A COURSE IN MATHEMATICAL ANALYSIS

VOLUME I

DERIVATIVES AND DIFFERENTIALS
DEFINITE INTEGRALS
EXPANSION IN SERIES
APPLICATIONS TO GEOMETRY

BY

ÉDOUARD GOURSAT

TRANSLATED BY
EARLE RAYMOND HEDRICK

DOVER PUBLICATIONS, INC.
NEW YORK

Published in Canada by General Publishing Company, Ltd., 30 Lesmill Road, Don Mills, Toronto, Ontario.
Published in the United Kingdom by Constable and Company, Ltd., 10 Orange Street, London WC 2.

This Dover edition, first published in 1959, is an unabridged and unaltered republication of the Hedrick translation of *Cours d'Analyse Mathématique,* Volume I. This translation, originally published in 1905, is reprinted by permission of Ginn and Company, the original publisher of this text.

International Standard Book Number: 0-486-60554-X

Library of Congress Catalog Card Number: 60-320

Manufactured in the United States of America
Dover Publications, Inc.
180 Varick Street
New York, N. Y. 10014

AUTHOR'S PREFACE

This book contains, with slight variations, the material given in my course at the University of Paris. I have modified somewhat the order followed in the lectures for the sake of uniting in a single volume all that has to do with functions of real variables, except the theory of differential equations. The differential notation not being treated in the "Classe de Mathématiques spéciales," * I have treated this notation from the beginning, and have presupposed only a knowledge of the formal rules for calculating derivatives.

Since mathematical analysis is essentially the science of the continuum, it would seem that every course in analysis should begin, logically, with the study of irrational numbers. I have supposed, however, that the student is already familiar with that subject. The theory of incommensurable numbers is treated in so many excellent well-known works † that I have thought it useless to enter upon such a discussion. As for the other fundamental notions which lie at the basis of analysis, — such as the upper limit, the definite integral, the double integral, etc., — I have endeavored to treat them with all desirable rigor, seeking to retain the elementary character of the work, and to avoid generalizations which would be superfluous in a book intended for purposes of instruction.

Certain paragraphs which are printed in smaller type than the body of the book contain either problems solved in detail or else

---

* An interesting account of French methods of instruction in mathematics will be found in an article by Pierpont, *Bulletin Amer. Math. Society*, Vol. VI, 2d series (1900), p. 225. — Trans.

† Such books are *not* common in English. The reader is referred to Pierpont, *Theory of Functions of Real Variables*, Ginn & Company, Boston, 1905; Tannery, *Leçons d'arithmétique*, 1900, and other foreign works on arithmetic and on real functions.

supplementary matter which the reader may omit at the first reading without inconvenience. Each chapter is followed by a list of examples which are directly illustrative of the methods treated in the chapter. Most of these examples have been set in examinations. Certain others, which are designated by an asterisk, are somewhat more difficult. The latter are taken, for the most part, from original memoirs to which references are made.

Two of my old students at the École Normale, M. Émile Cotton and M. Jean Clairin, have kindly assisted in the correction of proofs; I take this occasion to tender them my hearty thanks.

E. GOURSAT

JANUARY 27, 1902

TRANSLATOR'S PREFACE

The translation of this Course was undertaken at the suggestion of Professor W. F. Osgood, whose review of the original appeared in the July number of the *Bulletin of the American Mathematical Society* in 1903. The lack of standard texts on mathematical subjects in the English language is too well known to require insistence. I earnestly hope that this book will help to fill the need so generally felt throughout the American mathematical world. It may be used conveniently in our system of instruction as a text for a *second course in calculus*, and as a book of reference it will be found valuable to an American student throughout his work.

Few alterations have been made from the French text. Slight changes of notation have been introduced occasionally for convenience, and several changes and additions have been made at the suggestion of Professor Goursat, who has very kindly interested himself in the work of translation. To him is due all the additional matter not to be found in the French text, except the footnotes which are signed, and even these, though not of his initiative, were always edited by him. I take this opportunity to express my gratitude to the author for the permission to translate the work and for the sympathetic attitude which he has consistently assumed. I am also indebted to Professor Osgood for counsel as the work progressed and for aid in doubtful matters pertaining to the translation.

The publishers, Messrs. Ginn & Company, have spared no pains to make the typography excellent. Their spirit has been far from commercial in the whole enterprise, and it is their hope, as it is mine, that the publication of this book will contribute to the advance of mathematics in America.

E. R. HEDRICK

August, 1904

CONTENTS

A COURSE IN MATHEMATICAL ANALYSIS

VOLUME I

A COURSE IN MATHEMATICAL ANALYSIS

CHAPTER I

DERIVATIVES AND DIFFERENTIALS

I. FUNCTIONS OF A SINGLE VARIABLE

1. Limits. When the successive values of a variable x approach nearer and nearer a constant quantity a, in such a way that the absolute value of the difference $x - a$ finally becomes and remains less than any preassigned number, the constant a is called the *limit* of the variable x. This definition furnishes a criterion for determining whether a is the limit of the variable x. The necessary and sufficient condition that it should be, is that, given any positive number ϵ, no matter how small, the absolute value of $x - a$ should remain less than ϵ for all values which the variable x can assume, after a certain instant.

Numerous examples of limits are to be found in Geometry and Algebra. For example, the limit of the variable quantity $x = (a^2 - m^2)/(a - m)$, as m approaches a, is $2\,a$; for $x - 2\,a$ will be less than ϵ whenever $m - a$ is taken less than ϵ. Likewise, the variable $x = a - 1/n$, where n is a positive integer, approaches the limit a when n increases indefinitely; for $a - x$ is less than ϵ whenever n is greater than $1/\epsilon$. It is apparent from these examples that the successive values of the variable x, as it approaches its limit, may form a continuous or a discontinuous sequence.

It is in general very difficult to determine the limit of a variable quantity. The following proposition, which we will assume as self-evident, enables us, in many cases, to establish the existence of a limit.

Any variable quantity which never decreases, and which always remains less than a constant quantity L, approaches a limit l, which is less than or at most equal to L.

Similarly, *any variable quantity which never increases, and which always remains greater than a constant quantity L', approaches a limit l', which is greater than or else equal to L'.*

For example, if each of an infinite series of positive terms is less, respectively, than the corresponding term of another infinite series of positive terms which is known to converge, then the first series converges also; for the sum Σ_n of the first n terms evidently increases with n, and this sum is constantly less than the total sum S of the second series.

2. Functions. When two variable quantities are so related that the value of one of them depends upon the value of the other, they are said to be functions of each other. If one of them be supposed to vary arbitrarily, it is called the *independent variable*. Let this variable be denoted by x, and let us suppose, for example, that it can assume all values between two given numbers a and b $(a < b)$. Let y be another variable, such that to each value of x between a and b, and also for the values a and b themselves, there corresponds one definitely determined value of y. Then y is called a function of x, defined in the interval (a, b); and this dependence is indicated by writing the equation $y = f(x)$. For instance, it may happen that y is the result of certain arithmetical operations performed upon x. Such is the case for the very simplest functions studied in elementary mathematics, e.g. polynomials, rational functions, radicals, etc.

A function may also be defined graphically. Let two coördinate axes Ox, Oy be taken in a plane; and let us join any two points A and B of this plane by a curvilinear arc ACB, of any shape, which is not cut in more than one point by any parallel to the axis Oy. Then the ordinate of a point of this curve will be a function of the abscissa. The arc ACB may be composed of several distinct portions which belong to different curves, such as segments of straight lines, arcs of circles, etc.

In short, any absolutely arbitrary law may be assumed for finding the value of y from that of x. The word *function*, in its most general sense, means nothing more nor less than this: to every value of x corresponds a value of y.

3. Continuity. The definition of functions to which the infinitesimal calculus applies does not admit of such broad generality. Let $y = f(x)$ be a function defined in a certain interval (a, b), and let x_0 and $x_0 + h$ be two values of x in that interval. If the difference $f(x_0 + h) - f(x_0)$ approaches zero as the absolute value of h approaches zero, the function $f(x)$ is said to be *continuous for the value x_0*. From the very definition of a limit we may also say that *a function $f(x)$ is continuous for $x = x_0$ if, corresponding to every positive number ϵ, no matter how small, we can find a positive number η, such that*

$$|f(x_0 + h) - f(x_0)| < \epsilon$$

for every value of h less than η in absolute value. * We shall say that a function $f(x)$ is continuous in an interval (a, b) if it is continuous for every value of x lying in that interval, and if the differences

$$f(a + h) - f(a), \qquad f(b - h) - f(b)$$

each approach zero when h, which is now to be taken only positive, approaches zero.

In elementary text-books it is usually shown that polynomials, rational functions, the exponential and the logarithmic function, the trigonometric functions, and the inverse trigonometric functions are continuous functions, except for certain particular values of the variable. It follows directly from the definition of continuity that the sum or the product of any number of continuous functions is itself a continuous function; and this holds for the quotient of two continuous functions also, except for the values of the variable for which the denominator vanishes.

It seems superfluous to explain here the reasons which lead us to assume that functions which are defined by physical conditions are, at least in general, continuous.

Among the properties of continuous functions we shall now state only the two following, which one might be tempted to think were self-evident, but which really amount to actual theorems, of which rigorous demonstrations will be given later. †

I. *If the function $y = f(x)$ is continuous in the interval (a, b), and if N is a number between $f(a)$ and $f(b)$, then the equation $f(x) = N$ has at least one root between a and b.*

II. *There exists at least one value of x belonging to the interval (a, b), inclusive of its end points, for which y takes on a value M which is greater than, or at least equal to, the value of the function at any other point in the interval. Likewise, there exists a value of x for which y takes on a value m, than which the function assumes no smaller value in the interval.*

The numbers M and m are called the maximum and the minimum values of $f(x)$, respectively, in the interval (a, b). It is clear that

---

* The notation $|a|$ denotes the absolute value of a.

† See Chapter IV.

the value of x for which $f(x)$ assumes its maximum value M, or the value of x corresponding to the minimum m, may be at one of the end points, a or b. It follows at once from the two theorems above, that if N is a number between M and m, the equation $f(x) = N$ has at least one root which lies between a and b.

4. Examples of discontinuities. The functions which we shall study will be in general continuous, but they may cease to be so for certain exceptional values of the variable. We proceed to give several examples of the kinds of discontinuity which occur most frequently.

The function $y = 1/(x - a)$ is continuous for every value x_0 of x except a. The operation necessary to determine the value of y from that of x ceases to have a meaning when x is assigned the value a; but we note that when x is very near to a the absolute value of y is very large, and y is positive or negative with $x - a$. As the difference $x - a$ diminishes, the absolute value of y increases indefinitely, so as eventually to become and remain greater than any preassigned number. This phenomenon is described by saying that y *becomes infinite* when $x = a$. Discontinuity of this kind is of great importance in Analysis.

Let us consider next the function $y = \sin 1/x$. As x approaches zero, $1/x$ increases indefinitely, and y does not approach any limit whatever, although it remains between $+1$ and -1. The equation $\sin 1/x = A$, where $|A| < 1$, has an infinite number of solutions which lie between 0 and ϵ, no matter how small ϵ be taken. Whatever value be assigned to y when $x = 0$, the function under consideration cannot be made continuous for $x = 0$.

An example of a still different kind of discontinuity is given by the convergent infinite series

$$S(x) = x^2 + \frac{x^2}{1 + x^2} + \cdots + \frac{x^2}{(1 + x^2)^n} + \cdots.$$

When x approaches zero, $S(x)$ approaches the limit 1, although $S(0) = 0$. For, when $x = 0$, every term of the series is zero, and hence $S(0) = 0$. But if x be given a value different from zero, a geometric progression is obtained, of which the ratio is $1/(1 + x^2)$. Hence

$$S(x) = \frac{x^2}{1 - \dfrac{1}{1 + x^2}} = \frac{x^2(1 + x^2)}{x^2} = 1 + x^2\,;$$

and the limit of $S(x)$ is seen to be 1. Thus, in this example, the function approaches a definite limit as x approaches zero, but that limit is different from the value of the function for $x = 0$.

5. Derivatives. Let $f(x)$ be a continuous function. Then the two terms of the quotient

$$\frac{f(x+h)-f(x)}{h}$$

approach zero simultaneously, as the absolute value of h approaches zero, while x remains fixed. If this quotient approaches a limit, this limit is called the derivative of the function $f(x)$, and is denoted by y', or by $f'(x)$, in the notation due to Lagrange.

An important geometrical concept is associated with this analytic notion of derivative. Let us consider, in a plane XOY, the curve AMB, which represents the function $y = f(x)$, which we shall assume to be continuous in the interval (a, b). Let M and M' be two points on this curve, in the interval (a, b), and let their abscissæ be x and $x + h$, respectively. The slope of the straight line MM' is then precisely the quotient above. Now as h approaches zero the point M' approaches the point M; and, if the function has a derivative, the slope of the line MM' approaches the limit y'. The straight line MM', therefore, approaches a limiting position, which is called the *tangent to the curve*. It follows that the equation of the tangent is

$$Y - y = y'(X - x),$$

where X and Y are the running coördinates.

To generalize, let us consider any curve in space, and let

$$x = f(t), \qquad y = \phi(t), \qquad z = \psi(t)$$

be the coördinates of a point on the curve, expressed as functions of a variable parameter t. Let M and M' be two points of the curve corresponding to two values, t and $t + h$, of the parameter. The equations of the chord MM' are then

$$\frac{X - f(t)}{f(t+h)-f(t)} = \frac{Y - \phi(t)}{\phi(t+h)-\phi(t)} = \frac{Z - \psi(t)}{\psi(t+h)-\psi(t)}.$$

If we divide each denominator by h and then let h approach zero, the chord MM' evidently approaches a limiting position, which is given by the equations

$$\frac{X - f(t)}{f'(t)} = \frac{Y - \phi(t)}{\phi'(t)} = \frac{Z - \psi(t)}{\psi'(t)},$$

provided, of course, that each of the three functions $f(t)$, $\phi(t)$, $\psi(t)$ possesses a derivative. The determination of the tangent to a curve thus reduces, analytically, to the calculation of derivatives.

Every function which possesses a derivative is necessarily continuous, but the converse is not true. It is easy to give examples of continuous functions which do not possess derivatives for particular values of the variable. The function $y = x \sin 1/x$, for example, is a perfectly continuous function of x, for $x = 0$,* and y approaches zero as x approaches zero. But the ratio $y/x = \sin 1/x$ does not approach any limit whatever, as we have already seen.

Let us next consider the function $y = x^{\frac{2}{3}}$. Here y is continuous for every value of x; and $y = 0$ when $x = 0$. But the ratio $y/x = x^{-\frac{1}{3}}$ increases indefinitely as x approaches zero. For abbreviation the derivative is said to be infinite for $x = 0$; the curve which represents the function is tangent to the axis of y at the origin.

Finally, the function

$$y = \frac{x \, e^{\frac{1}{x}}}{1 + e^{\frac{1}{x}}}$$

is continuous at $x = 0$,* but the ratio y/x approaches two different limits according as x is always positive or always negative while it is approaching zero. When x is positive and small, $e^{1/x}$ is positive and very large, and the ratio y/x approaches 1. But if x is negative and very small in absolute value, $e^{1/x}$ is very small, and the ratio y/x approaches zero. There exist then two values of the derivative according to the manner in which x approaches zero: the curve which represents this function has a *corner* at the origin.

It is clear from these examples that there exist continuous functions which do not possess derivatives for particular values of the variable. But the discoverers of the infinitesimal calculus confidently believed that a continuous function had a derivative *in general*. Attempts at proof were even made, but these were, of course, fallacious. Finally, Weierstrass succeeded in settling the question conclusively by giving examples of continuous functions which do not possess derivatives for any values of the variable whatever.† But as these functions have not as yet been employed in any applications,

---

* After the value zero has been assigned to y for $x = 0$. — TRANSLATOR.

† Note read at the Academy of Sciences of Berlin, July 18, 1872. Other examples are to be found in the memoir by Darboux on discontinuous functions (*Annales de l'École Normale Supérieure*, Vol. IV, 2d series). One of Weierstrass's examples is given later (Chapter IX).

we shall not consider them here.   In the future, when we say that
a function $f(x)$ has a derivative in the interval (a, b), we shall mean
that it has an *unique finite derivative* for every value of x between
a and b and also for $x = a$ (h being positive) and for $x = b$ (h being
negative), unless an explicit statement is made to the contrary.

6. Successive derivatives. The derivative of a function $f(x)$ is **in**
general another function of x, $f'(x)$.   If $f'(x)$ in turn has a derivative, the new function is called the *second derivative* of $f(x)$, and is
represented by y'' or by $f''(x)$.   In the same way the third derivative y''', or $f'''(x)$, is defined to be the derivative of the second, and
so on.   In general, the nth derivative $y^{(n)}$, or $f^{(n)}(x)$, is the derivative of the derivative of order $(n-1)$.   If, in thus forming the
successive derivatives, we never obtain a function which has no
derivative, we may imagine the process carried on indefinitely.   In
this way we obtain an unlimited sequence of derivatives of the function $f(x)$ with which we started.   Such is the case for all functions
which have found any considerable application up to the present
time.

The above notation is due to Lagrange.   The notation $D_n y$, or
$D_n f(x)$, due to Cauchy, is also used occasionally to represent the
nth derivative.   Leibniz' notation will be given presently.

7. Rolle's theorem. The use of derivatives in the study of equations depends upon the following proposition, which is known **as**
Rolle's Theorem :

*Let a and b be two roots of the equation $f(x) = 0$.   If the function
$f(x)$ is continuous and possesses a derivative in the interval (a, b),
the equation $f'(x) = 0$ has at least one root which lies between a and b.*

For the function $f(x)$ vanishes, by hypothesis, for $x = a$ and $x = b$.
If it vanishes at every point of the interval (a, b), its derivative also
vanishes at every point of the interval, and the theorem is evidently
fulfilled.   If the function $f(x)$ does not vanish throughout the interval, it will assume either positive or negative values at some points.
Suppose, for instance, that it has positive values.   Then it will have
a maximum value M for some value of x, say x_1, which lies between
a and b (§ 3, Theorem II).   The ratio

$$\frac{f(x_1 + h) - f(x_1)}{h},$$

where h is taken positive, is necessarily negative or else zero. Hence the limit of this ratio, i.e. $f'(x_1)$, cannot be positive; i.e. $f'(x_1) \leqq 0$. But if we consider $f'(x_1)$ as the limit of the ratio

$$\frac{f(x_1 - h) - f(x_1)}{-h},$$

where h is positive, it follows in the same manner that $f'(x_1) \geqq 0$. From these two results it is evident that $f'(x_1) = 0$.

8. Law of the mean. It is now easy to deduce from the above theorem the important law of the mean: *

Let $f(x)$ be a continuous function which has a derivative in the interval (a, b). Then

(1) $$f(b) - f(a) = (b - a) f'(c),$$

where c is a number between a and b.

In order to prove this formula, let $\phi(x)$ be another function which has the same properties as $f(x)$, i.e. it is continuous and possesses a derivative in the interval (a, b). Let us determine three constants, A, B, C, such that the auxiliary function

$$\psi(x) = A f(x) + B \phi(x) + C$$

vanishes for $x = a$ and for $x = b$. The necessary and sufficient conditions for this are

$$A f(a) + B \phi(a) + C = 0, \qquad A f(b) + B \phi(b) + C = 0;$$

and these are satisfied if we set

$$A = \phi(a) - \phi(b), \qquad B = f(b) - f(a), \qquad C = f(a) \phi(b) - f(b) \phi(a).$$

The new function $\psi(x)$ thus defined is continuous and has a derivative in the interval (a, b). The derivative $\psi'(x) = A f'(x) + B \phi'(x)$ therefore vanishes for some value c which lies between a and b, whence, replacing A and B by their values, we find a relation of the form

(1') $$[\phi(b) - \phi(a)] f'(c) = [f(b) - f(a)] \phi'(c).$$

It is merely necessary to take $\phi(x) = x$ in order to obtain the equality which was to be proved. It is to be noticed that this demonstration does not presuppose the continuity of the derivative $f'(x)$.

---

* "Formule des accroissements finis." The French also use "Formule de la moyenne" as a synonym. Other English synonyms are "Average value theorem" and "Mean value theorem." — TRANS.

From the theorem just proven it follows that if the derivative $f'(x)$ is zero at each point of the interval (a, b), the function $f(x)$ has the same value at every point of the interval; for the application of the formula to two values x_1, x_2, belonging to the interval (a, b), gives $f(x_1) = f(x_2)$. Hence, if two functions have the same derivative, their difference is a constant; and the converse is evidently true also. *If a function $F(x)$ be given whose derivative is $f(x)$, all other functions which have the same derivative are found by adding to $F(x)$ an arbitrary constant.**

The geometrical interpretation of the equation (1) is very simple. Let us draw the curve AMB which represents the function $y = f(x)$ in the interval (a, b). Then the ratio $[f(b) - f(a)]/(b - a)$ is the slope of the chord AB, while $f'(c)$ is the slope of the tangent at a point C of the curve whose abscissa is c. Hence the equation (1) expresses the fact that *there exists a point C on the curve AMB, between A and B, where the tangent is parallel to the chord AB.*

If the derivative $f'(x)$ is continuous, and if we let a and b approach the same limit x_0 according to any law whatever, the number c, which lies between a and b, also approaches x_0, and the equation (1) shows that the limit of the ratio

$$\frac{f(b) - f(a)}{b - a}$$

is $f'(x_0)$. The geometrical interpretation is as follows. Let us consider upon the curve $y = f(x)$ a point M whose abscissa is x_0, and two points A and B whose abscissæ are a and b, respectively. The ratio $[f(b) - f(a)]/(b - a)$ is equal to the slope of the chord AB, while $f'(x_0)$ is the slope of the tangent at M. Hence, when the two points A and B approach the point M according to any law whatever, the secant AB approaches, as its limiting position, the tangent at the point M.

---

* This theorem is sometimes applied without due regard to the conditions imposed in its statement. Let $f(x)$ and $\phi(x)$, for example, be two continuous functions which have derivatives $f'(x)$, $\phi'(x)$ in an interval (a, b). If the relation $f'(x)\phi(x) - f(x)\phi'(x) = 0$ is satisfied by these four functions, it is sometimes accepted as proved that the derivative of the function f/ϕ, or $[f'(x)\phi(x) - f(x)\phi'(x)]/\phi^2$, is zero, and that accordingly f/ϕ is constant in the interval (a, b). But this conclusion is not absolutely rigorous unless the function $\phi(x)$ does not vanish in the interval (a, b). Suppose, for instance, that $\phi(x)$ and $\phi'(x)$ both vanish for a value c between a and b. A function $f(x)$ equal to $C_1\phi(x)$ between a and c, and to $C_2\phi(x)$ between c and b, where C_1 and C_2 are different constants, is continuous and has a derivative in the interval (a, b), and we have $f'(x)\phi(x) - f(x)\phi'(x) = 0$ for every value of x in the interval. The geometrical interpretation is apparent.

This does not hold in general, however, if the derivative is not continuous. For instance, if two points be taken on the curve $y = x^{\frac{2}{3}}$, on opposite sides of the y axis, it is evident from a figure that the direction of the secant joining them can be made to approach any arbitrarily assigned limiting value by causing the two points to approach the origin according to a suitably chosen law.

The equation $(1')$ is sometimes called the *generalized law of the mean.* From it de l'Hospital's theorem on indeterminate forms follows at once. For, suppose $f(a) = 0$ and $\phi(a) = 0$. Replacing b by x in $(1')$, we find

$$\frac{f(x)}{\phi(x)} = \frac{f'(x_1)}{\phi'(x_1)},$$

where x_1 lies between a and x. This equation shows that *if the ratio $f'(x)/\phi'(x)$ approaches a limit as x approaches a, the ratio $f(x)/\phi(x)$ approaches the same limit, if $f(a) = 0$ and $\phi(a) = 0$.*

9. Generalizations of the law of the mean. Various generalizations of the law of the mean have been suggested. The following one is due to Stieltjes (*Bulletin de la Société Mathématique,* Vol. XVI, p. 100). For the sake of definiteness consider three functions, $f(x)$, $g(x)$, $h(x)$, each of which has derivatives of the first and second orders. Let a, b, c be three particular values of the variable ($a < b < c$). Let A be a number defined by the equation

$$\begin{vmatrix} f(a) & g(a) & h(a) \\ f(b) & g(b) & h(b) \\ f(c) & g(c) & h(c) \end{vmatrix} - A \begin{vmatrix} 1 & a & a^2 \\ 1 & b & b^2 \\ 1 & c & c^2 \end{vmatrix} = 0,$$

and let

$$\phi(x) = \begin{vmatrix} f(a) & g(a) & h(a) \\ f(b) & g(b) & h(b) \\ f(x) & g(x) & h(x) \end{vmatrix} - A \begin{vmatrix} 1 & a & a^2 \\ 1 & b & b^2 \\ 1 & x & x^2 \end{vmatrix}$$

be an auxiliary function. Since this function vanishes when $x = b$ and when $x = c$, its derivative must vanish for some value ζ between b and c. Hence

$$\begin{vmatrix} f(a) & g(a) & h(a) \\ f(b) & g(b) & h(b) \\ f'(\zeta) & g'(\zeta) & h'(\zeta) \end{vmatrix} - A \begin{vmatrix} 1 & a & a^2 \\ 1 & b & b^2 \\ 0 & 1 & 2\zeta \end{vmatrix} = 0.$$

If b be replaced by x in the left-hand side of this equation, we obtain a function of x which vanishes when $x = a$ and when $x = b$. Its derivative therefore vanishes for some value of x between a and b, which we shall call ξ. The new equation thus obtained is

$$\begin{vmatrix} f(a) & g(a) & h(a) \\ f'(\xi) & g'(\xi) & h'(\xi) \\ f'(\zeta) & g'(\zeta) & h'(\zeta) \end{vmatrix} - A \begin{vmatrix} 1 & a & a^2 \\ 0 & 1 & 2\xi \\ 0 & 1 & 2\zeta \end{vmatrix} = 0.$$

Finally, replacing ζ by x in the left-hand side of this equation, we obtain a function of x which vanishes when $x = \xi$ and when $x = \zeta$. Its derivative vanishes for some value η, which lies between ξ and ζ and therefore between a and c. Hence A must have the value

$$A = \frac{1}{1.2} \begin{vmatrix} f\,(a) & g\,(a) & h\,(a) \\ f'\,(\xi) & g'\,(\xi) & h'\,(\xi) \\ f''(\eta) & g''(\eta) & h''(\eta) \end{vmatrix},$$

where ξ lies between a and b, and η lies between a and c.

This proof does not presuppose the continuity of the second derivatives $f''(x)$, $g''(x)$, $h''(x)$. If these derivatives are continuous, and if the values a, b, c approach the same limit x_0, we have, in the limit,

$$\lim A = \frac{1}{1.2} \begin{vmatrix} f\,(x_0) & g\,(x_0) & h\,(x_0) \\ f'\,(x_0) & g'\,(x_0) & h'\,(x_0) \\ f''(x_0) & g''(x_0) & h''(x_0) \end{vmatrix}$$

Analogous expressions exist for n functions and the proof follows the same lines. If only two functions $f(x)$ and $g(x)$ are taken, the formulæ reduce to the law of the mean if we set $g(x) = 1$.

An analogous generalization has been given by Schwarz (*Annali di Mathematica*, 2d series, Vol. X).

II. FUNCTIONS OF SEVERAL VARIABLES

10. Introduction. A variable quantity ω whose value depends on the values of several other variables, x, y, z, $\cdots$, t, which are independent of each other, is called *a function of the independent variables* x, y, z, $\cdots$, t; and this relation is denoted by writing $\omega = f(x, y, z, \cdots, t)$. For definiteness, let us suppose that $\omega = f(x, y)$ is a function of the two independent variables x and y. If we think of x and y as the Cartesian coördinates of a point in the plane, each pair of values (x, y) determines a point of the plane, and conversely. If to each point of a certain region A in the xy plane, bounded by one or more contours of any form whatever, there corresponds a value of ω, the function $f(x, y)$ is said to be defined in the region A.

Let (x_0, y_0) be the coördinates of a point M_0 lying in this region. *The function $f(x, y)$ is said to be continuous for the pair of values (x_0, y_0) if, corresponding to any preassigned positive number ϵ, another positive number η exists such that*

$$|f(x_0 + h,\, y_0 + k) - f(x_0,\, y_0)| < \epsilon$$

whenever $|h| < \eta$ and $|k| < \eta$.

This definition of continuity may be interpreted as follows. Let us suppose constructed in the xy plane a square of side $2\,\eta$ about M_0 as center, with its sides parallel to the axes. The point M', whose coördinates are $x_0 + h$, $y_0 + k$, will lie inside this square, if $|h| < \eta$ and $|k| < \eta$. To say that the function is continuous for the pair of values (x_0, y_0) amounts to saying that by taking this square sufficiently small we can make the difference between the value of the function at M_0 and its value at any other point of the square less than ϵ in absolute value.

It is evident that we may replace the square by a circle about (x_0, y_0) as center. For, if the above condition is satisfied for all points inside a square, it will evidently be satisfied for all points inside the inscribed circle. And, conversely, if the condition is satisfied for all points inside a circle, it will also be satisfied for all points inside the square inscribed in that circle. We might then define continuity by saying that an η exists for every ϵ, such that whenever $\sqrt{h^2 + k^2} < \eta$ we also have

$$|f(x_0 + h, y_0 + k) - f(x_0, y_0)| < \epsilon.$$

The definition of continuity for a function of 3, 4, $\cdots$, n independent variables is similar to the above.

It is clear that any continuous function of the two independent variables x and y is a continuous function of each of the variables taken separately. However, the converse does not always hold.*

11. Partial derivatives. If any constant value whatever be substituted for y, for example, in a continuous function $f(x, y)$, there results a continuous function of the single variable x. The derivative of this function of x, if it exists, is denoted by $f_x(x, y)$ or by ω_x. Likewise the symbol ω_y, or $f_y(x, y)$, is used to denote the derivative of the function $f(x, y)$ when x is regarded as constant and y as the independent variable. The functions $f_x(x, y)$ and $f_y(x, y)$ are called *the partial derivatives* of the function $f(x, y)$. They are themselves, in general, functions of the two variables x and y. If we form their partial derivatives in turn, we get the partial derivatives of the second order of the given function $f(x, y)$. Thus there are four partial derivatives of the second order, $f_{x^2}(x, y)$, $f_{xy}(x, y)$, $f_{yx}(x, y)$, $f_{y^2}(x, y)$. The partial derivatives of the third, fourth, and higher orders are

---

* Consider, for instance, the function $f(x, y)$, which is equal to $2xy / (x^2 + y^2)$ when the two variables x and y are not both zero, and which is zero when $x = y = 0$. It is evident that this is a continuous function of x when y is constant, and *vice versa*. Nevertheless it is not a continuous function of the two independent variables x and y for the pair of values $x = 0$, $y = 0$. For, if the point (x, y) approaches the origin upon the line $x = y$, the function $f(x, y)$ approaches the limit 1, and *not* zero. Such functions have been studied by Baire in his thesis.

defined similarly. In general, given a function $\omega = f(x, y, z, \cdots, t)$ of any number of independent variables, a partial derivative of the nth order is the result of n successive differentiations of the function f, in a certain order, with respect to any of the variables which occur in f. We will now show that the result does not depend upon the order in which the differentiations are carried out.

Let us first prove the following lemma:

Let $\omega = f(x, y)$ be a function of the two variables x and y. Then $f_{xy} = f_{yx}$, provided that these two derivatives are continuous.

To prove this let us first write the expression

$$U = f(x + \Delta x, y + \Delta y) - f(x, y + \Delta y) - f(x + \Delta x, y) + f(x, y)$$

in two different forms, where we suppose that x, y, Δx, Δy have definite values. Let us introduce the auxiliary function

$$\phi(v) = f(x + \Delta x, v) - f(x, v),$$

where v is an auxiliary variable. Then we may write

$$U = \phi(y + \Delta y) - \phi(y).$$

Applying the law of the mean to the function $\phi(v)$, we have

$$U = \Delta y \, \phi_y(y + \theta \Delta y), \qquad \text{where} \qquad 0 < \theta < 1;$$

or, replacing ϕ_y by its value,

$$U = \Delta y [f_y(x + \Delta x, y + \theta \Delta y) - f_y(x, y + \theta \Delta y)].$$

If we now apply the law of the mean to the function $f_y(u, y + \theta \Delta y)$, regarding u as the independent variable, we find

$$U = \Delta x \, \Delta y f_{yx}(x + \theta' \Delta x, y + \theta \Delta y), \qquad 0 < \theta' < 1.$$

From the symmetry of the expression U in x, y, Δx, Δy, we see that we would also have, interchanging x and y,

$$U = \Delta y \, \Delta x f_{xy}(x + \theta_1' \Delta x, y + \theta_1 \Delta y),$$

where θ_1 and θ_1' are again positive constants less than unity. Equating these two values of U and dividing by $\Delta x \, \Delta y$, we have

$$f_{xy}(x + \theta_1' \Delta x, y + \theta_1 \Delta y) = f_{yx}(x + \theta' \Delta x, y + \theta \Delta y).$$

Since the derivatives $f_{xy}(x, y)$ and $f_{yx}(x, y)$ are supposed continuous, the two members of the above equation approach $f_{xy}(x, y)$ and $f_{yx}(x, y)$, respectively, as Δx and Δy approach zero, and we obtain the theorem which we wished to prove.

It is to be noticed in the above demonstration that no hypothesis whatever is made concerning the other derivatives of the second order, f_{x^2} and f_{y^2}. The proof applies also to the case where the function $f(x, y)$ depends upon any number of other independent variables besides x and y, since these other variables would merely have to be regarded as constants in the preceding developments.

Let us now consider a function of any number of independent variables,

$$\omega = f(x, y, z, \cdots, t),$$

and let Ω be a partial derivative of order n of this function. Any permutation in the order of the differentiations which leads to Ω can be effected by a series of interchanges between two successive differentiations; and, since these interchanges do not alter the result, as we have just seen, the same will be true of the permutation considered. It follows that in order to have a notation which is not ambiguous for the partial derivatives of the nth order, it is sufficient to indicate the number of differentiations performed with respect to each of the independent variables. For instance, any nth derivative of a function of three variables, $\omega = f(x, y, z)$, will be represented by one or the other of the notations

$$f_{x^p y^q z^r}(x, y, z), \qquad D^n_{x^p y^q z^r} f(x, y, z),$$

where $p + q + r = n$.* Either of these notations represents the result of differentiating f successively p times with respect to x, q times with respect to y, and r times with respect to z, these operations being carried out in any order whatever. There are three distinct derivatives of the first order, f_x, f_y, f_z; six of the second order, $f_{x^2}, f_{y^2}, f_{z^2}, f_{xy}, f_{yz}, f_{xz}$; and so on.

In general, a function of p independent variables has just as many distinct derivatives of order n as there are distinct terms in a homogeneous polynomial of order n in p independent variables; that is,

$$\frac{(n+1)(n+2)\cdots(n+p-1)}{1.2.\cdots(p-2)(p-1)},$$

as is shown in the theory of combinations.

Practical rules. A certain number of practical rules for the calculation of derivatives are usually derived in elementary books on

---

* The notation $f_{x^p y^q z^r}(x, y, z)$ is used instead of the notation $f^{(n)}_{x^p y^q z^r}(x, y, z)$ for simplicity. Thus the notation $f_{xy}(x, y)$, used in place of $f''_{xy}(x, y)$, is simpler and equally clear. — TRANS.

the Calculus. A table of such rules is appended, the function and its derivative being placed on the same line:

$$y = x^a, \qquad\qquad y' = ax^{a-1};$$
$$y = a^x, \qquad\qquad y' = a^x \log a,$$

where the symbol log denotes the natural logarithm;

$$y = \log x, \qquad\qquad y' = \frac{1}{x};$$

$$y = \sin x, \qquad\qquad y' = \cos x;$$

$$y = \cos x, \qquad\qquad y' = -\sin x;$$

$$y = \text{arc } \sin x, \qquad\qquad y' = \frac{1}{\pm\sqrt{1-x^2}};$$

$$y = \text{arc } \tan x, \qquad\qquad y' = \frac{1}{1+x^2};$$

$$y = uv, \qquad\qquad y' = u'v + uv';$$

$$y = \frac{u}{v}, \qquad\qquad y' = \frac{u'v - uv'}{v^2};$$

$$y = f(u), \qquad\qquad y_x = f'(u)u_x;$$

$$y = f(u, v, w), \qquad\qquad y_x = u_x f_u + v_x f_v + w_x f_w.$$

The last two rules enable us to find the derivative of a function of a function and that of a composite function if f_u, f_v, f_w are continuous. Hence we can find the successive derivatives of the functions studied in elementary mathematics, — polynomials, rational and irrational functions, exponential and logarithmic functions, trigonometric functions and their inverses, and the functions derivable from all of these by combination.

For functions of several variables there exist certain formulæ analogous to the law of the mean. Let us consider, for definiteness, a function $f(x, y)$ of the two independent variables x and y. The difference $f(x + h, y + k) - f(x, y)$ may be written in the form

$$f(x + h, y + k) - f(x, y) = [f(x + h, y + k) - f(x, y + k)] + [f(x, y + k) - f(x, y)],$$

to each part of which we may apply the law of the mean. We thus find

$$f(x + h, y + k) - f(x, y) = h f_x(x + \theta h, y + k) + k f_y(x, y + \theta'k),$$

where θ and θ' each lie between zero and unity.

This formula holds whether the derivatives f_x and f_y are continuous or not. If these derivatives are continuous, another formula, similar to the above, but involving only one undetermined number θ, may be employed.* In order to derive this second formula, consider the auxiliary function $\phi(t) = f(x + ht, y + kt)$, where x, y, h, and k have determinate values and t denotes an auxiliary variable. Applying the law of the mean to this function, we find

$$\phi(1) - \phi(0) = \phi'(\theta), \qquad 0 < \theta < 1.$$

Now $\phi(t)$ is a composite function of t, and its derivative $\phi'(t)$ is equal to $h f_x(x + ht, y + kt) + k f_y(x + ht, y + kt)$; hence the preceding formula may be written in the form

$$f(x + h,\, y + k) - f(x, y) = h f_x(x + \theta h, y + \theta k) + k f_y(x + \theta h, y + \theta k).$$

12. Tangent plane to a surface. We have seen that the derivative of a function of a single variable gives the tangent to a plane curve. Similarly, the partial derivatives of a function of two variables occur in the determination of the tangent plane to a surface. Let

$$(2) \qquad z = F(x, y)$$

be the equation of a surface S, and suppose that the function $F(x, y)$, together with its first partial derivatives, is continuous at a point (x_0, y_0) of the xy plane. Let z_0 be the corresponding value of z, and M_0 (x_0, y_0, z_0) the corresponding point on the surface S. If the equations

$$(3) \qquad x = f(t), \quad y = \phi(t), \quad z = \psi(t)$$

represent a curve C on the surface S through the point M_0, the three functions $f(t)$, $\phi(t)$, $\psi(t)$, which we shall suppose continuous and differentiable, must reduce to x_0, y_0, z_0, respectively, for some value t_0 of the parameter t. The tangent to this curve at the point M_0 is given by the equations (§ 5)

$$(4) \qquad \frac{X - x_0}{f'(t_0)} = \frac{Y - y_0}{\phi'(t_0)} = \frac{Z - z_0}{\psi'(t_0)}.$$

Since the curve C lies on the surface S, the equation $\psi(t) = F[f(t), \phi(t)]$ must hold for all values of t; that is, this relation must be an identity

---

* Another formula may be obtained which involves only one undetermined number θ, and which holds even when the derivatives f_x and f_y are discontinuous. For the application of the law of the mean to the auxiliary function $\phi(t) = f(x + ht, y + k) + f(x, y + kt)$ gives

$$\phi(1) - \phi(0) = \phi'(\theta), \qquad\qquad\qquad 0 < \theta < 1,$$

or

$$f(x + h,\, y + k) - f(x, y) = h f_x(x + \theta h, y + k) + k f_y(x, y + \theta k), \quad 0 < \theta < 1.$$

The operations performed, and hence the final formula, all hold provided the derivatives f_x and f_y merely exist at the points $(x + ht, y + k)$, $(x, y + kt)$, $0 \leqq t \leqq 1$. — TRANS.

in t. Taking the derivative of the second member by the rule for the derivative of a composite function, and setting $t = t_0$, we have

(5) $$\psi'(t_0) = f'(t_0) F_{x_0} + \phi'(t_0) F_{y_0}.$$

We can now eliminate $f'(t_0)$, $\phi'(t_0)$, $\psi'(t_0)$ between the equations (4) and (5), and the result of this elimination is

(6) $$Z - z_0 = (X - x_0) F_{x_0} + (Y - y_0) F_{y_0}.$$

This is the equation of a plane which is the locus of the tangents to all curves on the surface through the point M_0. It is called *the tangent plane to the surface*.

13. Passage from increments to derivatives. We have defined the successive derivatives in terms of each other, the derivatives of order n being derived from those of order $(n-1)$, and so forth. It is natural to inquire whether we may not define a derivative of any order as the limit of a certain ratio directly, without the intervention of derivatives of lower order. We have already done something of this kind for f_{xy} (§ 11); for the demonstration given above shows that f_{xy} is the limit of the ratio

$$\frac{f(x + \Delta x, \, y + \Delta y) - f(x + \Delta x, \, y) - f(x, \, y + \Delta y) + f(x, \, y)}{\Delta x \, \Delta y}$$

as Δx and Δy both approach zero. It can be shown in like manner that the second derivative f'' of a function $f(x)$ of a single variable is the limit of the ratio

$$\frac{f(x + h_1 + h_2) - f(x + h_1) - f(x + h_2) + f(x)}{h_1 h_2}$$

as h_1 and h_2 both approach zero.

For, let us set

$$f_1(x) = f(x + h_1) - f(x),$$

and then write the above ratio in the form

$$\frac{f_1(x + h_2) - f_1(x)}{h_1 h_2} = \frac{f_1'(x + \theta h_2)}{h_1}, \qquad 0 < \theta < 1;$$

or

$$\frac{f'(x + h_1 + \theta h_2) - f'(x + \theta h_2)}{h_1} = f''(x + \theta' h_1 + \theta h_2), \quad 0 < \theta' < 1.$$

The limit of this ratio is therefore the second derivative f'', provided that derivative is continuous.

Passing now to the general case, let us consider, for definiteness, a function of three independent variables, $\omega = f(x, y, z)$. Let us set

$$\Delta_x^h \omega = f(x + h, \, y, \, z) - f(x, \, y, \, z),$$
$$\Delta_y^k \omega = f(x, \, y + k, \, z) - f(x, \, y, \, z),$$
$$\Delta_z^l \omega = f(x, \, y, \, z + l) - f(x, \, y, \, z),$$

where $\Delta_x^h \omega$, $\Delta_y^k \omega$, $\Delta_z^l \omega$ are the *first increments* of ω. If we consider h, k, l as given constants, then these three first increments are themselves functions of x, y, z, and we may form the relative increments of these functions corresponding to increments h_1, k_1, l_1 of the variables. This gives us the second increments, $\Delta_x^{h_1} \Delta_x^{h} \omega$, $\Delta_x^{h_1} \Delta_y^{k} \omega$, $\cdots$. This process can be continued indefinitely; an increment of order n would be defined as a first increment of an increment of order $(n-1)$. Since we may invert the order of any two of these operations, it will be sufficient to indicate the successive increments given to each of the variables. An increment of order n would be indicated by some such notation as the following:

$$\Delta^{(n)} \omega = \Delta_x^{h_1} \Delta_x^{h_2} \cdots \Delta_x^{h_p} \Delta_y^{k_1} \cdots \Delta_y^{k_q} \Delta_z^{l_1} \cdots \Delta_z^{l_r} f(x, y, z),$$

where $p + q + r = n$, and where the increments h, k, l may be either equal or unequal. This increment may be expressed in terms of a partial derivative of order n, being equal to the product

$$h_1 h_2 \cdots h_p k_1 \cdots k_q l_1 \cdots l_r$$
$$\times f_{x^p y^q z^r}(x + \theta_1 h_1 + \cdots + \theta_p h_p, \ y + \theta_1' k_1 + \cdots + \theta_q' k_q, \ z + \theta_1'' l_1 + \cdots + \theta_r'' l_r),$$

where every θ lies between 0 and 1. This formula has already been proved for first and for second increments. In order to prove it in general, let us assume that it holds for an increment of order $(n-1)$, and let

$$\phi(x, y, z) = \Delta_x^{h_2} \cdots \Delta_x^{h_p} \Delta_y^{k_1} \cdots \Delta_y^{k_q} \Delta_z^{l_1} \cdots \Delta_z^{l_r} f.$$

Then, by hypothesis,

$$\phi(x, y, z) = h_2 \cdots h_p k_1 \cdots k_q l_1 \cdots l_r f_{x^{p-1} y^q z^r}(x + \theta_2 h_2 + \cdots + \theta_p h_p, \ y + \cdots, z + \cdots).$$

But the nth increment considered is equal to $\phi(x + h_1, y, z) - \phi(x, y, z)$; and if we apply the law of the mean to this increment, we finally obtain the formula sought.

Conversely, the partial derivative $f_{x^p y^q z^r}$ is the limit of the ratio

$$\frac{\Delta_x^{h_1} \Delta_x^{h_2} \cdots \Delta_x^{h_p} \Delta_y^{k_1} \cdots \Delta_y^{k_q} \Delta_z^{l_1} \cdots \Delta_z^{l_r} f}{h_1 h_2 \cdots h_p k_1 k_2 \cdots k_q l_1 \cdots l_r},$$

as all the increments h, k, l approach zero.

It is interesting to notice that this definition is sometimes more general than the usual definition. Suppose, for example, that $\omega = f(x, y) = \phi(x) + \psi(y)$ is a function of x and y, where neither ϕ nor ψ has a derivative. Then ω also has no first derivative, and consequently second derivatives are out of the question, in the ordinary sense. Nevertheless, if we adopt the new definition, the derivative f_{xy} is the limit of the fraction

$$\frac{f(x+h, y+k) - f(x+h, y) - f(x, y+k) + f(x, y)}{hk},$$

which is equal to

$$\frac{\phi(x+h) + \psi(y+k) - \phi(x+h) - \psi(y) - \phi(x) - \psi(y+k) + \phi(x) + \psi(y)}{hk}.$$

But the numerator of this ratio is identically zero. Hence the ratio approaches zero as a limit, and we find $f_{xy} = 0$.*

---

* A similar remark may be made regarding functions of a single variable. For example, the function $f(x) = x^3 \cos 1/x$ has the derivative

$$f'(x) = 3 x^2 \cos \frac{1}{x} + x \sin \frac{1}{x},$$

and $f'(x)$ has no derivative for $x = 0$. But the ratio

$$\frac{f(2\alpha) - 2f(\alpha) + f(0)}{\alpha^2},$$

or $8 \alpha \cos(1/2\alpha) - 2\alpha \cos(1/\alpha)$, has the limit zero when α approaches zero.

III. THE DIFFERENTIAL NOTATION

The differential notation, which has been in use longer than any other,* is due to Leibniz. Although it is by no means indispensable, it possesses certain advantages of symmetry and of generality which are convenient, especially in the study of functions of several variables. This notation is founded upon the use of infinitesimals.

14. Differentials. Any *variable* quantity which approaches zero as a limit is called an *infinitely small quantity*, or simply an *infinitesimal*. The condition that the quantity be variable is essential, for a constant, however small, is not an infinitesimal unless it is zero.

Ordinarily several quantities are considered which approach zero simultaneously. One of them is chosen as the standard of comparison, and is called the *principal infinitesimal*. Let α be the principal infinitesimal, and β another infinitesimal. Then β is said to be an infinitesimal of higher order *with respect to* α, if the ratio β/α approaches zero with α. On the other hand, β is called an infinitesimal of the first order with respect to α, if the ratio β/α approaches a limit K different from zero as α approaches zero. In this case

$$\frac{\beta}{\alpha} = K + \epsilon,$$

where ϵ is another infinitesimal with respect to α. Hence

$$\beta = \alpha(K + \epsilon) = K\alpha + \alpha\epsilon,$$

and $K\alpha$ is called the *principal part* of β. The complementary term $\alpha\epsilon$ is an infinitesimal of higher order with respect to α. In general, if we can find a positive power of α, say α^n, such that β/α^n approaches a finite limit K different from zero as α approaches zero, β is called an infinitesimal of order n with respect to α. Then we have

$$\frac{\beta}{\alpha^n} = K + \epsilon,$$

or

$$\beta = \alpha^n(K + \epsilon) = K\alpha^n + \alpha^n\epsilon.$$

The term $K\alpha^n$ is again called the principal part of β.

Having given these definitions, let us consider a continuous function $y = f(x)$, which possesses a derivative $f'(x)$. Let Δx be an

---

* With the possible exception of Newton's notation. — TRANS.

increment of x, and let Δy denote the corresponding increment of y. From the very definition of a derivative, we have

$$\frac{\Delta y}{\Delta x} = f'(x) + \epsilon,$$

where ϵ approaches zero with Δx. If Δx be taken as the principal infinitesimal, Δy is itself an infinitesimal whose principal part is $f'(x)\,\Delta x$.* This principal part is called the *differential* of y and is denoted by dy.

$$dy = f'(x)\,\Delta x.$$

When $f(x)$ reduces to x itself, the above formula becomes $dx = \Delta x$; and hence we shall write, for symmetry,

$$dy = f'(x)\,dx,$$

where the increment dx of the independent variable x is to be given the same fixed value, which is otherwise arbitrary and of course variable, for all of the several dependent functions of x which may be under consideration at the same time.

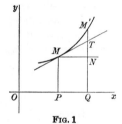

FIG. 1

Let us take a curve C whose equation is $y = f(x)$, and consider two points on it, M and M', whose abscissæ are x and $x + dx$, respectively. In the triangle MTN we have

$$NT = MN \tan \angle\, TMN = dx\, f'(x).$$

Hence NT represents the differential dy, while Δy is equal to NM'. It is evident from the figure that $M'T$ is an infinitesimal of higher order, in general, with respect to NT, as M' approaches M, unless MT is parallel to the x axis.

Successive differentials may be defined, as were successive derivatives, each in terms of the preceding. Thus we call the differential of the differential of the first order the *differential of the second order*, where dx is given the same value in both cases, as above. It is denoted by $d^2 y$:

$$d^2 y = d\,(dy) = \left[f''(x)\,dx \right] dx = f''(x)\,(dx)^2.$$

Similarly, the third differential is

$$d^3 y = d\,(d^2 y) = \left[f'''(x)\,dx^2 \right] dx = f'''(x)\,(dx)^3,$$

---

* Strictly speaking, we should here exclude the case where $f'(x) = 0$. It is, however, convenient to retain the same definition of $dy = f'(x)\,\Delta x$ in this case also, even though it is not the principal part of Δy. — TRANS.

and so on. In general, the differential of the differential of order $(n-1)$ is

$$d^n y = f^{(n)}(x)\, dx^n.$$

The derivatives $f'(x)$, $f''(x)$, $\cdots$, $f^{(n)}(x)$, $\cdots$ can be expressed, on the other hand, in terms of differentials, and we have a new notation for the derivatives:

$$y' = \frac{dy}{dx}, \qquad y'' = \frac{d^2 y}{dx^2}, \qquad \cdots, \qquad y^{(n)} = \frac{d^n y}{dx^n}, \qquad \cdots.$$

To each of the rules for the calculation of a derivative corresponds a rule for the calculation of a differential. For example, we have

$$d\, x^m = m x^{m-1} dx, \qquad\qquad d\, a^x = a^x \log a \, dx;$$

$$d \log x = \frac{dx}{x}, \qquad\qquad d \sin x = \cos x \, dx; \qquad \cdots;$$

$$d \arcsin x = \frac{dx}{\pm\sqrt{1-x^2}}, \qquad d \arctan x = \frac{dx}{1+x^2}.$$

Let us consider for a moment the case of a function of a function. Let $y = f(u)$, where u is a function of the independent variable x. Then

$$y_x = f'(u)\, u_x,$$

whence, multiplying both sides by dx, we get

$$y_x dx = f'(u) \times u_x dx;$$

that is,

$$dy = f'(u)\, du.$$

The formula for dy is therefore the same as if u were the independent variable. This is one of the advantages of the differential notation. In the derivative notation there are two distinct formulæ,

$$y_x = f'(x), \qquad y_x = f'(u)\, u_x,$$

to represent the derivative of y with respect to x, according as y is given directly as a function of x or is given as a function of x by means of an auxiliary function u. In the differential notation the same formula applies in each case.*

If $y = f(u, v, w)$ is a composite function, we have

$$y_x = u_x f_u + v_x f_v + w_x f_w,$$

at least if f_u, f_v, f_w are continuous, or, multiplying by dx,

$$y_x dx = u_x dx\, f_u + v_x dx\, f_v + w_x dx\, f_w;$$

---

* This particular advantage is slight, however; for the last formula above is equally well a general one and covers both the cases mentioned. — TRANS.

that is,

$$dy = f_u\,du + f_v\,dv + f_w\,dw.$$

Thus we have, for example,

$$d(uv) = u\,dv + v\,du, \qquad d\left(\frac{u}{v}\right) = \frac{v\,du - u\,dv}{v^2}.$$

The same rules enable us to calculate the successive differentials. Let us seek to calculate the successive differentials of a function $y = f(u)$, for instance. We have already

$$dy = f'(u)\,du.$$

In order to calculate d^2y, it must be noted that du cannot be regarded as fixed, since u is not the independent variable. We must then calculate the differential of the *composite* function $f'(u)\,du$, where u and du are the auxiliary functions. We thus find

$$d^2y = f''(u)\,du^2 + f'(u)\,d^2u.$$

To calculate d^3y, we must consider d^2y as a composite function, with u, du, d^2u as auxiliary functions, which leads to the expression

$$d^3y = f'''(u)\,du^3 + 3f''(u)\,du\,d^2u + f'(u)\,d^3u\,;$$

and so on. It should be noticed that these formulæ for d^2y, d^3y, etc., are not the same as if u were the independent variable, on account of the terms d^2u, d^3u, etc.*

A similar notation is used for the partial derivatives of a function of several variables. Thus the partial derivative of order n of $f(x, y, z)$, which is represented by $f_{x^p y^q z^r}$ in our previous notation, is represented by

$$\frac{\partial^n f}{\partial x^p\,\partial y^q\,\partial z^r}, \qquad p + q + r = n,$$

in the differential notation.† This notation is purely symbolic, and in no sense represents a quotient, as it does in the case of functions of a single variable.

15. Total differentials. Let $\omega = f(x, y, z)$ be a function of the three independent variables x, y, z. The expression

$$d\omega = \frac{\partial f}{\partial x}\,dx + \frac{\partial f}{\partial y}\,dy + \frac{\partial f}{\partial z}\,dz$$

---

* This disadvantage would seem completely to offset the advantage mentioned above. Strictly speaking, we should distinguish between $d_x^2 y$ and $d_u^2 y$, etc. — TRANS.

† This use of the letter ∂ to denote the partial derivatives of a function of several variables is due to Jacobi. Before his time the same letter d was used as is used for the derivatives of a function of a single variable.

is called the *total differential* of ω, where dx, dy, dz are three fixed increments, which are otherwise arbitrary, assigned to the three independent variables x, y, z. The three products

$$\frac{\partial f}{\partial x}\,dx, \qquad \frac{\partial f}{\partial y}\,dy, \qquad \frac{\partial f}{\partial z}\,dz$$

are called partial differentials.

The total differential of the second order $d^2\omega$ is the total differential of the total differential of the first order, the increments dx, dy, dz remaining the same as we pass from one differential to the next higher. Hence

$$d^2\omega = d(d\omega) = \frac{\partial\,d\omega}{\partial x}\,dx + \frac{\partial\,d\omega}{\partial y}\,dy + \frac{\partial\,d\omega}{\partial z}\,dz\,;$$

or, expanding,

$$
\begin{aligned}
d^2\omega = {} & \left(\frac{\partial^2 f}{\partial x^2}\,dx + \frac{\partial^2 f}{\partial x\,\partial y}\,dy + \frac{\partial^2 f}{\partial x\,\partial z}\,dz \right)dx \\
& + \left(\frac{\partial^2 f}{\partial x\,\partial y}\,dx + \frac{\partial^2 f}{\partial y^2}\,dy + \frac{\partial^2 f}{\partial y\,\partial z}\,dz \right)dy \\
& + \left(\frac{\partial^2 f}{\partial x\,\partial z}\,dx + \frac{\partial^2 f}{\partial y\,\partial z}\,dy + \frac{\partial^2 f}{\partial z^2}\,dz \right)dz \\
= {} & \frac{\partial^2 f}{\partial x^2}\,dx^2 + \frac{\partial^2 f}{\partial y^2}\,dy^2 + \frac{\partial^2 f}{\partial z^2}\,dz^2 \\
& + 2\,\frac{\partial^2 f}{\partial x\,\partial y}\,dx\,dy + 2\,\frac{\partial^2 f}{\partial x\,\partial z}\,dx\,dz + 2\,\frac{\partial^2 f}{\partial y\,\partial z}\,dy\,dz.
\end{aligned}
$$

If $\partial^2 f$ be replaced by ∂f^2, the right-hand side of this equation becomes the square of

$$\frac{\partial f}{\partial x}\,dx + \frac{\partial f}{\partial y}\,dy + \frac{\partial f}{\partial z}\,dz.$$

We may then write, symbolically,

$$d^2\omega = \left(\frac{\partial f}{\partial x}\,dx + \frac{\partial f}{\partial y}\,dy + \frac{\partial f}{\partial z}\,dz \right)^{(2)},$$

it being agreed that ∂f^2 is to be replaced by $\partial^2 f$ after expansion.

In general, if we call the total differential of the total differential of order $(n-1)$ *the total differential of order n,* and denote it by $d^n\omega$, we may write, in the same symbolism,

$$d^n\omega = \left(\frac{\partial f}{\partial x}\,dx + \frac{\partial f}{\partial y}\,dy + \frac{\partial f}{\partial z}\,dz \right)^{(n)},$$

where ∂f^n is to be replaced by $\partial^n f$ after expansion; that is, in our ordinary notation,

$$d^n \omega = \Sigma A_{pqr} \frac{\partial^n f}{\partial x^p \partial y^q \partial z^r} dx^p dy^q dz^r, \qquad p + q + r = n,$$

where

$$A_{pqr} = \frac{n!}{p!\, q!\, r!}$$

is the coefficient of the term $a^p b^q c^r$ in the development of $(a + b + c)^n$. For, suppose this formula holds for $d^n \omega$. We will show that it then holds for $d^{n+1} \omega$; and this will prove it in general, since we have already proved it for $n = 2$. From the definition, we find

$$d^{n+1} \omega = d(d^n \omega)$$

$$= \Sigma A_{pqr} \left[\frac{\partial^{n+1} f}{\partial x^{p+1} \partial y^q \partial z^r} dx^{p+1} dy^q dz^r + \frac{\partial^{n+1} f}{\partial x^p \partial y^{q+1} \partial z^r} dx^p dy^{q+1} dz^r \right.$$

$$\left. + \frac{\partial^{n+1} f}{\partial x^p \partial y^q \partial z^{r+1}} dx^p dy^q dz^{r+1} \right];$$

whence, replacing $\partial^{n+1} f$ by ∂f^{n+1}, the right-hand side becomes

$$\Sigma A_{pqr} \frac{\partial f^n}{\partial x^p \partial y^q \partial z^r} dx^p dy^q dz^r \left(\frac{\partial f}{\partial x} dx + \frac{\partial f}{\partial y} dy + \frac{\partial f}{\partial z} dz \right),$$

or

$$\left(\frac{\partial f}{\partial x} dx + \frac{\partial f}{\partial y} dy + \frac{\partial f}{\partial z} dz \right)^{(n)} \left(\frac{\partial f}{\partial x} dx + \frac{\partial f}{\partial y} dy + \frac{\partial f}{\partial z} dz \right).$$

Hence, using the same symbolism, we may write

$$d^{n+1} \omega = \left(\frac{\partial f}{\partial x} dx + \frac{\partial f}{\partial y} dy + \frac{\partial f}{\partial z} dz \right)^{(n+1)}.$$

Note. Let us suppose that the expression for $d\omega$, obtained in any way whatever, is

(7) $$d\omega = P\, dx + Q\, dy + R\, dz,$$

where P, Q, R are any functions x, y, z. Since by definition

$$d\omega = \frac{\partial \omega}{\partial x} dx + \frac{\partial \omega}{\partial y} dy + \frac{\partial \omega}{\partial z} dz,$$

we must have

$$\left(\frac{\partial \omega}{\partial x} - P \right) dx + \left(\frac{\partial \omega}{\partial y} - Q \right) dy + \left(\frac{\partial \omega}{\partial z} - R \right) dz = 0,$$

where dx, dy, dz are any constants. Hence

(8) $$\frac{\partial \omega}{\partial x} = P, \qquad \frac{\partial \omega}{\partial y} = Q, \qquad \frac{\partial \omega}{\partial z} = R.$$

The single equation (7) is therefore equivalent to the three separate equations (8); and it determines all three partial derivatives at once.

In general, if the nth total differential be obtained in any way whatever,

$$d^n \omega = \Sigma C_{pqr} dx^p dy^q dz^r ;$$

then the coefficients C_{pqr} are respectively equal to the corresponding nth derivatives multiplied by certain numerical factors. Thus all these derivatives are determined at once. We shall have occasion to use these facts presently.

16. Successive differentials of composite functions. Let $\omega = F(u, v, w)$ be a composite function, u, v, w being themselves functions of the independent variables x, y, z, t. The partial derivatives may then be written down as follows :

$$\frac{\partial \omega}{\partial x} = \frac{\partial F}{\partial u} \frac{\partial u}{\partial x} + \frac{\partial F}{\partial v} \frac{\partial v}{\partial x} + \frac{\partial F}{\partial w} \frac{\partial w}{\partial x},$$

$$\frac{\partial \omega}{\partial y} = \frac{\partial F}{\partial u} \frac{\partial u}{\partial y} + \frac{\partial F}{\partial v} \frac{\partial v}{\partial y} + \frac{\partial F}{\partial w} \frac{\partial w}{\partial y},$$

$$\frac{\partial \omega}{\partial z} = \frac{\partial F}{\partial u} \frac{\partial u}{\partial z} + \frac{\partial F}{\partial v} \frac{\partial v}{\partial z} + \frac{\partial F}{\partial w} \frac{\partial w}{\partial z},$$

$$\frac{\partial \omega}{\partial t} = \frac{\partial F}{\partial u} \frac{\partial u}{\partial t} + \frac{\partial F}{\partial v} \frac{\partial v}{\partial t} + \frac{\partial F}{\partial w} \frac{\partial w}{\partial t}.$$

If these four equations be multiplied by dx, dy, dz, dt, respectively, and added, the left-hand side becomes

$$\frac{\partial \omega}{\partial x} dx + \frac{\partial \omega}{\partial y} dy + \frac{\partial \omega}{\partial z} dz + \frac{\partial \omega}{\partial y} dt,$$

that is, $d\omega$; and the coefficients of

$$\frac{\partial F}{\partial u}, \qquad \frac{\partial F}{\partial v}, \qquad \frac{\partial F}{\partial w}$$

on the right-hand side are du, dv, dw, respectively. Hence

$$(9) \qquad d\omega = \frac{\partial F}{\partial u} du + \frac{\partial F}{\partial v} dv + \frac{\partial F}{\partial w} dw,$$

and we see that the expression of the total differential of the first order of a composite function is the same as if the auxiliary functions were the independent variables. This is one of the main advantages of the differential notation. The equation (9) does not depend, in form, either upon the number or upon the choice of the independent variables ; and it is equivalent to as many separate equations as there are independent variables.

To calculate $d^2\omega$, let us apply the rule just found for $d\omega$, noting that the second member of (9) involves the six auxiliary functions u, v, w, du, dv, dw. We thus find

$$d^2\omega = \quad \frac{\partial^2 F}{\partial u^2}\, du^2 \quad + \frac{\partial^2 F}{\partial u\, \partial v}\, du\, dv + \frac{\partial^2 F}{\partial u\, \partial w}\, du\, dw + \frac{\partial F}{\partial u}\, d^2u$$

$$+ \frac{\partial^2 F}{\partial u\, \partial v}\, du\, dv + \frac{\partial^2 F}{\partial v^2}\, dv^2 \quad + \frac{\partial^2 F}{\partial v\, \partial w}\, dv\, dw + \frac{\partial F}{\partial v}\, d^2v$$

$$+ \frac{\partial^2 F}{\partial u\, \partial w}\, du\, dw + \frac{\partial^2 F}{\partial v\, \partial w}\, dv\, dw + \frac{\partial^2 F}{\partial w^2}\, dw^2 \quad + \frac{\partial F}{\partial w}\, d^2w,$$

or, simplifying and using the same symbolism as above,

$$d^2\omega = \left(\frac{\partial F}{\partial u}\, du + \frac{\partial F}{\partial v}\, dv + \frac{\partial F}{\partial w}\, dw\right)^{(2)} + \frac{\partial F}{\partial u}\, d^2u + \frac{\partial F}{\partial v}\, d^2v + \frac{\partial F}{\partial w}\, d^2w.$$

This formula is somewhat complicated on account of the terms in d^2u, d^2v, d^2w, which drop out when u, v, w are the independent variables. This limitation of the differential notation should be borne in mind, and the distinction between $d^2\omega$ in the two cases carefully noted. To determine $d^3\omega$, we would apply the same rule to $d^2\omega$, noting that $d^2\omega$ depends upon the nine auxiliary functions u, v, w, du, dv, dw, d^2u, d^2v, d^2w; and so forth. The general expressions for these differentials become more and more complicated; $d^n\omega$ is an integral function of du, dv, dw, d^2u, $\cdots$, d^nu, d^nv, d^nw, and the terms containing d^nu, d^nv, d^nw are

$$\frac{\partial F}{\partial u}\, d^nu + \frac{\partial F}{\partial v}\, d^nv + \frac{\partial F}{\partial w}\, d^nw.$$

If, in the expression for $d^n\omega$, u, v, w, du, dv, dw, $\cdots$ be replaced by their values in terms of the independent variables, $d^n\omega$ becomes an integral polynomial in dx, dy, dz, $\cdots$ whose coefficients are equal (cf. *Note*, § 15) to the partial derivatives of ω of order n, multiplied by certain numerical factors. We thus obtain all these derivatives at once.

Suppose, for example, that we wished to calculate the first and second derivatives of a composite function $\omega = f(u)$, where u is a function of two independent variables $u = \phi(x, y)$. If we calculate these derivatives separately, we find for the two partial derivatives of the first order

$$(10) \qquad \frac{\partial \omega}{\partial x} = \frac{\partial \omega}{\partial u}\, \frac{\partial u}{\partial x}, \qquad \frac{\partial \omega}{\partial y} = \frac{\partial \omega}{\partial u}\, \frac{\partial u}{\partial y}.$$

Again, taking the derivatives of these two equations with respect to x, and then with respect to y, we find only the three following distinct equations, which give the second derivatives:

$$(11) \quad \begin{cases} \dfrac{\partial^2 \omega}{\partial x^2} = \dfrac{\partial^2 \omega}{\partial u^2}\left(\dfrac{\partial u}{\partial x}\right)^2 + \dfrac{\partial \omega}{\partial u}\,\dfrac{\partial^2 u}{\partial x^2}, \\[2mm] \dfrac{\partial^2 \omega}{\partial x\,\partial y} = \dfrac{\partial^2 \omega}{\partial u^2}\dfrac{\partial u}{\partial x}\dfrac{\partial u}{\partial y} + \dfrac{\partial \omega}{\partial u}\,\dfrac{\partial^2 u}{\partial x\,\partial y}, \\[2mm] \dfrac{\partial^2 \omega}{\partial y^2} = \dfrac{\partial^2 \omega}{\partial u^2}\left(\dfrac{\partial u}{\partial y}\right)^2 + \dfrac{\partial \omega}{\partial u}\,\dfrac{\partial^2 u}{\partial y^2}. \end{cases}$$

The second of these equations is obtained by differentiating the first of equations (10) with respect to y, or the second of them with respect to x. In the differential notation these five relations (10) and (11) may be written in the form

$$(12) \quad \begin{cases} d\omega = \dfrac{\partial \omega}{\partial u}\,du, \\[2mm] d^2\omega = \dfrac{\partial^2 \omega}{\partial u^2}\,du^2 + \dfrac{\partial \omega}{\partial u}\,d^2u. \end{cases}$$

If du and d^2u in these formulæ be replaced by

$$\frac{\partial u}{\partial x}\,dx + \frac{\partial u}{\partial y}\,dy \quad \text{and} \quad \frac{\partial^2 u}{\partial x^2}dx^2 + 2\,\frac{\partial^2 u}{\partial x\,\partial y}\,dx\,dy + \frac{\partial^2 u}{\partial y^2}\,dy^2,$$

respectively, the coefficients of dx and dy in the first give the first partial derivatives of ω, while the coefficients of dx^2, $2\,dx\,dy$, and dy^2 in the second give the second partial derivatives of ω.

17. Differentials of a product. The formula for the total differential of order n of a composite function becomes considerably simpler in certain special cases which often arise in practical applications. Thus, let us seek the differential of order n of the product of two functions $\omega = uv$. For the first values of n we have

$$d\omega = v\,du + u\,dv, \quad d^2\omega = v\,d^2u + 2\,du\,dv + u\,d^2v, \quad \cdots;$$

and, in general, it is evident from the law of formation that

$$d^n\omega = v\,d^n u + C_1\,dv\,d^{n-1}u + C_2\,d^2v\,d^{n-2}u + \cdots + u\,d^n v,$$

where C_1, C_2, $\cdots$ are positive integers. It might be shown by algebraic induction that these coefficients are equal to those of the expansion of $(a+b)^n$; but the same end may be reached by the following method, which is much more elegant, and which applies to many similar problems. Observing that C_1, C_2, $\cdots$ do not depend upon the particular functions u and v employed, let us take the special functions $u = e^x$, $v = e^y$, where x and y are the two independent variables, and determine the coefficients for this case. We thus find

$$\omega = e^{x+y}, \quad d\omega = e^{x+y}(dx+dy), \quad \cdots, \quad d^n\omega = e^{x+y}(dx+dy)^n,$$
$$du = e^x dx, \quad d^2 u = e^x dx^2, \quad \cdots,$$
$$dv = e^y dy, \quad d^2 v = e^y dy^2, \quad \cdots;$$

and the general formula, after division by e^{x+y}, becomes

$$(dx+dy)^n = dx^n + C_1 dy\, dx^{n-1} + C_2 dy^2 dx^{n-2} + \cdots + dy^n.$$

Since dx and dy are arbitrary, it follows that

$$C_1 = \frac{n}{1}, \quad C_2 = \frac{n(n-1)}{1.2}, \quad \cdots, \quad C_p = \frac{n(n-1)\cdots(n-p+1)}{1.2\cdots p}, \quad \cdots;$$

and consequently the general formula may be written

$$(13) \quad d^n(uv) = v\, d^n u + \frac{n}{1} dv\, d^{n-1}u + \frac{n(n-1)}{1.2} d^2 v\, d^{n-2}u + \cdots + u\, d^n v.$$

This formula applies for any number of independent variables. In particular, if u and v are functions of a single variable x, we have, after division by dx^n, the expression for the nth derivative of the product of two functions of a single variable.

It is easy to prove in a similar manner formulæ analogous to (13) for a product of any number of functions.

Another special case in which the general formula reduces to a simpler form is that in which u, v, w are integral linear functions of the independent variables x, y, z.

$$u = ax + by + cz + f,$$
$$v = a'x + b'y + c'z + f',$$
$$w = a''x + b''y + c''z + f'',$$

where the coefficients a, a', a'', b, b', $\cdots$ are constants. For then we have

$$du = a\, dx + b\, dy + c\, dz,$$
$$dv = a'dx + b'dy + c'dz,$$
$$dw = a''dx + b''dy + c''dz,$$

and all the differentials of higher order $d^n u$, $d^n v$, $d^n w$, where $n > 1$, vanish. Hence the formula for $d^n\omega$ is the same as if u, v, w were the independent variables; that is,

$$d^n \omega = \left(\frac{\partial F}{\partial u} \, du + \frac{\partial F}{\partial v} \, dv + \frac{\partial F}{\partial w} \, dw \right)^{(n)}.$$

We proceed to apply this remark.

18. Homogeneous functions. A function $\phi(x, y, z)$ is said to be homogeneous of degree m, if the equation

$$\phi(u, v, w) = t^m \phi(x, y, z)$$

is identically satisfied when we set

$$u = tx, \qquad v = ty, \qquad w = tz.$$

Let us equate the differentials of order n of the two sides of this equation with respect to t, noting that u, v, w are linear in t, and that

$$du = x \, dt, \qquad dv = y \, dt, \qquad dw = z \, dt.$$

The remark just made shows that

$$\left(x \frac{\partial \phi}{\partial u} + y \frac{\partial \phi}{\partial v} + z \frac{\partial \phi}{\partial w} \right)^{(n)} = m(m-1) \cdots (m-n+1) \, t^{m-n} \phi(x, y, z).$$

If we now set $t = 1$, u, v, w reduce to x, y, z, and any term of the development of the first member,

$$A_{pqr} \frac{\partial^n \phi}{\partial u^p \, \partial v^q \, \partial w^r} \, x^p \, y^q \, z^r,$$

becomes

$$A_{pqr} \frac{\partial^n \phi}{\partial x^p \, \partial y^q \, \partial z^r} \, x^p \, y^q \, z^r;$$

whence we may write, symbolically,

$$\left(x \frac{\partial \phi}{\partial x} + y \frac{\partial \phi}{\partial y} + z \frac{\partial \phi}{\partial z} \right)^{(n)} = m(m-1) \cdots (m-n+1) \, \phi(x, y, z),$$

which reduces, for $n = 1$, to the well-known formula

$$m \phi(x, y, z) = x \frac{\partial \phi}{\partial x} + y \frac{\partial \phi}{\partial y} + z \frac{\partial \phi}{\partial z}.$$

Various notations. We have then, altogether, three systems of notation for the partial derivatives of a function of several variables, — that of Leibniz, that of Lagrange, and that of Cauchy. Each of these is somewhat inconveniently long, especially in a complicated calculation. For this reason various shorter notations have been devised. Among these one first used by Monge for the first and second derivatives of a function of two variables is now in common use. If z be the function of the two variables x and y, we set

$$p = \frac{\partial z}{\partial x}, \quad q = \frac{\partial z}{\partial y}, \quad r = \frac{\partial^2 z}{\partial x^2}, \quad s = \frac{\partial^2 z}{\partial x\,\partial y}, \quad t = \frac{\partial^2 z}{\partial y^2};$$

and the total differentials dz and d^2z are given by the formulæ

$$dz = p\,dx + q\,dy,$$
$$d^2z = r\,dx^2 + 2\,s\,dx\,dy + t\,dy^2.$$

Another notation which is now coming into general use is the following. Let z be a function of any number of independent variables $x_1, x_2, x_3, \cdots, x_n$; then the notation

$$p_{a_1 a_2 \cdots a_n} = \frac{\partial^{a_1 + a_2 + \cdots + a_n} z}{\partial x_1^{a_1}\,\partial x_2^{a_2} \cdots \partial x_n^{a_n}}$$

is used, where some of the indices $\alpha_1, \alpha_2, \cdots, \alpha_n$ may be zeros.

19. Applications. Let $y = f(x)$ be the equation of a plane curve C with respect to a set of rectangular axes. The equation of the tangent at a point $M(x, y)$ is

$$Y - y = y'(X - x).$$

The slope of the normal, which is perpendicular to the tangent at the point of tangency, is $-1/y'$; and the equation of the normal is, therefore,

$$(Y - y)y' + (X - x) = 0.$$

Let P be the foot of the ordinate of the point M, and let T and N be the points of intersection of the x axis with the tangent and the normal, respectively.

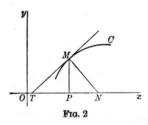

FIG. 2

The distance PN is called the subnormal; PT, the subtangent; MN, the normal; and MT, the tangent.

From the equation of the normal the abscissa of the point N is $x + yy'$, whence the subnormal is $\pm yy'$. If we agree to call the length PN the subnormal, and to attach the sign $+$ or the sign $-$ according as the direction PN is positive or negative, the subnormal will always be yy' for any position of the curve C. Likewise the subtangent is $-y/y'$.

The lengths MN and MT are given by the triangles MPN and MPT:

$$MN = \sqrt{\overline{MP}^2 + \overline{PN}^2} = y\sqrt{1 + y'^2},$$
$$MT = \sqrt{\overline{MP}^2 + \overline{PT}^2} = \frac{y}{y'}\sqrt{1 + y'^2}.$$

Various problems may be given regarding these lines. Let us find, for instance, all the curves for which the subnormal is constant and equal to a given number a. This amounts to finding all the functions $y = f(x)$ which satisfy the equation $yy' = a$. The left-hand side is the derivative of $y^2/2$, while the

right-hand side is the derivative of ax. These functions can therefore differ
only by a constant ; whence

$$y^2 = 2\,ax + C,$$

which is the equation of a parabola along the x axis.   Again, if we seek the
curves for which the subtangent is constant, we are led to write down the equation $y'/y = 1/a$; whence

$$\log y = \frac{x}{a} + \log C, \quad \text{or} \quad y = Ce^{\frac{x}{a}},$$

which is the equation of a transcendental curve to which the x axis is an asymptote.   To find the curves for which the normal is constant, we have the equation

$$y\,\sqrt{1 + y'^2} = a,$$

or

$$\frac{y\,y'}{\sqrt{a^2 - y^2}} = 1.$$

The first member is the derivative of $-\sqrt{a^2 - y^2}$; hence

$$-\sqrt{a^2 - y^2} = x + C,$$

or

$$(x + C)^2 + y^2 = a^2,$$

which is the equation of a circle of radius a, whose center lies on the x axis.

The curves for which the tangent is constant are transcendental curves, which we shall study later.

Let $y = f(x)$ and $Y = F(x)$ be the equations of two curves C and C', and let
M, M' be the two points which correspond to the same value of x.   In order that
the two subnormals should have equal lengths it is necessary and sufficient that

$$YY' = \pm\,yy' ;$$

that is, that $Y^2 = \pm\,y^2 + C$, where the double sign admits of the normals' being
directed in like or in opposite senses.   This relation is satisfied by the curves

$$y^2 = \frac{b^2}{a^2}(a^2 - x^2), \qquad Y^2 = \frac{b^2 x^2}{a^2},$$

and also by the curves

$$y^2 = \frac{b^2}{a^2}(x^2 - a^2), \qquad Y^2 = \frac{b^2 x^2}{a^2},$$

which gives an easy construction for the normal to the ellipse and to the hyperbola.

EXERCISES

1. Let $\rho = f(\theta)$ be the equation of a plane curve in polar coördinates.   Through
the pole O draw a line perpendicular to the radius
vector OM, and let T and N be the points where this
line cuts the tangent and the normal.   Find expressions for the distances OT, ON, MN, and MT in
terms of $f(\theta)$ and $f'(\theta)$.

Find the curves for which each of these distances,
in turn, is constant.

2. Let $y = f(x)$, $z = \phi(x)$ be the equations of a
skew curve Γ, i.e. of a general space curve.   Let N

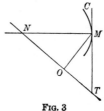

Fig. 3

be the point where the normal plane at a point M, that is, the plane perpendicular to the tangent at M, meets the z axis; and let P be the foot of the perpendicular from M to the z axis. Find the curves for which each of the distances PN and MN, in turn, is constant.

[*Note*. These curves lie on paraboloids of revolution or on spheres.]

3. Determine an integral polynomial $f(x)$ of the seventh degree in x, given that $f(x) + 1$ is divisible by $(x-1)^4$ and $f(x) - 1$ by $(x+1)^4$. Generalize the problem.

4. Show that if the two integral polynomials P and Q satisfy the relation

$$\sqrt{1 - P^2} = Q\sqrt{1 - x^2},$$

then

$$\frac{dP}{\sqrt{1 - P^2}} = \frac{n\,dx}{\sqrt{1 - x^2}},$$

where n is a positive integer.

[*Note*. From the relation

(a) $$1 - P^2 = Q^2(1 - x^2)$$

it follows that

(b) $$-2PP' = Q[2Q'(1 - x^2) - 2Qx].$$

The equation (a) shows that Q is prime to P; and (b) shows that P' is divisible by Q.]

5*. Let $R(x)$ be a polynomial of the fourth degree whose roots are all different, and let $x = U/V$ be a rational function of t, such that

$$\sqrt{R(x)} = \frac{P(t)}{Q(t)}\sqrt{R_1(t)},$$

where $R_1(t)$ is a polynomial of the fourth degree and P/Q is a rational function. Show that the function U/V satisfies a relation of the form

$$\frac{dx}{\sqrt{R(x)}} = \frac{k\,dt}{\sqrt{R_1(t)}},$$

where k is a constant.   [JACOBI.]

[*Note*. Each root of the equation $R(U/V) = 0$, since it cannot cause $R'(x)$ to vanish, must cause $UV' - VU'$, and hence also dx/dt, to vanish.]

6*. Show that the nth derivative of a function $y = \phi(u)$, where u is a function of the independent variable x, may be written in the form

(a) $$\frac{d^n y}{dx^n} = A_1\phi'(u) + \frac{A_2}{1\cdot2}\phi''(u) + \cdots + \frac{A_n}{1\cdot2\cdots n}\phi^{(n)}(u),$$

where

(b) $$\begin{cases} A_k = \dfrac{d^n u^k}{dx^n} - \dfrac{k}{1}u\dfrac{d^n u^{k-1}}{dx^n} + \dfrac{k(k-1)}{1\cdot2}u^2\dfrac{d^n u^{k-2}}{dx^n} + \cdots \\[2mm] \qquad + (-1)^{k-1}ku^{k-1}\dfrac{d^n u}{dx^n} \qquad (k = 1, 2, \cdots, n). \end{cases}$$

[First notice that the nth derivative may be written in the form (a), where the coefficients $A_1, A_2, \cdots, A_n$ are independent of the form of the function $\phi(u)$.

To find their values, set $\phi(u)$ equal to u, u^2, $\cdots$, u^n successively, and solve the resulting equations for A_1, A_2, $\cdots$, A_n. The result is the form (b).]

7*. Show that the nth derivative of $\phi(x^2)$ is

$$\frac{d^n \phi(x^2)}{dx^n} = (2\,x)^n \phi^{(n)}(x^2) + n\,(n-1)\,(2\,x)^{n-2}\,\phi^{(n-1)}(x^2) + \cdots$$
$$+ \frac{n\,(n-1)\cdots(n-2\,p+1)}{1\,.\,2\cdots p}\,(2\,x)^{n-2\,p}\,\phi^{(n-p)}(x^2) + \cdots,$$

where p varies from zero to the last positive integer not greater than $n/2$, and where $\phi^{(i)}(x^2)$ denotes the ith derivative with respect to x.

Apply this result to the functions e^{-x^2}, arc sin x, arc tan x.

8*. If $x = \cos u$, show that

$$\frac{d^{m-1}(1-x^2)^{m-\frac{1}{2}}}{dx^{m-1}} = (-1)^{m-1}\frac{1\,.\,3\,.\,5\cdots(2\,m-1)}{m}\,\sin mu.$$

[OLINDE RODRIGUES.]

9. Show that Legendre's polynomial,

$$X_n = \frac{1}{2\,.\,4\,.\,6\cdots 2\,n}\,\frac{d^n}{dx^n}\,(x^2-1)^n,$$

satisfies the differential equation

$$(1-x^2)\frac{d^2 X_n}{dx^2} - 2\,x\frac{d X_n}{dx} + n\,(n+1)\,X_n = 0.$$

Hence deduce the coefficients of the polynomial.

10. Show that the four functions

$$y_1 = \sin(n\text{ arc sin }x), \qquad\qquad y_3 = \sin(n\text{ arc cos }x),$$
$$y_2 = \cos(n\text{ arc sin }x), \qquad\qquad y_4 = \cos(n\text{ arc cos }x),$$

satisfy the differential equation

$$(1-x^2)\,y'' - xy' + n^2 y = 0.$$

Hence deduce the developments of these functions when they reduce to polynomials.

11*. Prove the formula

$$\frac{d^n}{dx^n}\left(x^{n-1}e^{\frac{1}{x}}\right) = (-1)^n\frac{e^{\frac{1}{x}}}{x^{n+1}}.$$

[HALPHEN.]

12. Every function of the form $z = x\,\phi\,(y/x) + \psi\,(y/x)$ satisfies the equation

$$rx^2 + 2\,sxy + ty^2 = 0,$$

whatever be the functions ϕ and ψ.

13. The function $z = x\,\phi(x+y) + y\,\psi(x+y)$ satisfies the equation

$$r - 2\,s + t = 0,$$

whatever be the functions ϕ and ψ,

14. The function $z = f[x + \phi(y)]$ satisfies the equation $ps = qr$, whatever be the functions f and ϕ.

15. The function $z = x^n \phi(y/x) + y^{-n} \psi(y/x)$ satisfies the equation

$$rx^2 + 2sxy + ty^2 + px + qy = n^2 z,$$

whatever be the functions ϕ and ψ.

16. Show that the function

$$y = |x - a_1| \phi_1(x) + |x - a_2| \phi_2(x) + \cdots + |x - a_n| \phi_n(x),$$

where $\phi_1(x)$, $\phi_2(x)$, $\cdots$, $\phi_n(x)$, together with their derivatives, $\phi_1'(x)$, $\phi_2'(x)$, $\cdots$, $\phi_n'(x)$, are continuous functions of x, has a derivative which is discontinuous for $x = a_1, a_2, \cdots, a_n$.

17. Find a relation between the first and second derivatives of the function $z = f(x_1, u)$, where $u = \phi(x_2, x_3)$; x_1, x_2, x_3 being three independent variables, and f and ϕ two arbitrary functions.

18. Let $f'(x)$ be the derivative of an arbitrary function $f(x)$. Show that

$$\frac{1}{u} \frac{d^2 u}{dx^2} = \frac{1}{v} \frac{d^2 v}{dx^2},$$

where $u = [f'(x)]^{-\frac{1}{2}}$ and $v = f(x) [f'(x)]^{-\frac{1}{2}}$.

19*. The nth derivative of a function of a function $u = \phi(y)$, where $y = \Psi(x)$, may be written in the form

$$D_x^n \phi = \sum \frac{n!}{i! \, j! \cdots k!} D_y^p \phi \left(\frac{\Psi'}{1}\right)^i \left(\frac{\Psi''}{1 \cdot 2}\right)^j \left(\frac{\Psi'''}{1 \cdot 2 \cdot 3}\right)^h \cdots \left(\frac{\Psi^{(l)}}{1 \cdot 2 \cdots l}\right)^k,$$

where the sign of summation extends over all the positive integral solutions of the equation $i + 2j + 3h + \cdots + lk = n$, and where $p = i + j + \cdots + k$.

[FAA DE BRUNO, *Quarterly Journal of Mathematics*, Vol. I, p. 359.]

CHAPTER II

IMPLICIT FUNCTIONS   FUNCTIONAL DETERMINANTS
CHANGE OF VARIABLE

I. IMPLICIT FUNCTIONS

20. A particular case. We frequently have to study functions for which no explicit expressions are known, but which are given by means of unsolved equations. Let us consider, for instance, an equation between the three variables x, y, z,

$$(1) \qquad F(x, y, z) = 0.$$

This equation defines, under certain conditions which we are about to investigate, a function of the two independent variables x and y. We shall prove the following theorem :

Let $x = x_0$, $y = y_0$, $z = z_0$ be a set of values which satisfy the equation (1), *and let us suppose that the function F, together with its first derivatives, is continuous in the neighborhood of this set of values.* * *If the derivative F_z does not vanish for $x = x_0$, $y = y_0$, $z = z_0$, there exists one and only one continuous function of the independent variables x and y which satisfies the equation* (1), *and which assumes the value z_0 when x and y assume the values x_0 and y_0, respectively.*

The derivative F_z not being zero for $x = x_0$, $y = y_0$, $z = z_0$, let us suppose, for definiteness, that it is positive. Since F, F_x, F_y, F_z are supposed continuous in the neighborhood, let us choose a positive number l so small that these four functions are continuous for all sets of values x, y, z which satisfy the relations

$$(2) \qquad |x - x_0| \leqq l, \qquad |y - y_0| \leqq l, \qquad |z - z_0| \leqq l,$$

and that, for these sets of values of x, y, z,

$$F_z(x, y, z) > P,$$

---

* In a recent article (*Bulletin de la Société Mathématique de France*, Vol. **XXXI**, 1903, pp. 184–192) Goursat has shown, by a method of successive approximations, that it is not necessary to make any assumption whatever regarding F_x and F_y, even as to their existence. His proof makes no use of the existence of F_x and F_y. His general theorem and a sketch of his proof are given in a footnote to § 25. — TRANS.

where P is some positive number. Let Q be another positive number greater than the absolute values of the other two derivatives F_x, F_y in the same region.

Giving x, y, z values which satisfy the relations (2), we may then write down the following identity:

$$F(x, y, z) - F(x_0, y_0, z_0) = F(x, y, z) - F(x_0, y, z) + F(x_0, y, z)$$
$$- F(x_0, y_0, z) + F(x_0, y_0, z) - F(x_0, y_0, z_0);$$

or, applying the law of the mean to each of these differences, and observing that $F(x_0, y_0, z_0) = 0$,

$$F(x, y, z) = \quad (x - x_0) F_x[x_0 + \theta(x - x_0), \ y, \ z]$$
$$+ (y - y_0) F_y[x_0, \ y_0 + \theta'(y - y_0), \ z]$$
$$+ (z - z_0) F_z[x_0, y_0, z_0 + \theta''(z - z_0)].$$

Hence $F(x, y, z)$ is of the form

$$(3) \quad \begin{cases} F(x, y, z) = \quad A(x, y, z)(x - x_0) \\ \qquad + B(x, y, z)(y - y_0) + C(x, y, z)(z - z_0), \end{cases}$$

where the absolute values of the functions $A(x, y, z)$, $B(x, y, z)$, $C(x, y, z)$ satisfy the inequalities

$$|A| < Q, \qquad |B| < Q, \qquad |C| > P$$

for all sets of values of x, y, z which satisfy (2). Now let ϵ be a positive number less than l, and η the smaller of the two numbers l and $P\epsilon/2Q$. Suppose that x and y in the equation (1) are given definite values which satisfy the conditions

$$|x - x_0| < \eta, \qquad |y - y_0| < \eta,$$

and that we seek the number of roots of that equation, z being regarded as the unknown, which lie between $z_0 - \epsilon$ and $z_0 + \epsilon$. In the expression (3), for $F(x, y, z)$ the sum of the first two terms is always less than $2Q\eta$ in absolute value, while the absolute value of the third term is greater than $P\epsilon$ when z is replaced by $z_0 \pm \epsilon$. From the manner in which η was chosen it is evident that this last term determines the sign of F. It follows, therefore, that $F(x, y, z_0 - \epsilon) < 0$ and $F(x, y, z_0 + \epsilon) > 0$; hence the equation (1) has at least one root which lies between $z_0 - \epsilon$ and $z_0 + \epsilon$. Moreover this root is unique, since the derivative F_z is positive for all values of z between $z_0 - \epsilon$ and $z_0 + \epsilon$. It is therefore clear that the equation (1) has one and only one root, and that this root approaches z_0 as x and y approach x_0 and y_0, respectively.

Let us investigate for just what values of the variables x and y the root whose existence we have just proved is defined. Let h be the smaller of the two numbers l and $Pl/2Q$; the foregoing reasoning shows that if the values of the variables x and y satisfy the inequalities $|x - x_0| < h$, $|y - y_0| < h$, the equation (1) will have one and only one root which lies between $z_0 - l$ and $z_0 + l$. Let R be a square of side $2\,h$, about the point $M_0(x_0, y_0)$, with its sides parallel to the axes. As long as the point (x, y) lies inside this square, the equation (1) uniquely determines a function of x and y, which remains between $z_0 - l$ and $z_0 + l$. This function is continuous, by the above, at the point M_0, and this is likewise true for any other point M_1 of R; for, by the hypotheses made regarding the function F and its derivatives, the derivative $F_z(x_1, y_1, z_1)$ will be positive at the point M_1, since $|x_1 - x_0| < l$, $|y_1 - y_0| < l$, $|z_1 - z_0| < l$. The condition of things at M_1 is then exactly the same as at M_0, and hence the root under consideration will be continuous for $x = x_1$, $y = y_1$.

Since the root considered is defined only in the interior of the region R, we have thus far only an *element* of an implicit function. In order to define this function outside of R, we proceed by successive steps, as follows. Let L be a continuous path starting at the point (x_0, y_0) and ending at a point (X, Y) outside of R. Let us suppose that the variables x and y vary simultaneously in such a way that the point (x, y) describes the path L. If we start at (x_0, y_0) with the value

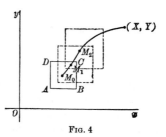

Fig. 4

z_0 of z, we have a definite value of this root as long as we remain inside the region R. Let $M_1(x_1, y_1)$ be a point of the path inside R, and z_1 the corresponding value of z. The conditions of the theorem being satisfied for $x = x_1$, $y = y_1$, $z = z_1$, there exists another region R_1, about the point M_1, inside which the root which reduces to z_1 for $x = x_1$, $y = y_1$ is uniquely determined. This new region R_1 will have, in general, points outside of R. Taking then such a point M_2 on the path L, inside R_1 but outside R, we may repeat the same construction and determine a new region R_2, inside of which the solution of the equation (1) is defined; and this process could be repeated indefinitely, as long as we did not find a set of values of x, y, z for which $F_z = 0$. We shall content ourselves for the present with these statements; we shall find occasion in later chapters to treat certain analogous problems in detail.

21. Derivatives of implicit functions. Let us return to the region R, and to the solution $z = \phi(x, y)$ of the equation (1), which is a continuous function of the two variables x and y in this region. This function possesses derivatives of the first order. For, keeping y fixed, let us give x an increment Δx. Then z will have an increment Δz, and we find, by the formula derived in § 20,

$$F(x + \Delta x, y, z + \Delta z) - F(x, y, z)$$
$$= \Delta x\, F_x(x + \theta \Delta x, y, z + \Delta z) + \Delta z\, F_z(x, y, z + \theta' \Delta z) = 0.$$

Hence

$$\frac{\Delta z}{\Delta x} = - \frac{F_x(x + \theta\, \Delta x, y, z + \Delta z)}{F_z(x, y, z + \theta' \Delta z)};$$

and when Δx approaches zero, Δz does also, since z is a continuous function of x. The right-hand side therefore approaches a limit, and z has a derivative with respect to x:

$$\frac{\partial z}{\partial x} = - \frac{F_x}{F_z}.$$

In a similar manner we find

$$\frac{\partial z}{\partial y} = - \frac{F_y}{F_z}.$$

Note. If the equation $F = 0$ is of degree m in z, it defines m functions of the variables x and y, and the partial derivatives $\partial z / \partial x$, $\partial z / \partial y$ also have m values for each set of values of the variables x and y. The preceding formulæ give these derivatives without ambiguity, if the variable z in the second member be replaced by the value of that function whose derivative is sought.

For example, the equation

$$x^2 + y^2 + z^2 - 1 = 0$$

defines the two continuous functions

$$+ \sqrt{1 - x^2 - y^2} \qquad \text{and} \qquad - \sqrt{1 - x^2 - y^2}$$

for values of x and y which satisfy the inequality $x^2 + y^2 < 1$. The first partial derivatives of the first are

$$\frac{- x}{\sqrt{1 - x^2 - y^2}}, \qquad \frac{- y}{\sqrt{1 - x^2 - y^2}},$$

and the partial derivatives of the second are found by merely changing the signs. The same results would be obtained by using the formulæ

$$\frac{\partial z}{\partial x} = -\frac{x}{z}, \qquad \frac{\partial z}{\partial y} = -\frac{y}{z},$$

replacing z by its two values, successively.

22. Applications to surfaces. If we interpret x, y, z as the Cartesian coördinates of a point in space, any equation of the form

$$(4) \qquad\qquad F(x, y, z) = 0$$

represents a surface S. Let (x_0, y_0, z_0) be the coördinates of a point A of this surface. If the function F, together with its first derivatives, is continuous in the neighborhood of the set of values x_0, y_0, z_0, and if all three of these derivatives do not vanish simultaneously at the point A, the surface S has a tangent plane at A. Suppose, for instance, that F_z is not zero for $x = x_0$, $y = y_0$, $z = z_0$. According to the general theorem we may think of the equation solved for z near the point A, and we may write the equation of the surface in the form

$$z = \phi(x, y),$$

where $\phi(x, y)$ is a continuous function; and the equation of the tangent plane at A is

$$Z - z_0 = \left(\frac{\partial z}{\partial x}\right)_0 (X - x_0) + \left(\frac{\partial z}{\partial y}\right)_0 (Y - y_0).$$

Replacing $\partial z / \partial x$ and $\partial z / \partial y$ by the values found above, the equation of the tangent plane becomes

$$(5) \quad \left(\frac{\partial F}{\partial x}\right)_0 (X - x_0) + \left(\frac{\partial F}{\partial y}\right)_0 (Y - y_0) + \left(\frac{\partial F}{\partial z}\right)_0 (Z - z_0) = 0.$$

If $F_z = 0$, but $F_x \neq 0$, at A, we would consider y and z as independent variables and x as a function of them. We would then find the same equation (5) for the tangent plane, which is also evident *a priori* from the symmetry of the left-hand side. Likewise the tangent to a plane curve $F(x, y) = 0$, at a point (x_0, y_0), is

$$(X - x_0)\left(\frac{\partial F}{\partial x}\right)_0 + (Y - y_0)\left(\frac{\partial F}{\partial y}\right)_0 = 0.$$

If the three first derivatives vanish simultaneously at the point A,

$$\left(\frac{\partial F}{\partial x}\right)_0 = \left(\frac{\partial F}{\partial y}\right)_0 = \left(\frac{\partial F}{\partial z}\right)_0 = 0,$$

the preceding reasoning is no longer applicable. We shall see later (Chapter III) that the tangents to the various curves which lie on the surface and which pass through A form, in general, a cone and not a plane.

In the demonstration of the general theorem on implicit functions we assumed that the derivative F_{z_0} did not vanish. Our geometrical intuition explains the necessity of this condition in general. For, if $F_{z_0} = 0$ but $F_{x_0} \neq 0$, the tangent plane is parallel to the z axis, and a line parallel to the z axis and near the line $x = x_0$, $y = y_0$ meets the surface, in general, in two points near the point of tangency. Hence, in general, the equation (4) would have two roots which both approach z_0 when x and y approach x_0 and y_0, respectively.

If the sphere $x^2 + y^2 + z^2 - 1 = 0$, for instance, be cut by the line $y = 0$, $x = 1 + \epsilon$, we find two values of z, which both approach zero with ϵ; they are real if ϵ is negative, and imaginary if ϵ is positive.

23. Successive derivatives. In the formulæ for the first derivatives,

$$\frac{\partial z}{\partial x} = -\frac{F_x}{F_z}, \qquad \frac{\partial z}{\partial y} = -\frac{F_y}{F_z},$$

we may consider the second members as composite functions, z being an auxiliary function. We might then calculate the successive derivatives, one after another, by the rules for composite functions. The existence of these partial derivatives depends, of course, upon the existence of the successive partial derivatives of $F(x, y, z)$.

The following proposition leads to a simpler method of determining these derivatives.

If several functions of an independent variable satisfy a relation $F = 0$, their derivatives satisfy the equation obtained by equating to zero the derivative of the left-hand side formed by the rule for differentiating composite functions. For it is clear that if F vanishes identically when the variables which occur are replaced by functions of the independent variable, then the derivative will also vanish identically. The same theorem holds even when the functions which satisfy the relation $F = 0$ depend upon several independent variables.

Now suppose that we wished to calculate the successive derivatives of an implicit function y of a single independent variable x defined by the relation

$$F(x, y) = 0.$$

We find successively

$$\frac{\partial F}{\partial x} + \frac{\partial F}{\partial y} y' = 0,$$

$$\frac{\partial^2 F}{\partial x^2} + 2\frac{\partial^2 F}{\partial x\,\partial y} y' + \frac{\partial^2 F}{\partial y^2} y'^2 + \frac{\partial F}{\partial y} y'' = 0,$$

$$\frac{\partial^3 F}{\partial x^3} + 3\frac{\partial^3 F}{\partial x^2\,\partial y} y' + 3\frac{\partial^3 F}{\partial x\,\partial y^2} y'^2 + 3\frac{\partial^2 F}{\partial x\,\partial y} y'' + \frac{\partial^3 F}{\partial y^3} y'^3$$

$$+ 3\frac{\partial^2 F}{\partial y^2} y' y'' + \frac{\partial F}{\partial y} y''' = 0,$$

. . . . ,

from which we could calculate successively y', y'', y''', $\cdots$.

Example. Given a function $y = f(x)$, we may, inversely, consider y as the independent variable and x as an implicit function of y defined by the equation $y = f(x)$. If the derivative $f'(x)$ does not vanish for the value x_0, where $y_0 = f(x_0)$, there exists, by the general theorem proved above, one and only one function of y which satisfies the relation $y = f(x)$ and which takes on the value x_0 for $y = y_0$. This function is called the *inverse* of the function $f(x)$. To calculate the successive derivatives x_y, x_{y^2}, x_{y^3}, $\cdots$ of this function, we need merely differentiate, regarding y as the independent variable, and we get

$$1 = f'(x)\ x_y,$$
$$0 = f''(x)\ (x_y)^2 + f'(x)\ x_{y^2},$$
$$0 = f'''(x)\ (x_y)^3 + 3f''(x)\ x_y\, x_{y^2} + f'(x)\ x_{y^3},$$
. . . . ,

whence

$$x_y = \frac{1}{f'(x)}, \qquad x_{y^2} = -\frac{f''(x)}{[f'(x)]^3}, \qquad x_{y^3} = \frac{3\,[f''(x)]^2 - f'(x)f'''(x)}{[f'(x)]^5}, \qquad \cdots.$$

It should be noticed that these formulæ are not altered if we exchange x_y and $f'(x)$, x_{y^2} and $f''(x)$, x_{y^3} and $f'''(x)$, $\cdots$, for it is evident that the relation between the two functions $y = f(x)$ and $x = \phi(y)$ is a reciprocal one.

As an application of these formulæ, let us determine all those functions $y = f(x)$ which satisfy the equation

$$y'y''' - 3y''^2 = 0.$$

Taking y as the independent variable and x as the function, this equation becomes

$$x_{y^3} = 0.$$

But the only functions whose third derivatives are zero are polynomials of at most the second degree. Hence x must be of the form

$$x = C_1 y^2 + C_2 y + C_3,$$

where C_1, C_2, C_3 are three arbitrary constants. Solving this equation for y, we see that the only functions $y = f(x)$ which satisfy the given equation are of the form

$$y = a \pm \sqrt{bx + c},$$

where a, b, c are three arbitrary constants. This equation represents a parabola whose axis is parallel to the x axis.

24. Partial derivatives. Let us now consider an implicit function of two variables, defined by the equation

$$(6) \qquad F(x, y, z) = 0.$$

The partial derivatives of the first order are given, as we have seen, by the equations

$$(7) \qquad \frac{\partial F}{\partial x} + \frac{\partial F}{\partial z} \frac{\partial z}{\partial x} = 0, \qquad \frac{\partial F}{\partial y} + \frac{\partial F}{\partial z} \frac{\partial z}{\partial y} = 0.$$

To determine the partial derivatives of the second order we need only differentiate the two equations (7) again with respect to x and with respect to y. This gives, however, only three new equations, for the derivative of the first of the equations (7) with respect to y is identical with the derivative of the second with respect to x. The new equations are the following:

$$(8) \quad \begin{cases} \dfrac{\partial^2 F}{\partial x^2} + 2 \dfrac{\partial^2 F}{\partial x \, \partial z} \dfrac{\partial z}{\partial x} + \dfrac{\partial^2 F}{\partial z^2} \left(\dfrac{\partial z}{\partial x} \right)^2 + \dfrac{\partial F}{\partial z} \dfrac{\partial^2 z}{\partial x^2} = 0, \\[2ex] \dfrac{\partial^2 F}{\partial x \, \partial y} + \dfrac{\partial^2 F}{\partial x \, \partial z} \dfrac{\partial z}{\partial y} + \dfrac{\partial^2 F}{\partial y \, \partial z} \dfrac{\partial z}{\partial x} + \dfrac{\partial^2 F}{\partial z^2} \dfrac{\partial z}{\partial x} \dfrac{\partial z}{\partial y} + \dfrac{\partial F}{\partial z} \dfrac{\partial^2 z}{\partial x \, \partial y} = 0, \\[2ex] \dfrac{\partial^2 F}{\partial y^2} + 2 \dfrac{\partial^2 F}{\partial y \, \partial z} \dfrac{\partial z}{\partial y} + \dfrac{\partial^2 F}{\partial z^2} \left(\dfrac{\partial z}{\partial y} \right)^2 + \dfrac{\partial F}{\partial z} \dfrac{\partial^2 z}{\partial y^2} = 0. \end{cases}$$

The third and higher derivatives may be found in a similar manner.

By the use of total differentials we can find all the partial derivatives of a given order at the same time. This depends upon the following theorem:

If several functions u, v, w, $\cdots$ of any number of independent variables x, y, z, $\cdots$ satisfy a relation $F = 0$, the total differentials satisfy the relation $dF = 0$, which is obtained by forming the total differential of F as if all the variables which occur in F were independent variables.

In order to prove this let $F(u, v, w) = 0$ be the given relation between the three functions u, v, w of the independent variables x, y, z, t. The first partial derivatives of u, v, w satisfy the four equations

$$\frac{\partial F}{\partial u} \frac{\partial u}{\partial x} + \frac{\partial F}{\partial v} \frac{\partial v}{\partial x} + \frac{\partial F}{\partial w} \frac{\partial w}{\partial x} = 0,$$

$$\frac{\partial F}{\partial u} \frac{\partial u}{\partial y} + \frac{\partial F}{\partial v} \frac{\partial v}{\partial y} + \frac{\partial F}{\partial w} \frac{\partial w}{\partial y} = 0,$$

$$\frac{\partial F}{\partial u}\frac{\partial u}{\partial z} + \frac{\partial F}{\partial v}\frac{\partial v}{\partial z} + \frac{\partial F}{\partial w}\frac{\partial w}{\partial z} = 0,$$

$$\frac{\partial F}{\partial u}\frac{\partial u}{\partial t} + \frac{\partial F}{\partial v}\frac{\partial v}{\partial t} + \frac{\partial F}{\partial w}\frac{\partial w}{\partial t} = 0.$$

Multiplying these equations by dx, dy, dz, dt, respectively, and adding, we find

$$\frac{\partial F}{\partial u}\,du + \frac{\partial F}{\partial v}\,dv + \frac{\partial F}{\partial w}\,dw = dF = 0.$$

This shows again the advantage of the differential notation, for the preceding equation is independent of the choice and of the number of independent variables. To find a relation between the second total differentials, we need merely apply the general theorem to the equation $dF = 0$, considered as an equation between u, v, w, du, dv, dw, and so forth. The differentials of higher order than the first of those variables which are chosen for independent variables must, of course, be replaced by zeros.

Let us apply this theorem to calculate the successive total differentials of the implicit function defined by the equation (6), where x and y are regarded as the independent variables. We find

$$\frac{\partial F}{\partial x}\,dx + \frac{\partial F}{\partial y}\,dy + \frac{\partial F}{\partial z}\,dz = 0,$$

$$\left(\frac{\partial F}{\partial x}\,dx + \frac{\partial F}{\partial y}\,dy + \frac{\partial F}{\partial z}\,dz\right)^{(2)} + \frac{\partial F}{\partial z}\,d^2z = 0,$$

$$. \quad . \quad . \quad . \quad . \quad . \quad . \quad . \quad . \quad . \quad . \quad . \quad . \quad . \quad ,$$

and the first two of these equations may be used instead of the five equations (7) and (8); from the expression for dz we may find the two first derivatives, from that for d^2z the three of the second order, etc. Consider for example, the equation

$$Ax^2 + A'y^2 + A''z^2 = 1,$$

which gives, after two differentiations,

$$Ax\,dx + A'y\,dy + A''z\,dz = 0,$$

$$A\,dx^2 + A'\,dy^2 + A''dz^2 + A''z\,d^2z = 0,$$

whence

$$dz = -\frac{Ax\,dx + A'y\,dy}{A''z};$$

and, introducing this value of dz in the second equation, we find

$$d^2z = -\frac{A\,(Ax^2 + A''z^2)\,dx^2 + 2\,A\,A'xy\,dx\,dy + A'(A'y^2 + A''z^2)\,dy^2}{A''^2\,z^3}.$$

Using Monge's notation, we have then

$$p = -\frac{A\,x}{A''z}, \qquad q = -\frac{A'y}{A''z},$$

$$r = -\frac{A\,(A\,x^2 + A''z^2)}{A''^2\,z^3}, \qquad s = -\frac{A\,A'\,xy}{A''^2\,z^3}, \qquad t = -\frac{A'(A'y^2 + A''z^2)}{A''^2\,z^3}.$$

This method is evidently general, whatever be the number of the independent variables or the order of the partial derivatives which it is desired to calculate.

Example. Let $z = f(x, y)$ be a function of x and y. Let us try to calculate the differentials of the first and second orders dx and d^2x, regarding y and z as the independent variables, and x as an implicit function of them. First of all, we have

$$dz = \frac{\partial f}{\partial x}\,dx + \frac{\partial f}{\partial y}\,dy.$$

Since y and z are now the independent variables, we must set

$$d^2y = d^2z = 0,$$

and consequently a second differentiation gives

$$0 = \frac{\partial^2 f}{\partial x^2}\,dx^2 + 2\,\frac{\partial^2 f}{\partial x\,\partial y}\,dx\,dy + \frac{\partial^2 f}{\partial y^2}\,dy^2 + \frac{\partial f}{\partial x}\,d^2x.$$

In Monge's notation, using p, q, r, s, t for the derivatives of $f(x, y)$, these equations may be written in the form

$$dz = p\,dx + q\,dy,$$
$$0 = r\,dx^2 + 2\,s\,dx\,dy + t\,dy^2 + p\,d^2x.$$

From the first we find

$$dx = \frac{dz - q\,dy}{p},$$

and, substituting this value of dx in the second equation,

$$d^2x = -\frac{r\,dz^2 + 2\,(p\,s - q\,r)\,dy\,dz + (q^2r - 2\,p\,q\,s + p^2t)\,dy^2}{p^3}.$$

The first and second partial derivatives of x, regarded as a function of y and z, therefore, have the following values:

$$\frac{\partial x}{\partial z} = \frac{1}{p}, \qquad \frac{\partial x}{\partial y} = -\frac{q}{p},$$

$$\frac{\partial^2 x}{\partial z^2} = -\frac{r}{p^3}, \qquad \frac{\partial^2 x}{\partial y\,\partial z} = \frac{q\,r - p\,s}{p^3}, \qquad \frac{\partial^2 x}{\partial y^2} = \frac{2\,p\,q\,s - p^2t - q^2r}{p^3}.$$

As an application of these formulæ, let us find all those functions $f(x, y)$ which satisfy the equation

$$q^2r + p^2t = 2\,pqs.$$

If, in the equation $z = f(x, y)$, x be considered as a function of the two independent variables y and z, the given equation reduces to $x_{y^2} = 0$. This means that x_y is independent of y; and hence $x_y = \phi(z)$, where $\phi(z)$ is an arbitrary function of z. This, in turn, may be written in the form

$$\frac{\partial}{\partial y}[x - y\,\phi(z)] = 0,$$

which shows that $x - y\,\phi(z)$ is independent of y. Hence we may write

$$x = y\,\phi(z) + \psi(z),$$

where $\psi(z)$ is another arbitrary function of z. It is clear, therefore, that all the functions $z = f(x, y)$ which satisfy the given equation, except those for which f_x vanishes, are found by solving this last equation for z. This equation represents a surface generated by a straight line which is always parallel to the xy plane.

25. The general theorem. *Let us consider a system of n equations*

(E) $\qquad \begin{cases} F_1(x_1, x_2, \cdots, x_p\,; \ u_1, u_2, \cdots, u_n) = 0, \\ F_2(x_1, x_2, \cdots, x_p\,; \ u_1, u_2, \cdots, u_n) = 0, \\ \ \cdot \ \ \cdot \ \ \cdot \ \ \cdot \ \ \cdot \ \ \cdot \ \ \cdot \ \ \cdot \ \ \cdot \ \ \cdot \ \ \cdot \ \ \cdot \ \ \cdot \ , \\ F_n(x_1, x_2, \cdots, x_p\,; \ u_1, u_2, \cdots, u_n) = 0, \end{cases}$

between the $n + p$ variables $u_1, u_2, \cdots, u_n$; $x_1, x_2, \cdots, x_p$. Suppose that these equations are satisfied for the values $x_1 = x_1^0, \cdots, x_p = x_p^0$, $u_1 = u_1^0, \cdots, u_n = u_n^0$; that the functions F_i are continuous and possess first partial derivatives which are continuous, in the neighborhood of this system of values; and, finally, that the determinant

$$\Delta = \begin{vmatrix} \dfrac{\partial F_1}{\partial u_1} & \dfrac{\partial F_1}{\partial u_2} & \cdots & \dfrac{\partial F_1}{\partial u_n} \\[2mm] \dfrac{\partial F_2}{\partial u_1} & \dfrac{\partial F_2}{\partial u_2} & \cdots & \dfrac{\partial F_2}{\partial u_n} \\[2mm] \cdot & \cdot & \cdot & \cdot \\ \dfrac{\partial F_n}{\partial u_1} & \dfrac{\partial F_n}{\partial u_2} & \cdots & \dfrac{\partial F_n}{\partial u_n} \end{vmatrix}$$

does not vanish for

$$x_i = x_i^0, \qquad u_k = u_k^0, \qquad (i = 1, 2, \cdots, p\,; \ k = 1, 2, \cdots, n).$$

Under these conditions there exists one and only one system of continuous functions $u_1 = \phi_1(x_1, x_2, \cdots, x_p), \cdots, u_n = \phi_n(x_1, x_2, \cdots, x_p)$ which satisfy the equations (E) *and which reduce to $u_1^0, u_2^0, \cdots, u_n^0$, for $x_1 = x_1^0, \cdots, x_p = x_p^0$.*[*]

---

[*] In his paper quoted above (ftn., p. 35) Goursat proves that the same conclusion may be reached without making any hypotheses whatever regarding the derivatives $\partial F_i / \partial x_j$ of the functions F_i with regard to the x's. Otherwise the hypotheses remain exactly as stated above. It is to be noticed that the later theorems regarding the existence of the derivatives of the functions ϕ would not follow, however, without some assumptions regarding $\partial F_i / \partial x_j$. The proof given is based on the following

The determinant Δ is called the *Jacobian*,* or the *Functional Determinant,* of the n functions F_1, F_2, $\cdots$, F_n with respect to the n variables u_1, u_2, $\cdots$, u_n. It is represented by the notation

$$\frac{D(F_1,\ F_2,\ \cdots,\ F_n)}{D(u_1,\ u_2,\ \cdots,\ u_n)}.$$

We will begin by proving the theorem in the special case of a system of two equations in three independent variables x, y, z and two unknowns u and v.

(9) $$F_1(x,\ y,\ z,\ u,\ v) = 0,$$

(10) $$F_2(x,\ y,\ z,\ u,\ v) = 0.$$

These equations are satisfied, by hypothesis, for $x = x_0, y = y_0, z = z_0$, $u = u_0$, $v = v_0$; and the determinant

$$\frac{\partial F_1}{\partial u}\frac{\partial F_2}{\partial v} - \frac{\partial F_1}{\partial v}\frac{\partial F_2}{\partial u}$$

does not vanish for this set of values. It follows that at least one of the derivatives $\partial F_1/\partial v$, $\partial F_2/\partial v$ does not vanish for these same values. Suppose, for definiteness, that $\partial F_1/\partial v$ does not vanish. According to the theorem proved above for a single equation, the relation (9) defines a function v of the variables x, y, z, u,

$$v = f(x,\ y,\ z,\ u),$$

which reduces to v_0 for $x = x_0$, $y = y_0$, $z = z_0$, $u = u_0$. Replacing v in the equation (10) by this function, we obtain an equation between x, y, z, and u,

$$\Phi(x,\ y,\ z,\ u) = F_2[x,\ y,\ z,\ u, f(x,\ y,\ z,\ u)] = 0,$$

---

lemma: *Let* $f_1(x_1, x_2, \cdots, x_p; u_1, u_2, \cdots, u_n)$, $\cdots$, $f_n(x_1, x_2, \cdots, x_p; u_1, u_2, \cdots, u_n)$ *be* n *functions of the* $n + p$ *variables* x_i *and* u_k, *which, together with the* n^2 *partial derivatives* $\partial f_i/\partial u_k$, *are continuous near* $x_1 = 0$, $x_2 = 0$, $\cdots$, $x_p = 0$, $u_1 = 0$, $\cdots$, $u_n = 0$. *If the* n *functions* f_i *and the* n^2 *derivatives* $\partial f_i/\partial u_k$ *all vanish for this system of values, then the* n *equations*

$$u_1 = f_1, \qquad u_2 = f_2, \qquad \cdots, \qquad u_n = f_n$$

admit one and only one system of solutions of the form

$$u_1 = \phi_1(x_1, x_2, \cdots, x_p), \qquad u_2 = \phi_2(x_1, x_2, \cdots, x_p), \qquad \cdots, \qquad u_n = \phi_n(x_1, x_2, \cdots, x_p),$$

where ϕ_1, ϕ_2, $\cdots$, ϕ_n *are continuous functions of the* p *variables* x_1, x_2, $\cdots$, x_p *which all approach zero as the variables all approach zero.* The lemma is proved by means of a suite of functions $u_i^{(m)} = f_i(x_1, x_2, \cdots, x_p; u_1^{(m-1)}, u_2^{(m-1)}, \cdots, u_n^{(m-1)})$ $(i = 1, 2, \cdots, n)$, where $u_i^{(0)} = 0$. It is shown that the suite of functions $u_i^{(m)}$ thus defined approaches a limiting function U_i, which 1) satisfies the given equations, and 2) constitutes the only solution. The passage from the lemma to the theorem consists in an easy transformation of the equations (E) into a form similar to that of the lemma. — Trans.

*Jacobi, *Crelle's Journal*, Vol. XXII.

which is satisfied for $x = x_0$, $y = y_0$, $z = z_0$, $u = u_0$. **Now**

$$\frac{\partial \Phi}{\partial u} = \frac{\partial F_2}{\partial u} + \frac{\partial F_2}{\partial v} \frac{\partial f}{\partial u};$$

and from equation (9),

$$\frac{\partial F_1}{\partial u} + \frac{\partial F_1}{\partial v} \frac{\partial f}{\partial u} = 0;$$

whence, replacing $\partial f / \partial u$ by this value in the expression for $\partial \Phi / \partial u$, we obtain

$$\frac{\partial \Phi}{\partial u} = - \frac{\dfrac{D(F_1, F_2)}{D(u, v)}}{\dfrac{\partial F_1}{\partial v}}.$$

It is evident that this derivative does not vanish for the values x_0, y_0, z_0, u_0. Hence the equation $\Phi = 0$ is satisfied when u is replaced by a certain continuous function $u = \phi(x, y, z)$, which is equal to u_0 when $x = x_0$, $y = y_0$, $z = z_0$; and, replacing u by $\phi(x, y, z)$ in $f(x, y, z, u)$, we obtain for v also a certain continuous function. The proposition is then proved for a system of two equations.

We can show, as in § 21, that these functions possess partial derivatives of the first order. Keeping y and z constant, let us give x an increment Δx, and let Δu and Δv be the corresponding increments of the functions u and v. The equations (9) and (10) then give us the equations

$$\Delta x \left(\frac{\partial F_1}{\partial x} + \epsilon \right) + \Delta u \left(\frac{\partial F_1}{\partial u} + \epsilon' \right) + \Delta v \left(\frac{\partial F_1}{\partial v} + \epsilon'' \right) = 0$$

$$\Delta x \left(\frac{\partial F_2}{\partial x} + \eta \right) + \Delta u \left(\frac{\partial F_2}{\partial u} + \eta' \right) + \Delta v \left(\frac{\partial F_2}{\partial v} + \eta'' \right) = 0,$$

where ϵ, ϵ', ϵ'', η, η', η'' approach zero with Δx, Δu, Δv. It follows that

$$\frac{\Delta u}{\Delta x} = - \frac{\left(\dfrac{\partial F_1}{\partial x} + \epsilon \right)\left(\dfrac{\partial F_2}{\partial v} + \eta'' \right) - \left(\dfrac{\partial F_1}{\partial v} + \epsilon'' \right)\left(\dfrac{\partial F_2}{\partial x} + \eta \right)}{\left(\dfrac{\partial F_1}{\partial u} + \epsilon' \right)\left(\dfrac{\partial F_2}{\partial v} + \eta'' \right) - \left(\dfrac{\partial F_1}{\partial v} + \epsilon'' \right)\left(\dfrac{\partial F_2}{\partial u} + \eta' \right)}.$$

When Δx approaches zero, Δu and Δv also approach zero; and hence ϵ, ϵ', ϵ'', η, η', η'' do so at the same time. The ratio $\Delta u / \Delta x$ therefore approaches a limit; that is, u possesses a derivative with respect to x:

$$\frac{\partial u}{\partial x} = - \frac{\dfrac{\partial F_1}{\partial x}\dfrac{\partial F_2}{\partial v} - \dfrac{\partial F_1}{\partial v}\dfrac{\partial F_2}{\partial x}}{\dfrac{\partial F_1}{\partial u}\dfrac{\partial F_2}{\partial v} - \dfrac{\partial F_1}{\partial v}\dfrac{\partial F_2}{\partial u}}.$$

It follows in like manner that the ratio $\Delta v / \Delta x$ approaches a finite limit $\partial v / \partial x$, which is given by an analogous formula. Practically, these derivatives may be calculated by means of the two equations

$$\frac{\partial F_1}{\partial x} + \frac{\partial F_1}{\partial u}\frac{\partial u}{\partial x} + \frac{\partial F_1}{\partial v}\frac{\partial v}{\partial x} = 0,$$

$$\frac{\partial F_2}{\partial x} + \frac{\partial F_2}{\partial u}\frac{\partial u}{\partial x} + \frac{\partial F_2}{\partial v}\frac{\partial v}{\partial x} = 0;$$

and the partial derivatives with respect to y and z may be found in a similar manner.

In order to prove the general theorem it will be sufficient to show that if the proposition holds for a system of $(n-1)$ equations, it will hold also for a system of n equations. Since, by hypothesis, the functional determinant Δ does not vanish for the initial values of the variables, at least one of the first minors corresponding to the elements of the last row is different from zero for these same values. Suppose, for definiteness, that it is the minor which corresponds to $\partial F_n / \partial u_n$ which is not zero. This minor is precisely

$$\frac{D(F_1, F_2, \cdots, F_{n-1})}{D(u_1, u_2, \cdots, u_{n-1})};$$

and, since the theorem is assumed to hold for a system of $(n-1)$ equations, it is clear that we may obtain solutions of the first $(n-1)$ of the equations (E) in the form

$$u_1 = \phi_1(x_1, x_2, \cdots, x_p; u_n), \quad \cdots, \quad u_{n-1} = \phi_{n-1}(x_1, x_2, \cdots, x_p; u_n),$$

where the functions ϕ_i are continuous. Then, replacing $u_1, \cdots, u_{n-1}$ by the functions $\phi_1, \cdots, \phi_{n-1}$ in the last of equations (E), we obtain a new equation for the determination of u_n,

$$\Phi(x_1, x_2, \cdots, x_p; u_n) = F_n(x_1, x_2, \cdots, x_p; \phi_1, \phi_2, \cdots, \phi_{n-1}, u_n) = 0.$$

It only remains for us to show that the derivative $\partial \Phi / \partial u_n$ does not vanish for the given set of values $x_1^0, x_2^0, \cdots, x_p^0, u_n^0$; for, if so, we can solve this last equation in the form

$$u_n = \psi(x_1, x_2, \cdots, x_p),$$

where ψ is continuous. Then, substituting this value of u_n in $\phi_1, \cdots, \phi_{n-1}$, we would obtain certain continuous functions for

$u_1, u_2, \cdots, u_{n-1}$ also. In order to show that the derivative in question does not vanish, let us consider the equation

$$(11) \qquad \frac{\partial \Phi}{\partial u_n} = \frac{\partial F_n}{\partial u_1} \frac{\partial \phi_1}{\partial u_n} + \cdots + \frac{\partial F_n}{\partial u_{n-1}} \frac{\partial \phi_{n-1}}{\partial u_n} + \frac{\partial F_n}{\partial u_n}.$$

The derivatives $\partial\phi_1/\partial u_n$, $\partial\phi_2/\partial u_n$, $\cdots$, $\partial\phi_{n-1}/\partial u_n$ are given by the $(n-1)$ equations

$$(12) \qquad \begin{cases} \dfrac{\partial F_1}{\partial u_1} \dfrac{\partial \phi_1}{\partial u_n} + \cdots + \dfrac{\partial F_1}{\partial u_{n-1}} \dfrac{\partial \phi_{n-1}}{\partial u_n} + \dfrac{\partial F_1}{\partial u_n} = 0, \\ \cdot \quad \cdot \quad \cdot \quad \cdot \quad \cdot \quad \cdot \quad \cdot \quad \cdot \quad \cdot \quad \cdot \quad \cdot \quad \cdot \quad \cdot \quad \cdot \quad \cdot \quad , \\ \dfrac{\partial F_{n-1}}{\partial u_1} \dfrac{\partial \phi_1}{\partial u_n} + \cdots + \dfrac{\partial F_{n-1}}{\partial u_{n-1}} \dfrac{\partial \phi_{n-1}}{\partial u_n} + \dfrac{\partial F_{n-1}}{\partial u_n} = 0; \end{cases}$$

and we may consider the equations (11) and (12) as n linear equations for $\partial\phi_1/\partial u_n$, $\cdots$, $\partial\phi_{n-1}/\partial u_n$, $\partial\Phi/\partial u_n$, from which we find

$$\frac{\partial \Phi}{\partial u_n} \frac{D(F_1, F_2, \cdots, F_{n-1})}{D(u_1, u_2, \cdots, u_{n-1})} = \frac{D(F_1, F_2, \cdots, F_n)}{D(u_1, u_2, \cdots, u_n)}.$$

It follows that the derivative $\partial\Phi/\partial u_n$ does not vanish for the initial values, and hence the general theorem is proved.

The successive derivatives of implicit functions defined by several equations may be calculated in a manner analogous to that used in the case of a single equation. When there are several independent variables it is advantageous to form the total differentials, from which the partial derivatives of the same order may be found. Consider the case of two functions u and v of the three variables x, y, z defined by the two equations

$$F(x, y, z, u, v) = 0,$$
$$\Phi(x, y, z, u, v) = 0.$$

The total differentials of the first order du and dv are given by the two equations

$$\frac{\partial F}{\partial x} dx + \frac{\partial F}{\partial y} dy + \frac{\partial F}{\partial z} dz + \frac{\partial F}{\partial u} du + \frac{\partial F}{\partial v} dv = 0,$$

$$\frac{\partial \Phi}{\partial x} dx + \frac{\partial \Phi}{\partial y} dy + \frac{\partial \Phi}{\partial z} dz + \frac{\partial \Phi}{\partial u} du + \frac{\partial \Phi}{\partial v} dv = 0.$$

Likewise, the second total differentials d^2u and d^2v are given by the equations

$$\left(\frac{\partial F}{\partial x}\,dx + \cdots + \frac{\partial F}{\partial v}\,dv\right)^{(2)} + \frac{\partial F}{\partial u}\,d^2u + \frac{\partial F}{\partial v}\,d^2v = 0,$$

$$\left(\frac{\partial \Phi}{\partial x}\,dx + \cdots + \frac{\partial \Phi}{\partial v}\,dv\right)^{(2)} + \frac{\partial \Phi}{\partial u}\,d^2u + \frac{\partial \Phi}{\partial v}\,d^2v = 0,$$

and so forth. In the equations which give $d^n u$ and $d^n v$ the determinant of the coefficients of those differentials is equal for all values of n to the Jacobian $D(F, \Phi)/D(u, v)$, which, by hypothesis, does not vanish.

26. Inversion. Let $u_1, u_2, \cdots, u_n$ be n functions of the n independent variables $x_1, x_2, \cdots, x_n$, such that the Jacobian $D(u_1, u_2, \cdots, u_n)/D(x_1, x_2, \cdots, x_n)$ does not vanish identically. The n equations

$$(13) \quad \begin{cases} u_1 = \phi_1(x_1, x_2, \cdots, x_n), \quad\quad u_2 = \phi_2(x_1, x_2, \cdots, x_n), \quad\quad \cdots, \\ \quad\quad\quad\quad u_n = \phi_n(x_1, x_2, \cdots, x_n) \end{cases}$$

define, inversely, $x_1, x_2, \cdots, x_n$ as functions of $u_1, u_2, \cdots, u_n$. For, taking any system of values $x_1^0, x_2^0, \cdots, x_n^0$, for which the Jacobian does not vanish, and denoting the corresponding values of $u_1, u_2, \cdots, u_n$ by $u_1^0, u_2^0, \cdots, u_n^0$, there exists, according to the general theorem, a system of functions

$$x_1 = \psi_1(u_1, u_2, \cdots, u_n), \quad x_2 = \psi_2(u_1, u_2, \cdots, u_n), \quad \cdots, \quad x_n = \psi_n(u_1, u_2, \cdots, u_n),$$

which satisfy (13), and which take on the values $x_1^0, x_2^0, \cdots, x_n^0$, respectively, when $u_1 = u_1^0, \cdots, u_n = u_n^0$. These functions are called the *inverses* of the functions $\phi_1, \phi_2, \cdots, \phi_n$, and the process of actually determining them is called an *inversion*.

In order to compute the derivatives of these inverse functions we need merely apply the general rule. Thus, in the case of two functions

$$u = f(x, y), \quad\quad\quad v = \phi(x, y),$$

if we consider u and v as the independent variables and x and y as inverse functions, we have the two equations

$$du = \frac{\partial f}{\partial x}\,dx + \frac{\partial f}{\partial y}\,dy, \quad\quad dv = \frac{\partial \phi}{\partial x}\,dx + \frac{\partial \phi}{\partial y}\,dy,$$

whence

$$dx = \frac{\dfrac{\partial \phi}{\partial y}\,du - \dfrac{\partial f}{\partial y}\,dv}{\dfrac{\partial f}{\partial x}\dfrac{\partial \phi}{\partial y} - \dfrac{\partial f}{\partial y}\dfrac{\partial \phi}{\partial x}}, \quad\quad dy = \frac{-\dfrac{\partial \phi}{\partial x}\,du + \dfrac{\partial f}{\partial x}\,dv}{\dfrac{\partial f}{\partial x}\dfrac{\partial \phi}{\partial y} - \dfrac{\partial f}{\partial y}\dfrac{\partial \phi}{\partial x}}.$$

We have then, finally, the formulæ

$$\frac{\partial x}{\partial u} = \frac{\dfrac{\partial \phi}{\partial y}}{\dfrac{\partial f}{\partial x}\dfrac{\partial \phi}{\partial y} - \dfrac{\partial f}{\partial y}\dfrac{\partial \phi}{\partial x}}, \quad\quad \frac{\partial x}{\partial v} = \frac{-\dfrac{\partial f}{\partial y}}{\dfrac{\partial f}{\partial x}\dfrac{\partial \phi}{\partial y} - \dfrac{\partial f}{\partial y}\dfrac{\partial \phi}{\partial x}},$$

$$\frac{\partial y}{\partial u} = \frac{-\dfrac{\partial \phi}{\partial x}}{\dfrac{\partial f}{\partial x}\dfrac{\partial \phi}{\partial y} - \dfrac{\partial f}{\partial y}\dfrac{\partial \phi}{\partial x}}, \qquad \frac{\partial y}{\partial v} = \frac{\dfrac{\partial f}{\partial x}}{\dfrac{\partial f}{\partial x}\dfrac{\partial \phi}{\partial y} - \dfrac{\partial f}{\partial y}\dfrac{\partial \phi}{\partial x}}.$$

27. Tangents to skew curves. Let us consider a curve C represented by the two equations

$$(14) \qquad \begin{cases} F_1(x, y, z) = 0, \\ F_2(x, y, z) = 0; \end{cases}$$

and let x_0, y_0, z_0 be the coördinates of a point M_0 of this curve, such that at least one of the three Jacobians

$$\frac{\partial F_1}{\partial y}\frac{\partial F_2}{\partial z} - \frac{\partial F_1}{\partial z}\frac{\partial F_2}{\partial y}, \qquad \frac{\partial F_1}{\partial z}\frac{\partial F_2}{\partial x} - \frac{\partial F_1}{\partial x}\frac{\partial F_2}{\partial z}, \qquad \frac{\partial F_1}{\partial x}\frac{\partial F_2}{\partial y} - \frac{\partial F_1}{\partial y}\frac{\partial F_2}{\partial x}$$

does not vanish when x, y, z are replaced by x_0, y_0, z_0, respectively. Suppose, for definiteness, that $D(F_1, F_2)/D(y, z)$ is one which does not vanish at the point M_0. Then the equations (14) may be solved in the form

$$y = \phi(x), \qquad z = \psi(x),$$

where ϕ and ψ are continuous functions of x which reduce to y_0 and z_0, respectively, when $x = x_0$. The tangent to the curve C at the point M_0 is therefore represented by the two equations

$$\frac{X - x_0}{1} = \frac{Y - y_0}{\phi'(x_0)} = \frac{Z - z_0}{\psi'(x_0)},$$

where the derivatives $\phi'(x)$ and $\psi'(\dot{x})$ may be found from the two equations

$$\frac{\partial F_1}{\partial x} + \frac{\partial F_1}{\partial y}\,\phi'(x) + \frac{\partial F_1}{\partial z}\,\psi'(x) = 0,$$

$$\frac{\partial F_2}{\partial x} + \frac{\partial F_2}{\partial y}\,\phi'(x) + \frac{\partial F_2}{\partial z}\,\psi'(x) = 0.$$

In these two equations let us set $x = x_0, y = y_0, z = z_0$, and replace $\phi'(x_0)$ and $\psi'(x_0)$ by $(Y - y_0)/(X - x_0)$ and $(Z - z_0)/(X - x_0)$, respectively. The equations of the tangent then become

$$(15) \qquad \begin{cases} \left(\dfrac{\partial F_1}{\partial x}\right)_0 (X - x_0) + \left(\dfrac{\partial F_1}{\partial y}\right)_0 (Y - y_0) + \left(\dfrac{\partial F_1}{\partial z}\right)_0 (Z - z_0) = 0, \\[2mm] \left(\dfrac{\partial F_2}{\partial x}\right)_0 (X - x_0) + \left(\dfrac{\partial F_2}{\partial y}\right)_0 (Y - y_0) + \left(\dfrac{\partial F_2}{\partial z}\right)_0 (Z - z_0) = 0, \end{cases}$$

or

$$\frac{X - x_0}{\left[\dfrac{D(F_1, F_2)}{D(y, z)}\right]_0} = \frac{Y - y_0}{\left[\dfrac{D(F_1, F_2)}{D(z, x)}\right]_0} = \frac{Z - z_0}{\left[\dfrac{D(F_1, F_2)}{D(x, y)}\right]_0}.$$

The geometrical interpretation of this result is very easy. The two equations (14) represent, respectively, two surfaces S_1 and S_2, of which C is the line of intersection. The equations (15) represent the two tangent planes to these two surfaces at the point M_0; and the tangent to C is the intersection of these two planes.

The formulæ become illusory when the three Jacobians above all vanish at the point M_0. In this case the two equations (15) reduce to a single equation, and the surfaces S_1 and S_2 are tangent at the point M_0. The intersection of the two surfaces will then consist, in general, as we shall see, of several distinct branches through the point M_0.

II. FUNCTIONAL DETERMINANTS

28. Fundamental property. We have just seen what an important rôle functional determinants play in the theory of implicit functions. All the above demonstrations expressly presuppose that a certain Jacobian does not vanish for the assumed set of initial values. Omitting the case in which the Jacobian vanishes only for certain particular values of the variables, we shall proceed to examine the very important case in which the Jacobian vanishes identically. The following theorem is fundamental.

Let u_1, u_2, $\cdots$, u_n be n functions of the n independent variables x_1, x_2, $\cdots$, x_n. In order that there exist between these n functions a relation $\Pi(u_1, u_2, \cdots, u_n) = 0$, which does not involve explicitly any of the variables x_1, x_2, $\cdots$, x_n, it is necessary and sufficient that the functional determinant

$$\frac{D(u_1, u_2, \cdots, u_n)}{D(x_1, x_2, \cdots, x_n)}$$

should vanish identically.

In the first place this condition is *necessary*. For, if such a relation $\Pi(u_1, u_2, \cdots, u_n) = 0$ exists between the n functions u_1, u_2, $\cdots$, u_n, the following n equations, deduced by differentiating with respect to each of the x's in order, must hold:

$$\frac{\partial \Pi}{\partial u_1}\frac{\partial u_1}{\partial x_1} + \frac{\partial \Pi}{\partial u_2}\frac{\partial u_2}{\partial x_1} + \cdots + \frac{\partial \Pi}{\partial u_n}\frac{\partial u_n}{\partial x_1} = 0,$$

$$\cdot \quad \cdot \quad \cdot \quad \cdot \quad \cdot \quad \cdot \quad \cdot \quad \cdot \quad \cdot \quad \cdot \quad \cdot \quad \cdot \quad \cdot \quad \cdot \quad \cdot \quad ,$$

$$\frac{\partial \Pi}{\partial u_1}\frac{\partial u_1}{\partial x_n} + \frac{\partial \Pi}{\partial u_2}\frac{\partial u_2}{\partial x_n} + \cdots + \frac{\partial \Pi}{\partial u_n}\frac{\partial u_n}{\partial x_n} = 0;$$

and, since we cannot have, at the same time,

$$\frac{\partial \Pi}{\partial u_1} = \frac{\partial \Pi}{\partial u_2} = \cdots = \frac{\partial \Pi}{\partial u_n} = 0,$$

since the relation considered would in that case reduce to a trivial identity, it is clear that the determinant of the coefficients, which is precisely the Jacobian of the theorem, must vanish.*

The condition is also *sufficient*. To prove this, we shall make use of certain facts which follow immediately from the general theorems.

1) Let u, v, w be three functions of the three independent variables x, y, z, such that the functional determinant $D(u, v, w)/D(x, y, z)$ is not zero. Then no relation of the form

$$\lambda \, du + \mu \, dv + \nu \, dw = 0$$

can exist between the total differentials du, dv, dw, except for $\lambda = \mu = \nu = 0$. For, equating the coefficients of dx, dy, dz in the foregoing equation to zero, there result three equations for λ, μ, ν which have no other solutions than $\lambda = \mu = \nu = 0$.

2) Let ω, u, v, w be four functions of the three independent variables x, y, z, such that the determinant $D(u, v, w)/D(x, y, z)$ is not zero. We can then express x, y, z inversely as functions of u, v, w; and substituting these values for x, y, z in ω, we obtain a function

$$\omega = \Phi(u, v, w)$$

of the three variables u, v, w. *If by any process whatever we can obtain a relation of the form*

$$(16) \qquad d\omega = P \, du + Q \, dv + R \, dw$$

---

* As Professor Osgood has pointed out, the reasoning here supposes that the partial derivatives $\partial \Pi / \partial u_1$, $\partial \Pi / \partial u_2$, $\cdots$, $\partial \Pi / \partial u_n$ do not all vanish simultaneously for any system of values which cause $\Pi(u_1, u_2, \cdots, u_n)$ to vanish. This supposition is certainly justified when the relation $\Pi = 0$ is solved for one of the variables u_i.

*between the total differentials $d\omega$, du, dv, dw, taken with respect to the
independent variables x, y, z, then the coefficients P, Q, R are equal,
respectively, to the three first partial derivatives of $\Phi(u, v, w)$:*

$$P = \frac{\partial \Phi}{\partial u}, \qquad Q = \frac{\partial \Phi}{\partial v}, \qquad R = \frac{\partial \Phi}{\partial w}.$$

For, by the rule for the total differential of a composite function
(§ 16), we have

$$d\omega = \frac{\partial \Phi}{\partial u}\, du + \frac{\partial \Phi}{\partial v}\, dv + \frac{\partial \Phi}{\partial w}\, dw\,;$$

and there cannot exist any other relation of the form (16) between
$d\omega$, du, dv, dw, for that would lead to a relation of the form

$$\lambda\, du + \mu\, dv + \nu\, dw = 0,$$

where λ, μ, ν do not all vanish. We have just seen that this is
impossible.

It is clear that these remarks apply to the general case of any
number of independent variables.

Let us then consider, for definiteness, a system of four functions
of four independent variables

$$(17) \qquad \begin{cases} X = F_1(x,\, y,\, z,\, t), \\[4pt] Y = F_2(x,\, y,\, z,\, t), \\[4pt] Z = F_3(x,\, y,\, z,\, t), \\[4pt] T = F_4(x,\, y,\, z,\, t), \end{cases}$$

where the Jacobian $D(F_1, F_2, F_3, F_4)/D(x, y, z, t)$ is identically
zero by hypothesis; and let us suppose, first, that one of the first
minors, say $D(F_1, F_2, F_3)/D(x, y, z)$, is not zero. We may then
think of the first three of equations (17) as solved for x, y, z as
functions of X, Y, Z, t; and, substituting these values for x, y, z in
the last of equations (17), we obtain T as a function of X, Y, Z, t:

$$(18) \qquad\qquad T = \Phi(X,\, Y,\, Z,\, t).$$

We proceed to show that this function Φ does not contain the variable t, that is, that $\partial \Phi / \partial t$ vanishes identically. For this purpose
let us consider the determinant

$$\Delta = \begin{vmatrix} \dfrac{\partial F_1}{\partial x} & \dfrac{\partial F_1}{\partial y} & \dfrac{\partial F_1}{\partial z} & dX \\[2ex] \dfrac{\partial F_2}{\partial x} & \dfrac{\partial F_2}{\partial y} & \dfrac{\partial F_2}{\partial z} & dY \\[2ex] \dfrac{\partial F_3}{\partial x} & \dfrac{\partial F_3}{\partial y} & \dfrac{\partial F_3}{\partial z} & dZ \\[2ex] \dfrac{\partial F_4}{\partial x} & \dfrac{\partial F_4}{\partial y} & \dfrac{\partial F_4}{\partial z} & dT \end{vmatrix}.$$

If, in this determinant, dX, dY, dZ, dT be replaced by their values

$$dX = \frac{\partial F_1}{\partial x}\,dx + \frac{\partial F_1}{\partial y}\,dy + \frac{\partial F_1}{\partial z}\,dz + \frac{\partial F_1}{\partial t}\,dt,$$

$$\cdot \quad \cdot \quad \cdot \quad \cdot \quad \cdot \quad \cdot \quad \cdot \quad \cdot \quad \cdot \quad \cdot \quad \cdot \quad \cdot \quad \cdot \quad \cdot \quad \cdot \quad ,$$

and if the determinant be developed in terms of dx, dy, dz, dt, it turns out that the coefficients of these four differentials are each zero; the first three being determinants with two identical columns, while the last is precisely the functional determinant. Hence $\Delta = 0$. But if we develop this determinant with respect to the elements of the last column, the coefficient of dT is not zero, and we obtain a relation of the form

$$dT = P\,dX + Q\,dY + R\,dZ.$$

By the remark made above, the coefficient of dt in the right-hand side is equal to $\partial \Phi / \partial t$. But this right-hand side does not contain dt, hence $\partial \Phi / \partial t = 0$. It follows that the relation (18) is of the form

$$T = \Phi(X, Y, Z),$$

which proves the theorem stated.

It can be shown that there exists no other relation, distinct from that just found, between the four functions X, Y, Z, T, independent of x, y, z, t. For, if one existed, and if we replaced T by $\Phi(X, Y, Z)$ in it, we would obtain a relation between X, Y, Z of the form $\Pi(X, Y, Z) = 0$, which is a contradiction of the hypothesis that $D(X, Y, Z) / D(x, y, z)$ does not vanish.

Let us now pass to the case in which all the first minors of the Jacobian vanish identically, but where at least one of the second minors, say $D(F_1, F_2) / D(x, y)$, is not zero. Then the first two of equations (17) may be solved for x and y as functions of X, Y, z, t, and the last two become

$$Z = \Phi_1(X, Y, z, t), \qquad T = \Phi_2(X, Y, z, t).$$

On the other hand we can show, as before, that the determinant

$$\begin{vmatrix} \dfrac{\partial F_1}{\partial x} & \dfrac{\partial F_1}{\partial y} & dX \\[2mm] \dfrac{\partial F_2}{\partial x} & \dfrac{\partial F_2}{\partial y} & dY \\[2mm] \dfrac{\partial F_3}{\partial x} & \dfrac{\partial F_3}{\partial y} & dZ \end{vmatrix}$$

vanishes identically ; and, developing it with respect to the elements of the last column, we find a relation of the form

$$dZ = P\,dX + Q\,dY,$$

whence it follows that

$$\frac{\partial \Phi_1}{\partial z} = 0, \qquad \frac{\partial \Phi_1}{\partial t} = 0.$$

In like manner it can be shown that

$$\frac{\partial \Phi_2}{\partial z} = 0, \qquad \frac{\partial \Phi_2}{\partial t} = 0;$$

and there exist in this case two distinct relations between the four functions X, Y, Z, T, of the form

$$Z = \Phi_1(X, Y), \qquad T = \Phi_2(X, Y).$$

There exists, however, no third relation distinct from these two; for, if there were, we could find a relation between X and Y, which would be in contradiction with the hypothesis that $D(X, Y)/D(x, y)$ is not zero.

Finally, if all the second minors of the Jacobian are zeros, but not all four functions X, Z, Y, T are constants, three of them are functions of the fourth. The above reasoning is evidently general. If the Jacobian of the n functions F_1, F_2, $\cdots$, F_n of the n independent variables x_1, x_2, $\cdots$, x_n, together with all its $(n-r+1)$-rowed minors, vanishes identically, but at least one of the $(n-r)$-rowed minors is not zero, there exist precisely r distinct relations between the n functions ; and certain r of them can be expressed in terms of the remaining $(n-r)$, between which there exists no relation.

The proof of the following proposition, which is similar to the above demonstration, will be left to the reader. *The necessary and sufficient condition that n functions of $n + p$ independent variables be connected by a relation which does not involve these variables is that every one of the Jacobians of these n functions, with respect to any **n*** *of the independent variables, should vanish identically.* In particular, the necessary and sufficient condition that two functions $F_1(x_1, x_2, \cdots, x_n)$ and $F_2(x_1, x_2, \cdots, x_n)$ should be functions of each other is that the corresponding partial derivatives $\partial F_1/\partial x_i$ and $\partial F_2/\partial x_i$ should be proportional.

Note. The functions $F_1, F_2, \cdots, F_n$ in the foregoing theorems may involve certain other variables $y_1, y_2, \cdots, y_m$, besides $x_1, x_2, \cdots, x_n$. If the Jacobian $D(F_1, F_2, \cdots, F_n)/D(x_1, x_2, \cdots, x_n)$ is zero, the functions $F_1, F_2, \cdots, F_n$ are connected by one or more relations which do not involve explicitly the variables $x_1, x_2, \cdots, x_n$, but which may involve the other variables $y_1, y_2, \cdots, y_m$.

Applications. The preceding theorem is of great importance. The fundamental property of the logarithm, for instance, can be demonstrated by means of it, without using the arithmetic definition of the logarithm. For it is proved at the beginning of the Integral Calculus that there exists a function which is defined for all positive values of the variable, which is zero when $x = 1$, and whose derivative is $1/x$. Let $f(x)$ be this function, and let

$$u = f(x) + f(y), \qquad v = xy.$$

Then

$$\frac{D(u, v)}{D(x, y)} = \begin{vmatrix} 1 & 1 \\ \frac{1}{x} & \frac{1}{y} \\ y & x \end{vmatrix} = 0.$$

Hence there exists a relation of the form

$$f(x) + f(y) = \phi(xy) ;$$

and to determine ϕ we need only set $y = 1$, which gives $f(x) = \phi(x)$. Hence, since x is arbitrary,

$$f(x) + f(y) = f(xy).$$

It is clear that the preceding definition might have led to the discovery of the fundamental properties of the logarithm had they not been known before the Integral Calculus.

As another application let us consider a system of n equations in n unknowns $u_1, u_2, \cdots, u_n$:

$$(19) \qquad \begin{cases} F_1(u_1, u_2, \cdots, u_n) = H_1, \\ F_2(u_1, u_2, \cdots, u_n) = H_2, \\ \cdots \cdots \cdots \cdots \cdots, \\ F_n(u_1, u_2, \cdots, u_n) = H_n, \end{cases}$$

where $H_1, H_2, \cdots, H_n$ are constants or functions of certain other variables $x_1, x_2, \cdots, x_m$, which may also occur in the functions F_i. If the Jacobian $D(F_1, F_2, \cdots, F_n)/D(u_1, u_2, \cdots, u_n)$ vanishes identically, there exist between the n functions F_i a certain number, say $n - k$, of distinct relations of the form

$$F_{k+1} = \Pi_1(F_1, \cdots, F_k), \cdots, F_n = \Pi_{n-k}(F_1, \cdots, F_k).$$

In order that the equations (19) be compatible, it is evidently necessary that

$$H_{k+1} = \Pi_1(H_1, \cdots, H_k), \cdots, H_n = \Pi_{n-k}(H_1, \cdots, H_k),$$

and, if this be true, the n equations (19) reduce to k distinct equations. We have then the same cases as in the discussion of a system of linear equations.

29. Another property of the Jacobian. The Jacobian of a system of n functions of n variables possesses properties analogous to those of the derivative of a function of a single variable. Thus the preceding theorem may be regarded as a generalization of the theorem of § 8.

The formula for the derivative of a function of a function may be extended to Jacobians. Let $F_1, F_2, \cdots, F_n$ be a system of n functions of the variables $u_1, u_2, \cdots, u_n$, and let us suppose that $u_1, u_2, \cdots, u_n$ themselves are functions of the n independent variables $x_1, x_2, \cdots, x_n$. Then the formula

$$\frac{D(F_1, F_2, \cdots, F_n)}{D(x_1, x_2, \cdots, x_n)} = \frac{D(F_1, F_2, \cdots, F_n)}{D(u_1, u_2, \cdots, u_n)} \cdot \frac{D(u_1, u_2, \cdots, u_n)}{D(x_1, x_2, \cdots, x_n)}$$

follows at once from the rule for the multiplication of determinants and the formula for the derivative of a composite function. For, let us write down the two functional determinants

$$\begin{vmatrix} \dfrac{\partial F_1}{\partial u_1} & \dfrac{\partial F_1}{\partial u_2} & \cdots & \dfrac{\partial F_1}{\partial u_n} \\ \cdots & \cdots & \cdots & \cdots \\ \dfrac{\partial F_n}{\partial u_1} & \dfrac{\partial F_n}{\partial u_2} & \cdots & \dfrac{\partial F_n}{\partial u_n} \end{vmatrix}, \quad \begin{vmatrix} \dfrac{\partial u_1}{\partial x_1} & \dfrac{\partial u_2}{\partial x_1} & \cdots & \dfrac{\partial u_n}{\partial x_1} \\ \cdots & \cdots & \cdots & \cdots \\ \dfrac{\partial u_1}{\partial x_n} & \dfrac{\partial u_2}{\partial x_n} & \cdots & \dfrac{\partial u_n}{\partial x_n} \end{vmatrix},$$

where the rows and the columns in the second have been interchanged. The first element of the product is equal to

$$\frac{\partial F_1}{\partial u_1}\frac{\partial u_1}{\partial x_1} + \frac{\partial F_1}{\partial u_2}\frac{\partial u_2}{\partial x_1} + \cdots + \frac{\partial F_1}{\partial u_n}\frac{\partial u_n}{\partial x_1};$$

that is, to $\partial F_1/\partial x_1$, and similarly for the other elements.

30. Hessians. Let $f(x, y, z)$ be a function of the three variables x, y, z. Then the functional determinant of the three first partial derivatives $\partial f/\partial x$, $\partial f/\partial y$, $\partial f/\partial z$,

$$k = \begin{vmatrix} \dfrac{\partial^2 f}{\partial x^2} & \dfrac{\partial^2 f}{\partial x\,\partial y} & \dfrac{\partial^2 f}{\partial x\,\partial z} \\ \dfrac{\partial^2 f}{\partial x\,\partial y} & \dfrac{\partial^2 f}{\partial y^2} & \dfrac{\partial^2 f}{\partial y\,\partial z} \\ \dfrac{\partial^2 f}{\partial x\,\partial z} & \dfrac{\partial^2 f}{\partial y\,\partial z} & \dfrac{\partial^2 f}{\partial z^2} \end{vmatrix},$$

is called the *Hessian* of $f(x, y, z)$. The Hessian of a function of n variables is defined in like manner, and plays a rôle analogous to that of the second derivative of a function of a single variable. We proceed to prove a remarkable invariant property of this determinant. Let us suppose the independent variables transformed by the linear substitution

$$(19')\qquad \begin{cases} x = \;\;\alpha X + \;\;\beta Y + \;\;\gamma Z, \\ y = \;\;\alpha' X + \;\;\beta' Y + \;\;\gamma' Z, \\ z = \;\;\alpha'' X + \;\;\beta'' Y + \;\;\gamma'' Z, \end{cases}$$

where X, Y, Z are the transformed variables, and $\alpha, \beta, \gamma, \cdots, \gamma''$ are constants such that the determinant of the substitution,

$$\Delta = \begin{vmatrix} \alpha & \beta & \gamma \\ \alpha' & \beta' & \gamma' \\ \alpha'' & \beta'' & \gamma'' \end{vmatrix},$$

is not zero. This substitution carries the function $f(x, y, z)$ over into a new function $F(X, Y, Z)$ of the three variables X, Y, Z. Let $H(X, Y, Z)$ be the Hessian of this new function. We shall show that we have identically

$$H(X, Y, Z) = \Delta^2 h(x, y, z),$$

where x, y, z are supposed replaced in $h(x, y, z)$ by their expressions from (19').
For we have

$$H = \frac{D\left(\dfrac{\partial F}{\partial X}, \dfrac{\partial F}{\partial Y}, \dfrac{\partial F}{\partial Z}\right)}{D(X, Y, Z)} = \frac{D\left(\dfrac{\partial F}{\partial X}, \dfrac{\partial F}{\partial Y}, \dfrac{\partial F}{\partial Z}\right)}{D(x, y, z)} \cdot \frac{D(x, y, z)}{D(X, Y, Z)};$$

and if we consider $\partial f/\partial x, \partial f/\partial y, \partial f/\partial z$, for a moment, as auxiliary variables, we may write

$$H = \frac{D\left(\dfrac{\partial F}{\partial X}, \dfrac{\partial F}{\partial Y}, \dfrac{\partial F}{\partial Z}\right)}{D\left(\dfrac{\partial f}{\partial x}, \dfrac{\partial f}{\partial y}, \dfrac{\partial f}{\partial z}\right)} \cdot \frac{D\left(\dfrac{\partial f}{\partial x}, \dfrac{\partial f}{\partial y}, \dfrac{\partial f}{\partial z}\right)}{D(x, y, z)} \cdot \frac{D(x, y, z)}{D(X, Y, Z)}.$$

But from the relation $F(X, Y, Z) = f(x, y, z)$, we find

$$\frac{\partial F}{\partial X} = \alpha \frac{\partial f}{\partial x} + \alpha' \frac{\partial f}{\partial y} + \alpha'' \frac{\partial f}{\partial z},$$

$$\frac{\partial F}{\partial Y} = \beta \frac{\partial f}{\partial x} + \beta' \frac{\partial f}{\partial y} + \beta'' \frac{\partial f}{\partial z},$$

$$\frac{\partial F}{\partial Z} = \gamma \frac{\partial f}{\partial x} + \gamma' \frac{\partial f}{\partial y} + \gamma'' \frac{\partial f}{\partial z},$$

whence

$$\frac{D\left(\dfrac{\partial F}{\partial X}, \dfrac{\partial F}{\partial Y}, \dfrac{\partial F}{\partial Z}\right)}{D\left(\dfrac{\partial f}{\partial x}, \dfrac{\partial f}{\partial y}, \dfrac{\partial f}{\partial z}\right)} = \begin{vmatrix} \alpha & \alpha' & \alpha'' \\ \beta & \beta' & \beta'' \\ \gamma & \gamma' & \gamma'' \end{vmatrix} = \Delta;$$

and hence, finally,

$$H = \Delta h \frac{D(x, y, z)}{D(X, Y, Z)} = \Delta^2 h.$$

It is clear that this theorem is general.

Let us now consider an application of this property of the Hessian. Let

$$f(x, y) = ax^3 + 3bx^2y + 3cxy^2 + dy^3$$

be a given binary cubic form whose coefficients a, b, c, d are any constants. Then, neglecting a numerical factor,

$$h = \begin{vmatrix} ax + by & bx + cy \\ bx + cy & cx + dy \end{vmatrix} = (ac - b^2)x^2 + (ad - bc)xy + (bd - c^2)y^2,$$

and the Hessian is seen to be a binary quadratic form. First, discarding the case in which the Hessian is a perfect square, we may write it as the product of two linear factors:

$$h = (mx + ny)(px + qy).$$

If, now, we perform the linear substitution

$$mx + ny = X, \qquad px + qy = Y,$$

the form $f(x, y)$ goes over into a new form,

$$F(X, Y) = AX^3 + 3BX^2Y + 3CXY^2 + DY^3,$$

whose Hessian is

$$H(X, Y) = (AC - B^2)X^2 + (AD - BC)XY + (BD - C^2)Y^2,$$

and this must reduce, by the invariant property proved above, to a product of the form KXY. Hence the coefficients A, B, C, D must satisfy the relations

$$B^2 - AC = 0, \qquad BD - C^2 = 0.$$

If one of the two coefficients B, C be different from zero, the other must be so, and we shall have

$$A = \frac{B^2}{C}, \qquad D = \frac{C^2}{B},$$

$$F(X, Y) = \frac{1}{BC}(B^3X^3 + 3B^2CX^2Y + 3BC^2XY^2 + C^3Y^3) = \frac{(BX + CY)^3}{BC},$$

whence $F(X, Y)$, and hence $f(x, y)$, will be a perfect cube. Discarding this particular case, it is evident that we shall have $B = C = 0$; and the polynomial $F(X, Y)$ will be of the canonical form

$$AX^3 + DY^3.$$

Hence the reduction of the form $f(x, y)$ to its canonical form only involves the solution of an equation of the second degree, obtained by equating the Hessian of the given form to zero. The canonical variables X, Y are precisely the two factors of the Hessian.

It is easy to see, in like manner, that the form $f(x, y)$ is reducible to the form $AX^3 + BX^2Y$ when the Hessian is a perfect square. When the Hessian vanishes identically $f(x, y)$ is a perfect cube:

$$f(x, y) = (\alpha x + \beta y)^3.$$

III. TRANSFORMATIONS

It often happens, in many problems which arise in Mathematical Analysis, that we are led to change the independent variables. It therefore becomes necessary to be able to express the derivatives with respect to the old variables in terms of the derivatives with respect to the new variables. We have already considered a problem of this kind in the case of inversion. Let us now consider the question from a general point of view, and treat those problems which occur most frequently.

31. Problem I. *Let y be a function of the independent variable x, and let t be a new independent variable connected with x by the relation $x = \phi(t)$. It is required to express the successive derivatives of y with respect to x in terms of t and the successive derivatives of y with respect to t.*

Let $y = f(x)$ be the given function, and $F(t) = f[\phi(t)]$ the function obtained by replacing x by $\phi(t)$ in the given function. By the rule for the derivative of a function of a function, we find

$$\frac{dy}{dt} = \frac{dy}{dx} \times \phi'(t),$$

whence

$$y_x = \frac{\dfrac{dy}{dt}}{\phi'(t)} = \frac{y_t}{\phi'(t)}.$$

This result may be stated as follows: *To find the derivative of y with respect to x, take the derivative of that function with respect to t and divide it by the derivative of x with respect to t.*

The second derivative d^2y/dx^2 may be found by applying this rule to the expression just found for the first derivative. We find:

$$\frac{d^2y}{dx^2} = \frac{\dfrac{d}{dt}(y_x)}{\phi'(t)} = \frac{y_{t^2}\phi'(t) - y_t\phi''(t)}{[\phi'(t)]^3};$$

and another application of the same rule gives the third derivative

$$\frac{d^3y}{dx^3} = \frac{\dfrac{d}{dt}(y_{x^2})}{\phi'(t)},$$

or, performing the operations indicated,

$$\frac{d^3y}{dx^3} = \frac{y_{t^3}[\phi'(t)]^2 - 3\,y_{t^2}\phi'(t)\,\phi''(t) + 3\,y_t[\phi''(t)]^2 - y_t\phi'(t)\,\phi'''(t)}{[\phi'(t)]^5}.$$

The remaining derivatives may be calculated in succession by repeated applications of the same rule. In general, the nth derivative of y with respect to x may be expressed in terms of $\phi'(t)$, $\phi''(t)$, $\cdots$, $\phi^{(n)}(t)$, and the first n successive derivatives of y with respect to t. These formulæ may be arranged in more symmetrical form. Denoting the successive differentials of x and y with respect to t by dx, dy, d^2x, d^2y, $\cdots$, d^nx, d^ny, and the successive derivatives of y with respect to x by y', y'', $\cdots$, $y^{(n)}$, we may write the preceding formulæ in the form

$$(20) \quad \begin{cases} y' = \dfrac{dy}{dx}, \\[2mm] y'' = \dfrac{dx\,d^2y - dy\,d^2x}{dx^3}, \\[2mm] y''' = \dfrac{d^3y\,dx^2 - 3\,d^2y\,dx\,d^2x + 3\,dy\,(d^2x)^2 - dy\,d^3x\,dx}{dx^5}, \\[2mm] \cdot\ \cdot\ \cdot\ \cdot\ \cdot\ \cdot\ \cdot\ \cdot\ \cdot\ \cdot\ \cdot\ \cdot\ \cdot\ \cdot\ \cdot\ \cdot \end{cases}$$

The independent variable t, with respect to which the differentials on the right-hand sides of these formulæ are formed, is entirely arbitrary; and we pass from one derivative to the next by the recurrent formula

$$y^{(n)} = \frac{d[y^{(n-1)}]}{dx},$$

the second member being regarded as the quotient of two differentials.

32. Applications. These formulæ are used in the study of plane curves, when the coördinates of a point of the curve are expressed in terms of an auxiliary variable t.

$$x = f(t), \qquad y = \phi(t).$$

In order to study this curve in the neighborhood of one of its points it is necessary to calculate the successive derivatives y', y'', $\cdots$ of y with respect to x at the given point. But the preceding formulæ give us precisely these derivatives, expressed in terms of the successive derivatives of the functions $f(t)$ and $\phi(t)$, without the necessity of having recourse to the explicit expression of y as a function of x, which it might be very difficult, practically, to obtain. Thus the first formula

$$y' = \frac{dy}{dx} = \frac{\phi'(t)}{f'(t)}$$

gives the slope of the tangent. The value of y'' occurs in an important geometrical concept, *the radius of curvature*, which is given by the formula

$$R = \frac{(1 + y'^2)^{\frac{3}{2}}}{|y''|},$$

which we shall derive later. In order to find the value of R, when the coördinates x and y are given as functions of a parameter t, we need only replace y' and y'' by the preceding expressions, and we find

$$R = \frac{(dx^2 + dy^2)^{\frac{3}{2}}}{|dx\,d^2y - dy\,d^2x|},$$

where the second member contains only the first and second derivatives of x and y with respect to t.

The following interesting remark is taken from M. Bertrand's *Traité de Calcul différentiel et intégral* (Vol. I, p. 170). Suppose that, in calculating some geometrical concept allied to a given plane curve whose coördinates x and y are supposed given in terms of a parameter t, we had obtained the expression

$$F(x, y, dx, dy, d^2x, d^2y, \cdots, d^n x, d^n y),$$

where all the differentials are taken with respect to t. Since, by hypothesis, this concept has a geometrical significance, its value cannot depend upon the choice of the independent variable t. But, if we take $x = t$, we shall have $dx = dt$, $d^2x = d^3x = \cdots = d^n x = 0$, and the preceding expression becomes

$$f(x, y, y', y'', \cdots, y^{(n)});$$

which is the same as the expression we would have obtained by supposing at the start that the equation of the given curve was solved with respect to y in the form $y = \Phi(x)$. To return from this particular case to the case where the independent variable is arbitrary, we need only replace $y', y'', \cdots$ by their values from the formulæ (20). Performing this substitution in

$$f(x, y, y', y'', \cdots, y^{(n)}),$$

we should get back to the expression $F(x, y, dx, dy, d^2x, d^2y, \cdots)$ with which we started. If we do not, we can assert that the result obtained is incorrect. For example, the expression

$$\frac{dx\,d^2y + dy\,d^2x}{(dx^2 + dy^2)^{\frac{3}{2}}}$$

cannot have any geometrical significance for a plane curve which is independent of the choice of the independent variable. For, if we set $x = t$, this expression reduces to $y'' / (1 + y'^2)^{\frac{3}{2}}$; and, replacing y' and y'' by their values from (20), we do not get back to the preceding expression.

33. The formulæ (20) are also used frequently in the study of differential equations. Suppose, for example, that we wished to determine all the functions y of the independent variable x, which satisfy the equation

$$(21) \qquad (1 - x^2)\frac{d^2y}{dx^2} - x\,\frac{dy}{dx} + n^2y = 0,$$

where n is a constant. Let us introduce a new independent variable t, where $x = \cos t$. Then we have

$$\frac{dy}{dx} = \frac{\dfrac{dy}{dt}}{-\sin t},$$

$$\frac{d^2y}{dx^2} = \frac{\sin t \dfrac{d^2y}{dt^2} - \cos t \dfrac{dy}{dt}}{\sin^3 t};$$

and the equation (21) becomes, after the substitution,

$$(22) \qquad \frac{d^2y}{dt^2} + n^2y = 0.$$

It is easy to find all the functions of t which satisfy this equation, for it may be written, after multiplication by $2\,dy/dt$,

$$2\frac{dy}{dt}\frac{d^2y}{dt^2} + 2\,n^2y\,\frac{dy}{dt} = \frac{d}{dt}\left[\left(\frac{dy}{dt}\right)^2 + n^2y^2\right] = 0,$$

whence

$$\left(\frac{dy}{dt}\right)^2 + n^2y^2 = n^2a^2,$$

where a is an arbitrary constant. Consequently

$$\frac{dy}{dt} = n\,\sqrt{a^2 - y^2},$$

or

$$\frac{\dfrac{dy}{dt}}{\sqrt{a^2 - y^2}} - n = 0.$$

The left-hand side is the derivative of $\operatorname{arc\,sin}(y/a) - nt$. It follows that this difference must be another arbitrary constant b, whence

$$y = a \sin(nt + b),$$

which may also be written in the form

$$y = A \sin nt + B \cos nt.$$

Returning to the original variable x, we see that all the functions of x which satisfy the given equation (21) are given by the formula

$$y = A \sin(n \operatorname{arc\,cos} x) + B \cos(n \operatorname{arc\,cos} x),$$

where A and B are two arbitrary constants.

34. Problem II. *To every relation between x and y there corresponds, by means of the transformation $x = f(t, u)$, $y = \phi(t, u)$, a relation between t and u. It is required to express the derivatives of y with respect to x in terms of t, u, and the derivatives of u with respect to t.*

This problem is seen to depend upon the preceding when it is noticed that the formulæ of transformation,

$$x = f(t, u), \qquad y = \phi(t, u),$$

give us the expressions for the original variables x and y as functions of the variable t, if we imagine that u has been replaced in these formulæ by its value as a function of t. We need merely apply the general method, therefore, always regarding x and y as composite functions of t, and u as an auxiliary function of t. We find then, first,

$$\frac{dy}{dx} = \frac{dy}{dt} : \frac{dx}{dt} = \frac{\dfrac{\partial \phi}{\partial t} + \dfrac{\partial \phi}{\partial u}\dfrac{du}{dt}}{\dfrac{\partial f}{\partial t} + \dfrac{\partial f}{\partial u}\dfrac{du}{dt}},$$

and then

$$\frac{d^2 y}{dx^2} = \frac{d}{dt}\left(\frac{dy}{dx}\right) : \frac{dx}{dt},$$

or, performing the operations indicated,

$$\frac{d^2 y}{dx^2} = \frac{\left(\dfrac{\partial f}{\partial t} + \dfrac{\partial f}{\partial u}\dfrac{du}{dt}\right)\left[\dfrac{\partial^2 \phi}{\partial t^2} + 2\dfrac{\partial^2 \phi}{\partial u\,\partial t}\dfrac{du}{dt} + \dfrac{\partial^2 \phi}{\partial u^2}\left(\dfrac{du}{dt}\right)^2 + \dfrac{\partial \phi}{\partial u}\dfrac{d^2 u}{dt^2}\right] - \left(\dfrac{\partial \phi}{\partial t} + \dfrac{\partial \phi}{\partial u}\dfrac{du}{dt}\right)\left[\dfrac{\partial^2 f}{\partial t^2} + \cdots\right]}{\left(\dfrac{\partial f}{\partial t} + \dfrac{\partial f}{\partial u}\dfrac{du}{dt}\right)^3}.$$

In general, the nth derivative $y^{(n)}$ is expressible in terms of t, u, and the derivatives du/dt, d^2u/dt^2, $\cdots$, d^nu/dt^n.

Suppose, for instance, that the equation of a curve be given in polar coördinates $\rho = f(\omega)$. The formulæ for the rectangular coördinates of a point are then the following:

$$x = \rho \cos \omega, \qquad y = \rho \sin \omega.$$

Let ρ', ρ'', $\cdots$ be the successive derivatives of ρ with respect to ω, considered as the independent variable. From the preceding formulæ we find

$$dx = \cos \omega \, d\rho \; - \rho \sin \omega \, d\omega,$$
$$dy = \sin \omega \, d\rho \; + \rho \cos \omega \, d\omega,$$
$$d^2x = \cos \omega \, d^2\rho - 2 \sin \omega \, d\omega \, d\rho - \rho \cos \omega \, d\omega^2,$$
$$d^2y = \sin \omega \, d^2\rho + 2 \cos \omega \, d\omega \, d\rho - \rho \sin \omega \, d\omega^2,$$

whence

$$dx^2 + dy^2 = d\rho^2 + \rho^2 \, d\omega^2,$$
$$dx \, d^2y - dy \, d^2x = 2 \, d\omega \, d\rho^2 - \rho \, d\omega \, d^2\rho + \rho^2 \, d\omega^3.$$

The expression found above for the radius of curvature becomes

$$R = \pm \frac{(\rho^2 + \rho'^2)^{\frac{3}{2}}}{\rho^2 + 2\,\rho'^2 - \rho\rho''}.$$

35. Transformations of plane curves. Let us suppose that to every point m of a plane we make another point M of the same plane correspond by some known construction. If we denote the coördinates of the point m by (x, y) and those of M by (X, Y), there will exist, in general, two relations between these coördinates of the form

$$(23) \qquad X = f(x, y), \qquad Y = \phi(x, y).$$

These formulæ define a *point transformation* of which numerous examples arise in Geometry, such as projective transformations, the transformation of reciprocal radii, etc. When the point m describes a curve c, the corresponding point M describes another curve C, whose properties may be deduced from those of the curve c and from the nature of the transformation employed. Let y', y'', $\cdots$ be the successive derivatives of y with respect to x, and Y', Y'', $\cdots$ the successive derivatives of Y with respect to X. To study the curve C it is necessary to be able to express Y', Y'', $\cdots$ in terms of x, y, y', y'', $\cdots$. This is precisely the problem which we have just discussed; and we find

$$Y' = \frac{\dfrac{dY}{dx}}{\dfrac{dX}{dx}} = \frac{\dfrac{\partial \phi}{\partial x} + \dfrac{\partial \phi}{\partial y}\, y'}{\dfrac{\partial f}{\partial x} + \dfrac{\partial f}{\partial y}\, y'},$$

$$Y'' = \frac{\dfrac{dY'}{dx}}{\dfrac{dX}{dx}} = \frac{\left(\dfrac{\partial f}{\partial x} + \dfrac{\partial f}{\partial y}\, y'\right)\left(\dfrac{\partial^2 \phi}{\partial x^2} + \cdots\right) - \cdots}{\left(\dfrac{\partial f}{\partial x} + \dfrac{\partial f}{\partial y}\, y'\right)^3},$$

and so forth. It is seen that Y' depends only on x, y, y'. Hence, if the transformation (23) be applied to two curves c, c', which are tangent at the point (x, y), the transformed curves C, C' will also be tangent at the corresponding point (X, Y). This remark enables us to replace the curve c by any other curve which is tangent to it in questions which involve only the tangent to the transformed curve C.

Let us consider, for example, the transformation defined by the formulæ

$$X = \frac{h^2 x}{x^2 + y^2}, \qquad Y = \frac{h^2 y}{x^2 + y^2},$$

which is the transformation of reciprocal radii, or *inversion*, with the origin as pole. Let m be a point of a curve c and M the corresponding point of the curve C. In order to find the tangent to this curve C we need only apply the result of ordinary Geometry, that an inversion carries a straight line into a circle through the pole.

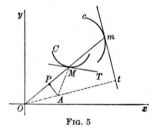

Fig. 5

Let us replace the curve c by its tangent mt. The inverse of mt is a circle through the two points M and O, whose center lies on the perpendicular Ot let fall from the origin upon mt. The tangent MT to this circle is perpendicular to AM, and the angles Mmt and mMT are equal, since each is the complement of the angle mOt. The tangents mt and MT are therefore antiparallel with respect to the radius vector.

36. Contact transformations. The preceding transformations are not the most general transformations which carry two tangent curves into two other tangent curves. Let us suppose that a point M is determined from each point m of a curve c by a construction

which depends not only upon the point m, but also upon the tangent
to the curve c at this point. The formulæ which define the transformation are then of the form

$$(24) \qquad X = f(x, y, y'), \qquad Y = \phi(x, y, y');$$

and the slope Y' of the tangent to the transformed curve is given
by the formula

$$Y' = \frac{dY}{dX} = \frac{\dfrac{\partial \phi}{\partial x} + \dfrac{\partial \phi}{\partial y} y' + \dfrac{\partial \phi}{\partial y'} y''}{\dfrac{\partial f}{\partial x} + \dfrac{\partial f}{\partial y} y' + \dfrac{\partial f}{\partial y'} y''}.$$

In general, Y' depends on the four variables x, y, y', y''; and if we
apply the transformation (24) to two curves c, c' which are tangent
at a point (x, y), the transformed curves C, C' will have a point
(X, Y) in common, but they will not be tangent, in general, unless
y'' happens to have the same value for each of the curves c and c'.
In order that the two curves C and C' should always be tangent, it
is necessary and sufficient that Y' should not depend on y''; that is,
that the two functions $f(x, y, y')$ and $\phi(x, y, y')$ should satisfy the
condition

$$\frac{\partial f}{\partial y'}\left(\frac{\partial \phi}{\partial x} + \frac{\partial \phi}{\partial y} y'\right) = \frac{\partial \phi}{\partial y'}\left(\frac{\partial f}{\partial x} + \frac{\partial f}{\partial y} y'\right).$$

In case this condition is satisfied, the transformation is called a
contact transformation. It is clear that a point transformation is a
particular case of a contact transformation.[*]

Let us consider, for example, Legendre's transformation, in which
the point M, which corresponds to a point (x, y) of a curve c, is given
by the equations

$$X = y', \qquad Y = xy' - y;$$

from which we find

$$Y' = \frac{dY}{dX} = \frac{xy''}{y''} = x,$$

which shows that the transformation is a contact transformation.
In like manner we find

$$Y'' = \frac{dY'}{dX} = \frac{dx}{y'' dx} = \frac{1}{y''},$$

$$Y''' = \frac{dY''}{dX} = -\frac{y'''}{y''^3},$$

---

[*] Legendre and Ampère gave many examples of contact transformations. Sophus
Lie developed the general theory in various works; see in particular his *Geometrie
der Berührungstransformationen.* See also JACOBI, *Vorlesungen über Dynamik.*

and so forth. From the preceding formulæ it follows that

$$x = Y', \qquad y = XY' - Y, \qquad y' = X,$$

which shows that the transformation is involutory.* All these properties are explained by the remark that the point whose coördinates are $X = y'$, $Y = xy' - y$ is the pole of the tangent to the curve c at the point (x, y) with respect to the parabola $x^2 - 2y = 0$. But, in general, if M denote the pole of the tangent at m to a curve c with respect to a directing conic Σ, then the locus of the point M is a curve C whose tangent at M is precisely the polar of the point m with respect to Σ. The relation between the two curves c and C is therefore a reciprocal one; and, further, if we replace the curve c by another curve c', tangent to c at the point m, the reciprocal curve C' will be tangent to the curve C at the point M.

Pedal curves. If, from a fixed point O in the plane of a curve c, a perpendicular OM be let fall upon the tangent to the curve at the point m, the locus of the foot M of this perpendicular is a curve C, which is called the *pedal of the given curve.* It would be easy to obtain, by a direct calculation, the coördinates of the point M, and to show that the transformation thus defined is a contact transfor-
mation, but it is simpler to proceed as follows.
Let us consider a circle γ of radius R, described about the point O as center; and let m_1
be a point on OM such that $Om_1 \times OM = R^2$.
The point m_1 is the pole of the tangent mt
with respect to the circle; and hence the
transformation which carries c into C is the
result of a transformation of reciprocal polars, followed by an inversion. When the
point m describes the curve c, the point m_1,
the pole of mt, describes a curve c_1 tangent
to the polar of the point m with respect to

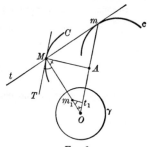

Fig. 6

the circle γ, that is, tangent to the straight line $m_1 t_1$, a perpendicular let fall from m_1 upon Om. The tangent MT to the curve C and the tangent $m_1 t_1$ to the curve c_1 make equal angles with the radius vector $Om_1 M$. Hence, if we draw the normal MA, the angles AMO and AOM are equal, since they are the complements of equal angles, and the point A is the middle point of the line Om. It follows that the normal to the pedal is found by joining the point M to the center of the line Om.

37. Projective transformations. Every function y which satisfies the equation $y'' = 0$ is a linear function of x, and conversely. But, if we subject x and y to the projective transformation

---

* That is, two successive applications of the transformation lead us back to the original coördinates. — TRANS.

$$x = \frac{a\,X + b\,Y + c}{a''\,X + b''\,Y + c''}, \qquad y = \frac{a'\,X + b'\,Y + c'}{a''\,X + b''\,Y + c''},$$

a straight line goes over into a straight line. Hence the equation $y'' = 0$ should become $d^2 Y / dX^2 = 0$. In order to verify this we will first remark that the general projective transformation may be resolved into a sequence of particular transformations of simple form. If the two coefficients a'' and b'' are not both zero, we will set $X_1 = a'' X + b'' Y + c''$; and since we cannot have at the same time $ab'' - ba'' = 0$ and $a'b'' - b'a'' = 0$, we will also set $Y_1 = a' X + b' Y + c'$, on the supposition that $a'b'' - b'a''$ is not zero. The preceding formulæ may then be written, replacing X and Y by their values in terms of X_1 and Y_1, in the form

$$y = \frac{Y_1}{X_1}, \qquad x = \frac{\alpha\,X_1 + \beta\,Y_1 + \gamma}{X_1} = \alpha + \beta\,\frac{Y_1}{X_1} + \frac{\gamma}{X_1}.$$

It follows that the general projective transformation can be reduced to a succession of integral transformations of the form

$$x = aX + bY + c, \qquad y = a'\,X + b'\,Y + c',$$

combined with the particular transformation

$$x = \frac{1}{X}, \qquad\qquad y = \frac{Y}{X}.$$

Performing this latter transformation, we find

$$y' = \frac{dy}{dx} = \frac{X\,Y' - Y}{X^2} : \frac{-1}{X^2} = Y - XY',$$

and

$$y'' = \frac{dy'}{dx} = -\,XY''(-\,X^2) = X^3\,Y''.$$

Likewise, performing an integral projective transformation, we have

$$y' = \frac{dy}{dx} = \frac{a' + b'\,Y'}{a + b\,Y'},$$

$$y'' = \frac{dy'}{dx} = \frac{(ab' - ba')\,Y''}{(a + b\,Y')^3}.$$

In each case the equation $y'' = 0$ goes over into $Y'' = 0$.

We shall now consider functions of several independent variables, and, for definiteness, we shall give the argument for a function of two variables.

38. Problem III. *Let $\omega = f(x, y)$ be a function of the two independent variables x and y, and let u and v be two new variables connected with the old ones by the relations*

$$x = \phi\,(u, v), \qquad y = \psi\,(u, v).$$

It is required to express the partial derivatives of ω with respect to the variables x and y in terms of u, v, and the partial derivatives of ω with respect to u and v.

Let $\omega = F(u, v)$ be the function which results from $f(x, y)$ by the substitution. Then the rule for the differentiation of composite functions gives

$$\frac{\partial \omega}{\partial u} = \frac{\partial \omega}{\partial x}\frac{\partial \phi}{\partial u} + \frac{\partial \omega}{\partial y}\frac{\partial \psi}{\partial u},$$

$$\frac{\partial \omega}{\partial v} = \frac{\partial \omega}{\partial x}\frac{\partial \phi}{\partial v} + \frac{\partial \omega}{\partial y}\frac{\partial \psi}{\partial v},$$

whence we may find $\partial \omega / \partial x$ and $\partial \omega / \partial y$; for, if the determinant $D(\phi, \psi)/D(u, v)$ vanished, the change of variables performed would have no meaning. Hence we obtain the equations

(25)
$$\begin{cases} \dfrac{\partial \omega}{\partial x} = A\,\dfrac{\partial \omega}{\partial u} + B\,\dfrac{\partial \omega}{\partial v}, \\[2mm] \dfrac{\partial \omega}{\partial y} = C\,\dfrac{\partial \omega}{\partial u} + D\,\dfrac{\partial \omega}{\partial v}, \end{cases}$$

where A, B, C, D are determinate functions of u and v; and these formulæ solve the problem for derivatives of the first order. They show that *the derivative of a function with respect to x is the sum of the two products formed by multiplying the two derivatives with respect to u and v by A and B, respectively.* The derivative with respect to y is obtained in like manner, using C and D instead of A and B, respectively. In order to calculate the second derivatives we need only apply to the first derivatives the rule expressed by the preceding formulæ; doing so, we find

$$\frac{\partial^2 \omega}{\partial x^2} = \frac{\partial}{\partial x}\left(\frac{\partial \omega}{\partial x}\right) = \frac{\partial}{\partial x}\left(A\,\frac{\partial \omega}{\partial u} + B\,\frac{\partial \omega}{\partial v}\right)$$
$$= A\,\frac{\partial}{\partial u}\left(A\,\frac{\partial \omega}{\partial u} + B\,\frac{\partial \omega}{\partial v}\right) + B\,\frac{\partial}{\partial v}\left(A\,\frac{\partial \omega}{\partial u} + B\,\frac{\partial \omega}{\partial v}\right), \quad .$$

or, performing the operations indicated,

$$\frac{\partial^2 \omega}{\partial x^2} = A\left(A\,\frac{\partial^2 \omega}{\partial u^2} + B\,\frac{\partial^2 \omega}{\partial u\, \partial v} + \frac{\partial A}{\partial u}\frac{\partial \omega}{\partial u} + \frac{\partial B}{\partial u}\frac{\partial \omega}{\partial v}\right)$$
$$+ B\left(A\,\frac{\partial^2 \omega}{\partial u\, \partial v} + B\,\frac{\partial^2 \omega}{\partial v^2} + \frac{\partial A}{\partial v}\frac{\partial \omega}{\partial u} + \frac{\partial B}{\partial v}\frac{\partial \omega}{\partial v}\right);$$

and we could find $\partial^2 \omega / \partial x\, \partial y$, $\partial^2 \omega / \partial y^2$ and the following derivatives in like manner. In all differentiations which are to be carried out we need only replace the operations $\partial / \partial x$ and $\partial / \partial y$ by the operations

$$A\,\frac{\partial}{\partial u} + B\,\frac{\partial}{\partial v}, \qquad C\,\frac{\partial}{\partial u} + D\,\frac{\partial}{\partial v},$$

respectively.   Hence everything depends upon the calculation of the coefficients A, B, C, D.

Example I. Let us consider the equation

(26)
$$a \frac{\partial^2 \omega}{\partial x^2} + 2 b \frac{\partial^2 \omega}{\partial x \partial y} + c \frac{\partial^2 \omega}{\partial y^2} = 0,$$

where the coefficients a, b, c are constants; and let us try to reduce this equation to as simple a form as possible.   We observe first that if $a = c = 0$, it would be superfluous to try to simplify the equation.   We may then suppose that c, for example, does not vanish.   Let us take two new independent variables u and v, defined by the equations

$$u = x + \alpha y, \qquad v = x + \beta y,$$

where α and β are constants.   Then we have

$$\frac{\partial \omega}{\partial x} = \frac{\partial \omega}{\partial u} + \frac{\partial \omega}{\partial v},$$
$$\frac{\partial \omega}{\partial y} = \alpha \frac{\partial \omega}{\partial u} + \beta \frac{\partial \omega}{\partial v},$$

and hence, in this case, $A = B = 1$, $C = \alpha$, $D = \beta$.   The general formulæ then give

$$\frac{\partial^2 \omega}{\partial x^2} = \frac{\partial^2 \omega}{\partial u^2} + 2 \frac{\partial^2 \omega}{\partial u \partial v} + \frac{\partial^2 \omega}{\partial v^2},$$
$$\frac{\partial^2 \omega}{\partial x \partial y} = \alpha \frac{\partial^2 \omega}{\partial u^2} + (\alpha + \beta) \frac{\partial^2 \omega}{\partial u \partial v} + \beta \frac{\partial^2 \omega}{\partial v^2},$$
$$\frac{\partial^2 \omega}{\partial y^2} = \alpha^2 \frac{\partial^2 \omega}{\partial u^2} + 2 \alpha\beta \frac{\partial^2 \omega}{\partial u \partial v} + \beta^2 \frac{\partial^2 \omega}{\partial v^2},$$

and the given equation becomes

$$(a + 2 b \alpha + c \alpha^2) \frac{\partial^2 \omega}{\partial u^2} + 2 [a + b (\alpha + \beta) + c \alpha\beta] \frac{\partial^2 \omega}{\partial u \partial v} + (a + 2 b \beta + c \beta^2) \frac{\partial^2 \omega}{\partial v^2} = 0.$$

It remains to distinguish several cases.

First case. Let $b^2 - ac > 0$.   Taking for α and β the two roots of the equation $a + 2 br + cr^2 = 0$, the given equation takes the simple form

$$\frac{\partial^2 \omega}{\partial u \partial v} = 0.$$

Since this may be written

$$\frac{\partial}{\partial v} \left(\frac{\partial \omega}{\partial u} \right) = 0,$$

we see that $\partial \omega / \partial u$ must be a function of the single variable, u, say $f(u)$.   Let $F(u)$ denote a function of u such that $F'(u) = f(u)$.   Then, since the derivative of $\omega - F(u)$ with respect to u is zero, this difference must be independent of u, and, accordingly, $\omega = F(u) + \Phi(v)$.   The converse is apparent.   Returning to the variables x and y, it follows that all the functions ω which satisfy the equation (26) are of the form

$$\omega = F(x + \alpha y) + \Phi(x + \beta y),$$

where F and Φ are arbitrary functions. For example, the general integral of the equation

$$\frac{\partial^2 \omega}{\partial y^2} = a^2 \frac{\partial^2 \omega}{\partial x^2},$$

which occurs in the theory of the stretched string, is

$$\omega = f(x + ay) + \phi(x - ay).$$

Second case. Let $b^2 - ac = 0$. Taking α equal to the double root of the equation $a + 2br + cr^2 = 0$, and β some other number, the coefficient of $\partial^2 \omega / \partial u \, \partial v$ becomes zero, for it is equal to $a + b\alpha + \beta(b + c\alpha)$. Hence the given equation reduces to $\partial^2 \omega / \partial v^2 = 0$. It is evident that ω must be a linear function of v, $\omega = vf(u) + \phi(u)$, where $f(u)$ and $\phi(u)$ are arbitrary functions. Returning to the variables x and y, the expression for ω becomes

$$\omega = (x + \beta y)f(x + \alpha y) + \phi(x + \alpha y),$$

which may be written

$$\omega = [x + \alpha y + (\beta - \alpha)y]f(x + \alpha y) + \phi(x + \alpha y),$$

or, finally,

$$\omega = yF(x + \alpha y) + \Phi(x + \alpha y).$$

Third case. If $b^2 - ac < 0$, the preceding transformation cannot be applied without the introduction of imaginary variables. The quantities α and β may then be determined by the equations

$$a + 2b\alpha + c\alpha^2 = a + 2b\beta + c\beta^2,$$

$$a + b(\alpha + \beta) + c\alpha\beta = 0,$$

which give

$$\alpha + \beta = -\frac{2b}{c}, \qquad \alpha\beta = \frac{2b^2 - ac}{c^2}.$$

The equation of the second degree,

$$r^2 + \frac{2b}{c}r + \frac{2b^2 - ac}{c^2} = 0,$$

whose roots are α and β, has, in fact, real roots. The given equation then becomes

$$\Delta\omega = \frac{\partial^2 \omega}{\partial u^2} + \frac{\partial^2 \omega}{\partial v^2} = 0.$$

This equation $\Delta\omega = 0$, which is known as *Laplace's Equation*, is of fundamental importance in many branches of mathematics and mathematical physics.

Example II. Let us see what form the preceding equation assumes when we set $x = \rho \cos\phi$, $y = \rho \sin\phi$. For the first derivatives we find

$$\frac{\partial \omega}{\partial \rho} = \frac{\partial \omega}{\partial x} \cos\phi + \frac{\partial \omega}{\partial y} \sin\phi,$$

$$\frac{\partial \omega}{\partial \phi} = -\frac{\partial \omega}{\partial x} \rho \sin\phi + \frac{\partial \omega}{\partial y} \rho \cos\phi,$$

or, solving for $\partial\omega/\partial x$ and $\partial\omega/\partial y$,

$$\frac{\partial\omega}{\partial x} = \cos\phi\,\frac{\partial\omega}{\partial\rho} - \frac{\sin\phi}{\rho}\,\frac{\partial\omega}{\partial\phi},$$

$$\frac{\partial\omega}{\partial y} = \sin\phi\,\frac{\partial\omega}{\partial\rho} + \frac{\cos\phi}{\rho}\,\frac{\partial\omega}{\partial\phi}.$$

Hence

$$\frac{\partial^2\omega}{\partial x^2} = \cos\phi\,\frac{\partial}{\partial\rho}\left(\cos\phi\,\frac{\partial\omega}{\partial\rho} - \frac{\sin\phi}{\rho}\,\frac{\partial\omega}{\partial\phi}\right) - \frac{\sin\phi}{\rho}\,\frac{\partial}{\partial\phi}\left(\cos\phi\,\frac{\partial\omega}{\partial\rho} - \frac{\sin\phi}{\rho}\,\frac{\partial\omega}{\partial\phi}\right)$$

$$= \cos^2\phi\,\frac{\partial^2\omega}{\partial\rho^2} + \frac{\sin^2\phi}{\rho^2}\,\frac{\partial^2\omega}{\partial\phi^2} - \frac{2\sin\phi\cos\phi}{\rho}\,\frac{\partial^2\omega}{\partial\rho\,\partial\phi} + \frac{2\sin\phi\cos\phi}{\rho^2}\,\frac{\partial\omega}{\partial\phi} + \frac{\sin^2\phi}{\rho}\,\frac{\partial\omega}{\partial\rho};$$

and the expression for $\partial^2\omega/\partial y^2$ is analogous to this. Adding the two, we find

$$\frac{\partial^2\omega}{\partial x^2} + \frac{\partial^2\omega}{\partial y^2} = \frac{\partial^2\omega}{\partial\rho^2} + \frac{1}{\rho^2}\,\frac{\partial^2\omega}{\partial\phi^2} + \frac{1}{\rho}\,\frac{\partial\omega}{\partial\rho}.$$

39. Another method. The preceding method is the most practical when the function whose partial derivatives are sought is unknown. But in certain cases it is more advantageous to use the following method.

Let $z = f(x, y)$ be a function of the two independent variables x and y. If x, y, and z are supposed expressed in terms of two auxiliary variables u and v, the total differentials dx, dy, dz satisfy the relation

$$dz = \frac{\partial f}{\partial x}\,dx + \frac{\partial f}{\partial y}\,dy,$$

which is equivalent to the two distinct equations

$$\frac{\partial z}{\partial u} = \frac{\partial f}{\partial x}\frac{\partial x}{\partial u} + \frac{\partial f}{\partial y}\frac{\partial y}{\partial u},$$

$$\frac{\partial z}{\partial v} = \frac{\partial f}{\partial x}\frac{\partial x}{\partial v} + \frac{\partial f}{\partial y}\frac{\partial y}{\partial v},$$

whence $\partial f/\partial x$ and $\partial f/\partial y$ may be found as functions of u, v, $\partial z/\partial u$, $\partial z/\partial v$, as in the preceding method. But to find the succeeding derivatives we will continue to apply the same rule. Thus, to find $\partial^2 f/\partial x^2$ and $\partial^2 f/\partial x\,\partial y$, we start with the identity

$$d\left(\frac{\partial f}{\partial x}\right) = \frac{\partial^2 f}{\partial x^2}\,dx + \frac{\partial^2 f}{\partial x\,\partial y}\,dy,$$

which is equivalent to the two equations

$$\frac{\partial\left(\dfrac{\partial f}{\partial x}\right)}{\partial u} = \frac{\partial^2 f}{\partial x^2}\frac{\partial x}{\partial u} + \frac{\partial^2 f}{\partial x\,\partial y}\,\frac{\partial y}{\partial u},$$

$$\frac{\partial\left(\dfrac{\partial f}{\partial x}\right)}{\partial v} = \frac{\partial^2 f}{\partial x^2}\frac{\partial x}{\partial v} + \frac{\partial^2 f}{\partial x\,\partial y}\frac{\partial y}{\partial v},$$

where it is supposed that $\partial f/\partial x$ has been replaced by its value calculated above. Likewise, we should find the values of $\partial^2 f/\partial x\,\partial y$ and $\partial^2 f/\partial y^2$ by starting with the identity

$$d\left(\frac{\partial f}{\partial y}\right) = \frac{\partial^2 f}{\partial x\,\partial y}\,dx + \frac{\partial^2 f}{\partial y^2}\,dy.$$

The work may be checked by the fact that the two values of $\partial^2 f/\partial x\,\partial y$ found must agree. Derivatives of higher order may be calculated in like manner.

Application to surfaces. The preceding method is used in the study of surfaces. Suppose that the coördinates of a point of a surface S are given as functions of two variable parameters u and v by means of the formulæ

$$(27) \qquad x = f(u, v), \qquad y = \phi(u, v), \qquad z = \psi(u, v).$$

The equation of the surface may be found by eliminating the variables u and v between the three equations (27); but we may also study the properties of the surface S directly from these equations themselves, without carrying out the elimination, which might be practically impossible. It should be noticed that the three Jacobians

$$\frac{D(f, \phi)}{D(u, v)}, \qquad \frac{D(\phi, \psi)}{D(u, v)}, \qquad \frac{D(f, \psi)}{D(u, v)}$$

cannot all vanish identically, for then the elimination of u and v would lead to two distinct relations between x, y, z, and the point whose coördinates are (x, y, z) would map out a curve, and not a surface. Let us suppose, for definiteness, that the first of these does not vanish: $D(f, \phi)/D(u, v) \neq 0$. Then the first two of equations (27) may be solved for u and v, and the substitution of these values in the third would give the equation of the surface in the form $z = F(x, y)$. In order to study this surface in the neighborhood of a point we need to know the partial derivatives p, q, r, s, t, $\cdots$ of this function $F(x, y)$ in terms of the parameters u and v. The first derivatives p and q are given by the equation

$$dz = p\,dx + q\,dy,$$

which is equivalent to the two equations

$$(28) \quad \begin{cases} \dfrac{\partial \psi}{\partial u} = p \dfrac{\partial f}{\partial u} + q \dfrac{\partial \phi}{\partial u}, \\[2mm] \dfrac{\partial \psi}{\partial v} = p \dfrac{\partial f}{\partial v} + q \dfrac{\partial \phi}{\partial v}, \end{cases}$$

from which p and q may be found. The equation of the tangent plane is found by substituting these values of p and q in the equation

$$Z - z = p(X - x) + q(Y - y),$$

and doing so we find the equation

$$(29) \quad (X - x)\frac{D(y, z)}{D(u, v)} + (Y - y)\frac{D(z, x)}{D(u, v)} + (Z - z)\frac{D(x, y)}{D(u, v)} = 0.$$

The equations (28) have a geometrical meaning which is easily remembered. They express the fact that the tangent plane to the surface contains the tangents to those two curves on the surface which are obtained by keeping v constant while u varies, and *vice versa*.*

Having found p and q, $p = f_1(u, v)$, $q = f_2(u, v)$, we may proceed to find r, s, t by means of the equations

$$dp = r\,dx + s\,dy,$$
$$dq = s\,dx + t\,dy,$$

each of which is equivalent to two equations; and so forth.

40. Problem IV. *To every relation between x, y, z there corresponds by means of the equations*

$$(30) \quad x = f(u, v, w), \qquad y = \phi(u, v, w), \qquad z = \psi(u, v, w),$$

a new relation between u, v, w. It is required to express the partial derivatives of z with respect to the variables x and y in terms of u, v, w, and the partial derivatives of w with respect to the variables u and v.

This problem can be made to depend upon the preceding. For, if we suppose that w has been replaced in the formulæ (30) by a function of u and v, we have x, y, z expressed as functions of the

---

* The equation of the tangent plane may also be found directly. Every curve on the surface is defined by a relation between u and v, say $v = \Pi(u)$; and the equations of the tangent to this curve are

$$\frac{X - x}{\dfrac{\partial f}{\partial u} + \dfrac{\partial f}{\partial v}\Pi'(u)} = \frac{Y - y}{\dfrac{\partial \phi}{\partial u} + \dfrac{\partial \phi}{\partial v}\Pi'(u)} = \frac{Z - z}{\dfrac{\partial \psi}{\partial u} + \dfrac{\partial \psi}{\partial v}\Pi'(u)}.$$

The elimination of $\Pi'(u)$ leads to the equation (29) of the tangent plane.

two parameters u and v; and we need only follow the preceding method, considering f, ϕ, ψ as composite functions of u and v, and w as an auxiliary function of u and v. In order to calculate the first derivatives p and q, for instance, we have the two equations

$$\frac{\partial \psi}{\partial u} + \frac{\partial \psi}{\partial w}\frac{\partial w}{\partial u} = p\left(\frac{\partial f}{\partial u} + \frac{\partial f}{\partial w}\frac{\partial w}{\partial u}\right) + q\left(\frac{\partial \phi}{\partial u} + \frac{\partial \phi}{\partial w}\frac{\partial w}{\partial u}\right),$$

$$\frac{\partial \psi}{\partial v} + \frac{\partial \psi}{\partial w}\frac{\partial w}{\partial v} = p\left(\frac{\partial f}{\partial v} + \frac{\partial f}{\partial w}\frac{\partial w}{\partial v}\right) + q\left(\frac{\partial \phi}{\partial v} + \frac{\partial \phi}{\partial w}\frac{\partial w}{\partial v}\right).$$

The succeeding derivatives may be calculated in a similar manner.

In geometrical language the above problem may be stated as follows: To every point m of space, whose coördinates are (x, y, z), there corresponds, by a given construction, another point M, whose coördinates are X, Y, Z. When the point m maps out a surface S, the point M maps out another surface Σ, whose properties it is proposed to deduce from those of the given surface S.

The formulæ which define the transformation are of the form

$$X = f(x, y, z), \qquad Y = \phi(x, y, z), \qquad Z = \psi(x, y, z).$$

Let
$$z = F(x, y), \qquad Z = \Phi(X, Y)$$

be the equations of the two surfaces S and Σ, respectively. The problem is to express the partial derivatives P, Q, R, S, T, $\cdots$ of the function $\Phi(X, Y)$ in terms of x, y, z and the partial derivatives p, q, r, s, t, $\cdots$ of the function $F(x, y)$. But this is precisely the above problem, except for the notation.

The first derivatives P and Q depend only on x, y, z, p, q; and hence the transformation carries tangent surfaces into tangent surfaces. But this is not the most general transformation which enjoys this property, as we shall see in the following example.

41. Legendre's transformation. Let $z = f(x, y)$ be the equation of a surface S, and let any point m (x, y, z) of this surface be carried into a point M, whose coördinates are X, Y, Z, by the transformation

$$X = p, \qquad Y = q, \qquad Z = px + qy - z.$$

Let $Z = \Phi(X, Y)$ be the equation of the surface Σ described by the point M. If we imagine z, p, q replaced by f, $\partial f/\partial x$, $\partial f/\partial y$, respectively, we have the three coördinates of the point M expressed as functions of the two independent variables x and y.

Let P, Q, R, S, T denote the partial derivatives of the function $\Phi(X, Y)$. Then the relation

$$dZ = P\,dX + Q\,dY$$

becomes

$$p\,dx + q\,dy + x\,dp + y\,dq - dz = P\,dp + Q\,dq,$$

or

$$x\,dp + y\,dq = P\,dp + Q\,dq.$$

Let us suppose that p and q, for the surface S, are not functions of each other, in which case there exists no identity of the form $\lambda\,dp + \mu\,dq = 0$, unless $\lambda = \mu = 0$. Then, from the preceding equation, it follows that

$$P = x, \qquad Q = y.$$

In order to find R, S, T we may start with the analogous relations

$$dP = R\,dX + S\,dY,$$
$$dQ = S\,dX + T\,dY,$$

which, when X, Y, P, Q are replaced by their values, become

$$dx = R(r\,dx + s\,dy) + S(s\,dx + t\,dy),$$
$$dy = S(r\,dx + s\,dy) + T(s\,dx + t\,dy);$$

whence

$$R\,r + S\,s = 1, \qquad R\,s + S\,t = 0,$$
$$S\,r + T\,s = 0, \qquad S\,s + T\,t = 1,$$

and consequently

$$R = \frac{t}{rt - s^2}, \qquad S = \frac{-s}{rt - s^2}, \qquad T = \frac{r}{rt - s^2}.$$

From the preceding formulæ we find, conversely,

$$x = P, \qquad y = Q, \qquad z = PX + QY - Z, \qquad p = X, \qquad q = Y,$$
$$r = \frac{T}{RT - S^2}, \qquad s = \frac{-S}{RT - S^2}, \qquad t = \frac{R}{RT - S^2},$$

which proves that the transformation is involutory. Moreover, it is a contact transformation, since X, Y, Z, P, Q depend only on x, y, z, p, q. These properties become self-explanatory, if we notice that the formulæ define a transformation of reciprocal polars with respect to the paraboloid

$$x^2 + y^2 - 2z = 0.$$

Note. The expressions for R, S, T become infinite, if the relation $rt - s^2 = 0$ holds at every point of the surface S. In this case the point M describes a curve, and not a surface, for we have

$$\frac{D(X,\,Y)}{D(x,\,y)} = \frac{D(p,\,q)}{D(x,\,y)} = rt - s^2 = 0,$$

and likewise

$$\frac{D(X,\,Z)}{D(x,\,y)} = \frac{D(p,\,px+qy-z)}{D(x,\,y)} = y(rt - s^2) = 0.$$

This is precisely the case which we had not considered.

42. Ampère's transformation. Retaining the notation of the preceding article, let us consider the transformation

$$X = x, \qquad Y = q, \qquad Z = qy - z.$$

The relation

$$dZ = P\,dX + Q\,dY$$

becomes

$$q\,dy + y\,dq - dz = P\,dx + Q\,dq,$$

or

$$y\,dq - p\,dx = P\,dx + Q\,dq.$$

Hence

$$P = -p, \qquad Q = y;$$

and conversely we find

$$x = X, \qquad y = Q, \qquad z = QY - Z, \qquad p = -P, \qquad q = Y.$$

It follows that this transformation also is an involutory contact transformation.

The relation

$$dP = R\,dX + S\,dY$$

next becomes

$$-r\,dx - s\,dy = R\,dx + S(s\,dx + t\,dy);$$

that is,

$$R + Ss = -r, \qquad St = -s,$$

whence

$$R = \frac{s^2 - rt}{t}, \qquad S = -\frac{s}{t}.$$

Starting with the relation $dQ = S\,dX + T\,dY$, we find, in like manner,

$$T = \frac{1}{t}.$$

As an application of these formulæ, let us try to find all the functions $f(x,\,y)$ which satisfy the equation $rt - s^2 = 0$. Let S be the surface represented by the equation $z = f(x,\,y)$, Σ the transformed surface, and $Z = \Phi(X,\,Y)$ the equation of Σ. From the formulæ for R it is clear that we must have

$$R = \frac{\partial^2 \Phi}{\partial X^2} = 0,$$

and Φ must be a linear function of X:

$$Z = X\phi(Y) + \psi(Y),$$

where ϕ and ψ are arbitrary functions of Y. It follows that

$$P = \phi(Y), \qquad Q = X\phi'(Y) + \psi'(Y);$$

and, conversely, the coördinates (x, y, z) of a point of the surface S are given as functions of the two variables X and Y by the formulæ

$$x = X, \quad y = X\phi'(Y) + \psi'(Y), \quad z = Y[X\phi'(Y) + \psi'(Y)] - X\phi(Y) - \psi(Y).$$

The equation of the surface may be obtained by eliminating X and Y; or, what amounts to the same thing, by eliminating α between the equations

$$z = \alpha y - x\phi(\alpha) - \psi(\alpha),$$
$$0 = \quad y - x\phi'(\alpha) - \psi'(\alpha).$$

The first of these equations represents a moving plane which depends upon the parameter α, while the second is found by differentiating the first with respect to this parameter. The surfaces defined by the two equations are the so-called *developable surfaces*, which we shall study later.

43. The potential equation in curvilinear coördinates. The calculation to which a change of variable leads may be simplified in very many cases by various devices. We shall take as an example the potential equation in orthogonal curvilinear coördinates.* Let

$$F(x, y, z) = \rho,$$
$$F_1(x, y, z) = \rho_1,$$
$$F_2(x, y, z) = \rho_2,$$

be the equations of three families of surfaces which form a triply orthogonal system, such that any two surfaces belonging to two different families intersect at right angles. Solving these equations for x, y, z as functions of the parameters ρ, ρ_1, ρ_2, we obtain equations of the form

(31)
$$\begin{cases} x = \phi(\rho, \rho_1, \rho_2), \\ y = \phi_1(\rho, \rho_1, \rho_2), \\ z = \phi_2(\rho, \rho_1, \rho_2); \end{cases}$$

and we may take ρ, ρ_1, ρ_2 as a system of orthogonal curvilinear coördinates.

Since the three given surfaces are orthogonal, the tangents to their curves of intersection must form a trirectangular trihedron. It follows that the equations

(32) $\quad S \dfrac{\partial\phi}{\partial\rho}\dfrac{\partial\phi}{\partial\rho_1} = 0, \qquad S \dfrac{\partial\phi}{\partial\rho_1}\dfrac{\partial\phi}{\partial\rho_2} = 0, \qquad S \dfrac{\partial\phi}{\partial\rho}\dfrac{\partial\phi}{\partial\rho_2} = 0,$

must be satisfied where the symbol S indicates that we are to replace ϕ by ϕ_1, then by ϕ_2, and add. These conditions for orthogonalism may be written in the following form, which is equivalent to the above:

(33)
$$\begin{cases} \dfrac{\partial\rho}{\partial x}\dfrac{\partial\rho_1}{\partial x} + \dfrac{\partial\rho}{\partial y}\dfrac{\partial\rho_1}{\partial y} + \dfrac{\partial\rho}{\partial z}\dfrac{\partial\rho_1}{\partial z} = 0, \\ \dfrac{\partial\rho}{\partial x}\dfrac{\partial\rho_2}{\partial x} + \cdots = 0, \qquad \dfrac{\partial\rho_1}{\partial x}\dfrac{\partial\rho_2}{\partial x} + \cdots = 0. \end{cases}$$

---

*Lamé, *Traité des coordonnées curvilignes.* See also Bertrand, *Traité de Calcul différentiel*, Vol. I, p. 181.

Let us then see what form the potential equation

$$\Delta_2 V = \frac{\partial^2 V}{\partial x^2} + \frac{\partial^2 V}{\partial y^2} + \frac{\partial^2 V}{\partial z^2} = 0$$

assumes in the variables ρ, ρ_1, ρ_2. First of all, we find

$$\frac{\partial V}{\partial x} = \frac{\partial V}{\partial \rho} \frac{\partial \rho}{\partial x} + \frac{\partial V}{\partial \rho_1} \frac{\partial \rho_1}{\partial x} + \frac{\partial V}{\partial \rho_2} \frac{\partial \rho_2}{\partial x},$$

and then

$$\begin{aligned}
\frac{\partial^2 V}{\partial x^2} = &\; \frac{\partial^2 V}{\partial \rho^2} \left(\frac{\partial \rho}{\partial x} \right)^2 + 2 \frac{\partial^2 V}{\partial \rho \, \partial \rho_1} \frac{\partial \rho}{\partial x} \frac{\partial \rho_1}{\partial x} + \frac{\partial V}{\partial \rho} \frac{\partial^2 \rho}{\partial x^2} \\
&+ \frac{\partial^2 V}{\partial \rho_1^2} \left(\frac{\partial \rho_1}{\partial x} \right)^2 + 2 \frac{\partial^2 V}{\partial \rho_1 \, \partial \rho_2} \frac{\partial \rho_1}{\partial x} \frac{\partial \rho_2}{\partial x} + \frac{\partial V}{\partial \rho_1} \frac{\partial^2 \rho_1}{\partial x^2} \\
&+ \frac{\partial^2 V}{\partial \rho_2^2} \left(\frac{\partial \rho_2}{\partial x} \right)^2 + 2 \frac{\partial^2 V}{\partial \rho \, \partial \rho_2} \frac{\partial \rho}{\partial x} \frac{\partial \rho_2}{\partial x} + \frac{\partial V}{\partial \rho_2} \frac{\partial^2 \rho_2}{\partial x^2}.
\end{aligned}$$

Adding the three analogous equations, the terms containing derivatives of the second order like $\partial^2 V / \partial \rho \, \partial \rho_1$ fall out, by reason of the relations (33), and we have

$$(34) \quad \left\{ \begin{aligned}
\frac{\partial^2 V}{\partial x^2} + \frac{\partial^2 V}{\partial y_2} + \frac{\partial^2 V}{\partial z^2} = &\; \Delta_1 (\rho) \frac{\partial^2 V}{\partial \rho^2} + \Delta_1 (\rho_1) \frac{\partial^2 V}{\partial \rho_1^2} + \Delta_1 (\rho_2) \frac{\partial^2 V}{\partial \rho_2^2} \\
&+ \Delta_2 (\rho) \frac{\partial V}{\partial \rho} + \Delta_2 (\rho_1) \frac{\partial V}{\partial \rho_1} + \Delta_2 (\rho_2) \frac{\partial V}{\partial \rho_2},
\end{aligned} \right.$$

where Δ_1 and Δ_2 denote *Lamé's differential parameters*:

$$\Delta_1 (f) = \left(\frac{\partial f}{\partial x} \right)^2 + \left(\frac{\partial f}{\partial y} \right)^2 + \left(\frac{\partial f}{\partial z} \right)^2, \qquad \Delta_2 (f) = \frac{\partial^2 f}{\partial x^2} + \frac{\partial^2 f}{\partial y^2} + \frac{\partial^2 f}{\partial z^2}.$$

The differential parameters of the first order $\Delta_1 (\rho)$, $\Delta_1 (\rho_1)$, $\Delta_1 (\rho_2)$ are easily calculated. From the equations (31) we have

$$\frac{\partial \phi}{\partial \rho} \frac{\partial \rho}{\partial x} + \frac{\partial \phi}{\partial \rho_1} \frac{\partial \rho_1}{\partial x} + \frac{\partial \phi}{\partial \rho_2} \frac{\partial \rho_2}{\partial x} = 1,$$

$$\frac{\partial \phi_1}{\partial \rho} \frac{\partial \rho}{\partial x} + \frac{\partial \phi_1}{\partial \rho_1} \frac{\partial \rho_1}{\partial x} + \frac{\partial \phi_1}{\partial \rho_2} \frac{\partial \rho_2}{\partial x} = 0,$$

$$\frac{\partial \phi_2}{\partial \rho} \frac{\partial \rho}{\partial x} + \frac{\partial \phi_2}{\partial \rho_1} \frac{\partial \rho_1}{\partial x} + \frac{\partial \phi_2}{\partial \rho_2} \frac{\partial \rho_2}{\partial x} = 0;$$

whence, multiplying by $\dfrac{\partial \phi}{\partial \rho}$, $\dfrac{\partial \phi_1}{\partial \rho}$, $\dfrac{\partial \phi_2}{\partial \rho}$, respectively, and adding, we find

$$\frac{\partial \rho}{\partial x} = \frac{\dfrac{\partial \phi}{\partial \rho}}{\left(\dfrac{\partial \phi}{\partial \rho} \right)^2 + \left(\dfrac{\partial \phi_1}{\partial \rho} \right)^2 + \left(\dfrac{\partial \phi_2}{\partial \rho} \right)^2}.$$

Then, calculating $\partial \rho / \partial y$ and $\partial \rho / \partial z$ in like manner, it is easy to see that

$$\left(\frac{\partial \rho}{\partial x} \right)^2 + \left(\frac{\partial \rho}{\partial y} \right)^2 + \left(\frac{\partial \rho}{\partial z} \right)^2 = \frac{1}{\left(\dfrac{\partial \phi}{\partial \rho} \right)^2 + \left(\dfrac{\partial \phi_1}{\partial \rho} \right)^2 + \left(\dfrac{\partial \phi_2}{\partial \rho} \right)^2}.$$

Let us now set

$$H = S\left(\frac{\partial\phi}{\partial\rho}\right)^2, \qquad H_1 = S\left(\frac{\partial\phi}{\partial\rho_1}\right)^2, \qquad H_2 = S\left(\frac{\partial\phi}{\partial\rho_2}\right)^2,$$

where the symbol S indicates, as before, that we are to replace ϕ by ϕ_1, then by ϕ_2, and add. Then the preceding equation and the two analogous equations may be written

$$\Delta_1(\rho) = \frac{1}{H}, \qquad \Delta_1(\rho_1) = \frac{1}{H_1}, \qquad \Delta_1(\rho_2) = \frac{1}{H_2}.$$

Lamé obtained the expressions for $\Delta_2(\rho)$, $\Delta_2(\rho_1)$, $\Delta_2(\rho_2)$ as functions of ρ, ρ_1, ρ_2 by a rather long calculation, which we may condense in the following form. In the identity (34)

$$\Delta_2 V = \frac{1}{H}\frac{\partial^2 V}{\partial\rho^2} + \frac{1}{H_1}\frac{\partial^2 V}{\partial\rho_1^2} + \frac{1}{H_2}\frac{\partial^2 V}{\partial\rho_2^2} + \Delta_2(\rho)\frac{\partial V}{\partial\rho} + \Delta_2(\rho_1)\frac{\partial V}{\partial\rho_1} + \Delta_2(\rho_2)\frac{\partial V}{\partial\rho_2},$$

let us set successively $V = x$, $V = y$, $V = z$. This gives the three equations

$$\frac{1}{H}\frac{\partial^2\phi}{\partial\rho^2} + \frac{1}{H_1}\frac{\partial^2\phi}{\partial\rho_1^2} + \frac{1}{H_2}\frac{\partial^2\phi}{\partial\rho_2^2} + \Delta_2(\rho)\frac{\partial\phi}{\partial\rho} + \Delta_2(\rho_1)\frac{\partial\phi}{\partial\rho_1} + \Delta_2(\rho_2)\frac{\partial\phi}{\partial\rho_2} = 0,$$

$$\frac{1}{H}\frac{\partial^2\phi_1}{\partial\rho^2} + \frac{1}{H_1}\frac{\partial^2\phi_1}{\partial\rho_1^2} + \frac{1}{H_2}\frac{\partial^2\phi_1}{\partial\rho_2^2} + \Delta_2(\rho)\frac{\partial\phi_1}{\partial\rho} + \Delta_2(\rho_1)\frac{\partial\phi_1}{\partial\rho_1} + \Delta_2(\rho_2)\frac{\partial\phi_1}{\partial\rho_2} = 0,$$

$$\frac{1}{H}\frac{\partial^2\phi_2}{\partial\rho^2} + \frac{1}{H_1}\frac{\partial^2\phi_2}{\partial\rho_1^2} + \frac{1}{H_2}\frac{\partial^2\phi_2}{\partial\rho_2^2} + \Delta_2(\rho)\frac{\partial\phi_2}{\partial\rho} + \Delta_2(\rho_1)\frac{\partial\phi_2}{\partial\rho_1} + \Delta_2(\rho_2)\frac{\partial\phi_2}{\partial\rho_2} = 0,$$

which we need only solve for $\Delta_2(\rho)$, $\Delta_2(\rho_1)$, $\Delta_2(\rho_2)$. For instance, multiplying by $\partial\phi/\partial\rho$, $\partial\phi_1/\partial\rho$, $\partial\phi_2/\partial\rho$, respectively, and adding, we find

$$\Delta_2(\rho) H + \frac{1}{H} S\frac{\partial\phi}{\partial\rho}\frac{\partial^2\phi}{\partial\rho^2} + \frac{1}{H_1} S\frac{\partial\phi}{\partial\rho}\frac{\partial^2\phi}{\partial\rho_1^2} + \frac{1}{H_2} S\frac{\partial\phi}{\partial\rho}\frac{\partial^2\phi}{\partial\rho_2^2} = 0.$$

Moreover, we have

$$S\frac{\partial\phi}{\partial\rho}\frac{\partial^2\phi}{\partial\rho^2} = \frac{1}{2}\frac{\partial H}{\partial\rho},$$

and differentiating the first of equations (32) with respect to ρ_1, we find

$$S\frac{\partial\phi}{\partial\rho}\frac{\partial^2\phi}{\partial\rho_1^2} = -S\frac{\partial\phi}{\partial\rho_1}\frac{\partial^2\phi}{\partial\rho\,\partial\rho_1} = -\frac{1}{2}\frac{\partial H_1}{\partial\rho}.$$

In like manner we have

$$S\frac{\partial\phi}{\partial\rho}\frac{\partial^2\phi}{\partial\rho_2^2} = -\frac{1}{2}\frac{\partial H_2}{\partial\rho},$$

and consequently

$$\Delta_2(\rho) = -\frac{1}{2H^2}\frac{\partial H}{\partial\rho} + \frac{1}{2HH_1}\frac{\partial H_1}{\partial\rho} + \frac{1}{2HH_2}\frac{\partial H_2}{\partial\rho} = -\frac{1}{2H}\frac{\partial}{\partial\rho}\left[\log\left(\frac{H}{H_1 H_2}\right)\right].$$

Setting

$$H = \frac{1}{h^2}, \qquad H_1 = \frac{1}{h_1^2}, \qquad H_2 = \frac{1}{h_2^2},$$

this formula becomes

$$\Delta_2(\rho) = h^2 \frac{\partial}{\partial \rho} \left(\log \frac{h}{h_1 h_2} \right);$$

and in like manner we find

$$\Delta_2(\rho_1) = h_1^2 \frac{\partial}{\partial \rho_1} \left(\log \frac{h_1}{h h_2} \right), \qquad \Delta_2(\rho_2) = h_2^2 \frac{\partial}{\partial \rho_2} \left(\log \frac{h_2}{h h_1} \right).$$

Hence the formula (34) finally becomes

$$(35) \quad \begin{cases} \dfrac{\partial^2 V}{\partial x^2} + \dfrac{\partial^2 V}{\partial y^2} + \dfrac{\partial^2 V}{\partial z^2} = \quad h^2 \left[\dfrac{\partial^2 V}{\partial \rho^2} + \dfrac{\partial}{\partial \rho} \left(\log \dfrac{h}{h_1 h_2} \right) \dfrac{\partial V}{\partial \rho} \right] \\ \qquad\qquad\qquad + h_1^2 \left[\dfrac{\partial^2 V}{\partial \rho_1^2} + \dfrac{\partial}{\partial \rho_1} \left(\log \dfrac{h_1}{h h_2} \right) \dfrac{\partial V}{\partial \rho_1} \right] \\ \qquad\qquad\qquad + h_2^2 \left[\dfrac{\partial^2 V}{\partial \rho_2^2} + \dfrac{\partial}{\partial \rho_2} \left(\log \dfrac{h_2}{h h_1} \right) \dfrac{\partial V}{\partial \rho_2} \right], \end{cases}$$

or, in condensed form,

$$\Delta_2 V = h h_1 h_2 \left[\frac{\partial}{\partial \rho} \left(\frac{h}{h_1 h_2} \frac{\partial V}{\partial \rho} \right) + \frac{\partial}{\partial \rho_1} \left(\frac{h_1}{h h_2} \frac{\partial V}{\partial \rho_1} \right) + \frac{\partial}{\partial \rho_2} \left(\frac{h_2}{h h_1} \frac{\partial V}{\partial \rho_2} \right) \right].$$

Let us apply this formula to polar coördinates. The formulæ of transformation are

$$x = \rho \sin \theta \cos \phi, \qquad y = \rho \sin \theta \sin \phi, \qquad z = \rho \cos \theta,$$

where θ and ϕ replace ρ_1 and ρ_2, and the coefficients h, h_1, h_2 have the following values:

$$h = 1, \qquad h_1 = \frac{1}{\rho}, \qquad h_2 = \frac{1}{\rho \sin \theta}.$$

Hence the general formula becomes

$$\Delta_2 V = \frac{1}{\rho^2 \sin \theta} \left[\frac{\partial}{\partial \rho} \left(\rho^2 \sin \theta \frac{\partial V}{\partial \rho} \right) + \frac{\partial}{\partial \theta} \left(\sin \theta \frac{\partial V}{\partial \theta} \right) + \frac{\partial}{\partial \phi} \left(\frac{1}{\sin \theta} \frac{\partial V}{\partial \phi} \right) \right];$$

or, expanding,

$$\Delta_2 V = \frac{\partial^2 V}{\partial \rho^2} + \frac{1}{\rho^2} \frac{\partial^2 V}{\partial \theta^2} + \frac{1}{\rho^2 \sin^2 \theta} \frac{\partial^2 V}{\partial \phi^2} + \frac{2}{\rho} \frac{\partial V}{\partial \rho} + \frac{\cot \theta}{\rho^2} \frac{\partial V}{\partial \theta},$$

which is susceptible of direct verification.

EXERCISES

1. Setting $u = x^2 + y^2 + z^2$, $v = x + y + z$, $w = xy + yz + zx$, the functional determinant $D(u, v, w) / D(x, y, z)$ vanishes identically. Find the relation which exists between u, v, w.

Generalize the problem.

2. Let

$$u_1 = \frac{x_1}{\sqrt{1 - x_1^2 - \cdots - x_n^2}}, \qquad \cdots, \qquad u_n = \frac{x_n}{\sqrt{1 - x_1^2 - \cdots - x_n^2}}.$$

Derive the equation

$$\frac{D(u_1, u_2, \cdots, u_n)}{D(x_1, x_2, \cdots, x_n)} = \frac{1}{(1 - x_1^2 - x_2^2 - \cdots - x_n^2)^{1 + \frac{n}{2}}}.$$

3. Using the notation

$$\begin{aligned}
x_1 &= \cos\phi_1, \\
x_2 &= \sin\phi_1 \cos\phi_2, \\
x_3 &= \sin\phi_1 \sin\phi_2 \cos\phi_3, \\
&\quad \cdot \ \cdot \ \cdot \ \cdot \ \cdot \ \cdot \ \cdot \ \cdot \ \cdot \ \cdot \ \cdot \ \cdot \ \cdot, \\
x_n &= \sin\phi_1 \sin\phi_2 \cdots \sin\phi_{n-1} \cos\phi_n,
\end{aligned}$$

show that

$$\frac{D(x_1, x_2, \cdots, x_n)}{D(\phi_1, \phi_2, \cdots, \phi_n)} = (-1)^n \sin^n\phi_1 \sin^{n-1}\phi_2 \sin^{n-2}\phi_3 \cdots \sin^2\phi_{n-1} \sin\phi_n.$$

4. Prove directly that the function $z = F(x, y)$ defined by the two equations

$$\begin{aligned}
z &= \alpha x + y f(\alpha) + \phi(\alpha), \\
0 &= x + y f'(\alpha) + \phi'(\alpha),
\end{aligned}$$

where α is an auxiliary variable, satisfies the equation $rt - s^2 = 0$, where $f(\alpha)$ and $\phi(\alpha)$ are arbitrary functions.

5. Show in like manner that any implicit function $z = F(x, y)$ defined by an equation of the form

$$y = x\,\phi(z) + \psi(z),$$

where $\phi(z)$ and $\psi(z)$ are arbitrary functions, satisfies the equation

$$rq^2 - 2\,pqs + tp^2 = 0.$$

6. Prove that the function $z = F(x, y)$ defined by the two equations

$$z\phi'(\alpha) = [y - \phi(\alpha)]^2, \qquad (x + \alpha)\phi'(\alpha) = y - \phi(\alpha),$$

where α is an auxiliary variable and $\phi(\alpha)$ an arbitrary function, satisfies the equation $pq = z$.

7. Prove that the function $z = F(x, y)$ defined by the two equations

$$[z - \phi(\alpha)]^2 = x^2(y^2 - \alpha^2), \qquad [z - \phi(\alpha)]\phi'(\alpha) = \alpha x^2$$

satisfies in like manner the equation $pq = xy$.

8*. Lagrange's formulæ. Let y be an implicit function of the two variables x and α, defined by the relation $y = \alpha + x\phi(y)$; and let $u = f(y)$ be any function of y whatever. Show that, in general,

$$\frac{\partial^n u}{\partial x^n} = \frac{\partial^{n-1}}{\partial \alpha^{n-1}} \left[\phi(y)^n \frac{\partial u}{\partial \alpha} \right].$$

[LAPLACE.]

Note. The proof is based upon the two formulæ

$$\frac{\partial}{\partial \alpha}\left[F(u)\frac{\partial u}{\partial x}\right] = \frac{\partial}{\partial x}\left[F(u)\frac{\partial u}{\partial \alpha}\right], \qquad \frac{\partial u}{\partial x} = \phi(y)\frac{\partial u}{\partial \alpha},$$

where u is any function of y whatever, and $F(u)$ is an arbitrary function of u. It is shown that if the formula holds for any value of n, it must hold for the value $n+1$.

Setting $x = 0$, y reduces to α and u to $f(\alpha)$; and the nth derivative of u with respect to x becomes

$$\left(\frac{\partial^n u}{\partial x^n}\right)_0 = \frac{\partial^{n-1}}{\partial \alpha^{n-1}}\left[\phi(\alpha)^n f'(\alpha)\right].$$

9. If $x = f(u, v)$, $y = \phi(u, v)$ are two functions which satisfy the equations

$$\frac{\partial f}{\partial u} = \frac{\partial \phi}{\partial v}, \qquad\qquad \frac{\partial f}{\partial v} = -\frac{\partial \phi}{\partial u},$$

show that the following equation is satisfied identically:

$$\frac{\partial^2 V}{\partial u^2} + \frac{\partial^2 V}{\partial v^2} = \left(\frac{\partial^2 V}{\partial x^2} + \frac{\partial^2 V}{\partial y^2}\right)\left[\left(\frac{\partial f}{\partial u}\right)^2 + \left(\frac{\partial f}{\partial v}\right)^2\right].$$

10. If the function $V(x, y, z)$ satisfies the equation

$$\Delta_2 V = \frac{\partial^2 V}{\partial x^2} + \frac{\partial^2 V}{\partial y^2} + \frac{\partial^2 V}{\partial z^2} = 0,$$

show that the function

$$\frac{1}{r}V\left(k^2\frac{x}{r^2},\ k^2\frac{y}{r^2},\ k^2\frac{z}{r^2}\right)$$

satisfies the same equation, where k is a constant and $r^2 = x^2 + y^2 + z^2$.

[LORD KELVIN.]

11. If $V(x, y, z)$ and $V_1(x, y, z)$ are two solutions of the equation $\Delta_2 V = 0$, show that the function

$$U = V(x, y, z) + (x^2 + y^2 + z^2)V_1(x, y, z)$$

satisfies the equation

$$\Delta_2 \Delta_2 U = 0.$$

12. What form does the equation

$$(x - x^3)y'' + (1 - 3x^2)y' - xy = 0$$

assume when we make the transformation $x = \sqrt{1 - t^2}$?

13. What form does the equation

$$\frac{\partial^2 z}{\partial x^2} + 2xy^2\frac{\partial z}{\partial x} + 2(y - y^3)\frac{\partial z}{\partial y} + x^2 y^2 z = 0$$

assume when we make the transformation $x = uv$, $y = 1/v$?

14*. Let $\phi(x_1, x_2, \cdots, x_n;\ u_1, u_2, \cdots, u_n)$ be a function of the $2n$ independent variables $x_1, x_2, \cdots, x_n, u_1, u_2, \cdots, u_n$, homogeneous and of the second degree with respect to the variables $u_1, u_2, \cdots, u_n$. If we set

$$\frac{\partial \phi}{\partial u_1} = p_1, \qquad \frac{\partial \phi}{\partial u_2} = p_2, \qquad \cdots, \qquad \frac{\partial \phi}{\partial u_n} = p_n,$$

and then take $p_1, p_2, \cdots, p_n$ as independent variables in the place of $u_1, u_2, \cdots, u_n$, the function ϕ goes over into a function of the form

$$\psi(x_1, x_2, \cdots, x_n; p_1, p_2, \cdots, p_n).$$

Derive the formulæ:

$$\frac{\partial \psi}{\partial p_k} = u_k, \qquad \frac{\partial \psi}{\partial x_k} = -\frac{\partial \phi}{\partial x_k}.$$

15. Let N be the point of intersection of a fixed plane P with the normal MN erected at any point M of a given surface S. Lay off on the perpendicular to the plane P at the point N a length $Nm = NM$. Find the tangent plane to the surface described by the point m, as M describes the surface S.

The preceding transformation is a contact transformation. Study the inverse transformation.

16. Starting from each point of a given surface S, lay off on the normal to the surface a constant length l. Find the tangent plane to the surface Σ (*the parallel surface*) which is the locus of the end points.

Solve the analogous problem for a plane curve.

17*. Given a surface S and a fixed point O; join the point O to any point M of the surface S, and pass a plane OMN through OM and the normal MN to the surface S at the point M. In this plane OMN draw through the point O a perpendicular to the line OM, and lay off on it a length $OP = OM$. The point P describes a surface Σ, which is called the *apsidal* surface to the given surface S. Find the tangent plane to this surface.

The transformation is a contact transformation, and the relation between the surfaces S and Σ is a reciprocal one. When the given surface S is an ellipsoid and the point O is its center, the surface Σ is Fresnel's wave surface.

18*. Halphen's differential invariants. Show that the differential equation

$$9\left(\frac{d^2 y}{dx^2}\right)^2 \frac{d^5 y}{dx^5} - 45 \frac{d^2 y}{dx^2} \frac{d^3 y}{dx^3} \frac{d^4 y}{dx^4} + 40 \left(\frac{d^3 y}{dx^3}\right)^3 = 0$$

remains unchanged when the variables x, y undergo any projective transformation (§ 37).

19. If in the expression $P\,dx + Q\,dy + R\,dz$, where P, Q, R are any functions of x, y, z, we set

$$x = f(u, v, w), \qquad y = \phi(u, v, w), \qquad z = \psi(u, v, w),$$

where u, v, w are new variables, it goes over into an expression of the form

$$P_1\,du + Q_1\,dv + R_1\,dw,$$

where P_1, Q_1, R_1 are functions of u, v, w. Show that the following equation is satisfied identically:

$$H_1 = \frac{D(x, y, z)}{D(u, v, w)} H,$$

where

$$H = P\left(\frac{\partial Q}{\partial z} - \frac{\partial R}{\partial y}\right) + Q\left(\frac{\partial R}{\partial x} - \frac{\partial P}{\partial z}\right) + R\left(\frac{\partial P}{\partial y} - \frac{\partial Q}{\partial x}\right),$$

$$H_1 = P_1\left(\frac{\partial Q_1}{\partial w} - \frac{\partial R_1}{\partial v}\right) + Q_1\left(\frac{\partial R_1}{\partial u} - \frac{\partial P_1}{\partial w}\right) + R_1\left(\frac{\partial P_1}{\partial v} - \frac{\partial Q_1}{\partial u}\right).$$

20*. Bilinear covariants. Let Θ_d be a linear differential form:

$$\Theta_d = X_1\,dx_1 + X_2\,dx_2 + \cdots + X_n\,dx_n,$$

where $X_1, X_2, \cdots, X_n$ are functions of the n variables $x_1, x_2, \cdots, x_n$. Let us consider the expression

$$H = \sum_{i=1}^{n}\sum_{k=1}^{n} a_{ik}\,dx_i\,\delta x_k,$$

where

$$a^{ik} = \frac{\partial X_i}{\partial x_k} - \frac{\partial X_k}{\partial x_i},$$

and where there are two systems of differentials, d and δ. If we make any transformation

$$x_i = \phi_i(y_1, y_2, \cdots, y_n), \qquad (i = 1, 2, \cdots, n),$$

the expression Θ_d goes over into an expression of the same form

$$\Theta'_d = Y_1\,dy_1 + \cdots + Y_n\,dy_n,$$

where $Y_1, Y_2, \cdots, Y_n$ are functions of $y_1, y_2, \cdots, y_n$. Let us also set

$$a'_{ik} = \frac{\partial Y_i}{\partial y_k} - \frac{\partial Y_k}{\partial y_i}$$

and

$$H' = \sum_i\sum_k a'_{ik}\,dy_i\,\delta y_k.$$

Show that $H = H'$, identically, provided that we replace dx_i and δx_k, respectively, by the expressions

$$\frac{\partial \phi_i}{\partial y_1}\,dy_1 + \frac{\partial \phi_i}{\partial y_2}\,dy_2 + \cdots + \frac{\partial \phi_i}{\partial y_n}\,dy_n,$$

$$\frac{\partial \phi_k}{\partial y_1}\,\delta y_1 + \frac{\partial \phi_k}{\partial y_2}\,\delta y_2 + \cdots + \frac{\partial \phi_k}{\partial y_n}\,\delta y_n.$$

The expression H is called a *bilinear covariant* of Θ_d.

21*. Beltrami's differential parameters. If in a given expression of the form

$$E\,dx^2 + 2\,F\,dx\,dy + G\,dy^2,$$

where E, F, G are functions of the variables x and y, we make a transformation $x = f(u, v)$, $y = \phi(u, v)$, we obtain an expression of the same form:

$$E_1\,du^2 + 2\,F_1\,du\,dv + G_1\,dv^2,$$

where E_1, F_1, G_1 are functions of u and v. Let $\theta(x, y)$ be any function of the variables x and y, and $\theta_1(u, v)$ the transformed function. Then we have, identically,

$$\frac{G\left(\dfrac{\partial\theta}{\partial x}\right)^2 - 2F\dfrac{\partial\theta}{\partial x}\dfrac{\partial\theta}{\partial y} + E\left(\dfrac{\partial\theta}{\partial y}\right)^2}{EG - F^2} = \frac{G_1\left(\dfrac{\partial\theta_1}{\partial u}\right)^2 - 2F_1\dfrac{\partial\theta_1}{\partial u}\dfrac{\partial\theta_1}{\partial v} + E_1\left(\dfrac{\partial\theta_1}{\partial v}\right)^2}{E_1 G_1 - F_1^2},$$

$$\frac{1}{\sqrt{EG - F^2}}\frac{\partial}{\partial x}\left(\frac{G\dfrac{\partial\theta}{\partial x} - F\dfrac{\partial\theta}{\partial y}}{\sqrt{EG - F^2}}\right) + \frac{1}{\sqrt{EG - F^2}}\frac{\partial}{\partial y}\left(\frac{E\dfrac{\partial\theta}{\partial y} - F\dfrac{\partial\theta}{\partial x}}{\sqrt{EG - F^2}}\right)$$

$$= \frac{1}{\sqrt{E_1 G_1 - F_1^2}}\frac{\partial}{\partial u}\left(\frac{G_1\dfrac{\partial\theta_1}{\partial u} - F_1\dfrac{\partial\theta_1}{\partial v}}{\sqrt{E_1 G_1 - F_1^2}}\right) + \frac{1}{\sqrt{E_1 G_1 - F_1^2}}\frac{\partial}{\partial v}\left(\frac{E_1\dfrac{\partial\theta_1}{\partial v} - F_1\dfrac{\partial\theta_1}{\partial u}}{\sqrt{E_1 G_1 - F_1^2}}\right).$$

22. Schwarzian. Setting $y = (ax + b)/(cx + b)$, where x is a function of t and a, b, c, d are arbitrary constants, show that the relation

$$\frac{x'''}{x'} - \frac{3}{2}\left(\frac{x''}{x'}\right)^2 = \frac{y'''}{y'} - \frac{3}{2}\left(\frac{y''}{y'}\right)^2$$

is identically satisfied, where x', x'', x''', y', y'', y''' denote the derivatives with respect to the variable t.

23*. Let u and v be any two functions of the two independent variables x and y, and let us set

$$U = \frac{au + bv + c}{a''u + b''v + c''}, \qquad V = \frac{a'u + b'v + c'}{a''u + b''v + c''},$$

where $a, b, c, \cdots, c''$ are constants. Prove the formulæ:

$$\frac{\dfrac{\partial^2 u}{\partial x^2}\dfrac{\partial v}{\partial x} - \dfrac{\partial^2 v}{\partial x^2}\dfrac{\partial u}{\partial x}}{(u, v)} = \frac{\dfrac{\partial^2 U}{\partial x^2}\dfrac{\partial V}{\partial x} - \dfrac{\partial^2 V}{\partial x^2}\dfrac{\partial U}{\partial x}}{(U, V)},$$

$$\frac{\dfrac{\partial^2 u}{\partial x^2}\dfrac{\partial v}{\partial y} - \dfrac{\partial^2 v}{\partial x^2}\dfrac{\partial u}{\partial y} + 2\left(\dfrac{\partial v}{\partial x}\dfrac{\partial^2 u}{\partial x\,\partial y} - \dfrac{\partial u}{\partial x}\dfrac{\partial^2 v}{\partial x\,\partial y}\right)}{(u, v)}$$

$$= \frac{\dfrac{\partial^2 U}{\partial x^2}\dfrac{\partial V}{\partial y} - \dfrac{\partial^2 V}{\partial x^2}\dfrac{\partial U}{\partial y} + 2\left(\dfrac{\partial V}{\partial x}\dfrac{\partial^2 U}{\partial x\,\partial y} - \dfrac{\partial U}{\partial x}\dfrac{\partial^2 V}{\partial x\,\partial y}\right)}{(U, V)},$$

and the analogous formulæ obtained by interchanging x and y, where

$$(u, v) = \frac{\partial u}{\partial x}\frac{\partial v}{\partial y} - \frac{\partial u}{\partial y}\frac{\partial v}{\partial x}, \qquad (U, V) = \frac{\partial U}{\partial x}\frac{\partial V}{\partial y} - \frac{\partial V}{\partial x}\frac{\partial U}{\partial y}.$$

[Goursat and Painlevé, *Comptes rendus*, 1887.]

CHAPTER III

TAYLOR'S SERIES   ELEMENTARY APPLICATIONS
MAXIMA AND MINIMA

I. TAYLOR'S SERIES WITH A REMAINDER
TAYLOR'S SERIES

44. Taylor's series with a remainder. In elementary texts on the Calculus it is shown that, if $f(x)$ is an integral polynomial of degree n, the following formula holds for all values of a and h:

$$(1) \quad f(a + h) = f(a) + \frac{h}{1} f'(a) + \frac{h^2}{1 \cdot 2} f''(a) + \cdots + \frac{h^n}{1 \cdot 2 \cdots n} f^{(n)}(a).$$

This development stops of itself, since all the derivatives past the $(n + 1)$th vanish. If we try to apply this formula to a function $f(x)$ which is not a polynomial, the second member contains an infinite number of terms. In order to find the proper value to assign to this development, we will first try to find an expression for the difference

$$f(a + h) - f(a) - \frac{h}{1} f'(a) - \frac{h^2}{1 \cdot 2} f''(a) - \cdots - \frac{h^n}{1 \cdot 2 \cdots n} f^{(n)}(a),$$

with the hypotheses that the function $f(x)$, together with its first n derivatives $f'(x), f''(x), \cdots, f^{(n)}(x)$, is continuous when x lies in the interval $(a, a + h)$, and that $f^{(n)}(x)$ itself possesses a derivative $f^{(n+1)}(x)$ in the same interval. The numbers a and $a + h$ being given, let us set

$$(2) \quad \begin{cases} f(a + h) = f(a) + \dfrac{h}{1} f'(a) + \dfrac{h^2}{1 \cdot 2} f''(a) + \cdots \\ \qquad + \dfrac{h^n}{1 \cdot 2 \cdots n} f^{(n)}(a) + \dfrac{h^p}{1 \cdot 2 \cdots n \cdot p} P, \end{cases}$$

where p is any positive integer, and where P is a number which is defined by this equation itself. Let us then consider the auxiliary function

$$\phi(x) = f(a+h) - f(x) - \frac{a+h-x}{1} f'(x) - \frac{(a+h-x)^2}{1.2} f''(x) - \cdots$$
$$- \frac{(a+h-x)^n}{1.2\cdots n} f^{(n)}(x) - \frac{(a+h-x)^p}{1.2\cdots n.p} P.$$

It is clear from equation (2), which defines the number P, that

$$\phi(a) = 0, \qquad \phi(a+h) = 0;$$

and it results from the hypotheses regarding $f(x)$ that the function $\phi(x)$ possesses a derivative throughout the interval $(a, a+h)$. Hence, by Rolle's theorem, the equation $\phi'(x) = 0$ must have a root $a + \theta h$ which lies in that interval, where θ is a positive number which lies between zero and unity. The value of $\phi'(x)$, after some easy reductions, turns out to be

$$\phi'(x) = \frac{(a+h-x)^{p-1}}{1.2\cdots n} \left[P - (a+h-x)^{n-p+1} f^{(n+1)}(x) \right].$$

The first factor $(a+h-x)^{p-1}$ cannot vanish for any value of x other than $a + h$. Hence we must have

$$P = h^{n-p+1}(1-\theta)^{n-p+1} f^{(n+1)}(a+\theta h), \quad \text{where} \quad 0 < \theta < 1;$$

whence, substituting this value for P in equation (2), we find

$$(3) \quad f(a+h) = f(a) + \frac{h}{1} f'(a) + \frac{h^2}{1.2} f''(a) + \cdots + \frac{h^n}{1.2\cdots n} f^{(n)}(a) + R_n,$$

where

$$R_n = \frac{h^{n+1}(1-\theta)^{n-p+1}}{1.2\cdots n.p} f^{(n+1)}(a+\theta h).$$

We shall call this formula *Taylor's series with a remainder*, and the last term or R_n the *remainder*. This remainder depends upon the positive integer p, which we have left undetermined. In practice, about the only values which are ever given to p are $p = n + 1$ and $p = 1$. Setting $p = n + 1$, we find the following expression for the remainder, which is due to Lagrange :

$$R_n = \frac{h^{n+1}}{1.2\cdots n(n+1)} f^{(n+1)}(a+\theta h);$$

setting $p = 1$, we find

$$R_n = \frac{h^{n+1}(1-\theta)^n}{1.2\cdots n} f^{(n+1)}(a+\theta h),$$

an expression for the remainder which is due to Cauchy. It is clear, moreover, that the number θ will not be the same, in general, in these two special formulæ. If we assume further that $f^{(n+1)}(x)$ is continuous when $x = a$, the remainder may be written in the form

$$R_n = \frac{h^{n+1}}{1 \cdot 2 \cdots (n+1)} \left[f^{(n+1)}(a) + \epsilon \right],$$

where ϵ approaches zero with h.

Let us consider, for definiteness, Lagrange's form. If, in the general formula (3), n be taken equal to 2, 3, 4, $\cdots$, successively, we get a succession of distinct formulæ which give closer and closer approximations for $f(a + h)$ for small values of h. Thus for $n = 1$ we find

$$f(a + h) = f(a) + \frac{h}{1} f'(a) + \frac{h^2}{1 \cdot 2} f''(a + \theta h),$$

which shows that the difference

$$f(a + h) - f(a) - \frac{h}{1} f'(a)$$

is an infinitesimal of at least the second order with respect to h, provided that f'' is finite near $x = a$. Likewise, the difference

$$f(a + h) - f(a) - \frac{h}{1} f'(a) - \frac{h^2}{1 \cdot 2} f''(a)$$

is an infinitesimal of the third order; and, in general, the expression

$$f(a + h) - f(a) - \frac{h}{1} f'(a) - \cdots - \frac{h^n}{n!} f^{(n)}(a)$$

is an infinitesimal of order $n + 1$. But, in order to have an exact idea of the approximation obtained by neglecting R, we need to know an upper limit of this remainder. Let us denote by M^* an upper limit of the absolute value of $f^{(n+1)}(x)$ in the neighborhood of $x = a$, say in the interval $(a - \eta, a + \eta)$. Then we evidently have

$$|R_n| \leqq \frac{|h|^{n+1}}{1 \cdot 2 \cdots (n+1)} M,$$

provided that $|h| < \eta$.

---

* That is, $M \geqq |f^{(n+1)}(x)|$ when $|x - a| < \eta$. The expression "*the* upper limit," defined in § 68, must be carefully distinguished from the expression "*an* upper limit," which is used here to denote a number greater than or equal to the absolute value of the function at any point in a certain interval. In this paragraph and in the next $f^{(n+1)}(x)$ is supposed to *have* an upper limit near $x = a$. — TRANS.

45. Application to curves. This result may be interpreted geometrically. Suppose that we wished to study a curve C, whose equation is $y = f(x)$, in the neighborhood of a point A, whose abscissa is a. Let us consider at the same time an auxiliary curve C', whose equation is

$$Y = f(a) + \frac{x-a}{1}f'(a) + \frac{(x-a)^2}{1.2}f''(a) + \cdots + \frac{(x-a)^n}{1.2\cdots n}f^{(n)}(a).$$

A line $x = a + h$, parallel to the axis of y, meets these two curves in two points M and M', which are near A. The difference of their ordinates, by the general formula, is equal to

$$y - Y = \frac{h^{n+1}}{1.2\cdots(n+1)}f^{(n+1)}(a + \theta h).$$

This difference is an infinitesimal of order not less than $n + 1$; and consequently, restricting ourselves to a small interval $(a - \eta, a + \eta)$, the curve C sensibly coincides with the curve C'. By taking larger and larger values of n we may obtain in this way curves which differ less and less from the given curve C; and this gives us a more and more exact idea of the *appearance* of the curve near the point A.

Let us first set $n = 1$. Then the curve C' is the tangent to the curve C at the point A:

$$Y = f(a) + (x - a)f'(a);$$

and the difference between the ordinates of the points M and M' of the curve and its tangent, respectively, which have the same abscissa $a + h$, is

$$y - Y = \frac{h^2}{1.2}f''(a + \theta h).$$

Let us suppose that $f''(a) \neq 0$, which is the case in general. The preceding formula may be written in the form

$$y - Y = \frac{h^2}{1.2}[f''(a) + \epsilon],$$

where ϵ approaches zero with h. Since $f''(a) \neq 0$, a positive number η can be found such that $|\epsilon| < |f''(a)|$, when h lies between $-\eta$ and $+\eta$. For such values of h the quantity $f''(a) + \epsilon$ will have the same sign as $f''(a)$, and hence $y - Y$ will also have the same sign as $f''(a)$. If $f''(a)$ is positive, the ordinate y of the curve is greater than the ordinate Y of the tangent, whatever the sign of h; and the curve C lies wholly above the tangent, near the point A. On the other hand, if $f''(a)$ is negative, y is less than Y, and the curve lies entirely below the tangent, near the point of tangency.

If $f''(a) = 0$, let $f^{(p)}(a)$ be the first succeeding derivative which does not vanish for $x = a$. Then we have, as before, if $f^{(p)}(x)$ is continuous when $x = a$,

$$y - Y = \frac{h^p}{1 \cdot 2 \cdots p} \left[f^{(p)}(a) + \epsilon \right];$$

and it can be shown, as above, that in a sufficiently small interval $(a - \eta, a + \eta)$ the difference $y - Y$ has the same sign as the product $h^p f^{(p)}(a)$. When p is even, this difference does not change sign with h, and the curve lies entirely on the same side of the tangent, near the point of tangency. But if p be odd, the difference $y - Y$ changes sign with h, and the curve C crosses its tangent at the point of tangency. In the latter case the point A is called a point of inflection; it occurs, for example, if $f'''(a) \neq 0$.

Let us now take $n = 2$. The curve C' is in this case a parabola:

$$Y = f(a) + (x - a)f'(a) + \frac{(x - a)^2}{1 \cdot 2} f''(a),$$

whose axis is parallel to the axis of y; and the difference of the ordinates is

$$y - Y = \frac{h^3}{1 \cdot 2 \cdot 3} \left[f'''(a) + \epsilon \right].$$

If $f'''(a)$ does not vanish, $y - Y$ has the same sign as $h^3 f'''(a)$ for sufficiently small values of h, and the curve C crosses the parabola C' at the point A. This parabola is called the *osculatory* parabola to the curve C; for, of the parabolas of the family

$$Y = mx^2 + nx + p,$$

this one comes nearest to coincidence with the curve C near the point A (see § 213).

46. General method of development. The formula (3) affords a method for the development of the infinitesimal $f(a + h) - f(a)$ according to ascending powers of h. But, still more generally, let x be a principal infinitesimal, which, to avoid any ambiguity, we will suppose positive; and let y be another infinitesimal of the form

$$(4) \qquad y = A_1 x^{n_1} + A_2 x^{n_2} + \cdots + x^{n_p} (A_p + \epsilon),$$

where $n_1, n_2, \cdots, n_p$ are ascending positive numbers, not necessarily integers, $A_1, A_2, \cdots, A_p$ are constants different from zero, and ϵ is another infinitesimal. The numbers $n_1, A_1, n_2, A_2, \cdots$ may be calculated successively by the following process. First of all, it is clear that n_1 is equal to the order of the infinitesimal y with respect to x, and that A_1 is equal to the limit of the ratio y / x^{n_1} when x approaches zero. Next we have

$$y - A_1 x^{n_1} = u_1 = A_2 x^{n_2} + \cdots + (A_p + \epsilon) x^{n_p},$$

which shows that n_2 is equal to the order of the infinitesimal u_1, and A_2 to the limit of the ratio u_1 / x^{n_2}. A continuation of this process gives the succeeding terms. It is then clear that an infinitesimal y does not admit of two essentially different developments of the form (4). If the developments have the same number of terms, they coincide; while if one of them has p terms and the other $p + q$ terms, the terms of the first occur also in the second. This method applies, in particular, to the development of $f(a + h) - f(a)$ according to powers of h; and it is not necessary to have obtained the general expression for the successive derivatives of the function $f(x)$ in advance. On the contrary, this method furnishes us a practical means of calculating the values of the derivatives $f'(a), f''(a), \cdots$.

Examples. Let us consider the equation

$$(5) \ F(x, y) = A x^n + B y + x y \, \Phi(x, y) + C x^{n+1} + \cdots + D y^2 + \cdots = 0,$$

where $\Phi(x, y)$ is an integral polynomial in x and y, and where the terms not written down consist of two polynomials $P(x)$ and $Q(y)$, which are divisible, respectively, by x^{n+1} and y^2. The coefficients A and B are each supposed to be different from zero. As x approaches zero there is one and only one root of the equation (5) which approaches zero (§ 20). In order to apply Taylor's series with a remainder to this root, we should have to know the successive derivatives, which could be calculated by means of the general rules. But we may proceed more directly by employing the preceding method. For this purpose we first observe that the principal part of the infinitesimal root is equal to $- (A/B)x^n$. For if in the equation (5) we make the substitution

$$y = x^n \left(-\frac{A}{B} + y_1 \right),$$

and then divide by x^n, we obtain an equation of the same form:

$$(6) \quad \begin{cases} F_1(x, y_1) = A_1 x^{n_1} + B y_1 + x y_1 \Phi_1(x, y_1) \\ \qquad\qquad + C_1 x^{n_1+1} + \cdots + D_1 y_1^2 + \cdots = 0, \end{cases}$$

which has only one term in y_1, namely $B y_1$. As x approaches zero the equation (6) possesses an infinitesimal root in y_1, and consequently the infinitesimal root of the equation (5) has the principal part $- (A/B)x^n$, as stated above. Likewise, the principal part of y_1 is $- (A_1/B)x^{n_1}$; and we may set

$$y = -\frac{A}{B} x^n + \left(-\frac{A_1}{B} + y_2 \right) x^{n+n_1},$$

where y_2 is another infinitesimal whose principal part may be found by making the substitution

$$y_1 = x^{n_1} \left(-\frac{A_1}{B} + y_2 \right)$$

in the equation (6).

Continuing in this way, we may obtain for this root y an expression of the form

$$y = \alpha x^n + \alpha_1 x^{n+n_1} + \alpha_2 x^{n+n_1+n_2} + \cdots + (\alpha_p + \epsilon) x^{n+n_1+\cdots+n_p},$$

which we may carry out as far as we wish. All the numbers n, $n_1, n_2, \cdots, n_p$ are indeed positive integers, as they should be, since we are working under conditions where the general formula (3) is applicable. In fact the development thus obtained is precisely the same as that which we should find by applying Taylor's series with a remainder, where $a = 0$ and $h = x$.

Let us consider a second example where the exponents are not necessarily positive integers. Let us set

$$y = \frac{A x^\alpha + B x^\beta + C x^\gamma + \cdots}{1 + B_1 x^{\beta_1} + C_1 x^{\gamma_1} + \cdots},$$

where α, β, γ, $\cdots$ and β_1, γ_1, $\cdots$ are two ascending series of positive numbers, and the coefficient A is not zero. It is clear that the principal part of y is Ax^α, and that we have

$$y - Ax^\alpha = \frac{Bx^\beta + Cx^\gamma + \cdots - Ax^\alpha(B_1x^{\beta_1} + C_1x^{\gamma_1} + \cdots)}{1 + B_1x^{\beta_1} + C_1x^{\gamma_1} + \cdots},$$

which is an expression of the same form as the original, and whose principal part is simply the term of least degree in the numerator. It is evident that we might go on to find by the same process as many terms of the development as we wished.

Let $f(x)$ be a function which possesses $n + 1$ successive derivatives. Then replacing a by x in the formula (3), we find

$$f(x + h) = f(x) + \frac{h}{1} f'(x) + \frac{h^2}{1 \cdot 2} f''(x) + \cdots + \frac{h^n}{1 \cdot 2 \cdots n} [f^{(n)}(x) + \epsilon],$$

where ϵ approaches zero with h. Let us suppose, on the other hand, that we had obtained by any process whatever another expression of the same form for $f(x + h)$:

$$f(x + h) = f(x) + h\phi_1(x) + h^2\phi_2(x) + \cdots + h^n[\phi_n(x) + \epsilon'].$$

These two developments must coincide term by term, and hence the coefficients ϕ_1, ϕ_2, $\cdots$, ϕ_n are equal, save for certain numerical factors, to the successive derivatives of $f(x)$:

$$\phi_1(x) = f'(x), \qquad \phi_2(x) = \frac{f''(x)}{1 \cdot 2}, \qquad \cdots, \qquad \phi_n(x) = \frac{f^{(n)}(x)}{1 \cdot 2 \cdots n}.$$

This remark is sometimes useful in the calculation of the derivatives of certain functions. Suppose, for instance, that we wished to calculate the nth derivative of a function of a function:

$$y = f(u), \qquad \text{where} \qquad u = \phi(x).$$

Neglecting the terms of order higher than n with respect to h, we have

$$k = \phi(x + h) - \phi(x) = \frac{h}{1} \phi'(x) + \frac{h^2}{1 \cdot 2} \phi''(x) + \cdots + \frac{h^n}{1 \cdot 2 \cdots n} \phi^{(n)}(x);$$

and likewise neglecting terms of order higher than n with respect to k,

$$f(u + k) - f(u) = \frac{k}{1} f'(u) + \frac{k^2}{1 \cdot 2} f''(u) + \cdots + \frac{k^n}{1 \cdot 2 \cdots n} f^{(n)}(u).$$

If in the right-hand side k be replaced by the expression

$$\frac{h}{1} \phi'(x) + \frac{h^2}{1 \cdot 2} \phi''(x) + \cdots + \frac{h^n}{1 \cdot 2 \cdots n} \phi^{(n)}(x),$$

and the resulting expression arranged according to ascending powers of h, it is evident that the terms omitted will not affect the terms in h, h^2, $\cdots$, h^n. The coefficient of h^n, for instance, will be equal to the nth derivative of $f[\phi(x)]$ divided by $1.2\cdots n$; and hence we may write

$$D^n\left\{f[\phi(x)]\right\} = 1.2\cdots n\left[A_1 f'(u) + A_2\frac{f''(u)}{1.2} + \cdots + \frac{A_n}{1.2\cdots n}f^{(n)}(u)\right],$$

where A_i denotes the coefficient of h^n in the development of

$$\left[\frac{h}{1}\phi'(x) + \cdots + \frac{h^n}{1.2\cdots n}\phi^{(n)}(x)\right]^i.$$

For greater detail concerning this method, the reader is referred to Hermite's *Cours d'Analyse* (p. 59).

47. Indeterminate forms.* Let $f(x)$ and $\phi(x)$ be two functions which vanish for the same value of the variable $x = a$. Let us try to find the limit approached by the ratio

$$\frac{f(a+h)}{\phi(a+h)}$$

as h approaches zero. This is merely a special case of the problem of finding the limit approached by the ratio of two infinitesimals The limit in question may be determined immediately if the principal part of each of the infinitesimals is known, which is the case whenever the formula (3) is applicable to each of the functions $f(x)$ and $\phi(x)$ in the neighborhood of the point a. Let us suppose that the first derivative of $f(x)$ which does not vanish for $x = a$ is that of order p, $f^{(p)}(a)$; and that likewise the first derivative of $\phi(x)$ which does not vanish for $x = a$ is that of order q, $\phi^{(q)}(a)$. Applying the formula (3) to each of the functions $f(x)$ and $\phi(x)$ and dividing, we find

$$\frac{f(a+h)}{\phi(a+h)} = h^{p-q}\frac{1.2\cdots q}{1.2\cdots p}\frac{f^{(p)}(a)+\epsilon}{\phi^{(q)}(a)+\epsilon'},$$

where ϵ and ϵ' are two infinitesimals. It is clear from this result that the given ratio increases indefinitely when h approaches zero, if q is greater than p; and that it approaches zero if q is less than p. If $q = p$, however, the given ratio approaches $f^{(p)}(a)/\phi^{(q)}(a)$ as its limit, and this limit is different from zero.

Indeterminate forms of this sort are sometimes encountered in finding the tangent to a curve. Let

$$x = f(t), \qquad y = \phi(t), \qquad z = \psi(t)$$

---

* See also § 7.

be the equations of a curve C in terms of a parameter t. The equations of the tangent to this curve at a point M, which corresponds to a value t_0 of the parameter, are, as we saw in § 5,

$$\frac{X - f(t_0)}{f'(t_0)} = \frac{Y - \phi(t_0)}{\phi'(t_0)} = \frac{Z - \psi(t_0)}{\psi'(t_0)}.$$

These equations reduce to identities if the three derivatives $f'(t)$, $\phi'(t)$, $\psi'(t)$ all vanish for $t = t_0$. In order to avoid this difficulty, let us review the reasoning by which we found the equations of the tangent. Let M' be a point of the curve C near to M, and let $t_0 + h$ be the corresponding value of the parameter. Then the equations of the secant MM' are

$$\frac{X - f(t_0)}{f(t_0 + h) - f(t_0)} = \frac{Y - \phi(t_0)}{\phi(t_0 + h) - \phi(t_0)} = \frac{Z - \psi(t_0)}{\psi(t_0 + h) - \psi(t_0)}.$$

For the sake of generality let us suppose that all the derivatives of order less than $p\,(p>1)$ of the functions $f(t)$, $\phi(t)$, $\psi(t)$ vanish for $t = t_0$, but that at least one of the derivatives of order p, say $f^{(p)}(t_0)$, is not zero. Dividing each of the denominators in the preceding equations by h^p and applying the general formula (3), we may then write these equations in the form

$$\frac{X - f(t_0)}{f^{(p)}(t_0) + \epsilon} = \frac{Y - \phi(t_0)}{\phi^{(p)}(t_0) + \epsilon'} = \frac{Z - \psi(t_0)}{\psi^{(p)}(t_0) + \epsilon''},$$

where ϵ, ϵ', ϵ'' are three infinitesimals. If we now let h approach zero, these equations become in the limit

$$\frac{X - f(t_0)}{f^{(p)}(t_0)} = \frac{Y - \phi(t_0)}{\phi^{(p)}(t_0)} = \frac{Z - \psi(t_0)}{\psi^{(p)}(t_0)},$$

in which form all indetermination has disappeared.

The points of a curve C where this happens are, in general, singular points where the curve has some peculiarity of form. Thus the plane curve whose equations are

$$x = t^2, \qquad y = t^3$$

passes through the origin, and $dx/dt = dy/dt = 0$ at that point. The tangent is the axis of x, and the origin is a cusp of the first kind.

48. Taylor's series. If the sequence of derivatives of the function $f(x)$ is unlimited in the interval $(a, a + h)$, the number n in the formula (3) may be taken as large as we please. *If the remainder R_n approaches zero when n increases indefinitely*, we are led to write down the following formula:

$$(7)\quad f(a+h) = f(a) + \frac{h}{1}f'(a) + \frac{h^2}{1.2}f''(a) + \cdots + \frac{h^n}{1.2\cdots n}f^{(n)}(a) + \cdots;$$

which expresses that the series

$$f(a) + \frac{h}{1}f'(a) + \cdots + \frac{h^n}{1.2\cdots n}f^{(n)}(a) + \cdots$$

is convergent, and that its "sum"* is the quantity $f(a + h)$. This formula (7) is *Taylor's series*, properly speaking. But it is not justifiable unless we can show that the remainder R_n approaches zero when n is infinite, whereas the general formula (3) assumes only the existence of the first $n + 1$ derivatives. Replacing a by x, the equation (7) may be written in the form

$$f(x + h) = f(x) + \frac{h}{1} f'(x) + \cdots + \frac{h^n}{1 . 2 \cdots n} f^{(n)}(x) + \cdots.$$

Or, again, replacing h by x and setting $a = 0$, we find the formula

$$(8) \quad f(x) = f(0) + \frac{x}{1} f'(0) + \cdots + \frac{x^n}{1 . 2 \cdots n} f^{(n)}(0) + \cdots.$$

This latter form is often called *Maclaurin's series;* but it should be noticed that all these different forms are essentially equivalent. The equation (8) gives the development of a function of x according to powers of x; the formula (7) gives the development of a function of h according to powers of h: a simple change of notation is all that is necessary in order to pass from one to the other of these forms.

It is only in rather specialized cases that we are able to show that the remainder R_n approaches zero when n increases indefinitely. If, for instance, the absolute value of any derivative whatever is less than a fixed number M when x lies between a and $a + h$, it follows, from Lagrange's form for the remainder, that

$$| R_n | < M \frac{| h |^{n+1}}{1 . 2 \cdots (n + 1)},$$

an inequality whose right-hand member is the general term of a convergent series.† Such is the case, for instance, for the functions e^x, $\sin x$, $\cos x$. All the derivatives of e^x are themselves equal to e^x, and have, therefore, the same maximum in the interval considered. In the case of $\sin x$ and $\cos x$ the absolute values never exceed unity. Hence the formula (7) is applicable to these three functions for all values of a and h. Let us restrict ourselves to the form (8) and apply it first to the function $f(x) = e^x$. We find

$$f(0) = 1, \qquad f'(0) = 1, \qquad \cdots, \qquad f^{(n)}(0) = 1, \qquad \cdots;$$

---

* That is to say, the limit of the sum of the first n terms as n becomes infinite. For a definition of the meaning of the technical phrase "*the sum of a series*," see § 157. — TRANS.

† The *order of choice* is a, h, M, n, not a, h, n, M. This is essential to the convergence of the series in question. — TRANS.

and consequently we have the formula

(9) $e^x = 1 + \dfrac{x}{1} + \dfrac{x^2}{1 \cdot 2} + \cdots + \dfrac{x^n}{1 \cdot 2 \cdots n} + \cdots,$

which applies to all values, positive or negative, of x. If a is any positive number, we have $a^x = e^{x \log a}$, and the preceding formula becomes

(10) $a^x = 1 + \dfrac{x \log a}{1} + \dfrac{(x \log a)^2}{1 \cdot 2} + \cdots + \dfrac{(x \log a)^n}{1 \cdot 2 \cdots n} + \cdots.$

Let us now take $f(x) = \sin x$. The successive derivatives form a recurrent sequence of four terms $\cos x$, $- \sin x$, $- \cos x$, $\sin x$; and their values for $x = 0$ form another recurrent sequence $1, 0, - 1, 0$. Hence for any positive or negative value of x we have

(11) $\sin x = \dfrac{x}{1} - \dfrac{x^3}{1 \cdot 2 \cdot 3} + \dfrac{x^5}{1 \cdot 2 \cdot 3 \cdot 4 \cdot 5} - \cdots$
$$+ (-1)^n \dfrac{x^{2n+1}}{1 \cdot 2 \cdot 3 \cdots (2n+1)} + \cdots;$$

and, similarly,

(12) $\cos x = 1 - \dfrac{x^2}{1 \cdot 2} + \dfrac{x^4}{1 \cdot 2 \cdot 3 \cdot 4} - \cdots + (-1)^n \dfrac{x^{2n}}{1 \cdot 2 \cdot 3 \cdots 2n} + \cdots.$

Let us return to the general case. The discussion of the remainder R_n is seldom so easy as in the preceding examples; but the problem is somewhat simplified by the remark that if the remainder approaches zero the series

$$f(a) + \dfrac{h}{1} f'(a) + \cdots + \dfrac{h^n}{1 \cdot 2 \cdots n} f^{(n)}(a) + \cdots$$

necessarily converges. In general it is better, before examining R_n, to see whether this series converges. If for the given values of a and h the series diverges, it is useless to carry the discussion further; we can say at once that R_n does *not* approach zero when n increases indefinitely.

49. Development of $\log(1 + x)$. The function $\log(1 + x)$, together with all its derivatives, is continuous provided that x is greater than -1. The successive derivatives are as follows:

$$f'(x) = \dfrac{1}{1 + x},$$

$$f''(x) = \frac{-1}{(1+x)^2},$$

$$f'''(x) = \frac{1 \cdot 2}{(1+x)^3},$$

$$\cdots \cdots \cdots,$$

$$f^{(n)}(x) = (-1)^{n-1} \frac{1 \cdot 2 \cdots (n-1)}{(1+x)^n},$$

$$f^{(n+1)}(x) = (-1)^n \frac{1 \cdot 2 \cdots n}{(1+x)^{n+1}}.$$

Let us see for what values of x Maclaurin's formula (8) may be applied to this function. Writing first the series with a remainder, we have, under any circumstances,

$$\log (1+x) = \frac{x}{1} - \frac{x^2}{2} + \frac{x^3}{3} + \cdots + (-1)^{n-1} \frac{x^n}{n} + R_n.$$

The remainder R_n does not approach zero unless the series

$$\frac{x}{1} - \frac{x^2}{2} + \frac{x^3}{3} + \cdots + (-1)^{n-1} \frac{x^n}{n} + \cdots$$

converges, which it does only for the values of x between -1 and $+1$, including the upper limit $+1$. When x lies in this interval the remainder may be written in the Cauchy form as follows:

$$R_n = \frac{x^{n+1}(1-\theta)^n}{1 \cdot 2 \cdots n} \frac{(-1)^n 1 \cdot 2 \cdots n}{(1+\theta x)^{n+1}} = (-1)^n \frac{x^{n+1}(1-\theta)^n}{(1+\theta x)^{n+1}},$$

or

$$R_n = (-1)^n x^{n+1} \left(\frac{1-\theta}{1+\theta x}\right)^n \frac{1}{1+\theta x}.$$

Let us consider first the case where $|x| < 1$. The first factor x approaches zero with x, and the second factor $(1-\theta)/(1+\theta x)$ is less than unity, whether x be positive or negative, for the numerator is always less than the denominator. The last factor remains finite, for it is always less than $1/(1-|x|)$. Hence the remainder R_n actually approaches zero when n increases indefinitely. This form of the remainder gives us no information as to what happens when $x = 1$; but if we write the remainder in Lagrange's form,

$$R_n = (-1)^n \frac{1}{n+1} \frac{1}{(1+\theta)^{n+1}},$$

it is evident that R_n approaches zero when n increases indefinitely. An examination of the remainder for $x = -1$ would be useless, since the series diverges for that value of x. We have then, when x lies between -1 and $+1$, the formula

$$(13) \quad \log(1+x) = \frac{x}{1} - \frac{x^2}{2} + \frac{x^3}{3} - \cdots + (-1)^{n-1}\frac{x^n}{n} + \cdots.$$

This formula still holds when $x = 1$, which gives the curious relation

$$(14) \quad \log 2 = 1 - \frac{1}{2} + \frac{1}{3} - \frac{1}{4} + \cdots + (-1)^{n-1}\frac{1}{n} + \cdots.$$

The formula (13), not holding except when x is less than or equal to unity, cannot be used for the calculation of logarithms of whole numbers. Let us replace x by $-x$. The new formula obtained,

$$(13') \quad \log(1-x) = -\frac{x}{1} - \frac{x^2}{2} - \frac{x^3}{3} - \cdots - \frac{x^n}{n} - \cdots,$$

still holds for values of x between -1 and $+1$; and, subtracting the corresponding sides, we find the formula

$$(15) \quad \log\left(\frac{1+x}{1-x}\right) = 2\left(\frac{x}{1} + \frac{x^3}{3} + \frac{x^5}{5} + \cdots + \frac{x^{2n+1}}{2n+1} + \cdots\right).$$

When x varies from 0 to 1 the rational fraction $(1+x)/(1-x)$ steadily increases from 1 to $+\infty$, and hence we may now easily calculate the logarithms of all integers. A still more rapidly converging series may be obtained, however, by forming the difference of the logarithms of two consecutive integers. For this purpose let us set

$$\frac{1+x}{1-x} = \frac{N+1}{N}, \quad \text{or} \quad x = \frac{1}{2N+1}.$$

Then the preceding formula becomes

$$\log(N+1) - \log N = 2\left[\frac{1}{2N+1} + \frac{1}{3(2N+1)^3} + \frac{1}{5(2N+1)^5} + \cdots\right],$$

an equation whose right-hand member is a series which converges very rapidly, especially for large values of N.

Note. Let us apply the general formula (3) to the function $\log(1+x)$, setting $a = 0$, $h = x$, $n = 1$, and taking Lagrange's form for the remainder. We find in this way

$$\log(1+x) = x - \frac{x^2}{2(1+\theta x)^2}.$$

If we now replace x by the reciprocal of an integer n, this may be written

$$\log\left(1 + \frac{1}{n}\right) = \frac{1}{n} - \frac{\theta_n}{2\,n^2},$$

where θ_n is a positive number less than unity. Some interesting consequences may be deduced from this equation.

1) The harmonic series being divergent, the sum

$$\Sigma_n = 1 + \frac{1}{2} + \frac{1}{3} + \cdots + \frac{1}{n}$$

increases indefinitely with n. But the difference

$$\Sigma_n - \log n$$

approaches a finite limit. For, let us write this difference in the form

$$\left(1 - \log\frac{2}{1}\right) + \left(\frac{1}{2} - \log\frac{3}{2}\right) + \cdots + \left(\frac{1}{p} - \log\frac{p+1}{p}\right) + \cdots$$
$$+ \left(\frac{1}{n} - \log\frac{n+1}{n}\right) + \log\frac{n+1}{n}.$$

Now $1/p - \log(1 + 1/p)$ is the general term of a convergent series, for by the equation above

$$\frac{1}{p} - \log\left(1 + \frac{1}{p}\right) = \frac{\theta_p}{2\,p^2},$$

which shows that this term is smaller than the general term of the convergent series $\Sigma(1/p^2)$. When n increases indefinitely the expression

$$\log\frac{n+1}{n} = \log\left(1 + \frac{1}{n}\right)$$

approaches zero. Hence the difference under consideration approaches a finite limit, which is called *Euler's constant*. Its exact value, to twenty places of decimals, is $C = 0.57721566490153286060$.

2) Consider the expression

$$\Sigma = \frac{1}{n+1} + \frac{1}{n+2} + \cdots + \frac{1}{n+p},$$

where n and p are two positive integers which are to increase indefinitely. Then we may write

$$\Sigma = \left(1 + \frac{1}{2} + \cdots + \frac{1}{n+p}\right) - \left(1 + \frac{1}{2} + \cdots + \frac{1}{n}\right),$$
$$1 + \frac{1}{2} + \cdots + \frac{1}{n+p} = \log(n+p) + \rho_{n+p},$$
$$1 + \frac{1}{2} + \cdots + \frac{1}{n} = \log n + \rho_n,$$

where ρ_{n+p} and ρ_n approach the same value C when n and p increase indefinitely. Hence we have also

$$\Sigma = \log\left(1 + \frac{p}{n}\right) + \rho_{n+p} - \rho_n.$$

Now the difference $\rho_{n+p} - \rho_n$ approaches zero. Hence the sum Σ approaches no limit unless the ratio p/n approaches a limit. If this ratio does approach a limit α, the sum Σ approaches the limit $\log(1 + \alpha)$.

Setting $p = n$, for instance, we see that the sum

$$\frac{1}{n+1} + \frac{1}{n+2} + \cdots + \frac{1}{2n}$$

approaches the limit $\log 2$.

50. Development of $(1 + x)^m$. The function $(1 + x)^m$ is defined and continuous, and its derivatives all exist and are continuous functions of x, when $1 + x$ is positive, for any value of m; for the derivatives are of the same form as the given function:

$$f'(x) = m(1 + x)^{m-1},$$
$$f''(x) = m(m - 1)(1 + x)^{m-2},$$
$$\cdot \quad \cdot \quad \cdot \quad \cdot \quad \cdot \quad \cdot \quad \cdot \quad \cdot \quad \cdot \quad \cdot \quad \cdot \quad \cdot \quad ,$$
$$f^{(n)}(x) = m(m - 1)\cdots(m - n + 1)(1 + x)^{m-n},$$
$$f^{(n+1)}(x) = m(m - 1)\cdots(m - n)(1 + x)^{m-n-1}.$$

Applying the general formula (3), we find

$$(1 + x)^m = 1 + \frac{m}{1}x + \frac{m(m-1)}{1.2}x^2 + \cdots$$
$$+ \frac{m(m-1)\cdots(m-n+1)}{1.2\cdots n}x^n + R_n;$$

and, in order that the remainder R_n should approach zero, it is first of all necessary that the series whose general term is

$$\frac{m(m-1)\cdots(m-n+1)}{1.2\cdots n}x^n$$

should converge. But the ratio of any term to the preceding is

$$\frac{m-n+1}{n}x,$$

which approaches $-x$ as n increases indefinitely. Hence, excluding the case where m is a positive integer, which leads to the elementary binomial theorem, the series in question cannot converge unless $|x| \leqq 1$. Let us restrict ourselves to the case in which $|x| < 1$.

To show that the remainder approaches zero, let us write it in the Cauchy form:

$$R_n = \frac{m(m-1)\cdots(m-n)}{1.2\cdots n}\, x^{n+1}\left(\frac{1-\theta}{1+\theta x}\right)^n (1+\theta x)^{m-1}.$$

The first factor

$$\frac{m(m-1)\cdots(m-n)}{1.2\cdots n}\, x^{n+1}$$

approaches zero since it is the general term of a convergent series. The second factor $(1-\theta)/(1+\theta x)$ is less than unity; and, finally, the last factor $(1+\theta x)^{m-1}$ is less than a fixed limit. For, if $m-1>0$, we have $(1+\theta x)^{m-1} < 2^{m-1}$; while if $m-1<0$, $(1+\theta x)^{m-1} < (1-|x|)^{m-1}$. Hence for every value of x between -1 and $+1$ we have the development

$$(16)\quad \begin{cases}(1+x)^m = 1 + \dfrac{m}{1}x + \dfrac{m(m-1)}{1.2}x^2 + \cdots \\ \qquad\qquad + \dfrac{m(m-1)\cdots(m-n+1)}{1.2\cdots n}x^n + \cdots.\end{cases}$$

We shall postpone the discussion of the case where $x = \pm 1$.

In the same way we might establish the following formulæ:

$$\arcsin x = x + \frac{1}{2}\frac{x^3}{3} + \frac{1.3}{2.4}\frac{x^5}{5} + \cdots$$
$$+ \frac{1.3.5\cdots(2n-1)}{2.4.6\cdots 2n}\frac{x^{2n+1}}{2n+1} + \cdots,$$
$$\arctan x = x - \frac{x^3}{3} + \frac{x^5}{5} - \frac{x^7}{7} + \cdots + (-1)^n \frac{x^{2n+1}}{2n+1} + \cdots,$$

which we shall prove later by a simpler process, and which hold for all values of x between -1 and $+1$.

Aside from these examples and a few others, the discussion of the remainder presents great difficulty on account of the increasing complication of the successive derivatives. It would therefore seem from this first examination as if the application of Taylor's series for the development of a function in an infinite series were of limited usefulness. Such an impression would, however, be utterly false ; for these developments, quite to the contrary, play a fundamental rôle in modern Mathematical Analysis. In order to appreciate their importance it is necessary to take another point of view and to study the properties of power series for their own sake, irrespective of their origin. We shall do this in several of the following chapters.

Just now we will merely remark that the series

$$f(0) + \frac{x}{1} f'(0) + \frac{x^2}{1.2} f''(0) + \cdots + \frac{x^n}{1.2\cdots n} f^{(n)}(0) + \cdots$$

may very well be convergent without representing the function $f(x)$ from which it was derived. The following example is due to Cauchy. Let $f(x) = e^{-1/x^2}$. Then $f'(x) = (2/x^3) e^{-1/x^2}$; and, in general, the nth derivative is of the form

$$f^{(n)}(x) = \frac{P}{x^m} e^{-\frac{1}{x^2}},$$

where P is a polynomial. All these derivatives vanish for $x = 0$, for the quotient of e^{-1/x^2} by any positive power of x approaches zero with x.* Indeed, setting $x = 1/z$, we may write

$$\frac{1}{x^m} e^{-\frac{1}{x^2}} = \frac{z^m}{e^{z^2}};$$

and it is well known that e^{z^2}/z^m increases indefinitely with z, no matter how large m may be. Again, let $\phi(x)$ be a function to which the formula (8) applies:

$$\phi(x) = \phi(0) + \frac{x}{1} \phi'(0) + \cdots + \frac{x^n}{1.2\cdots n} \phi^{(n)}(0) + \cdots.$$

Setting $F(x) = \phi(x) + e^{-1/x^2}$, we find

$$F(0) = \phi(0), \quad F'(0) = \phi'(0), \quad \cdots, \quad F^{(n)}(0) = \phi^{(n)}(0), \quad \cdots,$$

and hence the development of $F(x)$ by Maclaurin's series would coincide with the preceding. The sum of the series thus obtained represents an entirely different function from that from which the series was obtained.

In general, if two distinct functions $f(x)$ and $\phi(x)$, together with all their derivatives, are equal for $x = 0$, it is evident that the

---

* It is tacitly assumed that $f(0) = 0$, which is the only assignment which would render $f(x)$ continuous at $x = 0$. But it should be noticed that no further assignment is necessary for $f'(x)$, etc., at $x = 0$. For

$$f'(0) = \lim_{x = 0} \frac{f(x) - f(0)}{x} = 0,$$

which defines $f'(x)$ at $x = 0$ and makes $f'(x)$ continuous at $x = 0$, etc. — TRANS.

Maclaurin series developments for the two functions cannot both be valid, for the coefficients of the two developments coincide.

51. Extension to functions of several variables. Let us consider, for definiteness, a function $\omega = f(x, y, z)$ of the three independent variables x, y, z, and let us try to develop $f(x + h, y + k, z + l)$ according to powers of h, k, l, grouping together the terms of the same degree. Cauchy reduced this problem to the preceding by the following device. Let us give x, y, z, h, k, l definite values and let us set

$$\phi(t) = f(x + ht, y + kt, z + lt),$$

where t is an auxiliary variable. The function $\phi(t)$ depends on t alone; if we apply to it Taylor's series with a remainder, we find

$$(17) \quad \begin{cases} \phi(t) = \phi(0) + \dfrac{t}{1}\,\phi'(0) + \dfrac{t^2}{1 \cdot 2}\,\phi''(0) + \cdots \\ \qquad\qquad + \dfrac{t^n}{1 \cdot 2 \cdots n}\,\phi^{(n)}(0) + \dfrac{t^{n+1}}{1 \cdot 2 \cdots (n+1)}\,\phi^{(n+1)}(\theta t), \end{cases}$$

where $\phi(0)$, $\phi'(0)$, $\cdots$, $\phi^{(n)}(0)$ are the values of the function $\phi(t)$ and its derivatives, for $t = 0$; and where $\phi^{(n+1)}(\theta t)$ is the value of the derivative of order $n + 1$ for the value θt, where θ lies between zero and one. But we may consider $\phi(t)$ as a composite function of t, $\phi(t) = f(u, v, w)$, the auxiliary functions

$$u = x + ht, \qquad v = y + kt, \qquad w = z + lt$$

being *linear* functions of t. According to a previous remark, the expression for the differential of order m, $d^m\phi$, is the same as if u, v, w were the independent variables. Hence we have the symbolic equation

$$d^m\phi = \left(\frac{\partial f}{\partial u}\,du + \frac{\partial f}{\partial v}\,dv + \frac{\partial f}{\partial w}\,dw\right)^{(m)} = dt^m\left(\frac{\partial f}{\partial u}\,h + \frac{\partial f}{\partial v}\,k + \frac{\partial f}{\partial w}\,l\right)^{(m)},$$

which may be written, after dividing by dt^m, in the form

$$\phi^{(m)}(t) = \left(\frac{\partial f}{\partial u}\,h + \frac{\partial f}{\partial v}\,k + \frac{\partial f}{\partial w}\,l\right)^{(m)}.$$

For $t = 0$, u, v, w reduce, respectively, to x, y, z, and the above equation in the same symbolism becomes

$$\phi^{(m)}(0) = \left(\frac{\partial f}{\partial x}\,h + \frac{\partial f}{\partial y}\,k + \frac{\partial f}{\partial z}\,l\right)^{(m)}.$$

Similarly,

$$\phi^{(n+1)}(\theta t) = \left(\frac{\partial f}{\partial x} h + \frac{\partial f}{\partial y} k + \frac{\partial f}{\partial z} l\right)^{(n+1)},$$

where x, y, z are to be replaced, after the expression is developed, by

$$x + \theta h t, \qquad y + \theta k t, \qquad z + \theta l t,$$

respectively. If we now set $t = 1$ in (17), it becomes

$$(18) \begin{cases} f(x+h, y+k, z+l) = f(x, y, z) + \left(\frac{\partial f}{\partial x} h + \frac{\partial f}{\partial y} k + \frac{\partial f}{\partial z} l\right) + \cdots \\ \qquad\qquad + \frac{1}{1 \cdot 2 \cdots n} \left(\frac{\partial f}{\partial x} h + \frac{\partial f}{\partial y} k + \frac{\partial f}{\partial z} l\right)^{(n)} + R_n. \end{cases}$$

The remainder R_n may be written in the form

$$R_n = \frac{1}{1 \cdot 2 \cdots (n+1)} \left(\frac{\partial f}{\partial x} h + \frac{\partial f}{\partial y} k + \frac{\partial f}{\partial z} l\right)^{(n+1)},$$

where x, y, z are to be replaced by $x + \theta h$, $y + \theta k$, $z + \theta l$ after the expression is expanded.*

This formula (18) is exactly analogous to the general formula (3). If for a given set of values of x, y, z, h, k, l the remainder R_n approaches zero when n increases indefinitely, we have a development of $f(x + h, y + k, z + l)$ in a series each of whose terms is a homogeneous polynomial in h, k, l. But it is very difficult, in general, to see from the expression for R_n whether or not this remainder approaches zero.

52. From the formula (18) it is easy to draw certain conclusions analogous to those obtained from the general formula (3) in the case of a single independent variable. For instance, let $z = f(x, y)$ be the equation of a surface S. If the function $f(x, y)$, together with all its partial derivatives up to a certain order n, is continuous in the neighborhood of a point (x_0, y_0), the formula (18) gives

$$f(x_0 + h, y_0 + k) = f(x_0, y_0) + \left(h \frac{\partial f}{\partial x_0} + k \frac{\partial f}{\partial y_0}\right) + \frac{1}{1 \cdot 2} \left(\frac{\partial f}{\partial x_0} h + \frac{\partial f}{\partial y_0} k\right)^{(2)} + \cdots + R_n.$$

Restricting ourselves, in the second member, to the first two terms, then to the first three, etc., we obtain the equation of a plane, then

---

* It is assumed here that *all* the derivatives used exist and are continuous. — TRANS.

that of a paraboloid, etc., which differ very little from the given surface near the point (x_0, y_0). The plane in question is precisely the tangent plane; and the paraboloid is that one of the family

$$z = Ax^2 + 2\,Bxy + Cy^2 + 2\,Dx + 2\,Ey + F$$

which most nearly coincides with the given surface S.

The formula (18) is also used to determine the limiting value of a function which is given in indeterminate form. Let $f(x, y)$ and $\phi(x, y)$ be two functions which both vanish for $x = a$, $y = b$, but which, together with their partial derivatives up to a certain order, are continuous near the point (a, b). Let us try to find the limit approached by the ratio

$$\frac{f(x, y)}{\phi(x, y)}$$

when x and y approach a and b, respectively. Supposing, first, that the four first derivatives $\partial f/\partial a$, $\partial f/\partial b$, $\partial \phi/\partial a$, $\partial \phi/\partial b$ do not all vanish simultaneously, we may write

$$\frac{f(a + h, b + k)}{\phi(a + h, b + k)} = \frac{h\left(\dfrac{\partial f}{\partial a} + \epsilon\right) + k\left(\dfrac{\partial f}{\partial b} + \epsilon'\right)}{h\left(\dfrac{\partial \phi}{\partial a} + \epsilon_1\right) + k\left(\dfrac{\partial \phi}{\partial b} + \epsilon_1'\right)},$$

where ϵ, ϵ', ϵ_1, ϵ_1' approach zero with h and k. When the point (x, y) approaches (a, b), h and k approach zero; and we will suppose that the ratio k/h approaches a certain limit α, i.e. that the point (x, y) describes a curve which has a tangent at the point (a, b). Dividing each of the terms of the preceding ratio by h, it appears that the fraction $f(x, y)/\phi(x, y)$ approaches the limit

$$\frac{\dfrac{\partial f}{\partial a} + \alpha\,\dfrac{\partial f}{\partial b}}{\dfrac{\partial \phi}{\partial a} + \alpha\,\dfrac{\partial \phi}{\partial b}}.$$

This limit depends, in general, upon α, i.e. upon the manner in which x and y approach their limits a and b, respectively. In order that this limit should be independent of α it is necessary that the relation

$$\frac{\partial f}{\partial a}\frac{\partial \phi}{\partial b} - \frac{\partial f}{\partial b}\frac{\partial \phi}{\partial a} = 0$$

should hold; and such is not the case in general.

If the four first derivatives $\partial f/\partial a$, $\partial f/\partial b$, $\partial\phi/\partial a$, $\partial\phi/\partial b$ vanish simultaneously, we should take the terms of the second order in the formula (18) and write

$$\frac{f(a+h,\,b+k)}{\phi(a+h,\,b+k)} = \frac{\left(\dfrac{\partial^2 f}{\partial a^2}+\epsilon\right)h^2 + 2\left(\dfrac{\partial^2 f}{\partial a\,\partial b}+\epsilon'\right)hk + \left(\dfrac{\partial^2 f}{\partial b^2}+\epsilon''\right)k^2}{\left(\dfrac{\partial^2 \phi}{\partial a^2}+\epsilon_1\right)h^2 + 2\left(\dfrac{\partial^2 \phi}{\partial a\,\partial b}+\epsilon_1'\right)hk + \left(\dfrac{\partial^2 \phi}{\partial b^2}+\epsilon_1''\right)k^2},$$

where ϵ, ϵ', ϵ'', ϵ_1, ϵ_1', ϵ_1'' are infinitesimals. Then, if α be given the same meaning as above, the limit of the left-hand side is seen to be

$$\frac{\dfrac{\partial^2 f}{\partial a^2} + 2\dfrac{\partial^2 f}{\partial a\,\partial b}\,\alpha + \dfrac{\partial^2 f}{\partial b^2}\,\alpha^2}{\dfrac{\partial^2 \phi}{\partial a^2} + 2\dfrac{\partial^2 \phi}{\partial a\,\partial b}\,\alpha + \dfrac{\partial^2 \phi}{\partial b^2}\,\alpha^2},$$

which depends, in general, upon α.

II. SINGULAR POINTS   MAXIMA AND MINIMA

53. Singular points. Let $(x_0,\,y_0)$ be the coördinates of a point M_0 of a curve C whose equation is $F(x,\,y)=0$. If the two first partial derivatives $\partial F/\partial x$, $\partial F/\partial y$ do not vanish simultaneously at this point, we have seen (§ 22) that a single branch of the curve C passes through the point, and that the equation of the tangent at that point is

$$(X-x_0)\frac{\partial F}{\partial x_0} + (Y-y_0)\frac{\partial F}{\partial y_0} = 0,$$

where the symbol $\partial^{p+q}F/\partial x_0^p\,\partial y_0^q$ denotes the value of the derivative $\partial^{p+q}F/\partial x^p\,\partial y^q$ for $x=x_0$, $y=y_0$. If $\partial F/\partial x_0$ and $\partial F/\partial y_0$ both vanish, the point $(x_0,\,y_0)$ is, in general, a *singular point*.* Let us suppose that the three second derivatives do not all vanish simultaneously for $x=x_0$, $y=y_0$, and that these derivatives, together with the third derivatives, are continuous near that point. Then the equation of the curve may be written in the form.

---

* That is, the appearance of the curve is, in general, peculiar at that point. For an **exact** analytic definition of a *singular point*, see § 192. — TRANS.

$$(19) \begin{cases} 0 = F(x, y) \\ = \dfrac{1}{2}\left[\dfrac{\partial^2 F}{\partial x_0^2}(x-x_0)^2 + 2\dfrac{\partial^2 F}{\partial x_0\,\partial y_0}(x-x_0)(y-y_0) + \dfrac{\partial^2 F}{\partial y_0^2}(y-y_0)^2 \right] \\ \qquad + \dfrac{1}{1\,.\,2\,.\,3}\left[\dfrac{\partial F}{\partial x}(x-x_0) + \dfrac{\partial F}{\partial y}(y-y_0) \right]^{(3)}_{\substack{x_0+\theta(x-x_0),\\ y_0+\theta(y-y_0)}} , \end{cases}$$

where x and y are to be replaced in the third derivatives by $x_0 + \theta(x - x_0)$ and $y_0 + \theta(y - y_0)$, respectively. We may assume that the derivative $\partial^2 F / \partial y_0^2$ does not vanish; for, at any rate, we could always bring this about by a change of axes. Then, setting $y - y_0 = t(x - x_0)$ and dividing by $(x - x_0)^2$, the equation (19) becomes

$$(20) \quad \frac{\partial^2 F}{\partial x_0^2} + 2\,t\,\frac{\partial^2 F}{\partial x_0\,\partial y_0} + t^2\,\frac{\partial^2 F}{\partial y_0^2} + (x-x_0)\,P(x-x_0,\,t) = 0,$$

where $P(x - x_0, t)$ is a function which remains finite when x approaches x_0. Now let t_1 and t_2 be the two roots of the equation

$$\frac{\partial^2 F}{\partial x_0^2} + 2\,t\,\frac{\partial^2 F}{\partial x_0\,\partial y_0} + t^2\,\frac{\partial^2 F}{\partial y_0^2} = 0.$$

If these roots are real and unequal, i.e. if

$$\left(\frac{\partial^2 F}{\partial x_0\,\partial y_0} \right)^2 > \frac{\partial^2 F}{\partial x_0^2}\,\frac{\partial^2 F}{\partial y_0^2},$$

the equation (20) may be written in the form

$$\frac{\partial^2 F}{\partial y_0^2}(t-t_1)(t-t_2) + (x-x_0)\,P = 0.$$

For $x = x_0$ the above quadratic has two distinct roots $t = t_1$, $t = t_2$. As x approaches x_0 that equation has two roots which approach t_1 and t_2, respectively. The proof of this is merely a repetition of the argument for the existence of implicit functions. Let us set $t = t_1 + u$, for example, and write down the equation connecting x and u:

$$u(t_1 - t_2 + u) + (x - x_0)\,Q(x,\,u) = 0,$$

where $Q(x, u)$ remains finite, while x approaches x_0 and u approaches zero. Let us suppose, for definiteness, that $t_1 - t_2 > 0$; and let M denote an upper limit of the absolute value of $Q(x, u)$, and m a lower limit of $t_1 - t_2 + u$, when x lies between $x_0 - h$ and $x_0 + h$, and u between $-h$ and $+h$, where h is a positive number less than $t_1 - t_2$. Now let ϵ be a positive number less than h, and η another positive number which satisfies the two inequalities

$$\eta < h, \qquad \eta < \frac{m}{M}\,\epsilon.$$

If x be given such a value that $|x - x_0|$ is less than η, the left-hand side of the above equation will have different signs if $-\epsilon$ and then $+\epsilon$ be substituted for u. Hence that equation has a root which approaches zero as x approaches x_0, and the equation (19) has a root of the form

$$y = y_0 + (x - x_0)(t_1 + \alpha),$$

where α approaches zero with $x - x_0$. It follows that there is one branch of the curve C which is tangent to the straight line

$$y - y_0 = t_1(x - x_0)$$

at the point (x_0, y_0).

In like manner it is easy to see that another branch of the curve passes through this same point tangent to the straight line $y - y_0 = t_2(x - x_0)$. The point M_0 is called a *double point;* and the equation of the system of tangents at this point may be found by setting the terms of the second degree in $(x - x_0)$, $(y - y_0)$ in (19) equal to zero.

If

$$\left(\frac{\partial^2 F}{\partial x_0 \partial y_0}\right)^2 - \frac{\partial^2 F}{\partial x_0^2}\frac{\partial^2 F}{\partial y_0^2} < 0,$$

the point (x_0, y_0) is called an *isolated double point.* Inside a sufficiently small circle about the point M_0 as center the first member $F(x, y)$ of the equation (19) does not vanish except at the point M_0 itself. For, let us take

$$x = x_0 + \rho \cos \phi, \qquad y = y_0 + \rho \sin \phi$$

as the coördinates of a point near M_0. Then we find

$$F(x, y) = \frac{\rho^2}{2}\left(\frac{\partial^2 F}{\partial x_0^2}\cos^2 \phi + 2\,\frac{\partial^2 F}{\partial x_0 \partial y_0}\cos \phi \sin \phi + \frac{\partial^2 F}{\partial y_0^2}\sin^2 \phi + \rho L\right),$$

where L remains finite when ρ approaches zero. Let H be an upper limit of the absolute value of L when ρ is less than a certain positive number r. For all values of ϕ between 0 and 2π the expression

$$\frac{\partial^2 F}{\partial x_0^2}\cos^2 \phi + 2\,\frac{\partial^2 F}{\partial x_0 \partial y_0}\cos \phi \sin \phi + \frac{\partial^2 F}{\partial y_0^2}\sin^2 \phi$$

has the same sign, since its roots are imaginary. Let m be a lower limit of its absolute value. Then it is clear that the coefficient of ρ^2 cannot vanish for any point inside a circle of radius $\rho < m / H$. Hence the equation $F(x, y) = 0$ has no root other than $\rho = 0$, i.e. $x = x_0$, $y = y_0$, inside this circle.

In case we have

$$\left(\frac{\partial^2 F}{\partial x_0 \partial y_0} \right)^2 = \frac{\partial^2 F}{\partial x_0^2} \frac{\partial^2 F}{\partial y_0^2},$$

the two tangents at the double point coincide, and there are, in general, two branches of the given curve tangent to the same line, thus forming a cusp. The exhaustive study of this case is somewhat intricate and will be left until later. Just now we will merely remark that the variety of cases which may arise is much greater than in the two cases which we have just discussed, as will be seen from the following examples.

The curve $y^2 = x^3$ has a *cusp of the first kind* at the origin, both branches of the curve being tangent to the axis of x and lying on different sides of this tangent, to the right of the y axis. The curve $y^2 - 2 x^2 y + x^4 - x^5 = 0$ has a *cusp of the second kind*, both branches of the curve being tangent to the axis of x and lying on the same side of this tangent; for the equation may be written

$$y = x^2 \pm x^{\frac{5}{2}},$$

and the two values of y have the same sign when x is very small, but are not real unless x is positive. The curve

$$x^4 + x^2 y^2 - 6 x^2 y + y^2 = 0$$

has two branches tangent to the x axis at the origin, which do not possess any other peculiarity; for, solving for y, the equation becomes

$$y = \frac{3 x^2 \pm x^2 \sqrt{8 - x^2}}{1 + x^2},$$

and neither of the two branches corresponding to the two signs before the radical has any singularity whatever at the origin.

It may also happen that a curve is composed of two coincident branches. Such is the case for the curve represented by the equation

$$F(x, y) = y^2 - 2 x^2 y + x^4 = 0.$$

When the point (x, y) passes across the curve the first member $F(x, y)$ vanishes without changing sign.

Finally, the point (x_0, y_0) may be an isolated double point. Such is the case for the curve $y^2 + x^4 + y^4 = 0$, on which the origin is an isolated double point.

54. In like manner a point M_0 of a surface S, whose equation is $F(x, y, z) = 0$, is, in general, a singular point of that surface if the three first partial derivatives vanish for the coördinates x_0, y_0, z_0 of that point:

$$\frac{\partial F}{\partial x_0} = 0, \quad \frac{\partial F}{\partial y_0} = 0, \quad \frac{\partial F}{\partial z_0} = 0.$$

The equation of the tangent plane found above (§ 22) then reduces to an identity; and if the six second partial derivatives do not all vanish at the same point, the locus of the tangents to all curves on the surface S through the point M_0 is, in general, a cone of the second order. For, let

$$x = f(t), \qquad y = \phi(t), \qquad z = \psi(t)$$

be the equations of a curve C on the surface S. Then the three functions $f(t)$, $\phi(t)$, $\psi(t)$ satisfy the equation $F(x, y, z) = 0$, and the first and second differentials satisfy the two relations

$$\frac{\partial F}{\partial x} dx + \frac{\partial F}{\partial y} dy + \frac{\partial F}{\partial z} dz = 0,$$

$$\left(\frac{\partial F}{\partial x} dx + \frac{\partial F}{\partial y} dy + \frac{\partial F}{\partial z} dz \right)^{(2)} + \frac{\partial F}{\partial x} d^2x + \frac{\partial F}{\partial y} d^2y + \frac{\partial F}{\partial z} d^2z = 0.$$

For the point $x = x_0$, $y = y_0$, $z = z_0$ the first of these equations reduces to an identity, and the second becomes

$$\frac{\partial^2 F}{\partial x_0^2} dx^2 + \frac{\partial^2 F}{\partial y_0^2} dy^2 + \frac{\partial^2 F}{\partial z_0^2} dz^2$$
$$+ 2 \frac{\partial^2 F}{\partial x_0 \partial y_0} dx\, dy + 2 \frac{\partial^2 F}{\partial y_0 \partial z_0} dy\, dz + 2 \frac{\partial^2 F}{\partial x_0 \partial z_0} dx\, dz = 0.$$

The equation of the locus of the tangents is given by eliminating dx, dy, dz between the latter equation and the equation of a tangent line

$$\frac{X - x_0}{dx} = \frac{Y - y_0}{dy} = \frac{Z - z_0}{dz},$$

which leads to the equation of a cone T of the second degree:

$$(21) \begin{cases} \dfrac{\partial^2 F}{\partial x_0^2}(X-x_0)^2 + \dfrac{\partial^2 F}{\partial y_0^2}(Y-y_0)^2 + \dfrac{\partial^2 F}{\partial z_0^2}(Z-z_0)^2 \\[2mm] \quad + 2\,\dfrac{\partial^2 F}{\partial x_0 \partial y_0}(X-x_0)(Y-y_0) \\[2mm] \quad + 2\,\dfrac{\partial^2 F}{\partial y_0 \partial z_0}(Y-y_0)(Z-z_0) + 2\,\dfrac{\partial^2 F}{\partial x_0 \partial z_0}(X-x_0)(Z-z_0) = 0. \end{cases}$$

On the other hand, applying Taylor's series with a remainder and carrying the development to terms of the third order, the equation of the surface becomes

$$(22) \begin{cases} 0 = F(x,\,y,\,z) \\[2mm] \quad = \dfrac{1}{1.2}\left[\dfrac{\partial F}{\partial x_0}(x-x_0) + \dfrac{\partial F}{\partial y_0}(y-y_0) + \dfrac{\partial F}{\partial z_0}(z-z_0)\right]^{(2)} \\[2mm] \quad + \dfrac{1}{1.2.3}\left[\dfrac{\partial F}{\partial x}(x-x_0) + \dfrac{\partial F}{\partial y}(y-y_0) + \dfrac{\partial F}{\partial z}(z-z_0)\right]^{(3)}_{\substack{x_0+\theta(x-x_0),\\ y_0+\theta(y-y_0),\\ z_0+\theta(z-z_0)}} \end{cases}$$

where x, y, z in the terms of the third order are to be replaced by $x_0 + \theta(x-x_0)$, $y_0 + \theta(y-y_0)$, $z_0 + \theta(z-z_0)$, respectively. The equation of the cone T may be obtained by setting the terms of the second degree in $x-x_0$, $y-y_0$, $z-z_0$ in the equation (22) equal to zero.

Let us then, first, suppose that the equation (21) represents a real non-degenerate cone. Let the surface S and the cone T be cut by a plane P which passes through two distinct generators G and G' of the cone. In order to find the equation of the section of the surface S by this plane, let us imagine a transformation of coördinates carried out which changes the plane P into a plane parallel to the xy plane. It is then sufficient to substitute $z = z_0$ in the equation (22). It is evident that for this curve the point M_0 is a double point with real tangents; from what we have just seen, this section is composed of two branches tangent, respectively, to the two generators G, G'. The surface S near the point M_0 therefore resembles the two nappes of a cone of the second degree near its vertex. Hence the point M_0 is called a *conical point*.

When the equation (21) represents an imaginary non-degenerate cone, the point M_0 is an *isolated* singular point of the surface S. Inside a sufficiently small sphere about such a point there exists no set of solutions of the equation $F(x, y, z) = 0$ other than $x = x_0$, $y = y_0$, $z = z_0$. For, let M be a point in space near M_0, ρ the distance MM_0, and α, β, γ the direction cosines of the line $M_0 M$. Then if we substitute

$$x = x_0 + \rho\alpha, \qquad y = y_0 + \rho\beta, \qquad z = z_0 + \rho\gamma,$$

the function $F(x, y, z)$ becomes

$$F(x, y, z) = \frac{\rho^2}{2}\left(\frac{\partial^2 F}{\partial x_0^2}\,\alpha^2 + \frac{\partial^2 F}{\partial y_0^2}\,\beta^2 + \cdots + 2\,\frac{\partial^2 F}{\partial x_0 \partial z_0}\,\alpha\gamma + \rho L\right),$$

where L remains finite when ρ approaches zero. Since the equation (21) represents an imaginary cone, the expression

$$\frac{\partial^2 F}{\partial x_0^2}\,\alpha^2 + \cdots + 2\,\frac{\partial^2 F}{\partial x_0 \partial z_0}\,\alpha\gamma$$

cannot vanish when the point (α, β, γ) describes the sphere

$$\alpha^2 + \beta^2 + \gamma^2 = 1.$$

Let m be a lower limit of the absolute value of this polynomial, and let H be an upper limit of the absolute value of L near the point M_0. If a sphere of radius m/H be drawn about M_0 as center, it is evident that the coefficient of ρ^2 in the expression for $F(x, y, z)$ cannot vanish inside this sphere. Hence the equation

$$F(x, y, z) = 0$$

has no root except $\rho = 0$.

When the equation (21) represents two distinct real planes, two nappes of the given surface pass through the point M_0, each of which is tangent to one of the planes. Certain surfaces have a line of double points, at each of which the tangent cone degenerates into two planes. This line is a double curve on the surface along which two distinct nappes cross each other. For example, the circle whose equations are $z = 0$, $x^2 + y^2 = 1$ is a double line on the surface whose equation is

$$z^4 + 2\,z^2(x^2 + y^2) - (x^2 + y^2 - 1)^2 = 0.$$

When the equation (21) represents a system of two conjugate imaginary planes or a double real plane, a special investigation is necessary in each particular case to determine the form of the surface near the point M_0. The above discussion will be renewed in the paragraphs on extrema.

55. Extrema of functions of a single variable. Let the function $f(x)$ be continuous in the interval (a, b), and let c be a point of that interval.   The function $f(x)$ is said to have an *extremum* (i.e. a *maximum* or a *minimum*) for $x = c$ if a positive number η can be found such that the difference $f(c + h) - f(c)$, which vanishes for $h = 0$, has the same sign for all other values of h between $-\eta$ and $+\eta$.   If this difference is positive, the function $f(x)$ has a smaller value for $x = c$ than for any value of x near c; it is said to have a minimum at that point.   On the contrary, if the difference $f(c + h) - f(c)$ is negative, the function is said to have a maximum.

If the function $f(x)$ possesses a derivative for $x = c$, that derivative must vanish.   For the two quotients

$$\frac{f(c + h) - f(c)}{h}, \quad \frac{f(c - h) - f(c)}{-h},$$

each of which approaches the limit $f'(c)$ when h approaches zero, have different signs; hence their common limit $f'(c)$ must be zero.   Conversely, let c be a root of the equation $f'(x) = 0$ which lies between a and b, and let us suppose, for the sake of generality, that the first derivative which does not vanish for $x = c$ is that of order n, and that this derivative is continuous when $x = c$.   Then Taylor's series with a remainder, if we stop with n terms, gives

$$f(c + h) - f(c) = \frac{h^n}{1 . 2 \cdots n} f^{(n)}(c + \theta h),$$

which may be written in the form

$$f(c + h) - f(c) = \frac{h^n}{1 . 2 \cdots n} \left[f^{(n)}(c) + \epsilon \right],$$

where ϵ approaches zero with h.   Let η be a positive number such that $|f^{(n)}(c)|$ is greater than ϵ when x lies between $c - \eta$ and $c + \eta$.   For such values of x, $f^{(n)}(c) + \epsilon$ has the same sign as $f^{(n)}(c)$, and consequently $f(c + h) - f(c)$ has the same sign as $h^n f^{(n)}(c)$.   If n is odd, it is clear that this difference changes sign with h, and there is neither a maximum nor a minimum at $x = c$.   If n is even, $f(c + h) - f(c)$ has the same sign as $f^{(n)}(c)$, whether h be positive or negative; hence the function is a maximum if $f^{(n)}(c)$ is negative, and a minimum if $f^{(n)}(c)$ is positive.   It follows that the necessary and sufficient condition that the function $f(x)$ should have a maximum or a minimum for $x = c$ is that the first derivative which does **not** vanish for $x = c$ should be of *even order*.

Geometrically, the preceding conditions mean that the tangent to the curve $y = f(x)$ at the point A whose abscissa is c must be parallel to the axis of x, and moreover that the point A must not be a point of inflection.

Notes. When the hypotheses which we have made are not satisfied the function $f(x)$ may have a maximum or a minimum, although the derivative $f'(x)$ does not vanish. If, for instance, the derivative is infinite for $x = c$, the function will have a maximum or a minimum if the derivative changes sign. Thus the function $y = x^{\frac{2}{3}}$ is at a minimum for $x = 0$, and the corresponding curve has a cusp at the origin, the tangent being the y axis.

When, as in the statement of the problem, the variable x is restricted to values which lie between two limits a and b, it may happen that the function has its absolute maxima and minima precisely at these limiting points, although the derivative $f'(x)$ does not vanish there. Suppose, for instance, that we wished to find the shortest distance from a point P whose coördinates are $(a, 0)$ to a circle C whose equation is $x^2 + y^2 - R^2 = 0$. Choosing for our independent variable the abscissa of a point M of the circle C, we find

$$d^2 = \overline{PM}^2 = (x - a)^2 + y^2 = x^2 + y^2 - 2\,ax + a^2,$$

or, making use of the equation of the circle,

$$d^2 = R^2 + a^2 - 2\,ax.$$

The general rule would lead us to try to find the roots of the derived equation $2\,a = 0$, which is absurd. But the paradox is explained if we observe that by the very nature of the problem the variable x must lie between $-R$ and $+R$. If a is positive, d^2 has a minimum for $x = R$ and a maximum for $x = -R$.

56. Extrema of functions of two variables. Let $f(x, y)$ be a continuous function of x and y when the point M, whose coördinates are x and y, lies inside a region Ω bounded by a contour C. The function $f(x, y)$ is said to have an extremum at the point $M_0(x_0, y_0)$ of the region Ω if a positive number η can be found such that the difference

$$\Delta = f(x_0 + h,\, y_0 + k) - f(x_0,\, y_0),$$

which vanishes for $h = k = 0$, keeps the same sign for all other sets of values of the increments h and k which are each less than η in absolute value. Considering y for the moment as constant and equal to y_0, z becomes a function of the single variable x; and, by the above, the difference

$$f(x_0 + h, y_0) - f(x_0, y_0)$$

cannot keep the same sign for small values of h unless the derivative $\partial f / \partial x$ vanishes at the point M_0. Likewise, the derivative $\partial f / \partial y$ must vanish at M_0; and it is apparent that the only possible sets of values of x and y which can render the function $f(x, y)$ an extremum are to be found among the solutions of the two simultaneous equations

$$\frac{\partial f}{\partial x} = 0, \qquad \frac{\partial f}{\partial y} = 0.$$

Let $x = x_0$, $y = y_0$ be a set of solutions of these two equations. We shall suppose that the second partial derivatives of $f(x, y)$ do not all vanish simultaneously at the point M_0 whose coördinates are (x_0, y_0), and that they, together with the third derivatives, are all continuous near M_0. Then we have, from Taylor's expansion,

$$(23) \quad \left\{ \begin{aligned} \Delta &= f(x_0 + h, y_0 + k) - f(x_0, y_0) \\ &= \frac{1}{1 \cdot 2} \left(h^2 \frac{\partial^2 f}{\partial x_0^2} + 2\, hk \frac{\partial^2 f}{\partial x_0\, \partial y_0} + k^2 \frac{\partial^2 f}{\partial y_0^2} \right) \\ &\quad + \frac{1}{6} \left(h \frac{\partial f}{\partial x} + k \frac{\partial f}{\partial y} \right)^{(3)}_{\substack{x_0 + \theta h \\ y_0 + \theta k}} \end{aligned} \right.$$

We can foresee that the expression

$$h^2 \frac{\partial^2 f}{\partial x_0^2} + 2\, hk \frac{\partial^2 f}{\partial x_0\, \partial y_0} + k^2 \frac{\partial^2 f}{\partial y_0^2}$$

will, in general, dominate the whole discussion.

In order that there be an extremum at M_0 it is necessary and sufficient that the difference Δ should have the same sign when the point $(x_0 + h, y_0 + k)$ lies anywhere inside a sufficiently small square drawn about the point M_0 as center, except at the center, where $\Delta = 0$. Hence Δ must also have the same sign when the point $(x_0 + h, y_0 + k)$ lies anywhere inside a sufficiently small circle whose center is M_0; for such a square may always be replaced by its inscribed circle, and conversely. Then let C be a circle of radius r drawn about the point M_0 as center. All the points inside this circle are given by

$$h = \rho \cos \phi, \qquad k = \rho \sin \phi,$$

where ϕ is to vary from 0 to 2π, and ρ from $-r$ to $+r$. We might, indeed, restrict ρ to positive values, but it is better in what follows not to introduce this restriction. Making this substitution, the expression for Δ becomes

$$\Delta = \frac{\rho^2}{2}(A\cos^2\phi + 2B\sin\phi\cos\phi + C\sin^2\phi) + \frac{\rho^3}{6}L,$$

where

$$A = \frac{\partial^2 f}{\partial x_0^2}, \quad B = \frac{\partial^2 f}{\partial x_0\,\partial y_0}, \quad C = \frac{\partial^2 f}{\partial y_0^2},$$

and where L is a function whose extended expression it would be useless to write out, but which remains finite near the point (x_0, y_0). It now becomes necessary to distinguish several cases according to the sign of $B^2 - AC$.

First case. Let $B^2 - AC > 0$. Then the equation

$$A\cos^2\phi + 2B\sin\phi\cos\phi + C\sin^2\phi = 0$$

has two real roots in $\tan\phi$, and the first member is the difference of two squares. Hence we may write

$$\Delta = \frac{\rho^2}{2}\left[\alpha(a\cos\phi + b\sin\phi)^2 - \beta(a'\cos\phi + b'\sin\phi)^2\right] + \frac{\rho^3}{6}L,$$

where

$$\alpha > 0, \qquad \beta > 0, \qquad ab' - ba' \neq 0.$$

If ϕ be given a value which satisfies the equation

$$a\cos\phi + b\sin\phi = 0,$$

Δ will be negative for sufficiently small values of ρ; while, if ϕ be such that $a'\cos\phi + b'\sin\phi = 0$, Δ will be positive for infinitesimal values of ρ. Hence no number r can be found such that the difference Δ has the same sign for any value of ϕ when ρ is less than r. It follows that the function $f(x, y)$ has neither a maximum nor a minimum for $x = x_0$, $y = y_0$.

Second case. Let $B^2 - AC < 0$. The expression

$$A\cos^2\phi + 2B\cos\phi\sin\phi + C\sin^2\phi$$

cannot vanish for any value of ϕ. Let m be a lower limit of its absolute value, and, moreover, let H be an upper limit of the absolute value of the function L in a circle of radius R about (x_0, y_0) as center. Finally, let r denote a positive number less than R and less than $3\,m/H$. Then inside a circle of radius r the difference Δ will have the same sign as the coefficient of ρ^2, i.e. the same sign as A or C. Hence the function $f(x, y)$ has either a maximum or a minimum for $x = x_0$, $y = y_0$.

To recapitulate, if at the point (x_0, y_0) we have

$$\left(\frac{\partial^2 f}{\partial x_0 \partial y_0}\right)^2 - \frac{\partial^2 f}{\partial x_0^2}\frac{\partial^2 f}{\partial y_0^2} > 0,$$

there is neither a maximum nor a minimum. But if

$$\left(\frac{\partial^2 f}{\partial x_0 \partial y_0}\right)^2 - \frac{\partial^2 f}{\partial x_0^2}\frac{\partial^2 f}{\partial y_0^2} < 0,$$

there is either a maximum or a minimum, depending on the sign of the two derivatives $\partial^2 f/\partial x_0^2$, $\partial^2 f/\partial y_0^2$. There is a maximum if these derivatives are negative, a minimum if they are positive.

57. The ambiguous case. The case where $B^2 - AC = 0$ is not covered by the preceding discussion. The geometrical interpretation shows why there should be difficulty in this case. Let S be the surface represented by the equation $z = f(x, y)$. If the function $f(x, y)$ has a maximum or a minimum at the point (x_0, y_0), near which the function and its derivatives are continuous, we must have

$$\frac{\partial f}{\partial x_0} = 0, \quad \frac{\partial f}{\partial y_0} = 0,$$

which shows that the tangent plane to the surface S at the point M_0, whose coördinates are (x_0, y_0, z_0), must be parallel to the xy plane. In order that there should be a maximum or a minimum it is also necessary that the surface S, near the point M_0, should lie entirely on one side of the tangent plane; hence we are led to study the behavior of a surface with respect to its tangent plane near the point of tangency.

Let us suppose that the point of tangency has been moved to the origin and that the tangent plane is the xy plane. Then the equation of the surface is of the form

$$(24) \quad z = ax^2 + 2bxy + cy^2 + \alpha x^3 + 3\beta x^2 y + 3\gamma xy^2 + \delta y^3,$$

where a, b, c are constants, and where α, β, γ, δ are functions of x and y which remain finite when x and y approach zero. This equation is essentially the same as equation (19), where x_0 and y_0 have been replaced by zeros, and h and k by x and y, respectively.

In order to see whether or not the surface S lies entirely on one side of the xy plane near the origin, it is sufficient to study the section of the surface by that plane. This section is given by the equation

$$(25) \qquad ax^2 + 2bxy + cy^2 + \alpha x^3 + \cdots = 0;$$

hence it has a double point at the origin of coördinates. If $b^2 - ac$ is negative, the origin is an isolated double point (§ 53), and the equation (25) has no solution except $x = y = 0$, when the point (x, y) lies inside a circle C of sufficiently small radius r drawn about the origin as center. The left-hand side of the equation (25) keeps the same sign as long as the point (x, y) remains inside this circle, and all the points of the surface S which project into the interior of the circle C are on the same side of the xy plane except the origin itself. In this case there is an extremum, and the portion of the surface S near the origin resembles a portion of a sphere or an ellipsoid.

If $b^2 - ac > 0$, the intersection of the surface S by its tangent plane has two distinct branches C_1, C_2 which pass through the origin, and the tangents to these two branches are given by the equation

$$ax^2 + 2bxy + cy^2 = 0.$$

Let the point (x, y) be allowed to move about in the neighborhood of the origin. As it crosses either of the two branches C_1, C_2, the left-hand side of the equation (25) vanishes and changes sign. Hence, assigning to each region of the plane in the neighborhood of the origin the sign of the left-hand side of the equation (25), we find a configuration similar to Fig. 7. Among the points of the surface which project into points inside a circle about the origin in

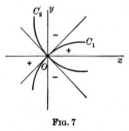

the xy plane there are always some which lie below and some which lie above the xy plane, no matter how small the circle be taken. The general aspect of the surface at this point with respect to its tangent plane resembles that of an unparted hyperboloid or an hyperbolic paraboloid. The function $f(x, y)$ has neither a maximum nor a minimum at the origin.

Fig. 7

The case where $b^2 - ac = 0$ is the case in which the curve of intersection of the surface by its tangent plane has a cusp at the origin. We will postpone the detailed discussion of this case. If the intersection is composed of two distinct branches through the origin, there can be no extremum, for the surface again cuts the tangent plane. If the origin is an isolated double point, the function $f(x, y)$ has an extremum for $x = y = 0$. It may also happen that the intersection of the surface with its tangent plane is composed of two coincident branches. For example, the surface $z = y^2 - 2 x^2 y + x^4$ is tangent to the plane $z = 0$ all along the parabola $y = x^2$. The function $y^2 - 2 x^2 y + x^4$ is zero at every point on this parabola, but is positive for all points near the origin which are not on the parabola.

58. In order to see which of these cases holds in a given example it is necessary to take into account the derivatives of the third and fourth orders, and sometimes derivatives of still higher order. The following discussion, which is usually sufficient in practice, is applicable only in the most general cases. When $b^2 - ac = 0$ the equation of the surface may be written in the following form by using Taylor's development to terms of the fourth order:

$$(26) \quad z = f(x, y) = A \left(x \sin \omega - y \cos \omega \right)^2 + \phi_3(x, y) + \frac{1}{24} \left(x \frac{\partial f}{\partial x} + y \frac{\partial f}{\partial y} \right)^{(4)}_{\substack{\theta x \\ \theta y}}.$$

Let us suppose, for definiteness, that A is positive. In order that the surface S should lie entirely on one side of the xy plane near the origin, it is necessary that all the curves of intersection of the surface by planes through the z axis should lie on the same side of the xy plane near the origin. But if the surface be cut by the secant plane

$$y = x \tan \phi,$$

the equation of the curve of intersection is found by making the substitution

$$x = \rho \cos \phi, \qquad y = \rho \sin \phi$$

in the equation (26), the new axes being the old z axis and the trace of the secant plane on the xy plane. Performing this operation, we find

$$z = A \rho^2 \left(\cos \phi \sin \omega - \cos \omega \sin \phi \right)^2 + K \rho^3 + L \rho^4,$$

where K is independent of ρ. If $\tan \omega \gtrless \tan \phi$, z is positive for sufficiently small values of ρ; hence all the corresponding sections lie above the xy plane near the origin. Let us now cut the surface by the plane

$$y = x \tan \omega.$$

If the corresponding value of K is not zero, the development of z is of the form

$$z = \rho^3 (K + \epsilon)$$

and changes sign with ρ. Hence the section of the surface by this plane has a point of inflection at the origin and crosses the xy plane. It follows that the function $f(x, y)$ has neither a maximum nor a minimum at the origin. Such is the case when the section of the surface by its tangent plane has a cusp of the first kind, for instance, for the surface

$$z = y^2 - x^3.$$

If $K = 0$ for the latter substitution, we would carry the development out to terms of the fourth order, and we would obtain an expression of the form

$$z = \rho^4 (K_1 + \epsilon'),$$

where K_1 is a constant which may be readily calculated from the derivatives of the fourth order. We shall suppose that K_1 is not zero. For infinitesimal values of ρ, z has the same sign as K_1; if K_1 is negative, the section in question lies beneath the xy plane near the origin, and again there is neither a maximum nor a minimum. Such is the case, for example, for the surface $z = y^2 - x^4$, whose intersection with the xy plane consists of the two parabolas $y = \pm x^2$. Hence, unless $K = 0$ and $K_1 > 0$ at the same time, it is evidently useless to carry the investigation farther, for we may conclude at once that the surface crosses its tangent plane near the origin.

But if $K = 0$ and $K_1 > 0$ at the same time, all the sections made by planes through the z axis lie above the xy plane near the origin. But that does not show conclusively that the surface does not cross its tangent plane, as is seen by considering the particular surface

$$z = (y - x^2)(y - 2x^2),$$

which cuts its tangent plane in two parabolas, one of which lies inside the other. In order that the surface should not cross its tangent plane it is also necessary that the section of the surface made by any cylinder whatever which passes through the z axis should lie wholly above the xy plane. Let $y = \phi(x)$ be the equation of the trace of this cylinder upon the xy plane, where $\phi(x)$ vanishes for $x = 0$. The function $F(x) = f[x, \phi(x)]$ must be at a minimum for $x = 0$, whatever be the function $\phi(x)$. In order to simplify the calculation we will suppose that the axes have been so chosen that the equation of the surface is of the form

$$z = Ay^2 + \phi_3(x, y) + \cdots,$$

where A is positive. With this system of axes we have

$$\frac{\partial f}{\partial x_0} = 0, \qquad \frac{\partial f}{\partial y_0} = 0, \qquad \frac{\partial^2 f}{\partial x_0^2} = 0, \qquad \frac{\partial^2 f}{\partial x_0 \partial y_0} = 0, \qquad \frac{\partial^2 f}{\partial y_0^2} > 0,$$

at the origin.

The derivatives of the function $F(x)$ are given by the formulæ

$$F'(x) = \frac{\partial f}{\partial x} + \frac{\partial f}{\partial y} \phi'(x),$$

$$F''(x) = \frac{\partial^2 f}{\partial x^2} + 2 \frac{\partial^2 f}{\partial x \partial y} \phi'(x) + \frac{\partial^2 f}{\partial y^2} \phi'^2(x) + \frac{\partial f}{\partial y} \phi''(x),$$

$$F'''(x) = \frac{\partial^3 f}{\partial x^3} + 3 \frac{\partial^3 f}{\partial x^2 \partial y} \phi'(x) + 3 \frac{\partial^3 f}{\partial x \partial y^2} \phi'^2(x) + \frac{\partial^3 f}{\partial y^3} \phi'^3(x)$$
$$+ 3 \frac{\partial^2 f}{\partial x \partial y} \phi''(x) + 3 \frac{\partial^2 f}{\partial y^2} \phi'\phi'' + \frac{\partial f}{\partial y} \phi'''(x),$$

$$F^{IV}(x) = \frac{\partial^4 f}{\partial x^4} + 4 \frac{\partial^4 f}{\partial x^3 \partial y} \phi'(x) + 6 \frac{\partial^4 f}{\partial x^2 \partial y^2} \phi'^2(x) + 4 \frac{\partial^4 f}{\partial x \partial y^3} \phi'^3(x) + \frac{\partial^4 f}{\partial y^4} \phi'^4(x)$$
$$+ 6 \frac{\partial^3 f}{\partial x^2 \partial y} \phi''(x) + 12 \frac{\partial^3 f}{\partial x \partial y^2} \phi'\phi'' + 6 \frac{\partial^3 f}{\partial y^3} \phi'^2\phi''$$
$$+ 4 \frac{\partial^2 f}{\partial x \partial y} \phi'''(x) + \frac{\partial^2 f}{\partial y^2} (4\phi'\phi''' + 3\phi''^2) + \frac{\partial f}{\partial y} \phi^{IV}(x),$$

from which, for $x = y = 0$, we obtain

$$F'(0) = 0, \qquad F''(0) = \frac{\partial^2 f}{\partial y_0^2}\,[\phi'(0)]^2.$$

If $\phi'(0)$ does not vanish, the function $F(x)$ has a minimum, as is also apparent from the previous discussion.   But if $\phi'(0) = 0$, we find the formulæ

$$F'(0) = 0, \qquad F''(0) = 0, \qquad F'''(0) = \frac{\partial^3 f}{\partial x_0^3},$$

$$F^{\mathrm{IV}}(0) = \frac{\partial^4 f}{\partial x_0^4} + 6\,\frac{\partial^3 f}{\partial x_0^2 \partial y_0}\,\phi''(0) + 3\,\frac{\partial^2 f}{\partial y_0^2}\,[\phi''(0)]^2.$$

Hence, in order that $F(x)$ be at a minimum, it is necessary that $\partial^3 f / \partial x_0^3$ vanish and that the following quadratic form in $\phi''(0)$,

$$\frac{\partial^4 f}{\partial x_0^4} + 6\,\frac{\partial^3 f}{\partial x_0^2 \partial y_0}\,\phi''(0) + 3\,\frac{\partial^2 f}{\partial y_0^2}\,[\phi''(0)]^2,$$

be positive for all values of $\phi''(0)$.

It is easy to show that these conditions are not satisfied for the above function $z = y^2 - 3\,x^2 y + 2\,x^4$, but that they are satisfied for the function $z = y^2 + x^4$. It is evident, in fact, that the latter surface lies entirely above the xy plane.

We shall not attempt to carry the discussion farther, for it requires extremely nice reasoning to render it absolutely rigorous.   The reader who wishes to examine the subject in greater detail is referred to an important memoir by Ludwig Scheffer, in Vol. XXXV of the *Mathematische Annalen.*

59. Functions of three variables.   Let $u = f(x, y, z)$ be a continuous function of the three variables x, y, z.   Then, as before, this function is said to have an extremum (maximum or minimum) for a set of values x_0, y_0, z_0 if a positive number η can be found so small that the difference

$$\Delta = f(x_0 + h,\, y_0 + k,\, z_0 + l) - f(x_0,\, y_0,\, z_0),$$

which vanishes for $h = k = l = 0$, has the same sign for all other sets of values of h, k, l, each of which is less in absolute value than η.   If only one of the variables x, y, z is given an increment, while the other two are regarded as constants, we find, as above, that u cannot be at an extremum unless the equations

$$\frac{\partial f}{\partial x_0} = 0, \quad \frac{\partial f}{\partial y_0} = 0, \quad \frac{\partial f}{\partial z_0} = 0$$

are all satisfied, provided, of course, that these derivatives are continuous near the point (x_0, y_0, z_0).   Let us now suppose that x_0, y_0, z_0 are a set of solutions of these equations, and let M_0 be the point whose coördinates are x_0, y_0, z_0.   There will be an extremum if a sphere can be drawn about M_0 so small that $f(x, y, z) - f(x_0, y_0, z_0)$

has the same sign for all points (x, y, z) except M_0 inside the sphere. Let the coördinates of a neighboring point be represented by the equations

$$x = x_0 + \rho\alpha, \qquad y = y_0 + \rho\beta, \qquad z = z_0 + \rho\gamma,$$

where α, β, γ satisfy the relation $\alpha^2 + \beta^2 + \gamma^2 = 1$; and let us replace $x - x_0$, $y - y_0$, $z - z_0$ in Taylor's expansion of $f(x, y, z)$ by $\rho\alpha$, $\rho\beta$, $\rho\gamma$, respectively. This gives the following expression for Δ:

$$\Delta = \rho^2[\phi(\alpha, \beta, \gamma) + \rho L],$$

where $\phi(\alpha, \beta, \gamma)$ denotes a quadratic form in α, β, γ whose coefficients are the second derivatives of $f(x, y, z)$, and where L is a function which remains finite near the point M_0. The quadratic form may be expressed as the sum of the squares of three distinct linear functions of α, β, γ, say P, P', P'', multiplied by certain constant factors a, a', a'', except in the particular case when the discriminant of the form is zero. Hence we may write, in general,

$$\phi(\alpha, \beta, \gamma) = aP^2 + a'P'^2 + a''P''^2,$$

where a, a', a'' are all different from zero. If the coefficients a, a', a'' have the same sign, the absolute value of the quadratic form ϕ will remain greater than a certain lower limit when the point α, β, γ describes the sphere

$$\alpha^2 + \beta^2 + \gamma^2 = 1,$$

and accordingly Δ has the same sign as a, a', a'' when ρ is less than a certain number. Hence the function $f(x, y, z)$ has an extremum.

If the three coefficients a, a', a'' do not all have the same sign, there will be neither a maximum nor a minimum. Suppose, for example, that $a > 0$, $a' < 0$, and let us take values of α, β, γ which satisfy the equations $P' = 0$, $P'' = 0$. These values cannot cause P to vanish, and Δ will be positive for small values of ρ. But if, on the other hand, values be taken for α, β, γ which satisfy the equations $P = 0$, $P'' = 0$, Δ will be negative for small values of ρ.

The method is the same for any number of independent variables: the discussion of a certain quadratic form always plays the principal rôle. In the case of a function $u = f(x, y, z)$ of only three independent variables it may be noticed that the discussion is equivalent to the discussion of the nature of a surface near a singular point. For consider a surface Σ whose equation is

$$F(x, y, z) = f(x, y, z) - f(x_0, y_0, z_0) = 0;$$

this surface evidently passes through the point M_0 whose coördinates are (x_0, y_0, z_0), and if the function $f(x, y, z)$ has an extremum there, the point M_0 is a singular point of Σ. Hence, if the cone of tangents at M_0 is imaginary, it is clear that $F(x, y, z)$ will keep the same sign inside a sufficiently small sphere about M_0 as center, and $f(x, y, z)$ will surely have a maximum or a minimum. But if the cone of tangents is real, or is composed of two real distinct planes, several nappes of the surface pass through M_0, and $F(x, y, z)$ changes sign as the point (x, y, z) crosses one of these nappes.

60. Distance from a point to a surface. Let us try to find the maximum and the minimum values of the distance from a fixed point (a, b, c) to a surface S whose equation is $F(x, y, z) = 0$. The square of this distance,

$$u = d^2 = (x - a)^2 + (y - b)^2 + (z - c)^2,$$

is a function of two independent variables only, — x and y, for example, if z be considered as a function of x and y defined by the equation $F = 0$. In order that u be at an extremum for a point (x, y, z) of the surface, we must have, for the coördinates of that point,

$$\frac{1}{2} \frac{\partial u}{\partial x} = (x - a) + (z - c) \frac{\partial z}{\partial x} = 0,$$
$$\frac{1}{2} \frac{\partial u}{\partial y} = (y - b) + (z - c) \frac{\partial z}{\partial y} = 0.$$

We find, in addition, from the equation $F = 0$, the relations

$$\frac{\partial F}{\partial x} + \frac{\partial F}{\partial z} \frac{\partial z}{\partial x} = 0, \quad \frac{\partial F}{\partial y} + \frac{\partial F}{\partial z} \frac{\partial z}{\partial y} = 0,$$

whence the preceding equations take the form

$$\frac{x - a}{\dfrac{\partial F}{\partial x}} = \frac{y - b}{\dfrac{\partial F}{\partial y}} = \frac{z - c}{\dfrac{\partial F}{\partial z}}.$$

This shows that the normal to the surface S at the point (x, y, z) passes through the point (a, b, c). Hence, omitting the singular points of the surface S, the points sought for are the feet of normals let fall from the point (a, b, c) upon the surface S. In order to see whether such a point actually corresponds to a maximum or to a minimum, let us take the point as origin and the tangent plane as the xy plane, so that the given point shall lie upon the axis of z. Then the function to be studied has the form

$$u = x^2 + y^2 + (z - c)^2,$$

where z is a function of x and y which, together with both its first derivatives, vanishes for $x = y = 0$. Denoting the second partial derivatives of z by r, s, t, we have, at the origin,

$$\frac{\partial^2 u}{\partial x^2} = 2(1 - cr), \quad \frac{\partial^2 u}{\partial x \, \partial y} = -2 cs, \quad \frac{\partial^2 u}{\partial y^2} = 2(1 - ct),$$

and it only remains to study the polynomial

$$\Delta(c) = c^2 s^2 - (1 - cr)(1 - ct) = c^2(s^2 - rt) + (r + t)c - 1.$$

The roots of the equation $\Delta(c) = 0$ are always real by virtue of the identity $(r + t)^2 + 4(s^2 - rt) = 4s^2 + (r - t)^2$. There are now several cases which must be distinguished according to the sign of $s^2 - rt$.

First case. Let $s^2 - rt < 0$. The two roots c_1 and c_2 of the equation $\Delta(c) = 0$ have the same sign, and we may write $\Delta(c) = (s^2 - rt)(c - c_1)(c - c_2)$. Let us now mark the two points A_1 and A_2 of the z axis whose coördinates are c_1 and c_2. These two points lie on the same side of the origin; and if we suppose, as is always allowable, that r and t are positive, they lie on the positive part of the z axis. If the given point A $(0, 0, c)$ lies outside the segment $A_1 A_2$, $\Delta(c)$ is negative, and the distance OA is a maximum or a minimum. In order to see which of the two it is we must consider the sign of $1 - cr$. This coefficient does not vanish except when $c = 1/r$; and this value of c lies between c_1 and c_2, since $\Delta(1/r) = s^2/r^2$. But, for $c = 0$, $1 - cr$ is positive; hence $1 - cr$ is positive, and the distance OA is a minimum if the point A and the origin lie on the same side of the segment $A_1 A_2$. On the other hand, the distance OA is a maximum if the point A and the origin lie on different sides of that segment. When the point A lies between A_1 and A_2 the distance is neither a minimum nor a maximum. The case where A lies at one of the points A_1, A_2 is left in doubt.

Second case. Let $s^2 - rt > 0$. One of the two roots c_1 and c_2 of $\Delta(c) = 0$ is positive and the other is negative, and the origin lies between the two points A_1 and A_2. If the point A does not lie between A_1 and A_2, $\Delta(c)$ is positive and there is neither a maximum nor a minimum. If A lies between A_1 and A_2, $\Delta(c)$ is negative, $1 - cr$ is positive, and hence the distance OA is a minimum.

Third case. Let $s^2 - rt = 0$. Then $\Delta(c) = (r + t)(c - c_1)$, and it is easily seen, as above, that the distance OA is a minimum if the point A and the origin lie on the same side of the point A_1, whose coördinates are $(0, 0, c_1)$, and that there is neither a maximum nor a minimum if the point A_1 lies between the point A and the origin.

The points A_1 and A_2 are of fundamental importance in the study of curvature; they are the *principal centers of curvature* of the surface S at the point O.

61. Maxima and minima of implicit functions. We often need to find the maxima and minima of a function of several variables which are connected by one or more relations. Let us consider, for example, a function $\omega = f(x, y, z, u)$ of the four variables x, y, z, u, which themselves satisfy the two equations

$$f_1(x, y, z, u) = 0, \qquad f_2(x, y, z, u) = 0.$$

For definiteness, let us think of x and y as the independent variables, and of z and u as functions of x and y defined by these equations. Then the necessary conditions that ω have an extremum are

$$\frac{\partial f}{\partial x} + \frac{\partial f}{\partial z}\frac{\partial z}{\partial x} + \frac{\partial f}{\partial u}\frac{\partial u}{\partial x} = 0, \qquad \frac{\partial f}{\partial y} + \frac{\partial f}{\partial z}\frac{\partial z}{\partial y} + \frac{\partial f}{\partial u}\frac{\partial u}{\partial y} = 0,$$

and the partial derivatives $\partial z / \partial x$, $\partial u / \partial x$, $\partial z / \partial y$, $\partial u / \partial y$ are given by the relations

$$\frac{\partial f_1}{\partial x} + \frac{\partial f_1}{\partial z}\frac{\partial z}{\partial x} + \frac{\partial f_1}{\partial u}\frac{\partial u}{\partial x} = 0, \qquad \frac{\partial f_2}{\partial x} + \frac{\partial f_2}{\partial z}\frac{\partial z}{\partial x} + \frac{\partial f_2}{\partial u}\frac{\partial u}{\partial x} = 0,$$

$$\frac{\partial f_1}{\partial y} + \frac{\partial f_1}{\partial z}\frac{\partial z}{\partial y} + \frac{\partial f_1}{\partial u}\frac{\partial u}{\partial y} = 0, \qquad \frac{\partial f_2}{\partial y} + \frac{\partial f_2}{\partial z}\frac{\partial z}{\partial y} + \frac{\partial f_2}{\partial u}\frac{\partial u}{\partial y} = 0.$$

The elimination of $\partial z / \partial x$, $\partial u / \partial x$, $\partial z / \partial y$, $\partial u / \partial y$ leads to the new equations of condition

$$(27) \qquad \frac{D(f, f_1, f_2)}{D(x, z, u)} = 0, \qquad \frac{D(f, f_1, f_2)}{D(y, z, u)} = 0,$$

which, together with the relations $f_1 = 0$, $f_2 = 0$, determine the values of x, y, z, u, which may correspond to extrema. But the equations (27) express the condition that we can find values of λ and μ which satisfy the equations

$$(28) \quad \begin{cases} \dfrac{\partial f}{\partial x} + \lambda \dfrac{\partial f_1}{\partial x} + \mu \dfrac{\partial f_2}{\partial x} = 0, & \dfrac{\partial f}{\partial y} + \lambda \dfrac{\partial f_1}{\partial y} + \mu \dfrac{\partial f_2}{\partial y} = 0, \\[2mm] \dfrac{\partial f}{\partial z} + \lambda \dfrac{\partial f_1}{\partial z} + \mu \dfrac{\partial f_2}{\partial z} = 0, & \dfrac{\partial f}{\partial u} + \lambda \dfrac{\partial f_1}{\partial u} + \mu \dfrac{\partial f_2}{\partial u} = 0; \end{cases}$$

hence the two equations (27) may be replaced by the four equations (28), where λ and μ are unknown auxiliary functions.

The proof of the general theorem is self-evident, and we may state the following practical rule:

Given a function

$$f(x_1, x_2, \cdots, x_n)$$

of n variables, connected by h distinct relations

$$\phi_1 = 0, \qquad \phi_2 = 0, \qquad \cdots, \qquad \phi_h = 0;$$

in order to find the values of x_1, x_2, $\cdots$, x_n which may render this function an extremum we must equate to zero the partial derivatives of the auxiliary function

$$f + \lambda_1\phi_1 + \cdots + \lambda_h\phi_h,$$

regarding λ_1, λ_2, $\cdots$, λ_h as constants.

62. Another example. We shall now take up another example, where the minimum is *not* necessarily given by equating the partial derivatives to zero. Given a triangle ABC; let us try to find a point P of the plane for which the sum $PA + PB + PC$ of the distances from P to the vertices of the triangle is a minimum. Let (a_1, b_1), (a_2, b_2), (a_3, b_3) be respectively the coördinates of the vertices A, B, C referred to a system of rectangular coördinates. Then the function whose minimum is sought is

$$(29) \quad z = \sqrt{(x-a_1)^2+(y-b_1)^2}+\sqrt{(x-a_2)^2+(y-b_2)^2}+\sqrt{(x-a_3)^2+(y-b_3)^2},$$

where each of the three radicals is to be taken with the positive sign. This equation (29) represents a surface S which is evidently entirely above the xy plane, and the whole question reduces to that of finding the point on this surface which is nearest the xy plane. From the relation (29) we find

$$\frac{\partial z}{\partial x} = \frac{x-a_1}{\sqrt{(x-a_1)^2+(y-b_1)^2}} + \frac{x-a_2}{\sqrt{(x-a_2)^2+(y-b_2)^2}} + \frac{x-a_3}{\sqrt{(x-a_3)^2+(y-b_3)^2}},$$

$$\frac{\partial z}{\partial y} = \frac{y-b_1}{\sqrt{(x-a_1)^2+(y-b_1)^2}} + \frac{y-b_2}{\sqrt{(x-a_2)^2+(y-b_2)^2}} + \frac{y-b_3}{\sqrt{(x-a_3)^2+(y-b_3)^2}};$$

and it is evident that these derivatives are continuous, except in the neighborhood of the points A, B, C, where they become indeterminate. The surface S, therefore, has three singular points which project into the vertices of the given triangle. The minimum of z is given by a point on the surface where the tangent plane is parallel to the xy plane, or else by one of these singular points. In order to solve the equations $\partial z/\partial x = 0$, $\partial z/\partial y = 0$, let us write them in the form

$$\frac{x-a_1}{\sqrt{(x-a_1)^2+(y-b_1)^2}} + \frac{x-a_2}{\sqrt{(x-a_2)^2+(y-b_2)^2}} = - \frac{x-a_3}{\sqrt{(x-a_3)^2+(y-b_3)^2}},$$

$$\frac{y-b_1}{\sqrt{(x-a_1)^2+(y-b_1)^2}} + \frac{y-b_2}{\sqrt{(x-a_2)^2+(y-b_2)^2}} = - \frac{y-b_3}{\sqrt{(x-a_3)^2+(y-b_3)^2}}.$$

Then squaring and adding, we find the condition

$$1 + 2 \frac{(x-a_1)(x-a_2)+(y-b_1)(y-b_2)}{\sqrt{(x-a_1)^2+(y-b_1)^2}\sqrt{(x-a_2)^2+(y-b_2)^2}} = 0.$$

The geometrical interpretation of this result is easy: denoting by α and β the cosines of the angles which the direction PA makes with the axes of x and y, respectively, and by α' and β' the cosines of the angles which PB makes with the same axes, we may write this last condition in the form

$$1 + 2(\alpha\alpha' + \beta\beta') = 0,$$

or, denoting the angle APB by ω,

$$2\cos\omega + 1 = 0.$$

Hence the condition in question expresses that the segment AB subtends an angle of 120° at the point P. For the same reason each of the angles BPC and CPA must be 120°.* It is clear that the point P must lie inside the triangle

---

* The reader is urged to draw the figure.

ABC, and that there is no point which possesses the required property if any angle of the triangle ABC is equal to or greater than 120°. In case none of the angles is as great as 120°, the point P is uniquely determined by an easy construction, as the intersection of two circles. In this case the minimum is given by the point P or by one of the vertices of the triangle. But it is easy to show that the sum $PA + PB + PC$ is less than the sum of two of the sides of the triangle. For, since the angles APB and APC are each 120°, we find, from the two triangles PAC and PBA, the formulæ

$$AB = \sqrt{a^2 + b^2 + ab}, \qquad AC = \sqrt{a^2 + c^2 + ac},$$

where $PA = a$, $PB = b$, $PC = c$. But it is evident that

$$\sqrt{a^2 + b^2 + ab} > b + \frac{a}{2}, \qquad \sqrt{a^2 + c^2 + ac} > c + \frac{a}{2},$$

and hence

$$AB + AC > a + b + c.$$

The point P therefore actually corresponds to a minimum.

When one of the angles of the triangle ABC is equal to or greater than 120° there exists no point at which each of the sides of the triangle ABC subtends an angle of 120°, and hence the surface S has no tangent plane which is parallel to the xy plane. In this case the minimum must be given by one of the vertices of the triangle, and it is evident, in fact, that this is the vertex of the obtuse angle. It is easy to verify this fact geometrically.

63. D'Alembert's theorem. Let $F(x, y)$ be a polynomial in the two variables x and y arranged into homogeneous groups of ascending order

$$F(x, y) = H + \phi_p(x, y) + \phi_{p+1}(x, y) + \cdots + \phi_m(x, y),$$

where H is a constant. If the equation $\phi_p(x, y) = 0$, considered as an equation in y/x, has a simple root, the function $F(x, y)$ cannot have a maximum or a minimum for $x = y = 0$. For it results from the discussion above that there exist sections of the surface $z + H = F(x, y)$ made by planes through the z axis, some of which lie above the xy plane and others below it near the origin. From this remark a demonstration of d'Alembert's theorem may be deduced. For, let $f(z)$ be an integral polynomial of degree m,

$$f(z) = A_0 + A_1 z + A_2 z^2 + \cdots + A_m z^m,$$

where the coefficients are entirely arbitrary. In order to separate the real and imaginary parts let us write this in the form

$$f(x + iy) = a_0 + ib_0 + (a_1 + ib_1)(x + iy) + \cdots + (a_m + ib_m)(x + iy)^m,$$

where $a_0, b_0, a_1, b_1, \cdots, a_m, b_m$ are real. We have then

$$f(z) = P + iQ,$$

where P and Q have the following meanings:

$$P = a_0 + a_1 x - b_1 y + \cdots,$$
$$Q = b_0 + b_1 x + a_1 y + \cdots;$$

and hence, finally,

$$|f(z)| = \sqrt{P^2 + Q^2}.$$

We will first show that $|f(z)|$, or, what amounts to the same thing, that $P^2 + Q^2$, cannot be at a minimum for $x = y = 0$ except when $a_0 = b_0 = 0$. For this purpose we shall introduce polar coördinates ρ and ϕ, and we shall suppose, for the sake of generality, that the first coefficient after A_0 which does not vanish is A_p. Then we may write the equations

$$P = a_0 + (a_p \cos p\phi - b_p \sin p\phi)\rho^p + \cdots,$$
$$Q = b_0 + (b_p \cos p\phi + a_p \sin p\phi)\rho^p + \cdots,$$
$$P^2 + Q^2 = a_0^2 + b_0^2 + 2\rho^p[(a_0 a_p + b_0 b_p)\cos p\phi + (b_0 a_p - a_0 b_p)\sin p\phi] + \cdots,$$

where the terms not written down are of degree higher than p with respect to ρ. But the equation

$$(a_0 a_p + b_0 b_p)\cos p\phi + (b_0 a_p - a_0 b_p)\sin p\phi = 0$$

gives $\tan p\phi = K$, which determines p straight lines which are separated by angles each equal to $2\pi/p$. It is therefore impossible by the above remark that $P^2 + Q^2$ should have a minimum for $x = y = 0$ unless the quantities

$$a_0 a_p + b_0 b_p, \qquad b_0 a_p - a_0 b_p$$

both vanish. But, since $a_p^2 + b_p^2$ is not zero, this would require that $a_0 = b_0 = 0$; that is, that the real and the imaginary parts of $f(z)$ should both vanish at the origin.

If $|f(z)|$ has a minimum for $x = \alpha$, $y = \beta$, the discussion may be reduced to the preceding by setting $z = \alpha + i\beta + z'$. It follows that $|f(z)|$ cannot be at a minimum unless P and Q vanish separately for $x = \alpha$, $y = \beta$.

The absolute value of $f(z)$ must pass through a minimum for at least one value of z, for it increases indefinitely as the absolute value of z increases indefinitely. In fact, we have

$$P^2 + Q^2 = (a_m^2 + b_m^2)\rho^{2m} + \cdots,$$

where the terms omitted are of degree less than $2m$ in ρ. This equation may be written in the form

$$\sqrt{P^2 + Q^2} = \rho^m(\sqrt{a_m^2 + b_m^2} + \epsilon),$$

where ϵ approaches zero as ρ increases indefinitely. Hence a circle may be drawn whose radius R is so large that the value of $\sqrt{P^2 + Q^2}$ is greater at every point of the circumference than it is at the origin, for example. It follows that there is at least one point

$$x = \alpha, \qquad y = \beta$$

inside this circle for which $\sqrt{P^2 + Q^2}$ is at a minimum. By the above it follows that the point $x = \alpha$, $y = \beta$ is a point of intersection of the two curves $P = 0$, $Q = 0$, which amounts to saying that $z = \alpha + \beta i$ is a root of the equation $f(z) = 0$.

In this example, as in the preceding, we have assumed that a function of the two variables x and y which is continuous in the interior of a limited region actually assumes a minimum value inside or on the boundary of that region. This is a statement which will be readily granted, and, moreover, it will be rigorously demonstrated a little later (Chapter VI).

EXERCISES

1. Show that the number θ, which occurs in Lagrange's form of the remainder, approaches the limit $1/(n+2)$ as h approaches zero, provided that $f^{(n+2)}(a)$ is not zero.

2. Let $F(x)$ be a determinant of order n, all of whose elements are functions of x. Show that the derivative $F'(x)$ is the sum of the n determinants obtained by replacing, successively, all of the elements of a single line by their derivatives. State the corresponding theorem for derivatives of higher order.

3. Find the maximum and the minimum values of the distance from a fixed point to a plane or a skew curve ; between two variable points on two curves ; between two variable points on two surfaces.

4. The points of a surface S for which the sum of the squares of the distances from n fixed points is an extremum are the feet of the normals let fall upon the surface from the center of mean distances of the given n fixed points.

5. Of all the quadrilaterals which can be formed from four given sides, that which is inscriptible in a circle has the greatest area. State the analogous theorem for polygons of n sides.

6. Find the maximum volume of a rectangular parallelopiped inscribed in an ellipsoid.

7. Find the axes of a central quadric from the consideration that the vertices are the points from which the distance to the center is an extremum.

8. Solve the analogous problem for the axes of a central section of an ellipsoid.

9. Find the ellipse of minimum area which passes through the three vertices of a given triangle, and the ellipsoid of minimum volume which passes through the four vertices of a given tetrahedron.

10. Find the point from which the sum of the distances to two given straight lines and the distance to a given point is a minimum.

[JOSEPH BERTRAND.]

11. Prove the following formulæ :

$$\log(x+2) = 2\log(x+1) - 2\log(x-1) + \log(x-2)$$
$$+ 2\left[\frac{2}{x^3-3x} + \frac{1}{3}\left(\frac{2}{x^3-3x}\right)^3 + \frac{1}{5}\left(\frac{2}{x^3-3x}\right)^5 + \cdots\right];$$

[BORDA's Series.]

$$\log(x+5) = \log(x+4) + \log(x+3) - 2\log x$$
$$+ \log(x-3) + \log(x-4) - \log(x-5)$$
$$- 2\left[\frac{72}{x^4-25x^2+72} + \frac{1}{3}\left(\frac{72}{x^4-25x^2+72}\right)^3 + \cdots\right].$$

[HARO's Series.]

CHAPTER IV

DEFINITE INTEGRALS

I. SPECIAL METHODS OF QUADRATURE

64. Quadrature of the parabola. The determination of the area bounded by a plane curve is a problem which has always engaged the genius of geometricians. Among the examples which have come down to us from the ancients one of the most celebrated is Archimedes' quadrature of the parabola. We shall proceed to indicate his method.

Let us try to find the area bounded by the arc ACB of a parabola and the chord AB. Draw the diameter CD, joining the middle point D of AB to the point C, where the tangent is parallel to AB. Connect AC and BC, and let E and E' be the points where the

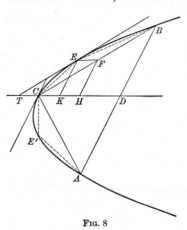

tangent is parallel to BC and AC, respectively. We shall first compare the area of the triangle BEC, for instance, with that of the triangle ABC. Draw the tangent ET, which cuts CD at T. Draw the diameter EF, which cuts CB at F; and, finally, draw EK and FH parallel to the chord AB. By an elementary property of the parabola $TC = CK$. Moreover, $CT = EF = KH$, and hence $EF = CH/2 = CD/4$. The areas of the two triangles BCE and BCD, since they have the

FIG. 8

same base BC, are to each other as their altitudes, or as EF is to CD. Hence the area of the triangle BCE is one fourth the area of the triangle BCD, or one eighth of the area S of the triangle ABC. The area of the triangle ACE' is evidently the same. Carrying out the same process upon each of the chords BE, CE, CE', $E'A$, we

obtain four new triangles, the area of each of which is $S/8^2$, and so
forth.   The nth operation gives rise to 2^n triangles, each having the
area $S/8^n$.   The area of the segment of the parabola is evidently
the limit approached by the sum of the areas of all these triangles
as n increases indefinitely; that is, the sum of the following descend-
ing geometrical progression :

$$S + \frac{S}{4} + \frac{S}{4^2} + \cdots + \frac{S}{4^n} + \cdots,$$

and this sum is $4\,S/3$.   It follows that *the required area is equal to
two thirds of the area of a parallelogram whose sides are AB and CD.*
   Although this method possesses admirable ingenuity, it must be
admitted that its success depends essentially upon certain special
properties of the parabola, and that it is lacking in generality.   The
other examples of quadratures which we might quote from ancient
writers would only go to corroborate this remark : each new curve
required some new device.   But whatever the device, the area to be
evaluated was always split up into elements the number of which
was made to increase indefinitely, and it was necessary to evaluate
the limit of the sum of these partial areas.   Omitting any further
particular cases,* we will proceed at once to give a general method
of subdivision, which will lead us naturally to the Integral Calculus.

   65. General method. For the sake of definiteness, let us try to
evaluate the area S bounded by a curvilinear arc AMB, an axis xx'
which does not cut that arc, and two perpendiculars AA_0 and BB_0 let

fall upon xx' from
the points A and B.
We will suppose
further that a par-
allel to these lines
AA_0, BB_0 cannot
cut the arc in more
than one point, as
indicated in Fig. 9.

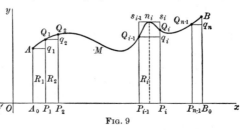

FIG. 9

Let us divide the segment A_0B_0 into a certain number of equal or
unequal parts by the points P_1, P_2, $\cdots$, P_{n-1}, and through these
points let us draw lines P_1Q_1, P_2Q_2, $\cdots$, $P_{n-1}Q_{n-1}$ parallel to AA_0
and meeting the arc AB in the points Q_1, Q_2, $\cdots$, Q_{n-1}, respectively.

---

   * A large number of examples of determinations of areas, arcs, and volumes by
the methods of ancient writers are to be found in Duhamel's *Traité*.

Now draw through A a line parallel to xx', cutting $P_1 Q_1$ at q_1; through Q_1 a parallel to xx', cutting $P_2 Q_2$ at q_2; and so on. We obtain in this way a sequence of rectangles $R_1, R_2, \cdots, R_i, \cdots, R_n$. Each of these rectangles may lie entirely inside the contour $ABB_0 A_0$, but some of them may lie partially outside that contour, as is indicated in the figure.

Let α_i denote the area of the rectangle R_i, and β_i the area bounded by the contour $P_{i-1} P_i Q_i Q_{i-1}$. In the first place, each of the ratios $\beta_1/\alpha_1, \beta_2/\alpha_2, \cdots, \beta_i/\alpha_i, \cdots$ approaches unity as the number of points of division increases indefinitely, if at the same time each of the distances $A_0 P_1, P_1 P_2, \cdots, P_{i-1} P_i, \cdots$ approaches zero. For the ratio β_i/α_i, for example, evidently lies between $l_i/P_{i-1} Q_{i-1}$ and $L_i/P_{i-1} Q_{i-1}$, where l_i and L_i are respectively the minimum and the maximum distances from a point of the arc $Q_{i-1} Q_i$ to the axis xx'. But it is clear that these two fractions each approach unity as the distance $P_{i-1} P_i$ approaches zero. It therefore follows that the ratio

$$\frac{\alpha_1 + \alpha_2 + \cdots + \alpha_n}{\beta_1 + \beta_2 + \cdots + \beta_n},$$

which lies between the largest and the least of the ratios α_1/β_1, $\alpha_2/\beta_2, \cdots, \alpha_n/\beta_n$, will also approach unity as the number of the rectangles is thus indefinitely increased. But the denominator of this ratio is constant and is equal to the required area S. Hence this area is also equal to the limit of the sum $\alpha_1 + \alpha_2 + \cdots + \alpha_n$, as the number of rectangles n is indefinitely increased in the manner specified above.

In order to deduce from this result an analytical expression for the area, let the curve AB be referred to a system of rectangular axes, the x axis Ox coinciding with xx', and let $y = f(x)$ be the equation of the curve AB. The function $f(x)$ is, by hypothesis, a continuous function of x between the limits a and b, the abscissæ of the points A and B. Denoting by $x_1, x_2, \cdots, x_{n-1}$ the abscissæ of the points of division $P_1, P_2, \cdots, P_{n-1}$, the bases of the above rectangles are $x_1 - a, x_2 - x_1, \cdots, x_i - x_{i-1}, \cdots, b - x_{n-1}$, and their altitudes are, in like manner, $f(a), f(x_1), \cdots, f(x_{i-1}), \cdots, f(x_{n-1})$. Hence the area S is equal to the limit of the following sum:

(1) $(x_1 - a)f(a) + (x_2 - x_1)f(x_1) + \cdots + (b - x_{n-1})f(x_{n-1})$,

as the number n increases indefinitely in such a way that each of the differences $x_1 - a, x_2 - x_1, \cdots$ approaches zero.

66. Examples. If the base AB be divided into n equal parts, each of length h $(b - a = nh)$, all the rectangles have the same base h, and their altitudes are, respectively,

$$f(a), \ f(a + h), \ f(a + 2\,h), \ \cdots, \ f[a + (n - 1)h].$$

It only remains to find the limit of the sum

$$h \{f(a) + f(a + h) + f(a + 2\,h) + \cdots + f[a + (n - 1)h]\},$$

where

$$h = \frac{b - a}{n},$$

as the integer n increases indefinitely. This calculation becomes easy if we know how to find the sum of a set of values $f(x)$ corresponding to a set of values of x which form an arithmetic progression; such is the case if $f(x)$ is simply an integral power of x, or, again, if $f(x) = \sin mx$ or $f(x) = \cos mx$, etc.

Let us reconsider, for example, the parabola $x^2 = 2\,py$, and let us try to find the area enclosed by an arc OA of this parabola, the axis of x, and the straight line $x = a$ which passes through the extremity A. The length being divided into n equal parts of length $h\,(nh = a)$, we must try to find by the above the limit of the sum

$$\frac{h}{2\,p}\,[h^2 + 4\,h^2 + \cdots + (n - 1)^2\,h^2] = \frac{h^3}{2\,p}\,[1 + 4 + 9 + \cdots + (n - 1)^2].$$

The quantity inside the parenthesis is the sum of the squares of the first $(n - 1)$ integers, that is, $n(n - 1)(2\,n - 1)/6$; and hence the foregoing sum is equal to

$$\frac{n(n - 1)(2\,n - 1)}{12\,pn^3}\,a^3.$$

As n increases indefinitely this sum evidently approaches the limit $a^3/6\,p = (1/3)(a \cdot a^2/2\,p)$, or one third of the rectangle constructed upon the two coördinates of the point A, which is in harmony with the result found above.

In other cases, as in the following example, which is due to Fermat, it is better to choose as points of division points whose abscissæ are in geometric progression.

Let us try to find the area enclosed by the curve $y = Ax^\mu$, the axis of x, and the two straight lines $x = a, x = b$ $(0 < a < b)$, where the exponent μ is arbitrary. In order to do so let us insert between a and b, $n-1$ geometric means so as to obtain the sequence

$$a, \ a(1+\alpha), \ a(1+\alpha)^2, \ \cdots, \ a(1+\alpha)^{n-1}, \ b,$$

where the number α satisfies the condition $a(1+\alpha)^n = b$. Taking this set of numbers as the abscissæ of the points of division, the corresponding ordinates have, respectively, the following values:

$$Aa^\mu, \ Aa^\mu(1+\alpha)^\mu, \ Aa^\mu(1+\alpha)^{2\mu}, \ \cdots,$$

and the area of the pth rectangle is

$$[a(1+\alpha)^p - a(1+\alpha)^{p-1}]Aa^\mu(1+\alpha)^{(p-1)\mu} = Aa^{\mu+1}\alpha(1+\alpha)^{(p-1)(\mu+1)}.$$

Hence the sum of the areas of all the rectangles is

$$Aa^{\mu+1}\alpha[1 + (1+\alpha)^{\mu+1} + (1+\alpha)^{2(\mu+1)} + \cdots + (1+\alpha)^{(n-1)(\mu+1)}].$$

If $\mu + 1$ is not zero, as we shall suppose first, the sum inside the parenthesis is equal to

$$\frac{(1+\alpha)^{n(\mu+1)} - 1}{(1+\alpha)^{\mu+1} - 1};$$

or, replacing $a(1+\alpha)^n$ by b, the original sum may be written in the form

$$A(b^{\mu+1} - a^{\mu+1}) \frac{\alpha}{(1+\alpha)^{\mu+1} - 1}.$$

As α approaches zero the quotient $[(1+\alpha)^{\mu+1} - 1]/\alpha$ approaches as its limit the derivative of $(1+\alpha)^{\mu+1}$ with respect to α for $\alpha = 0$, that is, $\mu + 1$; hence the required area is

$$\frac{A(b^{\mu+1} - a^{\mu+1})}{\mu + 1}.$$

If $\mu = -1$, this calculation no longer applies. The sum of the areas of the inscribed rectangles is equal to $nA\alpha$, and we have to find the limit of the product $n\alpha$ where n and α are connected by the relation

$$a(1+\alpha)^n = b.$$

From this it follows that

$$n\alpha = \log\frac{b}{a}\frac{\alpha}{\log(1+\alpha)} = \log\frac{b}{a}\frac{1}{\log(1+\alpha)^{\frac{1}{\alpha}}},$$

where the symbol log denotes the Naperian logarithm. As α approaches zero, $(1 + \alpha)^{1/\alpha}$ approaches the number e, and the product $n\alpha$ approaches $\log(b/a)$. Hence the required area is equal to $A \log(b/a)$.

67. Primitive functions. The invention of the Integral Calculus reduced the problem of evaluating a plane area to the problem of finding a function whose derivative is known. Let $y = f(x)$ be the equation of a curve referred to two rectangular axes, where the function $f(x)$ is continuous. Let us consider the area enclosed by this curve, the axis of x, a fixed ordinate M_0P_0, and a variable ordinate MP, as a function of the abscissa x of the variable ordinate.

In order to include all possible cases let us agree to
denote by A the sum of the
areas enclosed by the given
curve, the x axis, and the
straight lines M_0P_0, MP,
each of the portions of
this area being affected
by a certain sign: the
sign $+$ for the portions to

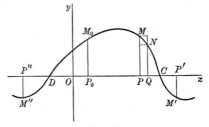

FIG. 10

the right of M_0P_0 and above Ox, the sign $-$ for the portions to the right of M_0P_0 and below Ox, and the opposite convention for portions to the left of M_0P_0. Thus, if MP were in the position $M'P'$, we would take A equal to the difference

$$M_0P_0C - M'P'C;$$

and likewise, if MP were at $M''P''$, $A = M''P''D - M_0P_0D$.

With these conventions we shall now show that the derivative of the continuous function A, defined in this way, is precisely $f(x)$. As in the figure, let us take two neighboring ordinates MP, NQ, whose abscissæ are x and $x + \Delta x$. The increment of the area ΔA evidently lies between the areas of the two rectangles which have the same base PQ, and whose altitudes are, respectively, the greatest and the least ordinates of the arc MN. Denoting the maximum ordinate by H and the minimum by h, we may therefore write

$$h\Delta x < \Delta A < H\Delta x,$$

or, dividing by Δx, $h < \Delta A / \Delta x < H$. As Δx approaches zero, H and h approach the same limit MP, or $f(x)$, since $f(x)$ is continuous.

Hence the derivative of A is $f(x)$.   The proof that the same result holds for any position of the point M is left to the reader.

If we already know a *primitive function* of $f(x)$, that is, a function $F(x)$ whose derivative is $f(x)$, the difference $A - F(x)$ is a constant, since its derivative is zero (§ 8).   In order to determine this constant, we need only notice that the area A is zero for the abscissa $x = a$ of the line MP.   Hence

$$A = F(x) - F(a).$$

It follows from the above reasoning, first, that the determination of a plane area may be reduced to the discovery of a primitive function; and, secondly (and this is of far greater importance for us), that *every continuous function $f(x)$ is the derivative of some other function*.   This fundamental theorem is proved here by means of a somewhat vague geometrical concept, — that of the area under a plane curve.   This demonstration was regarded as satisfactory for a long time, but it can no longer be accepted.   In order to have a stable foundation for the Integral Calculus it is imperative that this theorem should be given a purely analytic demonstration which does not rely upon any geometrical intuition whatever.   In giving the above geometrical proof the motive was not wholly its historical interest, however, for it furnishes us with the essential analytic argument of the new proof.   It is, in fact, the study of precisely such sums as (1) and sums of a slightly more general character which will be of preponderant importance.   Before taking up this study we must first consider certain questions regarding the general properties of functions and in particular of continuous functions.*

II. DEFINITE INTEGRALS   ALLIED GEOMETRICAL CONCEPTS

68. Upper and lower limits.   An assemblage of numbers is said to have an *upper limit* (see ftn., p. 91) if there exists a number N so large that no member of the assemblage exceeds N.   Likewise, an assemblage is said to have a *lower limit* if a number N' exists than which no member of the assemblage is smaller.   Thus the assemblage of all positive integers has a lower limit, but no upper limit;

---

* Among the most important works on the general notion of the definite integral there should be mentioned the memoir by Riemann: *Über die Möglichkeit, eine Function durch eine trigonometrische Reihe darzustellen* (*Werke*, 2d ed., Leipzig, 1892, p. 239; and also French translation by Laugel, p. 225); and the memoir by Darboux, to which we have already referred: *Sur les fonctions discontinues* (*Annales de l'École Normale Supérieure*, 2d series, Vol. IV).

the assemblage of all integers, positive and negative, has neither; and the assemblage of all rational numbers between 0 and 1 has both a lower and an upper limit.

Let (E) be an assemblage which has an upper limit. With respect to this assemblage all numbers may be divided into two classes. We shall say that a number α belongs to the first class if there are members of the assemblage (E) which are greater than α, and that it belongs to the second class if there is no member of the assemblage (E) greater than α. Since the assemblage (E) has an upper limit, it is clear that numbers of each class exist. If A be a number of the first class and B a number of the second class, it is evident that $A < B$; there exist members of the assemblage (E) which lie between A and B, but there is no member of the assemblage (E) which is greater than B. The number $C = (A + B)/2$ may belong to the first or to the second class. In the former case we should replace the interval (A, B) by the interval (C, B), in the latter case by the interval (A, C). The new interval (A_1, B_1) is half the interval (A, B) and has the same properties: there exists at least one member of the assemblage (E) which is greater than A_1, but none which is greater than B_1. Operating upon (A_1, B_1) in the same way that we operated upon (A, B), and so on indefinitely, we obtain an unlimited sequence of intervals (A, B), (A_1, B_1), (A_2, B_2), $\cdots$, each of which is half the preceding and possesses the same property as (A, B) with respect to the assemblage (E). Since the numbers $A, A_1, A_2, \cdots, A_n$ never decrease and are always less than B, they approach a limit λ (§ 1). Likewise, since the numbers $B, B_1, B_2, \cdots$ never increase and are always greater than A, they approach a limit λ'. Moreover, since the difference $B_n - A_n = (B - A)/2^n$ approaches zero as n increases indefinitely, these limits must be equal, i.e. $\lambda' = \lambda$. Let L be this common limit; then L is called *the upper limit* of the assemblage (E). From the manner in which we have obtained it, it is clear that L has the following two properties:

1) *No member of the assemblage (E) is greater than L.*

2) *There always exists a member of the assemblage (E) which is greater than $L - \epsilon$, where ϵ is any arbitrarily small positive number.*

For let us suppose that there were a member of the assemblage greater than L, say $L + h$ $(h > 0)$. Since B_n approaches L as n increases indefinitely, B_n will be less than $L + h$ after a certain value of n. But this is impossible since B_n is of the second class. On the other hand, let ϵ be any positive number. Then, after a certain value of n, A_n will be greater than $L - \epsilon$; and since there are members of (E) greater than A_n, these numbers will also be greater than $L - \epsilon$. It is evident that the two properties stated above cannot apply to any other number than L.

The upper limit may or may not belong to the assemblage (E). In the assemblage of all rational numbers which do not exceed 2, for instance, the number 2 is precisely the upper limit, and it belongs to the assemblage. On the other hand, the assemblage of all irrational numbers which do not exceed 2 has the upper limit 2, but this upper limit is not a member of the assemblage. It should be particularly noted that if the upper limit L does not belong to the assemblage, there are always an infinite number of members of (E) which are greater than $L - \epsilon$, no matter how small ϵ be taken. For if there were only a finite number, the upper limit would be the largest of these and not L. When the assemblage consists of n different numbers the upper limit is simply the largest of these n numbers.

It may be shown in like manner that there exists a number L', in case the assemblage has a lower limit, which has the following two properties:

1) *No member of the assemblage is less than L'.*

2) *There exists a member of the assemblage which is less than $L' + \epsilon$, where ϵ is an arbitrary positive number.**

This number L' is called *the lower limit* of the assemblage.

69. Oscillation. Let $f(x)$ be a function of x defined in the closed † interval (a, b); that is, to each value of x between a and b and to each of the limits a and b themselves there corresponds a uniquely determined value of $f(x)$. The function is said to be *finite* in this closed interval if all the values which it assumes lie between two fixed numbers A and B. Then the assemblage of values of the function has an upper and a lower limit. Let M and m be the upper and lower limits of this assemblage, respectively; then the difference

---

* Whenever *all* numbers can be separated into two classes A and B, according to any characteristic property, in such a way that any number of the class A is less than any number of the class B, the upper limit L of the numbers of the class A is at the same time the lower limit of the numbers of the class B. It is clear, first of all, that any number greater than L belongs to the class B. And if there were a number $L' < L$ belonging to the class B, then every number greater than L' would belong to the class B. Hence every number less than L belongs to the class A, every number greater than L belongs to the class B, and L itself may belong to either of the two classes.

† The word "closed" is used merely for emphasis. See § 2. — TRANS.

$\Delta = M - m$ is called the *oscillation* of the function $f(x)$ in the interval (a, b).

These definitions lead to several remarks. In order that a function be finite in a closed interval (a, b) it is not sufficient that it should have a finite value for every value of x. Thus the function defined in the closed interval $(0, 1)$ as follows:

$$f(0) = 0, \qquad f(x) = 1/x \quad \text{for} \quad x > 0,$$

has a finite value for each value of x; but nevertheless it is not finite in the sense in which we have defined the word, for $f(x) > A$ if we take $x < 1/A$. Again, a function which is finite in the closed interval (a, b) may take on values which differ as little as we please from the upper limit M or from the lower limit m and still never assume these values themselves. For instance, the function $f(x)$, defined in the closed interval $(0, 1)$ by the relations

$$f(0) = 0, \qquad f(x) = 1 - x \quad \text{for} \quad 0 < x \leqq 1,$$

has the upper limit $M = 1$, but never reaches that limit.

70. Properties of continuous functions. We shall now turn to the study of continuous functions in particular.

THEOREM A. *Let $f(x)$ be a function which is continuous in the closed interval (a, b) and ϵ an arbitrary positive number. Then we can always break up the interval (a, b) into a certain number of partial intervals in such a way that for any two values of the variable whatever, x' and x'', which belong to the same partial interval, we always have $|f(x') - f(x'')| < \epsilon$.*

Suppose that this were not true. Then let $c = (a + b)/2$; at least one of the intervals (a, c), (c, b) would have the same property as (a, b); that is, it would be impossible to break it up into partial intervals which would satisfy the statement of the theorem. Substituting it for the given interval (a, b) and carrying out the reasoning as above (§ 68), we could form an infinite sequence of intervals (a, b), (a_1, b_1), (a_2, b_2), $\cdots$, each of which is half the preceding and has the same property as the original interval (a, b). For any value of n we could always find in the interval (a_n, b_n) two numbers x' and x'' such that $|f(x') - f(x'')|$ would be larger than ϵ. Now let λ be the common limit of the two sequences of numbers $a, a_1, a_2, \cdots$ and $b, b_1, b_2, \cdots$. Since the function $f(x)$ is continuous for $x = \lambda$, we can find a number η such that $|f(x) - f(\lambda)| < \epsilon/2$

whenever $|x - \lambda|$ is less than η. Let us choose n so large that both a_n and b_n differ from λ by less than η. Then the interval (a_n, b_n) will lie wholly within the interval $(\lambda - \eta, \lambda + \eta)$; and if x' and x'' are any two values whatever in the interval (a_n, b_n), we must have

$$|f(x') - f(\lambda)| < \epsilon/2, \quad |f(x'') - f(\lambda)| < \epsilon/2,$$

and hence $|f(x') - f(x'')| < \epsilon$. It follows that the hypothesis made above leads to a contradiction; hence the theorem is proved.

Corollary I. Let $a, x_1, x_2, \cdots, x_{p-1}, b$ be a method of subdivision of the interval (a, b) into p subintervals, which satisfies the conditions of the theorem. In the interval (a, x_1) we shall have $|f(x)| < |f(a)| + \epsilon$; and, in particular, $|f(x_1)| < |f(a)| + \epsilon$. Likewise, in the interval (x_1, x_2) we shall have $|f(x)| < |f(x_1)| + \epsilon$, and, *a fortiori*, $|f(x)| < |f(a)| + 2\epsilon$; in particular, for $x = x_2$, $|f(x_2)| < |f(a)| + 2\epsilon$; and so forth. For the last interval we shall have

$$|f(x)| < |f(x_{p-1})| + \epsilon < |f(a)| + p\epsilon.$$

Hence the absolute value of $f(x)$ in the interval (a, b) always remains less than $|f(a)| + p\epsilon$. *It follows that every function which is continuous in a closed interval (a, b) is finite in that interval.*

Corollary II. Let us suppose the interval (a, b) split up into p subintervals $(a, x_1), (x_1, x_2), \cdots, (x_{p-1}, b)$ such that $|f(x') - f(x'')| < \epsilon/2$ for any two values of x which belong to the same closed subinterval. Let η be a positive number less than any of the differences $x_1 - a$, $x_2 - x_1 \cdots, b - x_{p-1}$. Then let us take any two numbers whatever in the interval (a, b) for which $|x' - x''| < \eta$, and let us try to find an upper limit for $|f(x') - f(x'')|$. If the two numbers x' and x'' fall in the same subinterval, we shall have $|f(x') - f(x'')| < \epsilon/2$. If they do not, x' and x'' must lie in two consecutive intervals, and it is easy to see that $|f(x') - f(x'')| < 2(\epsilon/2) = \epsilon$. Hence *corresponding to any positive number ϵ another positive number η can be found such that*

$$|f(x') - f(x'')| < \epsilon,$$

where x' and x'' are any two numbers of the interval (a, b) for which $|x' - x''| < \eta$. This property is also expressed by saying that the function $f(x)$ is *uniformly continuous* in the interval (a, b).

THEOREM B. *A function $f(x)$ which is continuous in a closed interval (a, b) takes on every value between $f(a)$ and $f(b)$ at least once for some value of x which lies between a and b.*

IV, §70] ALLIED GEOMETRICAL CONCEPTS **145**

Let us first consider a particular case. Suppose that $f(a)$ and $f(b)$ have opposite signs, — that $f(a) < 0$ and $f(b) > 0$, for instance. We shall then show that there exists at least one value of x between a and b for which $f(x) = 0$. Now $f(x)$ is negative near a and positive near b. Let us consider the assemblage of values of x between a and b for which $f(x)$ is positive, and let λ be the lower limit of this assemblage $(a < \lambda < b)$. By the very definition of a lower limit $f(\lambda - h)$ is negative or zero for every positive value of h. Hence $f(\lambda)$, which is the limit of $f(\lambda - h)$, is also negative or zero. But $f(\lambda)$ cannot be negative. For suppose that $f(\lambda) = -m$, where m is a positive number. Since the function $f(x)$ is continuous for $x = \lambda$, a number η can be found such that $|f(x) - f(\lambda)| < m$ whenever $|x - \lambda| < \eta$, and the function $f(x)$ would be negative for all values of x between λ and $\lambda + \eta$. Hence λ could not be the lower limit of the values of x for which $f(x)$ is positive. Consequently $f(\lambda) = 0$.

Now let N be any number between $f(a)$ and $f(b)$. Then the function $\phi(x) = f(x) - N$ is continuous and has opposite signs for $x = a$ and $x = b$. Hence, by the particular case just treated, it vanishes at least once in the interval (a, b).

THEOREM C. *Every function which is continuous in a closed interval (a, b) actually assumes the value of its upper and of its lower limit at least once.*

In the first place, every continuous function, since we have already proved that it is finite, has an upper limit M and a lower limit m. Let us show, for instance, that $f(x) = M$ for at least one value of x in the interval (a, b).

Taking $c = (a + b)/2$, the upper limit of $f(x)$ is equal to M for at least one of the intervals (a, c), (c, b). Let us replace (a, b) by this new interval, repeat the process upon it, and so forth. Reasoning as we have already done several times, we could form an infinite sequence of intervals (a, b), (a_1, b_1), (a_2, b_2), $\cdots$, each of which is half the preceding and in each of which the upper limit of $f(x)$ is M. Then, if λ is the common limit of the sequences a, a_1, $\cdots$, a_n, $\cdots$ and b, b_1, $\cdots$, b_n, $\cdots$, $f(\lambda)$ *is equal to M.* For suppose that $f(\lambda) = M - h$, where h is positive. We can find a positive number η such that $f(x)$ remains between $f(\lambda) + h/2$ and $f(\lambda) - h/2$, and therefore less than $M - h/2$ as long as x remains between $\lambda - \eta$ and $\lambda + \eta$. Let us now choose n so great that a_n and b_n differ from their common limit λ by less than η. Then the interval (a_n, b_n) lies wholly inside the interval $(\lambda - \eta, \lambda + \eta)$, and it follows at once that the upper limit of $f(x)$ in the interval (a_n, b_n) could not be equal to M.

Combining this theorem with the preceding, we see that *any function which is continuous in a closed interval* (a, b) *assumes, at least once, every value between its upper and its lower limit.* Moreover theorem A may be stated as follows : *Given a function which is continuous in a closed interval* (a, b), *it is possible to divide the interval into such small subregions that the oscillation of the function in any one of them will be less than an arbitrarily assigned positive number.* For the oscillation of a continuous function is equal to the difference of the values of $f(x)$ for two particular values of the variable.

71. The sums S and s. Let $f(x)$ be a finite function, continuous or discontinuous, in the interval (a, b), where $a < b$. Let us suppose the interval (a, b) divided into a number of smaller partial intervals $(a, x_1), (x_1, x_2), \cdots, (x_{p-1}, b)$, where each of the numbers $x_1, x_2, \cdots, x_{p-1}$ is greater than the preceding. Let M and m be the limits of $f(x)$ in the original interval, and M_i and m_i the limits in the interval (x_{i-1}, x_i), and let us set

$$S = M_1(x_1 - a) + M_2(x_2 - x_1) + \cdots + M_p(b - x_{p-1}),$$
$$s = m_1(x_1 - a) + m_2(x_2 - x_1) + \cdots + m_p(b - x_{p-1}).$$

To every method of division of (a, b) into smaller intervals there corresponds a sum S and a smaller sum s. It is evident that none of the sums S are less than $m(b - a)$, for none of the numbers M_i are less than m; hence these sums S have a lower limit I.* Likewise, the sums s, none of which exceed $M(b - a)$ have an upper limit I'. We proceed to show that I' *is at most equal to* I. For this purpose it is evidently sufficient to show that $s \leq S'$ and $s' \leq S$, where S, s and S', s' are the two sets of sums which correspond to any two given methods of subdivision of the interval (a, b).

In the first place, let us suppose each of the subintervals (a, x_1), (x_1, x_2), $\cdots$ redivided into still smaller intervals by new points of division and let

$$a, y_1, y_2, \cdots, y_{k-1}, x_1, y_{k+1}, \cdots, y_{l-1}, x_2, y_{l+1}, \cdots, b$$

---

* If $f(x)$ is a constant, $S = s$, $M = m$, and, in general, all the inequalities mentioned become equations. — TRANS.

be the new suite thus obtained. This new method of subdivision is called *consecutive* to the first. Let Σ and σ denote the sums analogous to S and s with respect to this new method of division of the interval (a, b), and let us compare S and s with Σ and σ. Let us compare, for example, the portions of the two sums S and Σ which arise from the interval (a, x_1). Let M_1' and m_1' be the limits of $f(x)$ in the interval (a, y_1), M_2' and m_2' the limits in the interval (y_1, y_2), $\cdots$, M_k' and m_k' the limits in the interval (y_{k-1}, x_1). Then the portion of Σ which comes from (a, x_1) is

$$M_1'(y_1 - a) + M_2'(y_2 - y_1) + \cdots + M_k'(x_1 - y_{k-1});$$

and since the numbers M_1', M_2', $\cdots$, M_k' cannot exceed M_1, it is clear that the above sum is at most equal to $M_1(x_1 - a)$. Likewise, the portion of Σ which arises from the interval (x_1, x_2) is at most equal to $M_2(x_2 - x_1)$, and so on. Adding all these inequalities, we find that $\Sigma \leqq S$, and it is easy to show in like manner that $\sigma \geqq s$.

Let us now consider any two methods of subdivision whatever, and let S, s and S', s' be the corresponding sums. Superimposing the points of division of these two methods of subdivision, we get a third method of subdivision, which may be considered as consecutive to either of the two given methods. Let Σ and σ be the sums with respect to this auxiliary division. By the above we have the relations

$$\Sigma \leqq S, \quad \sigma \geqq s, \quad \Sigma \leqq S', \quad \sigma \geqq s';$$

and, since Σ is not less than σ, it follows that $s' \leqq S$ and $s \leqq S'$. Since none of the sums S are less than any of the sums s, the limit I cannot be less than the limit I'; that is, $I \geqq I'$.

72. Integrable functions. A function which is finite in an interval (a, b) is said to be *integrable* in that interval if the two sums S and s approach the same limit when the number of the partial intervals is indefinitely increased in such a way that each of those partial intervals approaches zero.

The necessary and sufficient condition that a function be integrable in an interval is that corresponding to any positive number ϵ another number η exists such that $S - s$ is less than ϵ whenever each of the partial intervals is less than η.

This condition is, first, *necessary*, for if S and s have the same limit I, we can find a number η so small that $|S - I|$ and $|s - I|$ are each less than $\epsilon/2$ whenever each of the partial intervals is less than η. Then, *a fortiori*, $S - s$ is less than ϵ.

Moreover the condition is *sufficient*, for we may write *

$$S - s = S - I + I - I' + I' - s,$$

and since none of the numbers $S - I$, $I - I'$, $I' - s$ can be negative, each of them must be less than ϵ if their sum is to be less than ϵ. But since $I - I'$ is a fixed number and ϵ is an arbitrary positive number, it follows that we must have $I' = I$. Moreover $S - I < \epsilon$ and $I - s < \epsilon$ whenever each of the partial intervals is less than η, which is equivalent to saying that S and s have the same limit I.

The function $f(x)$ is then said to be *integrable* in the interval (a, b), and the limit I is called a *definite integral*. It is represented by the symbol

$$I = \int_a^b f(x)\, dx,$$

which suggests its origin, and which is read "the *definite integral* from a to b of $f(x)\, dx$." By its very definition I always lies between the two sums S and s for any method of subdivision whatever. If any number between S and s be taken as an approximate value of I, the error never exceeds $S - s$.

Every continuous function is integrable.

The difference $S - s$ is less than or equal to $(b - a)\omega$, where ω denotes the upper limit of the oscillation of $f(x)$ in the partial intervals. But η may be so chosen that the oscillation is less than a preassigned positive number in any interval less than η (§ 70). If then η be so chosen that the oscillation is less than $\epsilon/(b - a)$, the difference $S - s$ will be less than ϵ.

Any monotonically increasing or monotonically decreasing function in an interval is integrable in that interval.

A function $f(x)$ is said to *increase monotonically* in a given interval (a, b) if for any two values x', x'' in that interval $f(x') \geqq f(x'')$ whenever $x' > x''$. The function may be constant in certain portions of the interval, but if it is not constant it must increase with x. Dividing the interval (a, b) into n subintervals, each less than η, we may write

$$S = f(x_1)(x_1 - a) + f(x_2)(x_2 - x_1) + \cdots + f(b)(b - x_{n-1}),$$
$$s = f(a)(x_1 - a) + f(x_1)(x_2 - x_1) + \cdots + f(x_{n-1})(b - x_{n-1}),$$

---

* For the proof that I and I' exist, see § 73, which may be read before § 72. — TRANS.

for the upper limit of $f(x)$ in the interval (a, x_1), for instance, is precisely $f(x_1)$, the lower limit $f(a)$; and so on for the other subintervals. Hence, subtracting,

$$S - s = (x_1 - a)[f(x_1) - f(a)] + (x_2 - x_1)[f(x_2) - f(x_1)]$$
$$+ \cdots + (b - x_{n-1})[f(b) - f(x_{n-1})].$$

None of the differences which occur in the right-hand side of this equation are negative, and all of the differences $x_1 - a$, $x_2 - x_1$, $\cdots$ are less than η; consequently

$$S - s < \eta[f(x_1) - f(a) + f(x_2) - f(x_1) + \cdots + f(b) - f(x_{n-1})],$$

or

$$S - s < \eta[f(b) - f(a)],$$

and we need only take

$$\eta < \frac{\epsilon}{f(b) - f(a)}$$

in order to make $S - s < \epsilon$. The reasoning is the same for a monotonically decreasing function.

Let us return to the general case. In the definition of the integral the sums S and s may be replaced by more general expressions. Given any method of subdivision of the interval (a, b):

$$a, \ x_1, \ x_2, \ \cdots, \ x_{i-1}, \ x_i, \ \cdots, \ x_{n-1}, \ b;$$

let $\xi_1, \xi_2, \cdots, \xi_i, \cdots$ be values belonging to these intervals in order $(x_{i-1} \leqq \xi_i \leqq x_i)$. Then the sum

$$(2) \quad \begin{cases} \displaystyle\sum_{i=1}^{n} f(\xi_i)(x_i - x_{i-1}) = \\ f(\xi_1)(x_1 - a) + f(\xi_2)(x_2 - x_1) + \cdots + f(\xi_n)(b - x_{n-1}) \end{cases}$$

evidently lies between the sums S and s, for we always have $m_i \leqq f(\xi_i) \leqq M_i$. If the function is integrable, this new sum has the limit I. In particular, if we suppose that $\xi_1, \xi_2, \cdots, \xi_n$ coincide with $a, x_1, \cdots, x_{n-1}$, respectively, the sum (2) reduces to the sum (1) considered above (§ 65).

There are several propositions which result immediately from the definition of the integral. We have supposed that $a < b$; if we now interchange these two limits a and b, each of the factors $x_i - x_{i-1}$ changes sign; hence

$$\int_a^b f(x)\,dx = -\int_b^a f(x)\,dx.$$

It also evidently follows from the definition that

$$\int_a^b f(x)\,dx = \int_a^c f(x)\,dx + \int_c^b f(x)\,dx,$$

at least if c lies between a and b; the same formula still holds when b lies between a and c, for instance, provided that the function $f(x)$ is integrable between a and c, for it may be written in the form

$$\int_a^c f(x)\,dx = \int_a^b f(x)\,dx - \int_c^b f(x)\,dx = \int_a^b f(x)\,dx + \int_b^c f(x)\,dx.$$

If $f(x) = A\phi(x) + B\psi(x)$, where A and B are any two constants, we have

$$\int_a^b f(x)\,dx = A\int_a^b \phi(x)\,dx + B\int_a^b \psi(x)\,dx,$$

and a similar formula holds for the sum of any number of functions.

The expression $f(\xi_i)$ in (2) may be replaced by a still more general expression. The interval (a, b) being divided into n subintervals $(a, x_1), \cdots, (x_{i-1}, x_i), \cdots$, let us associate with each of the subintervals a quantity ζ_i, which approaches zero with the length $x_i - x_{i-1}$ of the subinterval in question. We shall say that ζ_i approaches zero *uniformly* if corresponding to every positive number ϵ another positive number η can be found independent of i and such that $|\zeta_i| < \epsilon$ whenever $x_i - x_{i-1}$ is less than η. We shall now proceed to show that the sum

$$S' = \sum_{i=1}^n \left[f(x_{i-1}) + \zeta_i \right](x_i - x_{i-1})$$

approaches the definite integral $\int_a^b f(x)\,dx$ as its limit provided that ζ_i approaches zero uniformly. For suppose that η is a number so small that the two inequalities

$$\left| \sum_{i=1}^n f(x_{i-1})(x_i - x_{i-1}) - \int_a^b f(x)\,dx \right| < \epsilon, \quad |\zeta_i| < \epsilon$$

are satisfied whenever each of the subintervals $x_i - x_{i-1}$ is less than η. Then we may write

$$S' - \int_a^b f(x)\,dx =$$
$$\left[\sum_{i=1}^n f(x_{i-1})(x_i - x_{i-1}) - \int_a^b f(x)\,dx \right] + \sum_{i=1}^n \zeta_i(x_i - x_{i-1}),$$

and it is clear that we shall have

$$\left| S' - \int_a^b f(x)\,dx \right| < \epsilon + \epsilon(b-a)$$

whenever each of the subintervals is less than η.   Thus the theorem is proved.*

73. Darboux's theorem.   Given any function $f(x)$ which is *finite* in an interval (a, b); the sums S and s approach their limits I and I', respectively, when the number of subintervals increases indefinitely in such a way that each of them approaches zero.   Let us prove this for the sum S, for instance.   We shall suppose that $a < b$, and that $f(x)$ is positive in the interval (a, b), which can be brought about by adding a suitable constant to $f(x)$, which, in turn, amounts to adding a constant to each of the sums S.   Then, since the number I is the lower limit of all the sums S, we can find a particular method of subdivision, say

$$a,\ x_1,\ x_2,\ \cdots,\ x_{p-1},\ b,$$

for which the sum S is less than $I + \epsilon/2$, where ϵ is a preassigned positive number.   Let us now consider a division of (a, b) into intervals less than η, and let us try to find an upper limit of the corresponding sum S'.   Taking first those intervals which do not include any of the points $x_1, x_2, \cdots, x_{p-1}$, and recalling the reasoning of § 71, it is clear that the portion of S' which comes from these intervals will be less than the original sum S, that is, less than $I + \epsilon/2$.   On the other hand, the number of intervals which include a point of the set $x_1, x_2, \cdots, x_{p-1}$ cannot exceed $p - 1$, and hence their contribution to the sum S' cannot exceed $(p - 1)M\eta$, where M is the upper limit of $f(x)$.   Hence

$$S' < I + \epsilon/2 + (p-1)M\eta,$$

and we need only choose η less than $\epsilon/2\,M(p-1)$ in order to make S' less than $I + \epsilon$.   Hence the lower limit I of *all* the sums S is also the limit of any sequence of S's which corresponds to uniformly infinitesimal subintervals.

It may be shown in a similar manner that the sums s have the limit I'. If the function $f(x)$ is any function whatever, these two limits I and I' are in general different.   In order that the function be integrable it is necessary and sufficient that $I' = I$.

74. First law of the mean for integrals.   From now on we shall assume, unless something is explicitly said to the contrary, that the functions under the integral sign are continuous.

---

* The above theorem can be extended without difficulty to double and triple integrals ; we shall make use of it in several places (§§ 80, 95, 97, 131, 144, etc.).

The proposition is essentially only an application of a theorem of Duhamel's according to which the limit of a sum of infinitesimals remains unchanged when each of the infinitesimals is replaced by another infinitesimal which differs from the given infinitesimal by an infinitesimal of higher order.   (See an article by W. F. Osgood, *Annals of Mathematics*, 2d series, Vol. IV, pp. 161–178 : *The Integral as the Limit of a Sum and a Theorem of Duhamel's*.)

Let $f(x)$ and $\phi(x)$ be two functions which are each continuous in the interval (a, b), one of which, say $\phi(x)$, has the same sign throughout the interval. And we shall suppose further, for the sake of definiteness, that $a < b$ and $\phi(x) > 0$.

Suppose the interval (a, b) divided into subintervals, and let $\xi_1, \xi_2, \cdots, \xi_i, \cdots$ be values of x which belong to each of these smaller intervals in order. All the quantities $f(\xi_i)$ lie between the limits M and m of $f(x)$ in the interval (a, b):

$$m \leq f(\xi_i) \leq M.$$

Let us multiply each of these inequalities by the factors

$$\phi(\xi_i)(x_i - x_{i-1}),$$

respectively, which are all positive by hypothesis, and then add them together. The sum $\Sigma f(\xi_i) \phi(\xi_i)(x_i - x_{i-1})$ evidently lies between the two sums $m\Sigma \phi(\xi_i)(x_i - x_{i-1})$ and $M\Sigma \phi(\xi_i)(x_i - x_{i-1})$. Hence, as the number of subintervals increases indefinitely, we have, in the limit,

$$m \int_a^b \phi(x)\,dx \leq \int_a^b f(x)\phi(x)\,dx \leq M \int_a^b \phi(x)\,dx,$$

which may be written

$$\int_a^b f(x)\phi(x)\,dx = \mu \int_a^b \phi(x)\,dx,$$

where μ lies between m and M. Since the function $f(x)$ is continuous, it assumes the value μ for some value ξ of the variable which lies between a and b; and hence we may write the preceding equation in the form

$$(3) \qquad \int_a^b f(x)\phi(x)\,dx = f(\xi) \int_a^b \phi(x)\,dx,$$

where ξ lies between a and b.* If, in particular, $\phi(x) = 1$, the integral $\int_a^b dx$ reduces to $(b - a)$ by the very definition of an integral, and the formula becomes

$$(4) \qquad \int_a^b f(x)\,dx = (b - a)f(\xi).$$

---

* The lower sign holds in the preceding relations only when $f(x) = k$. It is evident that the formula still holds, however, and that $a < \xi < b$ in any case. — TRANS.

75. Second law of the mean for integrals. There is a second formula, due to Bonnet, which he deduced from an important lemma of Abel's.

Lemma. *Let* $\epsilon_0, \epsilon_1, \cdots, \epsilon_p$ *be a set of monotonically decreasing positive quantities, and* $u_0, u_1, \cdots, u_p$ *the same number of arbitrary positive or negative quantities. If* A *and* B *are respectively the greatest and the least of all of the sums* $s_0 = u_0$, $s_1 = u_0 + u_1, \cdots, s_p = u_0 + u_1 + \cdots + u_p$, *the sum*

$$S = \epsilon_0 u_0 + \epsilon_1 u_1 + \cdots + \epsilon_p u_p$$

will lie between $A\epsilon_0$ *and* $B\epsilon_0$, *i.e.* $A\epsilon_0 \geqq S \geqq B\epsilon_0$.

For we have

$$u_0 = s_0, \qquad u_1 = s_1 - s_0, \qquad \cdots, \qquad u_p = s_p - s_{p-1},$$

whence the sum S is equal to

$$s_0 (\epsilon_0 - \epsilon_1) + s_1 (\epsilon_1 - \epsilon_2) + \cdots + s_{p-1} (\epsilon_{p-1} - \epsilon_p) + s_p \epsilon_p.$$

Since none of the differences $\epsilon_0 - \epsilon_1, \epsilon_1 - \epsilon_2, \cdots, \epsilon_{p-1} - \epsilon_p$ are negative, two limits for S are given by replacing $s_0, s_1, \cdots, s_p$ by their upper limit A and then by their lower limit B. In this way we find

$$S \leqq A (\epsilon_0 - \epsilon_1 + \epsilon_1 - \epsilon_2 + \cdots + \epsilon_{p-1} - \epsilon_p + \epsilon_p) = A\epsilon_0,$$

and it is likewise evident that $S \geqq B\epsilon_0$.

Now let $f(x)$ and $\phi(x)$ be two continuous functions of x, one of which, $\phi(x)$, is a positive monotonically decreasing function in the interval $a \leqq x \leqq b$. Then the integral $\int_a^b f(x) \phi(x) \, dx$ is the limit of the sum

$$f(a) \phi(a) (x_1 - a) + f(x_1) \phi(x_1) (x_2 - x_1) + \cdots.$$

The numbers $\phi(a), \phi(x_1), \cdots$ form a set of monotonically decreasing positive numbers; hence the above sum, by the lemma, lies between $A\phi(a)$ and $B\phi(a)$, where A and B are respectively the greatest and the least among the following sums:

$$f(a) (x_1 - a),$$
$$f(a) (x_1 - a) + f(x_1) (x_2 - x_1),$$
$$\cdots \cdots \cdots \cdots \cdots \cdots,$$
$$f(a) (x_1 - a) + f(x_1) (x_2 - x_1) + \cdots + f(x_{n-1}) (b - x_{n-1}).$$

Passing to the limit, it is clear that the integral in question must lie between $A_1 \phi(a)$ and $B_1 \phi(a)$, where A_1 and B_1 denote the maximum and the minimum, respectively, of the integral $\int_a^c f(x) \, dx$, as c varies from a to b. Since this integral is evidently a continuous function of its upper limit c (§ 76), we may write the following formula:

$$(5) \qquad \int_a^b f(x) \phi(x) \, dx = \phi(a) \int_a^{\xi} f(x) \, dx, \qquad a \leqq \xi \leqq b.$$

When the function $\phi(x)$ is a monotonically decreasing function, without being always positive, there exists a more general formula, due to **Weierstrass**. In such a case let us set $\phi(x) = \phi(b) + \psi(x)$. Then $\psi(x)$ is a positive monotonically decreasing function. Applying the formula (5) to it, we find

$$\int_a^b f(x) \psi(x) \, dx = [\phi(a) - \phi(b)] \int_a^{\xi} f(x) \, dx.$$

From this it is easy to derive the formula

$$\int_a^b f(x)\,\phi(x)\,dx = \int_a^b f(x)\,\phi(b)\,dx + [\phi(a) - \phi(b)]\int_a^\xi f(x)\,dx,$$

or

$$\int_a^b f(x)\,\phi(x)\,dx = \phi(a)\int_a^\xi f(x)\,dx + \phi(b)\int_\xi^b f(x)\,dx.$$

Similar formulæ exist for the case when the function $\phi(x)$ is increasing.

76. Return to primitive functions. We are now in a position to give a purely analytic proof of the fundamental existence theorem (§ 67). Let $f(x)$ be any continuous function. Then the definite integral

$$F(x) = \int_a^x f(t)\,dt,$$

where the limit a is regarded as fixed, is a function of the upper limit x. We proceed to show that *the derivative of this function is $f(x)$.* In the first place, we have

$$F(x + h) - F(x) = \int_x^{x+h} f(t)\,dt,$$

or, applying the first law of the mean (4),

$$F(x + h) - F(x) = hf(\xi),$$

where ξ lies between x and $x + h$. As h approaches zero, $f(\xi)$ approaches $f(x)$; hence the derivative of the function $F(x)$ is $f(x)$, which was to be proved.

All other functions which have this same derivative are given by adding an arbitrary constant C to $F(x)$. There is one such function, and only one, which assumes a preassigned value y_0 for $x = a$, namely, the function

$$y_0 + \int_a^x f(t)\,dt.$$

When there is no reason to fear ambiguity the same letter x is used to denote the upper limit and the variable of integration, and $\int_a^x f(x)\,dx$ is written in place of $\int_a^x f(t)\,dt$. But it is evident that a definite integral depends only upon the limits of integration and the form of the function under the sign of integration. The letter which denotes the variable of integration is absolutely immaterial.

Every function whose derivative is $f(x)$ is called an *indefinite integral* of $f(x)$, or a *primitive function* of $f(x)$, and is represented by the symbol

$$\int f(x)\,dx,$$

the limits not being indicated.   By the above we evidently have

$$\int f(x)\,dx = \int_a^x f(x)\,dx + C.$$

Conversely, if a function $F(x)$ whose derivative is $f(x)$ can be discovered by any method whatever, we may write

$$\int_a^x f(x)\,dx = F(x) + C.$$

In order to determine the constant C we need only note that the left-hand side vanishes for $x = a$.   Hence $C = -F(a)$, and the fundamental formula becomes

$$(6) \qquad \int_a^x f(x)\,dx = F(x) - F(a).$$

If in this formula $f(x)$ be replaced by $F'(x)$, it becomes

$$F(x) - F(a) = \int_a^x F'(x)\,dx,$$

or, applying the first law of the mean for integrals,

$$F(x) - F(a) = (x - a)\,F'(\xi),$$

where ξ lies between a and x.   This constitutes a new proof of the law of the mean for derivatives; but it is less general than the one given in section 8, for it is assumed here that the derivative $F'(x)$ is continuous.

We shall consider in the next chapter the simpler classes of functions whose primitives are known.   Just now we will merely state a few of those which are apparent at once :

$$\int A(x-a)^\alpha\,dx = A\,\frac{(x-a)^{\alpha+1}}{\alpha+1} + C, \qquad \alpha + 1 \neq 0;$$

$$\int A\,\frac{dx}{x-a} = A\log(x-a) + C;$$

$$\int \cos x\,dx = \sin x + C; \qquad \int \sin x\,dx = -\cos x + C;$$

$$\int e^{mx}\,dx = \frac{e^{mx}}{m} + C, \qquad m \neq 0;$$

$$\int \frac{dx}{1+x^2} = \text{arc tan } x + C; \qquad\qquad \int \frac{dx}{\sqrt{1-x^2}} = \text{arc sin } x + C;$$

$$\int \frac{dx}{\sqrt{x^2+A}} = \log(x + \sqrt{x^2+A}) + C; \quad \int \frac{f'(x)\,dx}{f(x)} = \log f(x) + C.$$

The proof of the fundamental formula (6) was based upon the assumption that the function $f(x)$ was continuous in the closed interval (a, b). If this condition be disregarded, results may be obtained which are paradoxical. Taking $f(x) = 1/x^2$, for instance, the formula (6) gives

$$\int_a^b \frac{dx}{x^2} = \frac{1}{a} - \frac{1}{b}.$$

The left-hand side of this equality has no meaning in our present system unless a and b have the same sign; but the right-hand side has a perfectly determinate value, even when a and b have different signs. We shall find the explanation of this paradox later in the study of definite integrals taken between imaginary limits.

Similarly, the formula (6) leads to the equation

$$\int_a^b \frac{f'(x)\,dx}{f(x)} = \log \left[\frac{f(b)}{f(a)} \right].$$

If $f(a)$ and $f(b)$ have opposite signs, $f(x)$ vanishes between a and b, and neither side of the above equality has any meaning for us at present. We shall find later the signification which it is convenient to give them.

Again, the formula (6) may lead to ambiguity. Thus, if $f(x) = 1/(1+x^2)$, we find

$$\int_a^b \frac{dx}{1+x^2} = \text{arc tan } b - \text{arc tan } a.$$

Here the left-hand side is perfectly determinate, while the right-hand side has an infinite number of determinations. To avoid this ambiguity, let us consider the function

$$F(x) = \int_0^x \frac{dx}{1+x^2}.$$

This function $F(x)$ is continuous in the whole interval and vanishes with x. Let us denote by arc tan x, on the other hand, an angle between $-\pi/2$ and $+\pi/2$. These two functions have the same derivative and they both vanish for $x = 0$. It follows that they are equal, and we may write the equality

$$\int_a^b \frac{dx}{1 + x^2} = \int_0^b \frac{dx}{1 + x^2} - \int_0^a \frac{dx}{1 + x^2} = \text{arc tan } b - \text{arc tan } a,$$

where the value to be assigned the arctangent always lies between $-\pi/2$ and $+\pi/2$.

In a similar manner we may derive the formula

$$\int_a^b \frac{dx}{\sqrt{1 - x^2}} = \text{arc sin } b - \text{arc sin } a,$$

where the radical is to be taken positive, where a and b each lie between -1 and $+1$, and where arc sin x denotes an angle which lies between $-\pi/2$ and $+\pi/2$.

77. Indices. In general, when the primitive $F(x)$ is multiply determinate, we should choose one of the initial values $F(a)$ and follow the continuous variation of this branch as x varies from a to b. Let us consider, for instance, the integral

$$\int_a^b \frac{P'Q - PQ'}{P^2 + Q^2} dx = \int_a^b \frac{f'(x)}{1 + f^2(x)} dx,$$

where

$$f(x) = \frac{P}{Q}$$

and where P and Q are two functions which are both continuous in the interval (a, b) and which do not both vanish at the same time. If Q does not vanish between a and b, $f(x)$ does not become infinite, and arc tan $f(x)$ remains between $-\pi/2$ and $+\pi/2$. But this is no longer true, in general, if the equation $Q = 0$ has roots in this interval. In order to see how the formula must be modified, let us retain the convention that arc tan signifies an angle between $-\pi/2$ and $+\pi/2$, and let us suppose, in the first place, that Q vanishes just once between a and b for a value $x = c$. We may write the integral in the form

$$\int_a^b \frac{f'(x)\, dx}{1 + f^2(x)} = \int_a^{c-\epsilon} + \int_{c-\epsilon}^{c+\epsilon'} + \int_{c+\epsilon'}^b,$$

where ϵ and ϵ' are two very small positive numbers. Since $f(x)$ does not become infinite between a and $c - \epsilon$, nor between $c + \epsilon'$ and b, this may again be written

$$\int_a^b \frac{f'dx}{1 + f^2} = \text{arc tan } f(c - \epsilon) - \text{arc tan } f(a)$$
$$+ \text{arc tan } f(b) - \text{arc tan } f(c + \epsilon') + \int_{c-\epsilon}^{c+\epsilon'}.$$

Several cases may now present themselves. Suppose, for the sake of definiteness, that $f(x)$ becomes infinite by passing from $+\infty$ to $-\infty$. Then $f(c - \epsilon)$ will be positive and very large, and arc tan $f(c - \epsilon)$ will be very near to $\pi/2$; while

$f(c + \epsilon')$ will be negative and very large, and arc tan $f(c + \epsilon')$ will be very near $-\pi/2$. Also, the integral $\int_{c-\epsilon}^{c+\epsilon'}$ will be very small in absolute value; and, passing to the limit, we obtain the formula

$$\int_a^b \frac{f'(x)\,dx}{1 + f^2(x)} = \pi + \text{arc tan} f(b) - \text{arc tan} f(a).$$

Similarly, it is easy to show that it would be necessary to *subtract* π if $f(x)$ passed from $-\infty$ to $+\infty$. In the general case we would divide the interval (a, b) into subintervals in such a way that $f(x)$ would become infinite just once in each of them. Treating each of these subintervals in the above manner and adding the results obtained, we should find the formula

$$\int_a^b \frac{f'(x)\,dx}{1 + f^2(x)} = \text{arc tan} f(b) - \text{arc tan} f(a) + (K - K')\,\pi,$$

where K denotes the number of times that $f(x)$ becomes infinite by passing from $+\infty$ to $-\infty$, and K' the number of times that $f(x)$ passes from $-\infty$ to $+\infty$. The number $K - K'$ is called the *index* of the function $f(x)$ between a and b.

When $f(x)$ reduces to a rational function V_1/V, this index may be calculated by elementary processes without knowing the roots of V. It is clear that we may suppose V_1 prime to and of less degree than V, for the removal of a polynomial does not affect the index. Let us then consider the series of divisions necessary to determine the greatest common divisor of V and V_1, the sign of the remainder being changed each time. First, we would divide V by V_1, obtaining a quotient Q_1 and a remainder $- V_2$. Then we would divide V_1 by V_2, obtaining a quotient Q_2 and a remainder $- V_3$; and so on. Finally we should obtain a constant remainder $- V_{n+1}$. These operations give the following set of equations:

$$\begin{aligned} V &= V_1 Q_1 - V_2, \\ V_1 &= V_2 Q_2 - V_3, \\ &\cdots\cdots\cdots\cdots, \\ V_{n-1} &= V_n Q_n - V_{n+1}. \end{aligned}$$

The sequence of polynomials

$$(7) \quad V, \quad V_1, \quad V_2, \quad \cdots, \quad V_{r-1}, \quad V_r, \quad V_{r+1}, \quad \cdots, \quad V_n, \quad V_{n+1}$$

has the essential characteristics of a Sturm sequence: 1) two consecutive polynomials of the sequence cannot vanish simultaneously, for if they did, it could be shown successively that this value of x would cause all the other polynomials to vanish, in particular V_{n+1}; 2) when one of the intermediate polynomials V_1, V_2, $\cdots$, V_n vanishes, the number of changes of sign in the series (7) is not altered, for if V_r vanishes for $x = c$, V_{r-1} and V_{r+1} have different signs for $x = c$. It follows that the number of changes of sign in the series (7) remains the same, except when x passes through a root of $V = 0$. If V_1/V passes from $+\infty$ to $-\infty$, this number increases by one, but it diminishes by one on the other hand if V_1/V passes from $-\infty$ to $+\infty$. Hence the index is equal to the difference of the number of changes of sign in the series (7) for $x = b$ and $x = a$.

78. Area of a curve. We can now give a purely analytic definition of the area bounded by a continuous plane curve, the area of the rectangle only being considered known. For this purpose we need

only translate into geometrical language the results of § 72. Let
$f(x)$ be a function which is continuous in the closed interval (a, b),
and let us suppose for definiteness that $a < b$ and that $f(x) > 0$ in
the interval. Let us consider, as above (Fig. 9, § 65), the portion of
the plane bounded by the contour $AMBB_0A_0$, composed of the segment A_0B_0 of the x axis, the straight lines AA_0 and BB_0 parallel to
the y axis, and having the abscissæ a and b, and the arc of the curve
AMB whose equation is $y = f(x)$. Let us mark off on A_0B_0 a certain
number of points of division $P_1, P_2, \cdots, P_{i-1}, P_i, \cdots$, whose abscissæ
are $x_1, x_2, \cdots, x_{i-1}, x_i, \cdots$, and through these points let us draw
parallels to the y axis which meet the arc AMB in the points
$Q_1, Q_2, \cdots, Q_{i-1}, Q_i, \cdots$, respectively. Let us then consider, in
particular, the portion of the plane bounded by the contour
$Q_{i-1}Q_iP_iP_{i-1}Q_{i-1}$, and let us mark upon the arc $Q_{i-1}Q_i$ the highest
and the lowest points, that is, the points which correspond to the
maximum M_i and to the minimum m_i of $f(x)$ in the interval
(x_{i-1}, x_i). (In the figure the lowest point coincides with Q_{i-1}.)
Let R_i be the area of the rectangle $P_{i-1}P_is_is_{i-1}$ erected upon the
base $P_{i-1}P_i$ with the altitude M_i, and let r_i be the area of the
rectangle $P_{i-1}P_iq_iQ_{i-1}$ erected upon the base $P_{i-1}P_i$ with the altitude m_i. Then we have

$$R_i = M_i(x_i - x_{i-1}), \quad r_i = m_i(x_i - x_{i-1}),$$

and the results found above (§ 72) may now be stated as follows :
whatever be the points of division, there exists a fixed number I
which is always less than ΣR_i and greater than Σr_i, and the two
sums ΣR_i and Σr_i approach I as the number of subintervals $P_{i-1}P_i$
increases in such a way that each of them approaches zero. We shall
call this common limit I of the two sums ΣR_i and Σr_i *the area of
the portion of the plane bounded by the contour $AMBB_0A_0A$.* Thus
the area under consideration is defined to be equal to the definite
integral $\int_a^b f(x)\,dx$.

This definition agrees with the ordinary notion of the area of a
plane curve. For one of the clearest points of this rather vague
notion is that the area bounded by the contour $P_{i-1}P_iQ_in_iQ_{i-1}P_{i-1}$
lies between the two areas R_i and r_i of the two rectangles $P_{i-1}P_is_is_{i-1}$
and $P_{i-1}P_iq_iQ_{i-1}$; hence the total area bounded by the contour
$AMBB_0A_0A$ must surely be a quantity which lies between the two
sums ΣR_i and Σr_i. But the definite integral I is the *only fixed* quantity which always lies between these two sums for any mode of
subdivision of A_0B_0, since it is the common limit of ΣR_i and Σr_i.

The given area may also be defined in an infinite number of other ways as the limit of a sum of rectangles. Thus we have seen that the definite integral I is also the limit of the sum

$$\Sigma(x_i - x_{i-1})f(\xi_i),$$

where ξ_i is any value whatever in the interval (x_{i-1}, x_i). But the element

$$(x_i - x_{i-1})f(\xi_i)$$

of this sum represents the area of a rectangle whose base is $P_{i-1}P_i$ and whose altitude is the ordinate of any point of the arc $Q_{i-1}n_iQ_i$. It should be noticed also that the definite integral I represents the area, whatever be the position of the arc AMB with respect to the x axis, provided that we adopt the convention made in § 67. Every definite integral therefore represents an area; hence the calculation of such an integral is called a *quadrature*.

The notion of area thus having been made rigorous once for all, there remains no reason why it should not be used in certain arguments which it renders nearly intuitive. For instance, it is perfectly clear that the area considered above lies between the areas of the two rectangles which have the common base A_0B_0, and which have the least and the greatest of the ordinates of the arc AMB, respectively, as their altitudes. It is therefore equal to the area of a rectangle whose base is A_0B_0 and whose altitude is the ordinate of a properly chosen point upon the arc AMB, — which is a restatement of the first law of the mean for integrals.

79. The following remark is also important. Let $f(x)$ be a function which is finite in the interval (a, b) and which is discontinuous

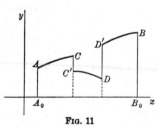

FIG. 11

in the manner described below for a finite number of values between a and b. Let us suppose that $f(x)$ is continuous from c to $c+k\,(k>0)$, and that $f(c + \epsilon)$ approaches a certain limit, which we shall denote by $f(c + 0)$, as ϵ approaches zero through positive values; and likewise let us suppose that $f(x)$ is continuous between $c-k$ and c and that $f(c - \epsilon)$ approaches a limit $f(c - 0)$ as ϵ approaches zero through positive values. If the two limits $f(c + 0)$ and $f(c - 0)$ are different, the function $f(x)$ is discontinuous for $x = c$. It is usually agreed to take for $f(c)$ the value $[f(c + 0) + f(c - 0)]/2$.   If the function $f(x)$ has a certain number of points of discontinuity of this kind, it will be represented graphically by several distinct arcs AC, $C'D$, $D'B$. Let c and d, for example, be the abscissæ of the points of discontinuity. Then we shall write

$$\int_a^b f(x)\,dx = \int_a^c f(x)\,dx + \int_c^d f(x)\,dx + \int_d^b f(x)\,dx,$$

in accordance with the definitions of §72. Geometrically, this definite integral represents the area bounded by the contour $ACC'DD'BB_0A_0A$.

If the upper limit b now be replaced by the variable x, the definite integral

$$F(x) = \int_a^x f(x)\,dx$$

is still a continuous function of x. In a point x where $f(x)$ is continuous we still have $F'(x) = f(x)$. For a point of discontinuity, $x = c$ for example, we shall have

$$F(c + h) - F(c) = \int_c^{c+h} f(x)\,dx = hf(c + \theta h), \qquad 0 < \theta < 1,$$

and the ratio $[F(c + h) - F(c)]/h$ approaches $f(c + 0)$ or $f(c - 0)$ according as h is positive or negative. This is an example of a function $F(x)$ whose derivative has two distinct values for certain values of the variable.

80. Length of a curvilinear arc. Given a curvilinear arc AB; let us take a certain number of intermediate points on this arc, m_1, m_2, $\cdots$, m_{n-1}, and let us construct the broken line $Am_1m_2 \cdots m_{n-1}B$ by connecting each pair of consecutive points by a straight line.

If the length of the perimeter of this broken line approaches a limit as the number of sides increases in such a way that each of them approaches zero, this limit is defined to be the *length of the arc AB*.

Let

$$x = f(t), \quad y = \phi(t), \quad z = \psi(t)$$

be the rectangular coördinates of a point of the arc AB expressed in terms of a parameter t, and let us suppose that as t varies from a to $b\,(a < b)$ the functions f, ϕ, and ψ are continuous and possess continuous first derivatives, and that the point (x, y, z) describes the arc AB without changing the sense of its motion. Let

$$a,\ t_1,\ t_2,\ \cdots,\ t_{i-1},\ t_i,\ \cdots,\ t_{n-1},\ b$$

be the values of t which correspond to the vertices of the broken line. Then the side c_i is given by the formula

$$c_i = \sqrt{(x_i - x_{i-1})^2 + (y_i - y_{i-1})^2 + (z_i - z_{i-1})^2},$$

or, applying the law of the mean to $x_i - x_{i-1}, \cdots,$

$$c_i = (t_i - t_{i-1}) \sqrt{[f'(\xi_i)]^2 + [\phi'(\eta_i)]^2 + [\psi'(\zeta_i)]^2},$$

where ξ_i, η_i, ζ_i lie between t_{i-1} and t_i. When the interval (t_{i-1}, t_i) is very small the radical differs very little from the expression

$$\sqrt{[f'(t_{i-1})]^2 + [\phi'(t_{i-1})]^2 + [\psi'(t_{i-1})]^2}.$$

In order to estimate the error we may write it in the form

$$\frac{[f'(\xi_i) - f'(t_{i-1})][f'(\xi_i) + f'(t_{i-1})] + \cdots}{\sqrt{f'^2(\xi_i) + \phi'^2(\eta_i) + \psi'^2(\zeta_i)} + \sqrt{f'^2(t_{i-1}) + \phi'^2(t_{i-1}) + \psi'^2(t_{i-1})}}.$$

But we have

$$|f'(\xi_i)| + |f'(t_{i-1})| < \sqrt{f'^2(\xi_i) + \cdots} + \sqrt{f'^2(t_{i-1}) + \cdots},$$

and consequently

$$\left| \frac{f'(\xi_i) + f'(t_{i-1})}{\sqrt{f'^2(\xi_i) + \cdots} + \sqrt{f'^2(t_{i-1}) + \cdots}} \right| < 1.$$

Hence, if each of the intervals be made so small that the oscillation of each of the functions $f'(t)$, $\phi'(t)$, $\psi'(t)$ is less than $\epsilon/3$ in any interval, we shall have

$$\sqrt{f'^2(\xi_i) + \cdots} = \sqrt{f'^2(t_{i-1}) + \cdots} + \epsilon_i,$$

where

$$|\epsilon_i| < \epsilon;$$

and the perimeter of the broken line is therefore equal to

$$\Sigma(t_i - t_{i-1}) \sqrt{f'^2(t_{i-1}) + \phi'^2(t_{i-1}) + \psi'^2(t_{i-1})} + \Sigma\epsilon_i(t_i - t_{i-1}).$$

The supplementary term $\Sigma\epsilon_i(t_i - t_{i-1})$ is less in absolute value than $\epsilon\Sigma(t_i - t_{i-1})$, that is, than $\epsilon(b - a)$. Since ϵ may be taken as small as we please, provided that the intervals be taken sufficiently small, it follows that this term approaches zero; hence the length S of the arc AB is equal to the definite integral

$$(8) \qquad S = \int_a^b \sqrt{f'^2 + \phi'^2 + \psi'^2} \, dt.$$

This definition may be extended to the case where the derivatives f', ϕ', ψ' are discontinuous in a finite number of points of the arc AB, which occurs when the curve has one or more corners. We need only divide the arc AB into several parts for each of which f', ϕ', ψ' are continuous.

It results from the formula (8) that the length S of the arc between a fixed point A and a variable point M, which corresponds to a value t of the parameter, is a function of t whose derivative is

$$\frac{dS}{dt} = \sqrt{f'^2 + \phi'^2 + \psi'^2};$$

whence, squaring and multiplying by dt^2, we find the formula

$$(9) \qquad dS^2 = dx^2 + dy^2 + dz^2,$$

which does not involve the independent variable. It is also easily remembered from its geometrical meaning, for it means that dS is the diagonal of a rectangular parallelopiped whose adjacent edges are dx, dy, dz.

Note. Applying the first law of the mean for integrals to the definite integral which represents the arc $M_0 M_1$, whose extremities correspond to the values t_0, t_1 of the parameter $(t_1 > t_0)$, we find

$$s = \text{arc } M_0 M_1 = (t_1 - t_0) \sqrt{f'^2(\theta) + \phi'^2(\theta) + \psi'^2(\theta)},$$

where θ lies in the interval (t_0, t_1). On the other hand, denoting the chord $M_0 M_1$ by c, we have

$$c^2 = [f(t_1) - f(t_0)]^2 + [\phi(t_1) - \phi(t_0)]^2 + [\psi(t_1) - \psi(t_0)]^2.$$

Applying the law of the mean for derivatives to each of the differences $f(t_1) - f(t_0)$, $\cdots$, we obtain the formula

$$c = (t_1 - t_0) \sqrt{f'^2(\xi) + \phi'^2(\eta) + \psi'^2(\zeta)},$$

where the three numbers ξ, η, ζ belong to the interval (t_0, t_1). By the above calculation the difference of the two radicals is less than ϵ, provided that the oscillation of each of the functions $f'(t)$, $\phi'(t)$, $\psi'(t)$ is less than $\epsilon/3$ in the interval (t_0, t_1). Consequently we have

$$s - c < \epsilon(t_1 - t_0),$$

or, finally,

$$1 - \frac{c}{s} < \frac{\epsilon}{\sqrt{f'^2(\theta) + \phi'^2(\theta) + \psi'^2(\theta)}}.$$

If the arc $M_0 M_1$ is infinitesimal, $t_1 - t_0$ approaches zero; hence ϵ, and therefore also $1 - c/s$, approaches zero. It follows that *the ratio of an infinitesimal arc to its chord approaches unity as its limit.*

Example. Let us find the length of an arc of a plane curve whose equation in polar coördinates is $\rho = f(\omega)$. Taking ω as independent variable, the curve is represented by the three equations $x = \rho \cos \omega$, $y = \rho \sin \omega$, $z = 0$; hence

$$ds^2 = dx^2 + dy^2 = (\cos \omega \, d\rho - \rho \sin \omega \, d\omega)^2 + (\sin \omega \, d\rho + \rho \cos \omega \, d\omega)^2,$$

or, simplifying,

$$ds^2 = d\rho^2 + \rho^2 d\omega^2.$$

Let us consider, for instance, the *cardioid*, whose equation is

$$\rho = R + R \cos \omega.$$

By the preceding formula we have

$$ds^2 = R^2 d\omega^2 [\sin^2 \omega + (1 + \cos \omega)^2] = 4 R^2 \cos^2 \frac{\omega}{2} d\omega^2,$$

or, letting ω vary from 0 to π only,

$$ds = 2 R \cos \frac{\omega}{2} d\omega;$$

and the length of the arc is

$$\left(4 R \sin \frac{\omega}{2} \right)_{\omega_0}^{\omega_1},$$

where ω_0 and ω_1 are the polar angles which correspond to the extremities of the arc. The total length of the curve is therefore $8 R$.

81. Direction cosines. In studying the properties of a curve we are often led to take the arc itself as the independent variable. Let us choose a certain sense along the curve as positive, and denote by s the length of the arc AM between a certain fixed point A and a variable point M, the sign being taken $+$ or $-$ according as M lies in the positive or in the negative direction from A. At any point M of the curve let us take the direction of the tangent which coincides with the direction in which the arc is increasing, and let α, β, γ be the angles which this direction makes with the positive directions of the three rectangular axes Ox, Oy, Oz. Then we shall have the following relations:

$$\frac{\cos \alpha}{dx} = \frac{\cos \beta}{dy} = \frac{\cos \gamma}{dz} = \pm \frac{1}{\sqrt{dx^2 + dy^2 + dz^2}} = \frac{\pm 1}{ds}.$$

To find which sign to take, suppose that the positive direction of the tangent makes an acute angle with the x axis; then x and s increase simultaneously, and the sign $+$ should be taken. If the angle α is obtuse, $\cos \alpha$ is negative, x decreases as s increases, dx/ds

is negative, and the sign + should be taken again. Hence in any case the following formulæ hold:

$$(10) \qquad \cos \alpha = \frac{dx}{ds}, \qquad \cos \beta = \frac{dy}{ds}, \qquad \cos \gamma = \frac{dz}{ds},$$

where dx, dy, dz, ds are differentials taken with respect to the same independent variable, which is otherwise arbitrary.

82. Variation of a segment of a straight line. Let MM_1 be a segment of a straight line whose extremities describe two curves C, C_1. On each of the two curves let us choose a point as origin and a positive sense of motion, and let us adopt the following notation: s, the arc AM; s_1, the arc A_1M_1, — the two arcs being taken with the same sign; l, the length MM_1; θ, the angle between MM_1 and the positive direction of the tangent MT; θ_1, the angle between M_1M and the positive direction of the tangent M_1T_1. We proceed to try to find a relation between θ, θ_1 and the differentials ds, ds_1, dl.

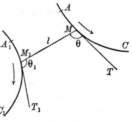

FIG. 12

Let (x, y, z), (x_1, y_1, z_1) be the coördinates of the points M, M_1, respectively, α, β, γ the direction angles of MT, and α_1, β_1, γ_1 the direction angles of M_1T_1. Then we have

$$l^2 = (x - x_1)^2 + (y - y_1)^2 + (z - z_1)^2,$$

from which we may derive the formula

$$l\,dl = (x - x_1)(dx - dx_1) + (y - y_1)(dy - dy_1) + (z - z_1)(dz - dz_1),$$

which, by means of the formulæ (10) and the analogous formulæ for C_1, may be written in the form

$$dl = \left(\frac{x - x_1}{l} \cos \alpha + \frac{y - y_1}{l} \cos \beta + \frac{z - z_1}{l} \cos \gamma \right) ds$$
$$+ \left(\frac{x_1 - x}{l} \cos \alpha_1 + \frac{y_1 - y}{l} \cos \beta_1 + \frac{z_1 - z}{l} \cos \gamma_1 \right) ds_1.$$

But $(x - x_1)/l$, $(y - y_1)/l$, $(z - z_1)/l$ are the direction cosines of M_1M, and consequently the coefficient of ds is $-\cos \theta$. Likewise the coefficient of ds_1 is $-\cos \theta_1$; hence the desired relation is

$$(10') \qquad dl = -\,ds \cos \theta - ds_1 \cos \theta_1.$$

We shall make frequent applications of this formula; one such we proceed to discuss immediately.

83. Theorems of Graves and of Chasles. Let E and E' be two confocal ellipses, and let the two tangents MA, MB to the interior ellipse E be drawn from a point

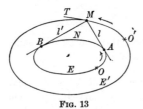

FIG. 13

M, which lies on the exterior ellipse E'. *The difference $MA + MB -$ arc ANB remains constant as the point M describes the ellipse E'.*

Let s and s' denote the arcs OA and OB, σ the arc $O'M$, l and l' the distances AM and BM, θ the angle between MB and the positive direction of the tangent MT. Since the ellipses are confocal the angle between MA and MT is equal to $\pi - \theta$. Noting that AM coincides with the positive direction of the tangent at A, and that BM is the negative direction of the tangent at B, we find from the formula (10'), successively,

$$dl = -ds + d\sigma \cos\theta,$$
$$dl' = ds' - d\sigma \cos\theta;$$

whence, adding,

$$d(l + l') = d(s' - s) = d(\text{arc } ANB),$$

which proves the proposition stated above.

The above theorem is due to an English geometrician, Graves. The following theorem, discovered by Chasles, may be proved in a similar manner. Given an ellipse and a confocal hyperbola which meets it at N. If from a point M on that branch of the hyperbola which passes through N the two tangents MA and MB be drawn to the ellipse, the difference of the arcs $NA - NB$ will be equal to the difference of the tangents $MA - MB$.

III. CHANGE OF VARIABLE   INTEGRATION BY PARTS

A large number of definite integrals which cannot be evaluated directly yield to the two general processes which we shall discuss in this section.

84. Change of variable. If in the definite integral $\int_a^b f(x)\,dx$ the variable x be replaced by a new independent variable t by means of the substitution $x = \phi(t)$, a new definite integral is obtained. Let us suppose that the function $\phi(t)$ is continuous and possesses a continuous derivative between α and β, and that $\phi(t)$ proceeds from a to b without changing sense as t goes from α to β.

The interval (α, β) having been broken up into subintervals by the intermediate values $\alpha, t_1, t_2, \cdots, t_{n-1}, \beta$, let $a, x_1, x_2, \cdots, x_{n-1}, b$ be the corresponding values of $x = \phi(t)$. Then, by the law of the mean, we shall have

$$x_i - x_{i-1} = (t_i - t_{i-1})\,\phi'(\theta_i),$$

where θ_i lies between t_{i-1} and t_i. Let $\xi_i = \phi(\theta_i)$ be the corresponding value of x which lies between x_{i-1} and x_i. Then the sum

$$f(\xi_1)(x_1 - a) + f(\xi_2)(x_2 - x_1) + \cdots + f(\xi_n)(b - x_{n-1})$$

approaches the given definite integral as its limit. But this sum may also be written

$$f[\phi(\theta_1)]\phi'(\theta_1)(t_1 - \alpha) + \cdots + f[\phi(\theta_i)]\phi'(\theta_i)(t_i - t_{i-1}) + \cdots,$$

and in this form we see that it approaches the new definite integral

$$\int_\alpha^\beta f[\phi(t)]\phi'(t)\,dt$$

as its limit. This establishes the equality

$$(11) \qquad \int_a^b f(x)\,dx = \int_\alpha^\beta f[\phi(t)]\phi'(t)\,dt,$$

which is called *the formula for the change of variable*. It is to be observed that the new differential under the sign of integration is obtained by replacing x and dx in the differential $f(x)\,dx$ by their values $\phi(t)$ and $\phi'(t)\,dt$, while the new limits of integration are the values of t which correspond to the old limits. By a suitable choice of the function $\phi(t)$ the new integral may turn out to be easier to evaluate than the old, but it is impossible to lay down any definite rules in the matter.

Let us take the definite integral

$$\int_0^x \frac{dx}{(x - \alpha)^2 + \beta^2},$$

for instance, and let us make the substitution $x = \alpha + \beta t$. It becomes

$$\int_0^x \frac{dx}{(x - \alpha)^2 + \beta^2} = \frac{1}{\beta}\int_{-\frac{\alpha}{\beta}}^t \frac{dt}{1 + t^2} = \frac{1}{\beta}\left(\arctan t + \arctan \frac{\alpha}{\beta}\right),$$

or, returning to the variable x,

$$\frac{1}{\beta}\left(\arctan \frac{x - \alpha}{\beta} + \arctan \frac{\alpha}{\beta}\right).$$

Not all the hypotheses made in establishing the formula (11) were necessary. Thus it is not necessary that the function $\phi(t)$ should always move in the same sense as t varies from α to β. For definiteness let us suppose that as t increases from α to γ ($\gamma < \beta$), $\phi(t)$ steadily increases from a to c ($c > b$); then as t increases from γ to β, $\phi(t)$ decreases from c to b. If the function $f(x)$ is continuous in the interval (a, c), the formula may be applied to each of the intervals (a, c), (c, b), which gives

$$\int_a^c f(x)\,dx = \int_\alpha^\gamma f[\phi(t)]\,\phi'(t)\,dt,$$

$$\int_c^b f(x)\,dx = \int_\gamma^\beta f[\phi(t)]\,\phi'(t)\,dt,$$

or, adding,

$$\int_a^b f(x)\,dx = \int_\alpha^\beta f[\phi(t)]\,\phi'(t)\,dt.$$

On the other hand, it is quite necessary that the function $\phi(t)$ should be uniquely defined for all values of t. If this condition be disregarded, fallacies may arise. For instance, if the formula be applied to the integral $\int_{-1}^{+1} dx$, using the transformation $x = t^{3/2}$, we should be led to write

$$\int_{-1}^{+1} dx = \int_1^1 \frac{3}{2}\,\sqrt{t}\,dt,$$

which is evidently incorrect, since the second integral vanishes. In order to apply the formula correctly we must divide the interval $(-1, +1)$ into the two intervals $(-1, 0)$, $(0, 1)$. In the first of these we should take $x = -\sqrt{t^3}$ and let t vary from 1 to 0. In the second half interval we should take $x = \sqrt{t^3}$ and let t vary from 0 to 1. We then find a correct result, namely

$$\int_{-1}^{+1} dx = 3 \int_0^1 \sqrt{t}\,dt = \left[2t^{\frac{3}{2}}\right]_0^1 = 2.$$

Note. If the upper limits b and β be replaced by x and t in the formula (11), it becomes

$$\int_a^x f(x)\,dx = \int_\alpha^t f[\phi(t)]\,\phi'(t)\,dt,$$

which shows that the transformation $x = \phi(t)$ carries a function $F(x)$, whose derivative is $f(x)$, into a function $\Phi(t)$ whose derivative is $f[\phi(t)]\,\phi'(t)$. This also follows at once from the formula for the derivative of a function of a function. Hence we may write, in general,

$$\int f(x)\,dx = \int f[\phi(t)]\,\phi'(t)\,dt,$$

which is the formula for the change of variable in indefinite integrals.

85. Integration by parts. Let u and v be two functions which, together with their derivatives u' and v', are continuous between a and b. Then we have

$$\frac{d(uv)}{dx} = u\frac{dv}{dx} + v\frac{du}{dx},$$

whence, integrating both sides of this equation, we find

$$\int_a^b \frac{d(uv)}{dx}\, dx = \int_a^b u\frac{dv}{dx}\, dx + \int_a^b v\frac{du}{dx}\, dx.$$

This may be written in the form

$$(12) \qquad \int_a^b u\, dv = [uv]_a^b - \int_a^b v\, du,$$

where the symbol $\left[F(x)\right]_a^b$ denotes, in general, the difference

$$F(b) - F(a).$$

If we replace the limit b by a variable limit x, but keep the limit a constant, which amounts to passing from definite to indefinite integrals, this formula becomes

$$(13) \qquad \int u\, dv = uv - \int v\, du.$$

Thus the calculation of the integral $\int u\, dv$ is reduced to the calculation of the integral $\int v\, du$, which may be easier. Let us try, for example, to calculate the definite integral

$$\int_a^b x^m \log x\, dx, \qquad m + 1 \neq 0.$$

Setting $u = \log x$, $v = x^{m+1}/(m+1)$, the formula (12) gives

$$\int_a^b \log x \cdot x^m dx = \left[\frac{x^{m+1}\log x}{m+1}\right]_a^b - \frac{1}{m+1}\int_a^b x^m dx$$
$$= \left[\frac{x^{m+1}\log x}{m+1} - \frac{x^{m+1}}{(m+1)^2}\right]_a^b.$$

This formula is not applicable if $m + 1 = 0$; in that particular case we have

$$\int_a^b \log x\, \frac{dx}{x} = \left[\frac{1}{2}(\log x)^2\right]_a^b.$$

It is possible to generalize the formula (12). Let the successive derivatives of the two functions u and v be represented by $u', u'', \cdots, u^{(n+1)}$; $v', v'', \cdots, v^{(n+1)}$. Then the application of the formula (12) to the integrals $\int u\,dv^{(n)}$, $\int u'\,dv^{(n-1)}$, $\cdots$ leads to the following equations:

$$\int_a^b uv^{(n+1)}\,dx = \int_a^b u\,dv^{(n)} = \left[uv^{(n)}\right]_a^b - \int_a^b u'v^{(n)}\,dx,$$

$$\int_a^b u'v^{(n)}\,dx = \int_a^b u'\,dv^{(n-1)} = \left[u'v^{(n-1)}\right]_a^b - \int_a^b u''v^{(n-1)}\,dx,$$

$$\cdots \cdots \cdots \cdots \cdots \cdots \cdots \cdots \cdots,$$

$$\int_a^b u^{(n)}v'\,dx = \int_a^b u^{(n)}\,dv = \left[u^{(n)}v\right]_a^b - \int_a^b u^{(n+1)}v\,dx.$$

Multiplying these equations through by $+1$ and -1 alternately, and then adding, we find the formula

$$(14) \quad \begin{cases} \int_a^b uv^{(n+1)}\,dx = \left[uv^{(n)} - u'v^{(n-1)} + u''v^{(n-2)} - \cdots + (-1)^n u^{(n)}v\right]_a^b \\ \qquad\qquad + (-1)^{n+1}\int_a^b u^{(n+1)}v\,dx, \end{cases}$$

which reduces the calculation of the integral $\int uv^{(n+1)}\,dx$ to the calculation of the integral $\int u^{(n+1)}v\,dx$.

In particular this formula applies when the function under the integral sign is the product of a polynomial of at most the nth degree and the derivative of order $(n+1)$ of a known function v. For then $u^{(n+1)} = 0$, and the second member contains no integral signs. Suppose, for instance, that we wished to evaluate the definite integral

$$\int_a^b e^{\omega x}f(x)\,dx,$$

where $f(x)$ is a polynomial of degree n. Setting $u=f(x)$, $v=e^{\omega x}/\omega^{n+1}$, the formula (14) takes the following form after $e^{\omega x}$ has been taken out as a factor:

$$(15)\quad \int_a^b e^{\omega x}f(x)\,dx = \left\{ e^{\omega x}\left[\frac{f(x)}{\omega} - \frac{f'(x)}{\omega^2} + \cdots + (-1)^n \frac{f^{(n)}(x)}{\omega^{n+1}}\right]\right\}_a^b.$$

The same method, or, what amounts to the same thing, a series of integrations by parts, enables us to evaluate the definite integrals

$$\int_a^b \cos mx\, f(x)\,dx, \qquad \int_a^b \sin mx\, f(x)\,dx,$$

where $f(x)$ is a polynomial.

86. Taylor's series with a remainder. In the formula (14) let us replace u by a function $F(x)$ which, together with its first $n+1$ derivatives, is continuous between a and b, and let us set $v = (b-x)^n$. Then we have

$$v' = -n(b-x)^{n-1}, \quad v'' = n(n-1)(b-x)^{n-2}, \quad \cdots,$$
$$v^{(n)} = (-1)^n 1 . 2 \cdots n, \quad v^{(n+1)} = 0,$$

and, noticing that $v, v', v'', \cdots, v^{(n-1)}$ vanish for $x = b$, we obtain the following equation from the general formula:

$$0 = (-1)^n \left[n! F(b) - n! F(a) - n! F'(a)(b-a) \right.$$
$$\left. - \frac{n!}{2} F''(a)(b-a)^2 \cdots - F^{(n)}(a)(b-a)^n \right]$$
$$+ (-1)^{n+1} \int_a^b F^{(n+1)}(x)(b-x)^n dx,$$

which leads to the equation

$$F(b) = F(a) + \frac{b-a}{1} F'(a) + \cdots$$
$$+ \frac{(b-a)^n}{n!} F^{(n)}(a) + \frac{1}{n!} \int_a^b F^{(n+1)}(x)(b-x)^n dx.$$

Since the factor $(b-x)^n$ keeps the same sign as x varies from a to b, we may apply the law of the mean to the integral on the right, which gives

$$\int_a^b F^{(n+1)}(x)(b-x)^n dx = F^{(n+1)}(\xi) \int_a^b (b-x)^n dx$$
$$= \frac{1}{n+1}(b-a)^{n+1} F^{(n+1)}(\xi),$$

where ξ lies between a and b. Substituting this value in the preceding equation, we find again exactly Taylor's formula, with Lagrange's form of the remainder.

87. Transcendental character of e. From the formula (15) we can prove a famous theorem due to Hermite: *The number e is not a root of any algebraic equation whose coefficients are all integers.*[*]

Setting $a = 0$ and $\omega = -1$ in the formula (15), it becomes

$$\int_0^b e^{-x} f(x) dx = -[e^{-x} F(x)]_0^b,$$

---

[*] The present proof is due to D. Hilbert, who drew his inspiration from the method used by Hermite.

where

$$F(x) = f(x) + f'(x) + \cdots + f^{(n)}(x);$$

and this again may be written in the form

(16) $$F(b) = e^b F(0) - e^b \int_0^b f(x) e^{-x} dx.$$

Now let us suppose that e were the root of an algebraic equation whose coefficients are all integers:

$$c_0 + c_1 e + c_2 e^2 + \cdots + c_m e^m = 0.$$

Then, setting $b = 0, 1, 2, \cdots, m$, successively, in the formula (16), and adding the results obtained, after multiplying them respectively by $c_0, c_1, \cdots, c_m$, we obtain the equation

(17) $$c_0 F(0) + c_1 F(1) + \cdots + c_m F(m) + \sum_{i=0}^{i=m} c_i e^i \int_0^i f(x) e^{-x} dx = 0,$$

where the index i takes on only the integral values $0, 1, 2, \cdots, m$. We proceed to show that such a relation is impossible if the polynomial $f(x)$, which is up to the present arbitrary, be properly chosen.

Let us choose it as follows:

$$f(x) = \frac{1}{(p-1)!} x^{p-1} (x-1)^p (x-2)^p \cdots (x-m)^p,$$

where p is a prime number greater than m. This polynomial is of degree $mp + p - 1$, and all of the coefficients of its successive derivatives past the pth are integral multiples of p, since the product of p successive integers is divisible by $p!$. Moreover $f(x)$, together with its first $(p-1)$ derivatives, vanishes for $x = 1, 2, \cdots, m$, and it follows that $F(1), F(2), \cdots, F(m)$ are all integral multiples of p. It only remains to calculate $F(0)$, that is,

$$F(0) = f(0) + f'(0) + \cdots + f^{(p-1)}(0) + f^{(p)}(0) + f^{(p+1)}(0) + \cdots.$$

In the first place, $f(0) = f'(0) = \cdots = f^{(p-2)}(0) = 0$, while $f^{(p)}(0), f^{(p+1)}(0), \cdots$ are all integral multiples of p, as we have just shown. To find $f^{(p-1)}(0)$ we need only multiply the coefficient of x^{p-1} in $f(x)$ by $(p-1)!$, which gives $\pm (1 . 2 \cdots m)^p$. Hence the sum

$$c_0 F(0) + c_1 F(1) + \cdots + c_m F(m)$$

is equal to an integral multiple of p increased by

$$\pm c_0 (1 . 2 \cdots m)^p.$$

If p be taken greater than either m or c_0, the above number cannot be divisible by p; hence the first portion of the sum (17) will be an *integer different from zero*.

We shall now show that the sum

$$\sum_{i=0}^{m} c_i e^i \int_0^i f(x) e^{-x} dx$$

can be made smaller than any preassigned quantity by taking p sufficiently large. As x varies from 0 to i each factor of $f(x)$ is less than m; hence we have

$$|f(x)| < \frac{1}{(p-1)!} m^{mp+p-1},$$

$$\left| \int_0^i f(x)\, e^{-x}\, dx \right| < \frac{1}{(p-1)!} m^{mp+p-1} \int_0^i e^{-x}\, dx < \frac{1}{(p-1)!} m^{mp+p-1},$$

from which it follows that

$$\left| \Sigma\, c_i e^i \int_0^i f(x)\, e^{-x}\, dx \right| < M \frac{m^{mp+p-1}}{(p-1)!}\, e^m = \phi\,(p),$$

where M is an upper limit of $|c_0| + |c_1| + \cdots + |c_m|$. As p increases indefinitely the function $\phi\,(p)$ approaches zero, for it is the general term of a convergent series in which the ratio of one term to the preceding approaches zero. It follows that we can find a prime number p so large that the equation (17) is impossible; hence Hermite's theorem is proved.

88. Legendre's polynomials. Let us consider the integral

$$\int_a^b Q\, P_n\, dx,$$

where $P_n(x)$ is a polynomial of degree n and Q is a polynomial of degree less than n, and let us try to determine $P_n(x)$ in such a way that the integral vanishes for any polynomial Q. We may consider $P_n(x)$ as the nth derivative of a polynomial R of degree $2\,n$, and this polynomial R is not completely determined, for we may add to it an arbitrary polynomial of degree $(n-1)$ without changing its nth derivative. We may therefore set $P_n = d^n R/dx^n$, where the polynomial R, together with its first $(n-1)$ derivatives, vanishes for $x = a$. But integrating by parts we find

$$\int_a^b Q \frac{d^n R}{dx^n}\, dx = \left[Q \frac{d^{n-1} R}{dx^{n-1}} - Q' \frac{d^{n-2} R}{dx^{n-2}} + \cdots \pm R \frac{d^{n-1} Q}{dx^{n-1}} \right]_a^b;$$

and since, by hypothesis,

$$R(a) = 0, \qquad R'(a) = 0, \qquad \cdots, \qquad R^{(n-1)}(a) = 0,$$

the expression

$$Q(b)\, R^{(n-1)}(b) - Q'(b)\, R^{(n-2)}(b) + \cdots \pm Q^{(n-1)}(b)\, R(b)$$

must also vanish if the integral is to vanish.

Since the polynomial Q of degree $n-1$ is to be arbitrary, the quantities $Q(b)$, $Q'(b)$, $\cdots$, $Q^{(n-1)}(b)$ are themselves arbitrary; hence we must also have

$$R(b) = 0, \qquad R'(b) = 0, \qquad \cdots, \qquad R^{(n-1)}(b) = 0.$$

The polynomial $R(x)$ is therefore equal, save for a constant factor, to the product $(x-a)^n (x-b)^n$; and the required polynomial $P_n(x)$ is completely determined, save for a constant factor, in the form

$$P_n = C \frac{d^n}{dx^n} [(x-a)^n (x-b)^n].$$

If the limits a and b are -1 and $+1$, respectively, the polynomials P_n are Legendre's polynomials. Choosing the constant C with Legendre, we will set

$$(18) \qquad X_n = \frac{1}{2 \cdot 4 \cdot 6 \cdots 2\,n} \frac{d^n}{dx^n} [(x^2 - 1)^n].$$

If we also agree to set $X_0 = 1$, we shall have

$$X_0 = 1, \qquad X_1 = x, \qquad X_2 = \frac{3x^2 - 1}{2}, \qquad X_3 = \frac{5x^3 - 3x}{2}, \qquad \cdots.$$

In general, X_n is a polynomial of degree n, all the exponents of x being even or odd with n. Leibniz' formula for the nth derivative of a product of two factors (§ 17) gives at once the formulæ

$$(19) \qquad\qquad X_n(1) = 1, \qquad X_n(-1) = (-1)^n.$$

By the general property established above,

$$(20) \qquad\qquad \int_{-1}^{+1} X_n \phi(x)\, dx = 0,$$

where $\phi(x)$ is any polynomial of degree less than n. In particular, if m and n are two different integers, we shall always have

$$(21) \qquad\qquad \int_{-1}^{+1} X_m X_n\, dx = 0.$$

This formula enables us to establish a very simple recurrent formula between three successive polynomials X_n. Observing that any polynomial of degree n can be written as a linear function of $X_0, X_1, \cdots, X_n$, it is clear that we may set

$$xX_n = C_0 X_{n+1} + C_1 X_n + C_2 X_{n-1} + C_3 X_{n-2} + \cdots,$$

where $C_0, C_1, C_2, \cdots$ are constants. In order to find C_3, for example, let us multiply both sides of this equation by X_{n-2}, and then integrate between the limits -1 and $+1$. By virtue of (20) and (21), all that remains is

$$C_3 \int_{-1}^{+1} X_{n-2}^2\, dx = 0,$$

and hence $C_3 = 0$. It may be shown in the same manner that $C_4 = 0$, $C_5 = 0$, $\cdots$. The coefficient C_1 is zero also, since the product xX_n does not contain x^n. Finally, to find C_0 and C_2 we need only equate the coefficients of x^{n+1} and then equate the two sides for $x = 1$. Doing this, we obtain the recurrent formula

$$(22) \qquad (n+1)X_{n+1} - (2n+1)xX_n + nX_{n-1} = 0,$$

which affords a simple means of calculating the polynomials X_n successively.

The relation (22) shows that the sequence of polynomials

$$(23) \qquad\qquad X_0, \qquad X_1, \qquad X_2, \qquad \cdots, \qquad X_n$$

possesses the properties of a Sturm sequence. As x varies continuously from -1 to $+1$, the number of changes of sign in this sequence is unaltered except when x passes through a root of $X_n = 0$. But the formulæ (19) show that there are n changes of sign in the sequence (23) for $x = -1$, and none for $x = 1$. Hence the equation $X_n = 0$ has n real roots between -1 and $+1$, which also readily follows from Rolle's theorem.

IV. GENERALIZATIONS OF THE IDEA OF AN INTEGRAL
IMPROPER INTEGRALS   LINE INTEGRALS*

89. The integrand becomes infinite. Up to the present we have supposed that the integrand remained finite between the limits of integration. In certain cases, however, the definition may be extended to functions which become infinite between the limits. Let us first consider the following particular case: $f(x)$ is continuous for every value of x which lies between a and b, and for $x = b$, but it becomes infinite for $x = a$. We will suppose for definiteness that $a < b$. Then the integral of $f(x)$ taken between the limits $a + \epsilon$ and b $(\epsilon > 0)$ has a definite value, no matter how small ϵ be taken. If this integral approaches a limit as ϵ approaches zero, it is usual and natural to denote that limit by the symbol

$$\int_a^b f(x)\,dx.$$

If a primitive of $f(x)$, say $F(x)$, be known, we may write

$$\int_{a+\epsilon}^b f(x)\,dx = F(b) - F(a + \epsilon),$$

and it is sufficient to examine $F(a + \epsilon)$ for convergence toward a limit as ϵ approaches zero. We have, for example,

$$\int_{a+\epsilon}^b \frac{M\,dx}{(x-a)^\mu} = -\frac{M}{\mu - 1}\left[\frac{1}{(b-a)^{\mu-1}} - \frac{1}{\epsilon^{\mu-1}}\right], \qquad \mu \neq 1.$$

If $\mu > 1$, the term $1/\epsilon^{\mu-1}$ increases indefinitely as ϵ approaches zero. But if μ is less than unity, we may write $1/\epsilon^{\mu-1} = \epsilon^{1-\mu}$, and it is clear that this term approaches zero with ϵ. Hence in this case the definite integral approaches a limit, and we may write

$$\int_a^b \frac{M\,dx}{(x-a)^\mu} = \frac{M(b-a)^{1-\mu}}{1-\mu}.$$

If $\mu = 1$, we have

$$\int_{a+\epsilon}^b \frac{M\,dx}{x-a} = M \log\left(\frac{b-a}{\epsilon}\right),$$

and the right-hand side increases indefinitely when ϵ approaches zero. To sum up, *the necessary and sufficient condition that the given integral should approach a limit is that μ should be less than unity.*

---

* It is possible, if desired, to read the next chapter before reading the closing sections of this chapter.

The straight line $x = a$ is an asymptote of the curve whose equation is

$$y = \frac{M}{(x-a)^\mu},$$

if μ is positive. It follows from the above that the area bounded by the x axis, the fixed line $x = b$, the curve, and its asymptote, has a finite value provided that $\mu < 1$.

If a primitive of $f(x)$ is not known, we may compare the given integral with known integrals. The above integral is usually taken as a comparison integral, which leads to certain practical rules which are sufficient in many cases. In the first place, the upper limit b does not enter into the reasoning, since everything depends upon the manner in which $f(x)$ becomes infinite for $x = a$. We may therefore replace b by any number whatever between a and b, which amounts to writing $\int_{a+\epsilon}^b = \int_{a+\epsilon}^c + \int_c^b$. In particular, unless $f(x)$ has an infinite number of roots near $x = a$, we may suppose that $f(x)$ keeps the same sign between a and c.

We will first prove the following lemma :

Let $\phi(x)$ be a function which is positive in the interval (a, b), and suppose that the integral $\int_{a+\epsilon}^b \phi(x)\,dx$ approaches a limit as ϵ approaches zero. Then, if $|f(x)| < \phi(x)$ throughout the whole interval, the definite integral $\int_{a+\epsilon}^b f(x)\,dx$ also approaches a limit.

If $f(x)$ is positive throughout the interval (a, b), the demonstration is immediate. For, since $f(x)$ is less than $\phi(x)$, we have

$$\int_{a+\epsilon}^b f(x)\,dx < \int_{a+\epsilon}^b \phi(x)\,dx.$$

Moreover $\int_{a+\epsilon}^b f(x)\,dx$ increases as ϵ diminishes, since all of its elements are positive. But the above inequality shows that it is constantly less than the second integral; hence it also approaches a limit. If $f(x)$ were always negative between a and b, it would be necessary merely to change the sign of each element. Finally, if the function $f(x)$ has an infinite number of roots near $x = a$, we may write down the equation

$$\int_{a+\epsilon}^b f(x)\,dx = \int_{a+\epsilon}^b [f(x) + |f(x)|]\,dx - \int_{a+\epsilon}^b |f(x)|\,dx.$$

The second integral on the right approaches a limit, since $|f(x)| < \phi(x)$. Now the function $f(x) + |f(x)|$ is either positive or zero between a and b, and its value cannot exceed $2\,\phi(x)$; hence the integral

$$\int_{a+\epsilon}^{b} \left[f(x) + |f(x)| \right] dx$$

also approaches a limit, and the lemma is proved.

It follows from the above that if a function $f(x)$ does not approach any limit whatever for $x = a$, but always remains less than a fixed number, the integral approaches a limit. Thus the integral $\int_{0}^{1} \sin(1/x)\,dx$ has a perfectly definite value.

Practical rule. Suppose that the function $f(x)$ can be written in the form

$$f(x) = \frac{\psi(x)}{(x-a)^{\mu}},$$

where the function $\psi(x)$ remains finite when x approaches a.

If $\mu < 1$ and the function $\psi(x)$ remains less in absolute value than a fixed number M, the integral approaches a limit. But if $\mu \geqq 1$ and the absolute value of $\psi(x)$ is greater than a positive number m, the integral approaches no limit.

The first part of the theorem is very easy to prove, for the absolute value of $f(x)$ is less than $M/(x-a)^{\mu}$, and the integral of the latter function approaches a limit, since $\mu < 1$.

In order to prove the second part, let us first observe that $\psi(x)$ keeps the same sign near $x = a$, since its absolute value always exceeds a positive number m. We shall suppose that $\psi(x) > 0$ between a and b. Then we may write

$$\int_{a+\epsilon}^{b} f(x)\,dx > \int_{a+\epsilon}^{b} \frac{m\,dx}{(x-a)^{\mu}},$$

and the second integral increases indefinitely as ϵ decreases.

These rules are sufficient for all cases in which we can find an exponent μ such that the product $(x-a)^{\mu} f(x)$ approaches, for $x = a$, a limit K different from zero. If μ is less than unity, the limit b may be taken so near a that the inequality

$$|f(x)| < \frac{L}{(x-a)^{\mu}}$$

holds inside the interval (a, b), where L is a positive number greater than $|K|$. Hence the integral approaches a limit. On the other hand, if $\mu \geqq 1$, b may be taken so near to a that

$$|f(x)| > \frac{l}{(x-a)^\mu}$$

inside the interval (a, b), where l is a positive number less than $|K|$. Moreover the function $f(x)$, being continuous, keeps the same sign; hence the integral $\int_{a+\epsilon}^b f(x)\,dx$ increases indefinitely in absolute value.*

Examples. Let $f(x) = P/Q$ be a rational function. If a is a root of order m of the denominator, the product $(x-a)^m f(x)$ approaches a limit different from zero for $x = a$. Since m is at least equal to unity, it is clear that the integral $\int_{a+\epsilon}^b f(x)\,dx$ increases beyond all limit as ϵ approaches zero. But if we consider the function

$$f(x) = \frac{P(x)}{\sqrt{R(x)}},$$

where P and R are two polynomials and $R(x)$ is prime to its derivative, the product $(x-a)^{1/2} f(x)$ approaches a limit for $x = a$ if a is a root of $R(x)$, and the integral itself approaches a limit. Thus the integral

$$\int_{-1+\epsilon}^0 \frac{dx}{\sqrt{1-x^2}}$$

approaches $\pi/2$ as ϵ approaches zero.

Again, consider the integral $\int_\epsilon^1 \log x\,dx$. The product $x^{1/2} \log x$ has the limit zero. Starting with a sufficiently small value of x, we may therefore write $\log x < M x^{-1/2}$, where M is a positive number chosen at random. Hence the integral approaches a limit.

Everything which has been stated for the lower limit a may be repeated without modification for the upper limit b. If the function $f(x)$ is infinite for $x = b$, we would define the integral $\int_a^b f(x)\,dx$ to be the limit of the integral $\int_a^{b-\epsilon'} f(x)\,dx$ as ϵ' approaches zero. If $f(x)$ is infinite at each limit, we would define $\int_a^b f(x)\,dx$ as the limit of the integral $\int_{a+\epsilon}^{b-\epsilon'} f(x)\,dx$ as ϵ and ϵ' both approach zero independently of each other. Let c be any number between a and b. Then we may write

---

*The first part of the proposition may also be stated as follows: the integral has a limit if an exponent μ can be found $(0 < \mu < 1)$ such that the product $(x-a)^\mu f(x)$ approaches a limit A as x approaches a, — the case where $A = 0$ not being excluded.

$$\int_{a+\epsilon}^{b-\epsilon'} f(x)\, dx = \int_{a+\epsilon}^{c} f(x)\, dx + \int_{c}^{b-\epsilon'} f(x)\, dx,$$

and each of the integrals on the right should approach a limit in this case.

Finally, if $f(x)$ becomes infinite for a value c between a and b, we would define the integral $\int_a^b f(x)\, dx$ as the sum of the limits of the two integrals $\int_a^{c-\epsilon'} f(x)\, dx$, $\int_{c+\epsilon}^{b} f(x)\, dx$, and we would proceed in a similar manner if any number of discontinuities whatever lay between a and b.

It should be noted that the fundamental formula (6), which was established under the assumption that $f(x)$ was continuous between a and b, still holds when $f(x)$ becomes infinite between these limits, provided that the primitive function $F(x)$ remains continuous. For the sake of definiteness let us suppose that the function $f(x)$ becomes infinite for just one value c between a and b. Then we have

$$\int_a^b f(x)\, dx = \lim_{\epsilon'=0} \int_a^{c-\epsilon'} f(x)\, dx + \lim_{\epsilon=0} \int_{c+\epsilon}^b f(x)\, dx \,;$$

and if $F(x)$ is a primitive of $f(x)$, this may be written as follows:

$$\int_a^b f(x)\, dx = \lim_{\epsilon'=0} F(c-\epsilon') - F(a) + F(b) - \lim_{\epsilon=0} F(c+\epsilon).$$

Since the function $F(x)$ is supposed continuous for $x = c$, $F(c+\epsilon)$ and $F(c-\epsilon')$ have the same limit $F(c)$, and the formula again becomes

$$\int_a^b f(x)\, dx = F(b) - F(a).$$

The following example is illustrative:

$$\int_{-1}^{+1} \frac{dx}{x^{\frac{2}{3}}} = \left[3x^{\frac{1}{3}}\right]_{-1}^{+1} = 6.$$

If the primitive function $F(x)$ itself becomes infinite between a and b, the formula ceases to hold, for the integral on the left has as yet no meaning in that case.

The formulæ for change of variable and for integration by parts may be extended to the new kinds of integrals in a similar manner by considering them as the limits of ordinary integrals.

90. Infinite limits of integration. Let $f(x)$ be a function of x which is continuous for all values of x greater than a certain number a. Then the integral $\int_a^l f(x)\, dx$, where $l > a$, has a definite value, no matter how large l be taken. If this integral approaches a limit as l increases indefinitely, that limit is represented by the symbol

$$\int_a^{+\infty} f(x)\, dx.$$

If a primitive of $f(x)$ be known, it is easy to decide whether the integral approaches a limit. For instance, in the example

$$\int_0^l \frac{dx}{1 + x^2} = \text{arc tan } l$$

the right-hand side approaches $\pi/2$ as l increases indefinitely, and this is expressed by writing the equation

$$\int_0^{+\infty} \frac{dx}{1 + x^2} = \frac{\pi}{2}.$$

Likewise, if a is positive and $\mu - 1$ is different from zero, we have

$$\int_a^l \frac{k\, dx}{x^\mu} = \frac{k}{1 - \mu}\left(\frac{1}{l^{\mu-1}} - \frac{1}{a^{\mu-1}}\right).$$

If μ is greater than unity, the right-hand side approaches a limit as l increases indefinitely, and we may write

$$\int_a^{+\infty} \frac{k\, dx}{x^\mu} = \frac{k}{(\mu - 1)\, a^{\mu-1}}.$$

On the other hand, if μ is less than one, the integral increases indefinitely with l. The same is true for $\mu = 1$, for the integral then results in a logarithm.

When no primitive of $f(x)$ is known, we again proceed by comparison, noting that the lower limit a may be taken as large as we please. Our work will be based upon the following lemma:

Let $\phi(x)$ be a function which is positive for $x > a$, and suppose that the integral $\int_a^l \phi(x)\, dx$ approaches a limit. Then the integral $\int_a^l f(x)\, dx$ also approaches a limit provided that $|f(x)| \leqq \phi(x)$ for all values of x greater than a.

The proof of this proposition is exactly similar to that given above. If the function $f(x)$ can be put into the form

$$f(x) = \frac{\psi(x)}{x^\mu},$$

where the function $\psi(x)$ remains finite when x is infinite, the following theorems can be demonstrated, but we shall merely state them:

If the absolute value of $\psi(x)$ is less than a fixed number M and μ is greater than unity, the integral approaches a limit.

If the absolute value of $\psi(x)$ is greater than a positive number m and μ is less than or equal to unity, the integral approaches no limit.

For instance, the integral

$$\int_0^l \frac{\cos ax}{1+x^2}\,dx$$

approaches a limit, for the integrand may be written

$$\frac{\cos ax}{1+x^2} = \frac{1}{x^2}\,\frac{\cos ax}{1+\dfrac{1}{x^2}},$$

and the coefficient of $1/x^2$ is less than unity in absolute value.

The above rule is sufficient whenever we can find a positive number μ for which the product $x^\mu f(x)$ approaches a limit *different from zero* as x becomes infinite. The integral approaches a limit if μ is greater than unity, but it approaches no limit if μ is less than or equal to unity.*

For example, the necessary and sufficient condition that the integral of a rational fraction approach a limit when the upper limit increases indefinitely is that the degree of the denominator should exceed that of the numerator by at least *two units*. Finally, if we take

$$f(x) = \frac{P(x)}{\sqrt{R(x)}},$$

where P and R are two polynomials of degree p and r, respectively, the product $x^{r/2-p} f(x)$ approaches a limit different from zero when x becomes infinite. The necessary and sufficient condition that the integral approach a limit is that p be less than $r/2-1$.

91. The rules stated above are not always sufficient for determining whether or not an integral approaches a limit. In the example $f(x) = (\sin x)/x$, for instance, the product $x^\mu f(x)$ approaches zero if μ is less than one, and can take on values greater than any given number if μ is greater than one. If $\mu = 1$, it oscillates between $+1$ and -1. None of the above rules apply, but the integral does approach a limit. Let us consider the slightly more general integral

---

* The integral also approaches a limit if the product $x^\mu f(x)$ (where $\mu > 1$) approaches zero as x becomes infinite.

$$A = \int_0^l e^{-\alpha x} \frac{\sin x}{x} dx, \qquad \alpha \geqq 0.$$

The integrand changes sign for $x = k\pi$. We are therefore led to study the alternating series

(24) $$a_0 - a_1 + a_2 - a_3 + \cdots + (-1)^n a_n + \cdots,$$

where the notation used is the following:

$$a_0 = \int_0^\pi e^{-\alpha x} \frac{\sin x}{x} dx, \qquad a_1 = -\int_\pi^{2\pi} e^{-\alpha x} \frac{\sin x}{x} dx, \qquad \cdots,$$

$$a_n = \left| \int_{n\pi}^{(n+1)\pi} e^{-\alpha x} \frac{\sin x}{x} dx \right|.$$

Substituting $y + n\pi$ for x, the general term a_n may be written

$$a_n = \int_0^\pi e^{-\alpha y - n\alpha\pi} \frac{\sin y}{y + n\pi} dy.$$

It is evident that the integrand decreases as n increases, and hence $a_{n+1} < a_n$. Moreover the general term a_n is less than $\int_0^\pi (1/n\pi) dy$, that is, than $1/n$. Hence the above series is convergent, since the absolute values of the terms decrease as we proceed in the series, and the general term approaches zero. If the upper limit l lies between $n\pi$ and $(n+1)\pi$, we shall have

$$\int_0^l e^{-\alpha x} \frac{\sin x}{x} dx = S_n \pm \theta a_n, \qquad 0 < \theta < 1,$$

where S_n denotes the sum of the first n terms of the series (24). As l increases indefinitely, n does the same, a_n approaches zero, and the integral approaches the sum S of the series (24).

In a similar manner it may be shown that the integrals

$$\int_0^{+\infty} \sin x^2 dx, \qquad \int_0^{+\infty} \cos x^2 dx,$$

which occur in the theory of diffraction, each have finite values. The curve $y = \sin x^2$, for example, has the undulating form of a sine curve, but the undulations become sharper and sharper as we go out, since the difference $\sqrt{(n+1)\pi} - \sqrt{n\pi}$ of two consecutive roots of $\sin x^2$ approaches zero as n increases indefinitely.

Remark. This last example gives rise to an interesting remark. As x increases indefinitely $\sin x^2$ oscillates between -1 and $+1$. Hence an integral may approach a limit even if the integrand does not approach zero, that is, even if the x axis is not an asymptote to the curve $y = f(x)$. The following is an example of the same kind in which the function $f(x)$ does not change sign. The function

$$f(x) = \frac{x}{1 + x^6 \sin^2 x}$$

remains positive when x is positive, and it does not approach zero, since $f(k\pi) = k\pi$. In order to show that the integral approaches a limit, let us consider, as above, the series

$$a_0 + a_1 + \cdots + a_n + \cdots,$$

where

$$a_n = \int_{n\pi}^{(n+1)\pi} \frac{x\,dx}{1 + x^6 \sin^2 x}.$$

As x varies from $n\pi$ to $(n + 1)\pi$, x^6 is constantly greater than $n^6 \pi^6$, and we may write

$$a_n < (n + 1)\pi \int_{n\pi}^{(n+1)\pi} \frac{dx}{1 + n^6 \pi^6 \sin^2 x}.$$

A primitive function of the new integrand is

$$\frac{1}{\sqrt{1 + n^6 \pi^6}} \arctan\left(\sqrt{1 + n^6 \pi^6}\, \tan x\right),$$

and as x varies from $n\pi$ to $(n + 1)\pi$, $\tan x$ becomes infinite just once, passing from $+\infty$ to $-\infty$. Hence the new integral is equal (§ 77) to $\pi/\sqrt{1 + n^6 \pi^6}$, and we have

$$a_n < \frac{(n + 1)\pi^2}{\sqrt{1 + n^6 \pi^6}} < \frac{(n + 1)}{n^3 \pi}.$$

It follows that the series Σa_n is convergent, and hence the integral $\int_0^l f(x)\,dx$ approaches a limit.

On the other hand, it is evident that the integral cannot approach any limit if $f(x)$ approaches a limit h different from zero when x becomes infinite. For beyond a certain value of x, $f(x)$ will be greater than $|h/2|$ in absolute value and will not change sign.

The preceding developments bear a close analogy to the treatment of infinite series. The intimate connection which exists between these two theories is brought out by a theorem of Cauchy's which will be considered later (Chapter VIII). We shall then also find new criteria which will enable us to determine whether or not an integral approaches a limit in more general cases than those treated above.

92. The function Γ(a). The definite integral

$$(25) \qquad \Gamma(a) = \int_0^{+\infty} x^{a-1} e^{-x} dx$$

has a determinate value provided that a is positive.

For, let us consider the two integrals

$$\int_\epsilon^1 x^{a-1} e^{-x} dx, \qquad \int_1^l x^{a-1} e^{-x} dx,$$

where ϵ is a very small positive number and l is a very large positive number. The second integral always approaches a limit, for past a sufficiently large value of x we have $x^{a-1}e^{-x} < 1/x^2$, that is, $e^x > x^{a+1}$. As for the first integral, the product $x^{1-a}f(x)$ approaches the limit 1 as x approaches zero, and the necessary and sufficient condition that the integral approach a limit is that $1-a$ be less than unity, that is, that a be positive. Let us suppose this condition satisfied. Then the sum of these two limits is the function $\Gamma(a)$, which is also called *Euler's integral of the second kind*. This function $\Gamma(a)$ becomes infinite as a approaches zero, it is positive when a is positive, and it becomes infinite with a. It has a minimum for $a = 1.4616321\cdots$, and the corresponding value of $\Gamma(a)$ is $0.8856032\cdots$

Let us suppose that $a > 1$, and integrate by parts, considering $e^{-x}dx$ as the differential of $-e^{-x}$. This gives

$$\Gamma(a) = -[x^{a-1}e^{-x}]_0^{+\infty} + (a-1)\int_0^{+\infty} x^{a-2}e^{-x}dx,$$

but the product $x^{a-1}e^{-x}$ vanishes at both limits, since $a > 1$, and there remains only the formula

(26) $$\Gamma(a) = (a-1)\,\Gamma(a-1).$$

The repeated application of this formula reduces the calculation of $\Gamma(a)$ to the case in which the argument a lies between 0 and 1. Moreover it is easy to determine the value of $\Gamma(a)$ when a is an integer. For, in the first place,

$$\Gamma(1) = \int_0^{+\infty} e^{-x}dx = -[e^{-x}]_0^{+\infty} = 1,$$

and the foregoing formula therefore gives, for $a = 2, 3, \cdots, n\cdots$,

$$\Gamma(2) = \Gamma(1) = 1, \qquad \Gamma(3) = 2\Gamma(2) = 1.2\,;$$

and, in general, if n is a positive integer,

(27) $$\Gamma(n) = 1.2.3\cdots(n-1) = (n-1)!.$$

93. Line integrals. Let AB be an arc of a continuous plane curve, and let $P(x, y)$ be a continuous function of the two variables x and y along AB, where x and y denote the coördinates of a point of AB with respect to a set of axes in its plane. On the arc AB let us take a certain number of points of division $m_1, m_2, \cdots, m_i, \cdots$, whose coördinates are $(x_1, y_1), (x_2, y_2), \cdots, (x_i, y_i), \cdots$, and then upon each of the arcs $m_{i-1}m_i$ let us choose another point n_i (ξ_i, η_i) at random. Finally, let us consider the sum

(28) $$\begin{cases} P(\xi_1, \eta_1)(x_1 - a) + P(\xi_2, \eta_2)(x_2 - x_1) + \cdots \\ \qquad\qquad + P(\xi_i, \eta_i)(x_i - x_{i-1}) + \cdots \end{cases}$$

extended over all these partial intervals. When the number of points of division is increased indefinitely in such a way that each of the differences $x_i - x_{i-1}$ approaches zero, the above sum approaches a limit which is called the *line integral* of $P(x, y)$ extended over the arc AB, and which is represented by the symbol

$$\int_{AB} P(x, y)\, dx.$$

In order to establish the existence of this limit, let us first suppose that a line parallel to the y axis cannot meet the arc AB in more than one point. Let a and b be the abscissæ of the points A and B, respectively, and let $y = \phi(x)$ be the equation of the curve AB. Then $\phi(x)$ is a continuous function of x in the interval (a, b), by hypothesis, and if we replace y by $\phi(x)$ in the function $P(x, y)$, the resulting function $\Phi(x) = P[x, \phi(x)]$ is also continuous. Hence we have

$$P(\xi_i, \eta_i) = P[\xi_i, \phi(\xi_i)] = \Phi(\xi_i),$$

and the preceding sum may therefore be written in the form

$$\Phi(\xi_1)(x_1 - a) + \Phi(\xi_2)(x_2 - x_1) + \cdots + \Phi(\xi_i)(x_i - x_{i-1}) + \cdots.$$

It follows that this sum approaches as its limit the ordinary definite integral

$$\int_a^b \Phi(x)\, dx = \int_a^b P[x, \phi(x)]\, dx,$$

and we have finally the formula

$$\int_{AB} P(x, y)\, dx = \int_a^b P[x, \phi(x)]\, dx.$$

If a line parallel to the y axis can meet the arc AB in more than one point, we should divide the arc into several portions, each of which is met in but one point by any line parallel to the y axis. If the given arc is of the form $ACDB$ (Fig. 14), for instance, where C and D are points at which the abscissa has an extremum, each of the arcs AC, CD, DB satisfies the above condition, and we may write

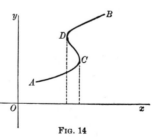

Fig. 14

$$\int_{ACDB} P(x, y)\, dx = \int_{AC} P(x, y)\, dx + \int_{CD} P(x, y)\, dx + \int_{DB} P(x, y)\, dx.$$

But it should be noticed that in the calculation of the three integrals on the right-hand side the variable y in the function $P(x, y)$ must be replaced by three different functions of the variable x, respectively.

Curvilinear integrals of the form $\int_{AB} Q(x, y)\,dy$ may be defined in a similar manner. It is clear that these integrals reduce at once to ordinary definite integrals, but their usefulness justifies their introduction. We may also remark that the arc AB may be composed of portions of different curves, such as straight lines, arcs of circles, and so on.

A case which occurs frequently in practice is that in which the coördinates of a point of the curve AB are given as functions of a variable parameter

$$x = \phi(t), \qquad y = \psi(t),$$

where $\phi(t)$ and $\psi(t)$, together with their derivatives $\phi'(t)$ and $\psi'(t)$, are continuous functions of t. We shall suppose that as t varies from α to β the point (x, y) describes the arc AB without changing the sense of its motion. Let the interval (α, β) be divided into a certain number of subintervals, and let t_{i-1} and t_i be two consecutive values of t to which correspond, upon the arc AB, two points m_{i-1} and m_i whose coördinates are (x_{i-1}, y_{i-1}) and (x_i, y_i), respectively. Then we have

$$x_i - x_{i-1} = \phi'(\theta_i)\,(t_i - t_{i-1}),$$

where θ_i lies between t_{i-1} and t_i. To this value θ_i there corresponds a point (ξ_i, η_i) of the arc $m_{i-1}m_i$; hence we may write

$$\Sigma P(\xi_i, \eta_i)\,(x_i - x_{i-1}) = \Sigma P[\phi(\theta_i), \psi(\theta_i)]\,\phi'(\theta_i)\,(t_i - t_{i-1}),$$

or, passing to the limit,

$$\int_{AB} P(x, y)\,dx = \int_\alpha^\beta P[\phi(t), \psi(t)]\,\phi'(t)\,dt.$$

An analogous formula for $\int Q\,dy$ may be obtained in a similar manner. Adding the two, we find the formula

$$(29) \qquad \int_{AB} P\,dx + Q\,dy = \int_\alpha^\beta [P\phi'(t) + Q\psi'(t)]\,dt,$$

which is the formula for change of variable in line integrals. Of course, if the arc AB is composed of several portions of different curves, the functions $\phi(t)$ and $\psi(t)$ will not have the same form along the whole of AB, and the formula should be applied in that case to each portion separately.

94. Area of a closed curve. We have already defined the area of a portion of the plane bounded by an arc AMB, a straight line which does not cut that arc, and the two perpendiculars AA_0, BB_0 let fall from the points A and B upon the straight line (§§ 65, 78, Fig. 9). Let us now consider a continuous closed curve of any shape, by which we shall understand the locus described by a point M whose coördinates are continuous functions $x = f(t)$, $y = \phi(t)$ of a parameter t which assume the same values for two values t_0 and T of the parameter t. The functions $f(t)$ and $\phi(t)$ may have several distinct forms between the limits t_0 and T; such will be the case, for instance, if the closed contour C be composed of portions of several distinct curves. Let $M_0, M_1, M_2, \cdots, M_{i-1}, M_i, \cdots, M_{n-1}, M_0$ denote points upon the curve C corresponding, respectively, to the values $t_0, t_1, t_2, \cdots, t_{i-1}, t_i, \cdots, t_{n-1}, T$ of the parameter, which increase from t_0 to T. Connecting these points in order by straight lines, we obtain a polygon inscribed in the curve. The limit approached by the area of this polygon, as the number of sides is indefinitely increased in such a way that each of them approaches zero, is called the *area of the closed curve C.*[*] This definition is seen to agree with that given in the particular case treated above. For if the polygon $A_0 A Q_1 Q_2 \cdots B B_0 A_0$ (Fig. 9) be broken up into small trapezoids by lines parallel to AA_0, the area of one of these trapezoids is $(x_i - x_{i-1})[f(x_i) + f(x_{i-1})]/2$, or $(x_i - x_{i-1})f(\xi_i)$, where ξ_i lies between x_{i-1} and x_i. Hence the area of the whole polygon, in this special case, approaches the definite integral $\int f(x)\,dx$.

Let us now consider a closed curve C which is cut in at most two points by any line parallel to a certain fixed direction. Let us choose as the axis of y a line parallel to this direction, and as the axis of x a line perpendicular to it, in such a way that the entire curve C lies in the quadrant xOy (Fig. 15).

The points of the contour C project into a segment ab of the axis Ox, and any line parallel to the axis of y meets the contour C in at most two points, m_1 and m_2. Let $y_1 = \psi_1(x)$ and $y_2 = \psi_2(x)$ be the equations of the two arcs Am_1B and Am_2B, respectively, and let us suppose for simplicity that the points A and B of the curve C which project into a and b are taken as two of the vertices of the

---

[*] It is supposed, of course, that the curve under consideration has no double point, and that the sides of the polygon have been chosen so small that the polygon itself has no double point.

polygon. The area of the inscribed polygon is equal to the difference between the areas of the two polygons formed by the lines Aa,
ab, bB with the broken lines inscribed in the two arcs Am_2B and
Am_1B, respectively. Passing to the limit, it is clear that the area
of the curve C is equal to the difference between the two areas
bounded by the contours Am_2BbaA and Am_1BbaA, respectively, that

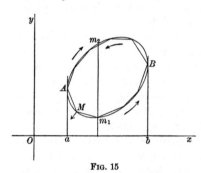

is, to the difference between
the corresponding definite integrals

$$\int_a^b \psi_2(x)\,dx - \int_a^b \psi_1(x)\,dx.$$

These two integrals represent
the curvilinear integral $\int y\,dx$
taken first along Am_2B and
then along Am_1B. If we
agree to say that the contour
C is described in the positive

Fig. 15

sense when an observer standing upon the plane and walking around
the curve in that sense has the enclosed area constantly on his left
hand (the axes being taken as usual, as in the figure), then the above
result may be expressed as follows: the area Ω enclosed by the
contour C is given by the formula

(30) $$\Omega = - \int_{(C)} y\,dx,$$

where the line integral is to be taken along the closed contour C in
the positive sense.   Since this integral is unaltered when the origin
is moved in any way, the axes remaining parallel to their original
positions, this same formula holds whatever be
the position of the contour C with respect to
the coördinate axes.

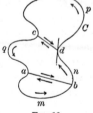

Let us now consider a contour C of any form
whatever.   We shall suppose that it is possible
to draw a finite number of lines connecting
pairs of points on C in such a way that the
resulting subcontours are each met in at most
two points by any line parallel to the y axis.
Such is the case for the region bounded by the

Fig. 16

contour C in Fig. 16, which we may divide into three subregions
bounded by the contours $amba$, $abndcqa$, $cdpc$, by means of the

transversals ab and cd. Applying the preceding formula to each of these subregions and adding the results thus obtained, the line integrals which arise from the auxiliary lines ab and cd cancel each other, and the area bounded by the closed curve C is still given by the line integral $-\int y\,dx$ taken along the contour C in the positive sense.

Similarly, it may be shown that this same area is given by the formula

$$(31) \qquad \Omega = \int_{(C)} x\,dy\,;$$

and finally, combining these two formulæ, we have

$$(32) \qquad \Omega = \frac{1}{2} \int_{(C)} x\,dy - y\,dx,$$

where the integrals are always taken in the positive sense. This last formula is evidently independent of the choice of axes.

If, for instance, an ellipse be given in the form

$$x = a \cos t, \qquad y = b \sin t,$$

its area is

$$\Omega = \frac{1}{2} \int_0^{2\pi} ab(\cos^2 t + \sin^2 t)\,dt = \pi ab.$$

95. Area of a curve in polar coördinates. Let us try to find the area enclosed by the contour $OAMBO$ (Fig. 17), which is composed of the two straight lines OA, OB, and the arc AMB, which is met in at most one point by any radius vector. Let us take O as the pole and a straight line Ox as the initial line, and let $\rho = f(\omega)$ be the equation of the arc AMB.

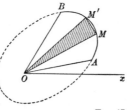
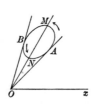

FIG. 17

Inscribing a polygon in the arc AMB, with A and B as two of the vertices, the area to be evaluated is the limit of the sum of such triangles as OMM'. But the area of the triangle OMM' is

$$\frac{1}{2} \rho(\rho + \Delta\rho) \sin \Delta\omega = \Delta\omega\left(\frac{\rho^2}{2} + \epsilon\right),$$

where ϵ approaches zero with $\Delta\omega$. It is easy to show that all the quantities analogous to ϵ are less than any preassigned number η provided that the angles $\Delta\omega$ are taken sufficiently small, and that we may therefore neglect the term $\epsilon\Delta\omega$ in evaluating the limit. Hence the area sought is the limit of the sum $\Sigma\rho^2\Delta\omega/2$, that is, it is equal to the definite integral

$$\frac{1}{2}\int_{\omega_1}^{\omega_2}\rho^2 d\omega,$$

where ω_1 and ω_2 are the angles which the straight lines OA and OB make with the line Ox.

An area bounded by a contour of any form is the algebraic sum of a certain number of areas bounded by curves like the above. If we wish to find the area of a closed contour surrounding the point O, which is cut in at most two points by any line through O, for example, we need only let ω vary from 0 to 2π. The area of a convex closed contour not surrounding O (Fig. 17) is equal to the difference of the two sectors $OAMBO$ and $OANBO$, each of which may be calculated by the preceding method. In any case the area is represented by the line integral

$$\frac{1}{2}\int\rho^2 d\omega$$

taken over the curve C in the positive sense. This formula does not differ essentially from the previous one. For if we pass from rectangular to polar coördinates we have

$$x = \rho\cos\omega, \qquad y = \rho\sin\omega,$$
$$dx = \cos\omega\, d\rho - \rho\sin\omega\, d\omega, \qquad dy = \sin\omega\, d\rho + \rho\cos\omega\, d\omega,$$
$$x\, dy - y\, dx = \rho^2 d\omega.$$

Finally, let us consider an arc AMB whose equation in oblique coördinates is $y = f(x)$. In order to find the area bounded by this arc AMB, the x axis, and the two lines AA_0, BB_0, which are parallel to the y axis, let us imagine a polygon inscribed in the arc AMB, and let us break up the area of this polygon into small trapezoids by lines parallel to the y axis. The area of one of these trapezoids is

$$\frac{f(x_{i-1}) + f(x_i)}{2}(x_i - x_{i-1})\sin\theta,$$

which may be written in the form $(x_{i-1} - x_i) f(\xi_i) \sin \theta$, where ξ lies in the interval (x_{i-1}, x_i). Hence the area in question is equal to the definite integral

$$\sin \theta \int_{x_0}^{X} f(x)\, dx,$$

where x_0 and X denote the abscissæ of the points A and B, respectively.

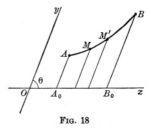

Fig. 18

It may be shown as in the similar case above that the area bounded by any closed contour C whatever is given by the formula

$$\frac{\sin \theta}{2} \int_{(C)} x\, dy - y\, dx.$$

Note. Given a closed curve C (Fig. 15), let us draw at any point M the portion of the normal which extends toward the exterior, and let α, β be the angles which this direction makes with the axes of x and y, respectively, counted from 0 to π. Along the arc Am_1B the angle β is obtuse and $dx = - ds \cos \beta$. Hence we may write

$$\int_{(Am_1 B)} y\, dx = - \int y \cos \beta\, ds.$$

Along Bm_2A the angle β is acute, but dx is negative along Bm_2A in the line integral. If we agree to consider ds always as positive, we shall still have $dx = - ds \cos \beta$. Hence the area of the closed curve may be represented by the integral

$$\int y \cos \beta\, ds,$$

where the angle β is defined as above, and where ds is essentially positive. This formula is applicable, as in the previous case, to a contour of any form whatever, and it is also obvious that the same area is given by the formula

$$\int x \cos \alpha\, ds.$$

These statements are absolutely independent of the choice of axes.

96. Value of the integral $\int x\, dy - y\, dx$. It is natural to inquire what will be represented by the integral $\int x\, dy - y\, dx$, taken over any curve whatever, closed or unclosed.

Let us consider, for example, the two closed curves $OAOBO$ and $ApBqCrAsBtCuA$ (Fig. 19) which have one and three double points, respectively. It is clear that we may replace either of these curves by a combination of two closed curves without double points. Thus the closed contour $OAOBO$

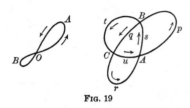

is equivalent to a combination of the two contours OAO and OBO. The integral taken over the whole contour is equal to the area of the portion OAO less the area of the portion OBO. Likewise, the other contour may be replaced by the two closed curves $ApBqCrA$ and $AsBtCuA$, and the integral taken over the whole con-

FIG. 19

tour is equal to the sum of the areas of $ApBsA$, $BtCqB$, and $ArCuA$, plus twice the area of the portion $AsBqCuA$. This reasoning is, moreover, general. Any closed contour with any number of double points determines a certain number of partial areas σ_1, σ_2, $\cdots$, σ_p, of each of which it forms all the boundaries. The integral taken over the whole contour is equal to a sum of the form

$$m_1\sigma_1 + m_2\sigma_2 + \cdots + m_p\sigma_p,$$

where m_1, m_2, $\cdots$, m_p are positive or negative integers which may be found by the following rule: *Given two adjacent areas σ, σ', separated by an arc ab of the contour C, imagine an observer walking on the plane along the contour in the sense determined by the arrows; then the coefficient of the area at his left is one greater than that of the area at his right.* Giving the area outside the contour the coefficient zero, the coefficients of all the other portions may be determined successively.

If the given arc AB is not closed, we may transform it into a closed curve by joining its extremities to the origin, and the preceding formula is applicable to this new region, for the integral $\int x\,dy - y\,dx$ taken over the radii vectores OA and OB evidently vanishes.

V. FUNCTIONS DEFINED BY DEFINITE INTEGRALS

97. Differentiation under the integral sign. We frequently have to deal with integrals in which the function to be integrated depends not only upon the variable of integration but also upon one or more other variables which we consider as parameters. Let $f(x, \alpha)$ be a continuous function of the two variables x and α when x varies from x_0 to X and α varies between certain limits α_0 and α_1. We proceed to study the function of the variable α which is defined by the definite integral

$$F(\alpha) = \int_{x_0}^{X} f(x, \alpha)\,dx,$$

where α is supposed to have a definite value between α_0 and α_1, and where the limits x_0 and X are independent of α.

We have then

$$(33) \quad F(\alpha + \Delta\alpha) - F(\alpha) = \int_{x_0}^{X} \left[f(x, \alpha + \Delta\alpha) - f(x, \alpha) \right] dx.$$

Since the function $f(x, \alpha)$ is continuous, this integrand may be made less than any preassigned number ϵ by taking $\Delta\alpha$ sufficiently small. Hence the increment $\Delta F(\alpha)$ will be less than $\epsilon |X - x_0|$ in absolute value, which shows that the function $F(\alpha)$ is continuous.

If the function $f(x, \alpha)$ has a derivative with respect to α, let us write

$$f(x, \alpha + \Delta\alpha) - f(x, \alpha) = \Delta\alpha \left[f_\alpha(x, \alpha) + \epsilon \right],$$

where ϵ approaches zero with $\Delta\alpha$. Dividing both sides of (33) by $\Delta\alpha$, we find

$$\frac{F(\alpha + \Delta\alpha) - F(\alpha)}{\Delta\alpha} = \int_{x_0}^{X} f_\alpha(x, \alpha)\, dx + \int_{x_0}^{X} \epsilon\, dx\,;$$

and if η be the upper limit of the absolute values of ϵ, the absolute value of the last integral will be less than $\eta |X - x_0|$. Passing to the limit, we obtain the formula

$$(34) \qquad \frac{dF}{d\alpha} = \int_{x_0}^{X} f_\alpha(x, \alpha)\, dx.$$

In order to render the above reasoning perfectly rigorous we must show that it is possible to choose $\Delta\alpha$ so small that the quantity ϵ will be less than any preassigned number η for all values of x between the given limits x_0 and X. This condition will certainly be satisfied if the derivative $f_\alpha(x, \alpha)$ itself is continuous. For we have from the law of the mean

$$f(x, \alpha + \Delta\alpha) - f(x, \alpha) = \Delta\alpha f_\alpha(x, \alpha + \theta\Delta\alpha), \qquad 0 < \theta < 1,$$

and hence

$$\epsilon = f_\alpha(x, \alpha + \theta\Delta\alpha) - f_\alpha(x, \alpha).$$

If the function f_α is continuous, this difference ϵ will be less than η for any values of x and α, provided that $|\Delta\alpha|$ is less than a properly chosen positive number h (see Chapter VI, § 120).

Let us now suppose that the limits X and x_0 are themselves functions of α. If ΔX and Δx_0 denote the increments which correspond to an increment $\Delta\alpha$, we shall have

$$F(\alpha + \Delta\alpha) - F(\alpha) = \int_{x_0}^{X} \left[f(x,\, \alpha + \Delta\alpha) - f(x,\, \alpha) \right] dx$$

$$+ \int_{X}^{X+\Delta X} f(x,\, \alpha + \Delta\alpha)\, dx$$

$$- \int_{x_0}^{x_0 + \Delta x_0} f(x,\, \alpha + \Delta\alpha)\, dx\,;$$

or, applying the first law of the mean for integrals to each of the last two integrals and dividing by $\Delta\alpha$,

$$\frac{F(\alpha + \Delta\alpha) - F(\alpha)}{\Delta\alpha} = \int_{x_0}^{X} \frac{f(x,\, \alpha + \Delta\alpha) - f(x,\, \alpha)}{\Delta\alpha}\, dx$$

$$+ \frac{\Delta X}{\Delta\alpha} f(X + \theta\,\Delta X,\; \alpha + \Delta\alpha)$$

$$- \frac{\Delta x_0}{\Delta\alpha} f(x_0 + \theta'\Delta x_0,\; \alpha + \Delta\alpha).$$

As $\Delta\alpha$ approaches zero the first of these integrals approaches the limit found above, and passing to the limit we find the formula

$$(35) \quad \frac{dF}{d\alpha} = \int_{x_0}^{X} f_\alpha(x,\, \alpha)\, dx + \frac{dX}{d\alpha} f(X,\, \alpha) - \frac{dx_0}{d\alpha} f(x_0,\, \alpha),$$

which is the general formula for *differentiation under the integral sign*.

Since a line integral may always be reduced to a sum of ordinary definite integrals, it is evident that the preceding formula may be extended to line integrals. Let us consider, for instance, the line integral

$$F(\alpha) = \int_{AB} P(x,\, y,\, \alpha)\, dx + Q(x,\, y,\, \alpha)\, dy$$

taken over a curve AB which is independent of α. It is evident that we shall have

$$F'(\alpha) = \int_{AB} P_\alpha(x,\, y,\, \alpha)\, dx + Q_\alpha(x,\, y,\, \alpha)\, dy,$$

where the integral is to be extended over the same curve. On the other hand, the reasoning presupposes that the limits are finite and that the function to be integrated does not become infinite between the limits of integration. We shall take up later (Chapter VIII, § 175) the cases in which these conditions are not satisfied.

The formula (35) is frequently used to evaluate certain definite integrals by reducing them to others which are more easily calculated. Thus, if a is positive, we have

$$\int_0^x \frac{dx}{x^2 + a} = \frac{1}{\sqrt{a}} \arctan \frac{x}{\sqrt{a}},$$

whence, applying the formula (34) $n - 1$ times, we find

$$(-1)^{n-1} 1 . 2 \cdots (n-1) \int_0^x \frac{dx}{(x^2 + a)^n} = \frac{d^{n-1}}{da^{n-1}}\left(\frac{1}{\sqrt{a}} \arctan \frac{x}{\sqrt{a}}\right).$$

98. Examples of discontinuity. If the conditions imposed are not satisfied for all values between the limits of integration, it may happen that the definite integral defines a discontinuous function of the parameter. Let us consider, for example, the definite integral

$$F(\alpha) = \int_{-1}^{+1} \frac{\sin \alpha \, dx}{1 - 2x \cos \alpha + x^2}.$$

This integral always has a finite value, for the roots of the denominator are imaginary except when $\alpha = k\pi$, in which case it is evident that $F(\alpha) = 0$. Supposing that $\sin \alpha \neq 0$ and making the substitution $x = \cos \alpha + t \sin \alpha$, the indefinite integral becomes

$$\int \frac{\sin \alpha \, dx}{1 - 2x \cos \alpha + x^2} = \int \frac{dt}{1 + t^2} = \arctan t.$$

Hence the definite integral $F(\alpha)$ has the value

$$\arctan\left(\frac{1 - \cos \alpha}{\sin \alpha}\right) - \arctan\left(\frac{-1 - \cos \alpha}{\sin \alpha}\right),$$

where the angles are to be taken between $-\pi/2$ and $\pi/2$. But

$$\frac{1 - \cos \alpha}{\sin \alpha} \times \frac{-1 - \cos \alpha}{\sin \alpha} = -1,$$

and hence the difference of these angles is $\pm \pi/2$. In order to determine the sign uniquely we need only notice that the sign of the integral is the same as that of $\sin \alpha$. Hence $F(\alpha) = \pm \pi/2$ according as $\sin \alpha$ is positive or negative. It follows that the function $F(\alpha)$ is discontinuous for all values of α of the form $k\pi$. This result does not contradict the above reasoning in the least, however. For when x varies from -1 to $+1$ and α varies from $-\epsilon$ to $+\epsilon$, for example, the function under the integral sign assumes an indeterminate form for the sets of values $\alpha = 0, x = -1$ and $\alpha = 0, x = +1$ which belong to the region in question for any value of ϵ.

It would be easy to give numerous examples of this nature. Again, consider the integral

$$\int_{-\infty}^{+\infty} \frac{\sin mx}{x} \, dx.$$

Making the substitution $mx = y$, we find

$$\int_{-\infty}^{+\infty} \frac{\sin mx}{x}\, dx = \pm \int_{-\infty}^{+\infty} \frac{\sin y}{y}\, dy,$$

where the sign to be taken is the sign of m, since the limits of the transformed integral are the same as those of the given integral if m is positive, but should be interchanged if m is negative. We have seen that the integral in the second member is a positive number N (§ 91). Hence the given integral is equal to $\pm N$ according as m is positive or negative. If $m = 0$, the value of the integral is zero. It is evident that the integral is discontinuous for $m = 0$.

VI. APPROXIMATE EVALUATION OF DEFINITE INTEGRALS

99. Introduction. When no primitive of $f(x)$ is known we may resort to certain methods for finding an approximate value of the definite integral $\int_a^b f(x)\, dx$. The theorem of the mean for integrals furnishes two limits between which the value of the integral must lie, and by a similar process we may obtain an infinite number of others. Let us suppose that $\phi(x) < f(x) < \psi(x)$ for all values of x between a and b ($a < b$). Then we shall also have

$$\int_a^b \phi(x)\, dx < \int_a^b f(x)\, dx < \int_a^b \psi(x)\, dx.$$

If the functions $\phi(x)$ and $\psi(x)$ are the derivatives of two known functions, this formula gives two limits between which the value of the integral must lie. Let us consider, for example, the integral

$$I = \int_0^1 \frac{dx}{\sqrt{1 - x^4}}.$$

Now $\sqrt{1 - x^4} = \sqrt{1 - x^2}\,\sqrt{1 + x^2}$, and the factor $\sqrt{1 + x^2}$ lies between 1 and $\sqrt{2}$ for all values of x between zero and unity. Hence the given integral lies between the two integrals

$$\int_0^1 \frac{dx}{\sqrt{1 - x^2}}, \qquad \frac{1}{\sqrt{2}} \int_0^1 \frac{dx}{\sqrt{1 - x^2}},$$

that is, between $\pi/2$ and $\pi/(2\sqrt{2})$. Two even closer limits may be found by noticing that $(1 + x^2)^{-1/2}$ is greater than $1 - x^2/2$, which results from the expansion of $(1 + u)^{-1/2}$ by means of Taylor's series with a remainder carried to two terms. Hence the integral I is greater than the expression

$$\int_0^1 \frac{dx}{\sqrt{1 - x^2}} - \frac{1}{2} \int_0^1 \frac{x^2\, dx}{\sqrt{1 - x^2}}.$$

The second of these integrals has the value $\pi/4$ (§ 105); hence I lies between $\pi/2$ and $3\pi/8$.

It is evident that the preceding methods merely lead to a rough idea of the exact value of the integral. In order to obtain closer approximations we may break up the interval (a, b) into smaller subintervals, to each of which the theorem of the mean for integrals may be applied. For definiteness let us suppose that the function $f(x)$ constantly increases as x increases from a to b. Let us divide the interval (a, b) into n equal parts $(b - a = nh)$. Then, by the very definition of an integral, $\int_a^b f(x)\,dx$ lies between the two sums

$$s = h\{f(a) \quad\quad + f(a + h) \ + \cdots + f[a + (n - 1)h]\},$$
$$S = h\{f(a + h) + f(a + 2h) + \cdots + f(a + nh)\}.$$

If we take $(S + s)/2$ as an approximate value of the integral, the error cannot exceed $|S - s|/2 = |[(b - a)/2n][f(b) - f(a)]|$. The value of $(S + s)/2$ may be written in the form

$$h\left\{\frac{f(a) + f(a + h)}{2} + \frac{f(a + h) + f(a + 2h)}{2} + \cdots \right.$$
$$\left. + \frac{f[a + (n - 1)h] + f(a + nh)}{2}\right\}.$$

Observing that $\{f(a + ih) + f[a + (i + 1)h]\}h/2$ is the area of the trapezoid whose height is h and whose bases are $f(a + ih)$ and $f(a + ih + h)$, we may say that the whole method amounts to replacing the area under the curve $y = f(x)$ between two neighboring ordinates by the area of the trapezoid whose bases are the two ordinates. This method is quite practical when a high degree of approximation is not necessary.

Let us consider, for example, the integral

$$\int_0^1 \frac{dx}{1 + x^2}.$$

Taking $n = 4$, we find as the approximate value of the integral

$$\frac{1}{4}\left(\frac{1}{2} + \frac{16}{17} + \frac{4}{5} + \frac{16}{25} + \frac{1}{4}\right) = 0.78279 \cdots,$$

and the error is less than $1/16 = .0625.$* This gives an approximate value of π which is correct to one decimal place, — $3.1311 \cdots$.

---

* Found from the formula $|S - s|/2$. In fact, the error is about .00260, the exact value being $\pi/4$. — TRANS.

If the function $f(x)$ does not increase (or decrease) constantly as x increases from a to b, we may break up the interval into sub-intervals for each of which that condition is satisfied.

100. Interpolation. Another method of obtaining an approximate value of the integral $\int_a^b f(x)\,dx$ is the following. Let us determine a parabolic curve of order n,

$$y = \phi(x) = a_0 + a_1 x + \cdots + a_n x^n,$$

which passes through $(n+1)$ points $B_0, B_1, \cdots, B_n$ of the curve $y = f(x)$ between the two points whose abscissæ are a and b. These points having been chosen in any manner, an approximate value of the given integral is furnished by the integral $\int_a^b \phi(x)\,dx$, which is easily calculated.

Let $(x_0, y_0), (x_1, y_1), \cdots, (x_n, y_n)$ be the coördinates of the $(n+1)$ points $B_0, B_1, \cdots, B_n$. The polynomial $\phi(x)$ is determined by Lagrange's interpolation formula in the form

$$\phi(x) = y_0 X_0 + y_1 X_1 + \cdots + y_i X_i + \cdots + y_n X_n,$$

where the coefficient of y_i is a polynomial of degree n,

$$X_i = \frac{(x - x_0) \cdots (x - x_{i-1})(x - x_{i+1}) \cdots (x - x_n)}{(x_i - x_0) \cdots (x_i - x_{i-1})(x_i - x_{i+1}) \cdots (x_i - x_n)},$$

which vanishes for the given values $x_0, x_1, \cdots, x_n$, except for $x = x_i$, and which is equal to unity when $x = x_i$. Hence we have

$$\int_a^b \phi(x)\,dx = \sum_{i=0}^n y_i \int_a^b X_i\,dx.$$

The numbers x_i are of the form

$$x_0 = a + \theta_0(b - a), \quad x_1 = a + \theta_1(b - a), \quad \cdots, \quad x_n = a + \theta_n(b - a),$$

where $0 \leqq \theta_0 < \theta_1 < \cdots < \theta_n \leqq 1$. Setting $x = a + (b - a)t$, the approximate value of the given integral takes the form

$$(36) \qquad (b - a)(K_0 y_0 + K_1 y_1 + \cdots + K_n y_n),$$

where K_i is given by the formula

$$K_i = \int_0^1 \frac{(t - \theta_0) \cdots (t - \theta_{i-1})(t - \theta_{i+1}) \cdots (t - \theta_n)}{(\theta_i - \theta_0) \cdots (\theta_i - \theta_{i-1})(\theta_i - \theta_{i+1}) \cdots (\theta_i - \theta_n)}\,dt.$$

If we divide the main interval (a, b) into subintervals whose ratios are the same constants for any given function $f(x)$ whatever, the numbers $\theta_0, \theta_1, \cdots, \theta_n$, and hence also the numbers K_i, are independent of $f(x)$. Having calculated these coefficients once for all, it only remains to replace $y_0, y_1, \cdots, y_n$ by their respective values in the formula (36).

If the curve $f(x)$ whose area is to be evaluated is given graphically, it is convenient to divide the interval (a, b) into equal parts, and it is only necessary to measure certain equidistant ordinates of this curve. Thus, dividing it into halves, we should take $\theta_0 = 0$, $\theta_1 = 1/2$, $\theta_2 = 1$, which gives the following formula for the approximate value of the integral:

$$I = \frac{b - a}{6} (y_0 + 4y_1 + y_2).$$

Likewise, for $n = 3$ we find the formula

$$I = \frac{b - a}{8} (y_0 + 3y_1 + 3y_2 + y_3),$$

and for $n = 4$

$$I = \frac{b - a}{90} (7y_0 + 32y_1 + 12y_2 + 32y_3 + 7y_4).$$

The preceding method is due to Cotes. The following method, due to Simpson, is slightly different. Let the interval (a, b) be divided into $2n$ equal parts, and let $y_0, y_1, y_2, \cdots, y_{2n}$ be the ordinates of the corresponding points of division. Applying Cotes' formula to the area which lies between two ordinates whose indices are consecutive even numbers, such as y_0 and y_2, y_2 and y_4, etc., we find an approximate value of the given area in the form

$$I = \frac{b - a}{6n} \big[(y_0 + 4y_1 + y_2) + (y_2 + 4y_3 + y_4) + \cdots$$
$$+ (y_{2n-2} + 4y_{2n-1} + y_{2n}) \big],$$

whence, upon simplification, we find Simpson's formula:

$$I = \frac{b - a}{6n} \big[y_0 + y_{2n} + 2(y_2 + y_4 + \cdots + y_{2n-2})$$
$$+ 4(y_1 + y_3 + \cdots + y_{2n-1}) \big].$$

101. Gauss' method. In Gauss' method other values are assigned the quantities θ_i. The argument is as follows: Suppose that we can find polynomials of increasing degree which differ less and less from the given integrand $f(x)$ in the interval (a, b). Suppose, for instance, that we can write

$$f(x) = \alpha_0 + \alpha_1 x + \alpha_2 x^2 + \cdots + \alpha_{2n-1} x^{2n-1} + R_{2n}(x),$$

where the remainder $R_{2n}(x)$ is less than a fixed number ϵ_n for all values of x between a and b.* The coefficients α_i will be in general unknown, but they do not occur in the calculation, as we shall see. Let $x_0, x_1, \cdots, x_{n-1}$ be values of x between a and b, and let $\phi(x)$ be a polynomial of degree $n-1$ which assumes the same values as does $f(x)$ for these values of x. Then Lagrange's interpolation formula shows that this polynomial may be written in the form

$$\phi(x) = \sum_{m=0}^{2n-1} \alpha_m \phi_m(x) + R_{2n}(x_0)\Psi_0(x) + \cdots + R_{2n}(x_{n-1})\Psi_{n-1}(x),$$

where ϕ_m and Ψ_k are at most polynomials of degree $n-1$. It is clear that the polynomial $\phi_m(x)$ depends only upon the choice of $x_0, x_1, \cdots, x_{n-1}$. On the other hand, this polynomial $\phi_m(x)$ must assume the same values as does x^m for $x = x_0$, $x = x_1$, $\cdots$, $x = x_{n-1}$. For, supposing that all the α's except α_m and also $R_{2n}(x)$ vanish, $f(x)$ reduces to $\alpha_m x^m$ and $\phi(x)$ reduces to $\alpha_m \phi_m(x)$. Hence the difference $x^m - \phi_m(x)$ must be divisible by the product

$$P_n(x) = (x - x_0)(x - x_1) \cdots (x - x_{n-1}).$$

It follows that $x^m - \phi_m(x) = P_n Q_{m-n}(x)$, where $Q_{m-n}(x)$ is a polynomial of degree $m - n$, if $m \geq n$; and that $x^m - \phi_m(x) = 0$ if $m \leq n-1$. The error made in replacing $\int_a^b f(x)\,dx$ by $\int_a^b \phi(x)\,dx$ is evidently given by the formula

$$(37) \qquad \sum_{m=0}^{2n-1} \alpha_m \int_a^b [x^m - \phi_m(x)]\,dx + \int_a^b R_{2n}(x)\,dx$$
$$- \sum_{i=0}^{n-1} R_{2n}(x_i) \int_a^b \Psi_i(x)\,dx.$$

The terms which depend upon the coefficients $\alpha_0, \alpha_1, \cdots, \alpha_{n-1}$ vanish identically, and hence the error depends only upon the coefficients $\alpha_n, \alpha_{n+1}, \cdots, \alpha_{2n-1}$ and the remainder $R_{2n}(x)$. But this remainder is very small, in general, with respect to the coefficients $\alpha_n, \alpha_{n+1}, \cdots, \alpha_{2n-1}$. Hence the chances are good for obtaining a high degree of approximation if we can dispose of the quantities $x_0, x_1, \cdots, x_{n-1}$ in such a way that the terms which depend upon $\alpha_n, \alpha_{n+1}, \cdots, \alpha_{2n-1}$ also vanish identically. For this purpose it is necessary and sufficient that the n integrals

$$\int_a^b P_n Q_0\,dx, \qquad \int_a^b P_n Q_1\,dx, \qquad \cdots, \qquad \int_a^b P_n Q_{n-1}\,dx$$

* This is a property of any function which is continuous in the interval (a, b), according to a theorem due to Weierstrass (see Chapter IX, § 199).

should vanish, where Q_i is a polynomial of degree i. We have already seen (§ 88) that this condition is satisfied if we take P_n of the form

$$P_n = \frac{d^n}{dx^n} \left[(x - a)^n (x - b)^n \right].$$

It is therefore sufficient to take for $x_0, x_1, \cdots, x_{n-1}$ the n roots of the equation $P_n = 0$, and these roots all lie between a and b.

We may assume that $a = -1$ and $b = +1$, since all other cases may be reduced to this by the substitution $x = (b+a)/2 + t(b-a)/2$. In the special case the values of $x_0, x_1, \cdots, x_{n-1}$ are the roots of Legendre's polynomial X_n. The values of these roots and the values of K_i for the formula (36), up to $n = 5$, are to be found to seven and eight places of decimals in Bertrand's *Traité de Calcul intégral* (p. 342).

Thus the error in Gauss' method is

$$\int_a^b R_{2n}(x)\,dx - \sum_{i=0}^{n-1} R_{2n}(x_i) \int_a^b \Psi_i(x)\,dx,$$

where the functions $\Psi_i(x)$ are independent of the given integrand. In order to obtain a limit of error it is sufficient to find a limit of $R_{2n}(x)$, that is, to know the degree of approximation with which the function $f(x)$ can be represented as a polynomial of degree $2n - 1$ in the interval (a, b). But it is not necessary to know this polynomial itself.

Another process for obtaining an approximate numerical value of a given definite integral is to develop the function $f(x)$ in series and integrate the series term by term. We shall see later (Chapter VIII) under what conditions this process is justifiable and the degree of approximation which it gives.

102. Amsler's planimeter. A great many machines have been invented to measure mechanically the area bounded by a closed plane curve.* One of the most ingenious of these is Amsler's planimeter, whose theory affords an interesting application of line integrals.

Let us consider the areas A_1 and A_2 bounded by the curves described by two points A_1 and A_2 of a rigid straight line which moves in a plane in any manner and finally returns to its original position. Let (x_1, y_1) and (x_2, y_2) be the coördinates of the points A_1 and A_2, respectively, with respect to a set of rectangular axes. Let l be the distance $A_1 A_2$, and θ the angle which $A_1 A_2$ makes with

---

* A description of these instruments is to be found in a work by Abdank-Abakanowicz: *Les intégraphes, la courbe intégrale et ses applications* (Gauthier-Villars, 1886).

the positive x axis. In order to define the motion of the line analytically, x_1, y_1, and θ must be supposed to be periodic functions of a certain variable parameter t which resume the same values when t is increased by T. We have $x_2 = x_1 + l\cos\theta$, $y_2 = y_1 + l\sin\theta$, and hence

$$x_2\,dy_2 - y_2\,dx_2 = x_1\,dy_1 - y_1\,dx_1 + l^2\,d\theta$$
$$+ l(\cos\theta\,dy_1 - \sin\theta\,dx_1 + x_1\cos\theta\,d\theta + y_1\sin\theta\,d\theta).$$

The areas A_1 and A_2 of the curves described by the points A_1 and A_2, under the general conventions made above (§ 96), have the following values:

$$A_1 = \frac{1}{2}\int x_1\,dy_1 - y_1\,dx_1, \qquad A_2 = \frac{1}{2}\int x_2\,dy_2 - y_2\,dx_2.$$

Hence, integrating each side of the equation just found, we obtain the equation

$$A_2 = A_1 + \frac{l^2}{2}\int d\theta + \frac{l}{2}\left[\int\cos\theta\,dy_1 - \sin\theta\,dx_1 + \int(x_1\cos\theta + y_1\sin\theta)\,d\theta\right],$$

where the limits of each of the integrals correspond to the values t_0 and $t_0 + T$ of the variable t. It is evident that $\int d\theta = 2K\pi$, where K is an integer which depends upon the way in which the straight line moves. On the other hand, integration by parts leads to the formulæ

$$\int x_1\cos\theta\,d\theta = \quad x_1\sin\theta - \int\sin\theta\,dx_1,$$
$$\int y_1\sin\theta\,d\theta = -\,y_1\cos\theta + \int\cos\theta\,dy_1.$$

But $x_1\sin\theta$ and $y_1\cos\theta$ have the same values for $t = t_0$ and $t = t_0 + T$. Hence the preceding equation may be written in the form

$$A_2 = A_1 + K\pi l^2 + l\int\cos\theta\,dy_1 - \sin\theta\,dx_1.$$

Now let s be the length of the arc described by A_1 counted positive in a certain sense from any fixed point as origin, and let α be the angle which the positive direction of the tangent makes with the positive x axis. Then we shall have

$$\cos\theta\,dy_1 - \sin\theta\,dx_1 = (\sin\alpha\cos\theta - \sin\theta\cos\alpha)\,ds = \sin V\,ds,$$

where V is the angle which the positive direction of the tangent makes with the positive direction $A_1 A_2$ of the straight line taken as in Trigonometry. The preceding equation, therefore, takes the form

$$(38) \qquad\qquad A_2 = A_1 + K\pi l^2 + l\int\sin V\,ds.$$

Similarly, the area of the curve described by any third point A_3 of the straight line is given by the formula

$$(39) \qquad\qquad A_3 = A_1 + K\pi l'^2 + l'\int\sin V\,ds,$$

where l' is the distance $A_1 A_3$. Eliminating the unknown quantity $\int\sin V\,ds$ between these two equations, we find the formula

$$l'A_2 - lA_3 = (l' - l)A_1 + K\pi ll'(l - l'),$$

which may be written in the form

(40) $A_1(23) + A_2(31) + A_3(12) + K\pi(12)(23)(31) = 0$,

where (ik) denotes the distance between the points A_i and A_k (i, $k = 1, 2, 3$) taken with its proper sign. As an application of this formula, let us consider a straight line A_1A_2 of length $(a + b)$, whose extremities A_1 and A_2 describe the same closed convex curve C. The point A_3, which divides the line into segments of length a and b, describes a closed curve C' which lies wholly inside C. In this case we have

$A_2 = A_1$, $(12) = a + b$, $(23) = -b$, $(31) = -a$, $K = 1$;

whence, dividing by $a + b$,

$$A_1 - A_3 = \pi ab.$$

But $A_1 - A_3$ is the area between the two curves C and C'. Hence this area is independent of the form of the curve C. This theorem is due to Holditch.

If, instead of eliminating $\int \sin V \, ds$ between the equations (38) and (39), we eliminate A_1, we find the formula

(41) $A_3 = A_2 + K\pi(l'^2 - l^2) + (l' - l)\int \sin V \, ds$.

Amsler's planimeter affords an application of this formula. Let $A_1A_2A_3$ be a rigid rod joined at A_2 with another rod OA_2. The point O being fixed, the point A_3, to which is attached a sharp pointer, is made to describe the curve whose area is sought. The point A_2 then describes an arc of a circle or an entire circumference, according to the nature of the motion. In any case the quantities A_2, K, l, l' are all known, and the area A_3 can be calculated if the integral $\int \sin V \, ds$, which is to be taken over the curve C_1 described by the point A_1, can be evaluated. This end A_1 carries a graduated circular cylinder whose axis coincides with the axis of the rod A_1A_3, and which can turn about this axis.

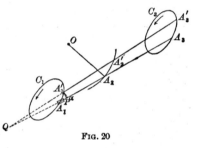

FIG. 20

Let us consider a small displacement of the rod which carries $A_1A_2A_3$ into the position $A_1'A_2'A_3'$. Let Q be the intersection of these straight lines. About Q as center draw the circular arc $A_1'\alpha$ and drop the perpendicular $A_1'P$ from A_1' upon A_1A_2. We may imagine the motion of the rod to consist of a sliding along its own direction until A_1 comes to α, followed by a rotation about Q which brings α to A_1'. In the first part of this process the cylinder would slide, without turning, along one of its generators. In the second part the rotation of the cylinder is measured by the arc $\alpha A_1'$. The two ratios $\alpha A_1'/A_1'P$ and $A_1'P/\text{arc } A_1A_1'$ approach 1 and $\sin V$, respectively, as the arc $A_1'A_1$ approaches zero. Hence $\alpha A_1' = \Delta s(\sin V + \epsilon)$, where ϵ approaches zero with Δs. It follows that the total rotation of the cylinder is proportional to the limit of the sum $\Sigma \Delta s(\sin V + \epsilon)$, that is, to the integral $\int \sin V \, ds$. Hence the measurement of this rotation is sufficient for the determination of the given area.

EXERCISES

1. Show that the sum $1/n + 1/(n + 1) + \cdots + 1/2n$ approaches $\log 2$ as n increases indefinitely.

[Show that this sum approaches the definite integral $\int_0^1 [1/(1 + x)]\, dx$ as its limit.]

2. As in the preceding exercise, find the limits of each of the sums

$$\frac{n}{n^2 + 1} + \frac{n}{n^2 + 2^2} + \cdots + \frac{n}{n^2 + (n - 1)^2},$$

$$\frac{1}{\sqrt{n^2 - 1}} + \frac{1}{\sqrt{n^2 - 2^2}} + \cdots + \frac{1}{\sqrt{n^2 - (n - 1)^2}},$$

by connecting them with certain definite integrals. In general, the limit of the sum

$$\sum_{i=0}^{n} \phi(i, n),$$

as n becomes infinite, is equal to a certain definite integral whenever $\phi(i, n)$ is a homogeneous function of degree -1 in i and n.

3. Show that the value of the definite integral $\int_0^{\pi/2} \log \sin x \, dx$ is $-(\pi/2) \log 2$.

[This may be proved by starting with the known trigonometric formula

$$\sin \frac{\pi}{n} \sin \frac{2\pi}{n} \cdots \sin \frac{(n - 1)\pi}{n} = \frac{n}{2^{n-1}},$$

or else by use of the following almost self-evident equalities:

$$\int_0^{\frac{\pi}{2}} \log \sin x \, dx = \int_0^{\frac{\pi}{2}} \log \cos x \, dx = \frac{1}{2} \int_0^{\frac{\pi}{2}} \log \left(\frac{\sin 2x}{2} \right) dx. \,]$$

4. By the aid of the preceding example evaluate the definite integral

$$\int_0^{\frac{\pi}{2}} \left(x - \frac{\pi}{2} \right) \tan x \, dx.$$

5. Show that the value of the definite integral

$$\int_0^1 \frac{\log (1 + x)}{1 + x^2} \, dx$$

is $(\pi/8) \log 2$.

[Set $x = \tan \phi$ and break up the transformed integral into three parts.]

6*. Evaluate the definite integral

$$\int_0^{\pi} \log (1 - 2\alpha \cos x + \alpha^2) \, dx.$$

[POISSON.]

[Dividing the interval from 0 to π into n equal parts and applying a well-known formula of trigonometry, we are led to seek the limit of the expression

$$\frac{\pi}{n} \log \left[\frac{\alpha - 1}{\alpha + 1} (\alpha^{2n} - 1) \right]$$

as n becomes infinite. If α lies between -1 and $+1$, this limit is zero. If $\alpha^2 > 1$, it is $\pi \log \alpha^2$. Compare § 140.]

7. Show that the value of the definite integral

$$\int_0^\pi \frac{\sin x \, dx}{\sqrt{1 - 2\alpha \cos x + \alpha^2}},$$

where α is positive, is 2 if $\alpha \leq 1$, and is $2/\alpha$ if $\alpha > 1$.

8*. Show that a necessary and sufficient condition that $f(x)$ should be integrable in an interval (a, b) is that, corresponding to any preassigned number ϵ, a subdivision of the interval can be found such that the difference $S - s$ of the corresponding sums S and s is less than ϵ.

9. Let $f(x)$ and $\phi(x)$ be two functions which are continuous in the interval (a, b), and let $(a, x_1, x_2, \cdots, b)$ be a method of subdivision of that interval. If ξ_i, η_i are any two values of x in the interval (x_{i-1}, x_i), the sum $\Sigma f(\xi_i) \phi(\eta_i) (x_i - x_{i-1})$ approaches the definite integral $\int_a^b f(x) \phi(x) \, dx$ as its limit.

10. Let $f(x)$ be a function which is continuous and positive in the interval (a, b). Show that the product of the two definite integrals

$$\int_a^b f(x) \, dx, \qquad \int_a^b \frac{dx}{f(x)}$$

is a minimum when the function is a constant.

11. Let the symbol $I_{x_0}^{x_1}$ denote the index of a function (§ 77) between x_0 and x_1. Show that the following formula holds:

$$I_{x_0}^{x_1} f(x) + I_{x_0}^{x_1} \frac{1}{f(x)} = \epsilon,$$

where $\epsilon = + 1$ if $f(x_0) > 0$ and $f(x_1) < 0$, $\epsilon = - 1$ if $f(x_0) < 0$ and $f(x_1) > 0$, and $\epsilon = 0$ if $f(x_0)$ and $f(x_1)$ have the same sign.

[Apply the last formula in the second paragraph of § 77 to each of the functions $f(x)$ and $1/f(x)$.]

12*. Let U and V be two polynomials of degree n and $n - 1$, respectively, which are prime to each other. Show that the index of the rational fraction V/U between the limits $-\infty$ and $+\infty$ is equal to the difference between the number of imaginary roots of the equation $U + iV = 0$ in which the coefficient of i is positive and the number in which the coefficient of i is negative.

[Hermite, *Bulletin de la Société mathématique*, Vol. VII, p. 128.]

13*. Derive the second theorem of the mean for integrals by integration by parts.

[Let $f(x)$ and $\phi(x)$ be two functions each of which is continuous in the interval (a, b) and the first of which, $f(x)$, constantly increases (or decreases) and has a continuous derivative. Introducing the auxiliary function

$$\Phi(x) = \int_a^x \phi(x)\, dx$$

and integrating by parts, we find the equation

$$\int_a^b f(x)\, \phi(x)\, dx = f(b)\, \Phi(b) - \int_a^b f'(x)\, \Phi(x)\, dx.$$

Since $f'(x)$ always has the same sign, it only remains to apply the first theorem of the mean for integrals to the new integral.]

14. Show directly that the definite integral $\int x\, dy - y\, dx$ extended over a closed contour goes over into an integral of the same form when the axes are replaced by any other set of rectangular axes which have the same aspect.

15. Given the formula

$$\int_a^b \cos \lambda x\, dx = \frac{1}{\lambda}(\sin \lambda b - \sin \lambda a),$$

evaluate the integrals

$$\int_a^b x^{2p+1} \sin \lambda x\, dx, \qquad \int_a^b x^{2p} \cos \lambda x\, dx.$$

16. Let us associate the points (x, y) and (x', y') upon any two given curves C and C', respectively, at which the tangents are parallel. The point whose coördinates are $x_1 = px + qx'$, $y_1 = py + qy'$, where p and q are given constants, describes a new curve C_1. Show that the following relation holds between the corresponding arcs of the three curves:

$$s_1 = \pm\, ps \pm qs'.$$

17. Show that corresponding arcs of the two curves

$$C \begin{cases} x = tf'(t) - f(t) + \phi'(t), \\ y = f'(t) - t\phi'(t) + \phi(t), \end{cases} \qquad C' \begin{cases} x' = tf'(t) - f(t) - \phi'(t), \\ y' = f'(t) + t\phi'(t) - \phi(t) \end{cases}$$

have the same length whatever be the functions $f(t)$ and $\phi(t)$.

18. From a point M of a plane let us draw the normals $MP_1, \cdots, MP_n$ to n given curves $C_1, C_2, \cdots, C_n$ which lie in the same plane, and let l_i be the distance MP_i. The locus of the points M, for which a relation of the form $F(l_1, l_2, \cdots, l_n) = 0$ holds between the n distances l_i, is a curve Γ. If lengths proportional to $\partial F/\partial l_i$ be laid off upon the lines MP_i, respectively, according to a definite convention as to sign, show that the resultant of these n vectors gives the direction of the normal to Γ at the point M. Generalize the theorem for surfaces in space.

19. Let C be any closed curve, and let us select two points p and p' upon the tangent to C at a point m, on either side of m, making $mp = mp'$. Supposing that the distance mp varies according to any arbitrary law as m describes the curve C, show that the points p and p' describe curves of equal area. Discuss the special case where mp is constant.

20. Given any closed convex curve, let us draw a parallel curve by laying off a constant length l upon the normals to the given curve. Show that the area between the two curves is equal to $\pm \pi l^2 + sl$, where s is the length of the given curve.

21. Let C be any closed curve. Show that the locus of the points A, for which the corresponding pedal has a constant area, is a circle whose center is fixed.

[Take the equation of the curve C in the tangential form

$$x \cos t + y \sin t = f(t).]$$

22. Let C be any closed curve, C_1 its pedal with respect to a point A, and C_2 the locus of the foot of a perpendicular let fall from A upon a normal to C. Show that the areas of these three curves satisfy the relation $\mathsf{A} = \mathsf{A}_1 - \mathsf{A}_2$.

[By a property of the pedal (§ 36), if ρ and ω are the polar coördinates of a point on C_1, the coördinates of the corresponding point of C_2 are ρ' and $\omega + \pi/2$, and those of the corresponding point of C are $r = \sqrt{\rho^2 + \rho'^2}$ and $\phi = \omega + \arctan \rho'/\rho$.]

23. If a curve C rolls without slipping on a straight line, every point A which is rigidly connected to the curve C describes a curve which is called a *roulette*. Show that the area between an arc of the roulette and its base is twice the area of the corresponding portion of the pedal of the point A with respect to C. Also show that the length of an arc of the roulette is equal to the length of the corresponding arc of the pedal.

[STEINER.]

[In order to prove these theorems analytically, let X and Y be the coördinates of the point A with respect to a moving system of axes formed of the tangent and normal at a point M on C. Let s be the length of the arc OM counted from a fixed point O on C, and let ω be the angle between the tangents at O and M. First establish the formulæ

$$ds + dX = Y \, d\omega, \qquad dY + X \, d\omega = 0,$$

and then deduce the theorems from them.]

24*. The error made in Gauss' method of quadrature may be expressed in the form

$$\frac{f^{(2n)}(\xi)}{1 \cdot 2 \cdots 2n} \times \frac{2}{2n + 1} \left[\frac{1 \cdot 2 \cdot 3 \cdots n}{1 \cdot 2 \cdots (2n - 1)} \right]^2,$$

where ξ lies between -1 and $+1$.   [MANSION, *Comptes rendus*, 1886.]

CHAPTER V

INDEFINITE INTEGRALS

We shall review in this chapter the general classes of elementary functions whose integrals can be expressed in terms of elementary functions. Under the term *elementary functions* we shall include the rational and irrational algebraic functions, the exponential function and the logarithm, the trigonometric functions and their inverses, and all those functions which can be formed by a finite number of combinations of those already named. When the indefinite integral of a function $f(x)$ cannot be expressed in terms of these functions, it constitutes a new transcendental function. The study of these transcendental functions and their classification is one of the most important problems of the Integral Calculus.

I. INTEGRATION OF RATIONAL FUNCTIONS

103. General method. Every rational function $f(x)$ is the sum of an integral function $E(x)$ and a rational fraction $P(x)/Q(x)$, where $P(x)$ is prime to and of less degree than $Q(x)$. If the real and imaginary roots of the equation $Q(x)$ be known, the rational fraction may be decomposed into a sum of simple fractions of one or the other of the two types

$$\frac{A}{(x-a)^m}, \quad \frac{Mx+N}{[(x-\alpha)^2+\beta^2]^n}.$$

The fractions of the first type correspond to the real roots, those of the second type to pairs of imaginary roots. The integral of the integral function $E(x)$ can be written down at once. The integrals of the fractions of the first type are given by the formulæ

$$\int \frac{A\,dx}{(x-a)^m} = -\frac{A}{(m-1)(x-a)^{m-1}}, \quad \text{if } m > 1;$$

$$\int \frac{A\,dx}{x-a} = A\log(x-a), \quad \text{if } m = 1.$$

For the sake of simplicity we have omitted the arbitrary constant C, which belongs on the right-hand side. It merely remains to examine the simple fractions which arise from pairs of imaginary roots. In order to simplify the corresponding integrals, let us make the substitution

$$x = \alpha + \beta t, \quad dx = \beta\, dt.$$

The integral in question then becomes

$$\int \frac{Mx + N}{[(x-\alpha)^2 + \beta^2]^n}\, dx = \frac{1}{\beta^{2n-1}} \int \frac{M\alpha + N + M\beta t}{(1+t^2)^n}\, dt,$$

and there remain two kinds of integrals:

$$\int \frac{t\, dt}{(1+t^2)^n}, \quad \int \frac{dt}{(1+t^2)^n}.$$

Since $t\, dt$ is half the differential of $1 + t^2$, the first of these integrals is given, if $n > 1$, by the formula

$$\int \frac{t\, dt}{(1+t^2)^n} = -\frac{1}{2(n-1)(1+t^2)^{n-1}} = -\frac{\beta^{2n-2}}{2(n-1)[(x-\alpha)^2+\beta^2]^{n-1}},$$

or, if $n = 1$, by the formula

$$\int \frac{t\, dt}{1+t^2} = \frac{1}{2}\log(1+t^2) = \frac{1}{2}\log\left(\frac{(x-\alpha)^2+\beta^2}{\beta^2}\right).$$

The only integrals which remain are those of the type

$$\int \frac{dt}{(1+t^2)^n}.$$

If $n = 1$, the value of this integral is

$$\int \frac{dt}{1+t^2} = \arctan t = \arctan \frac{x-\alpha}{\beta}.$$

If n is greater than unity, the calculation of the integral may be reduced to the calculation of an integral of the same form, in which the exponent of $(1+t^2)$ is decreased by unity. Denoting the integral in question by I_n, we may write

$$I_n = \int \frac{dt}{(1+t^2)^n} = \int \frac{1+t^2-t^2}{(1+t^2)^n}\, dt = \int \frac{dt}{(1+t^2)^{n-1}} - \int \frac{t^2\, dt}{(1+t^2)^n}.$$

From the last of these integrals, taking

$$u = t, \quad dv = \frac{t\, dt}{(1+t^2)^n}, \quad v = -\frac{1}{2(n-1)(1+t^2)^{n-1}},$$

and integrating by parts, we find the formula

$$\int \frac{t^2 dt}{(1+t^2)^n} = -\frac{t}{2(n-1)(1+t^2)^{n-1}} + \frac{1}{2(n-1)} \int \frac{dt}{(1+t^2)^{n-1}}.$$

Substituting this value in the equation for I_n, that equation becomes

$$I_n = \frac{2n-3}{2n-2} I_{n-1} + \frac{t}{2(n-1)(1+t^2)^{n-1}}.$$

Repeated applications of this formula finally lead to the integral $I_1 = \operatorname{arc\,tan} t$. Retracing our steps, we find the formula

$$I_n = \frac{(2n-3)(2n-5)\cdots 3 . 1}{(2n-2)(2n-4)\cdots 4 . 2} \operatorname{arc\,tan} t + R(t),$$

where $R(t)$ is a rational function of t which is easily calculated. We will merely observe that the denominator is $(1+t^2)^{n-1}$, and that the numerator is of degree less than $2n-2$ (see § 97, p. 192).

It follows that the integral of a rational function consists of terms which are themselves rational, and transcendental terms of one of the following forms:

$$\log(x-a), \quad \log[(x-\alpha)^2 + \beta^2], \quad \operatorname{arc\,tan} \frac{x-\alpha}{\beta}.$$

Let us consider, for example, the integral $\int [1/(x^4-1)] dx$. The denominator has two real roots $+1$ and -1, and two imaginary roots $+i$ and $-i$. We may therefore write

$$\frac{1}{x^4-1} = \frac{A}{x-1} + \frac{B}{x+1} + \frac{Cx+D}{1+x^2}.$$

In order to determine A, multiply both sides by $x-1$ and then set $x=1$. This gives $A = 1/4$, and similarly $B = -1/4$. The identity assumed may therefore be written in the form

$$\frac{1}{x^4-1} - \frac{1}{4}\left(\frac{1}{x-1} - \frac{1}{x+1}\right) = \frac{Cx+D}{1+x^2},$$

or, simplifying the left-hand side,

$$\frac{-1}{2(1+x^2)} = \frac{Cx+D}{1+x^2}.$$

It follows that $C = 0$ and $D = -1/2$, and we have, finally,

$$\frac{1}{x^4-1} = \frac{1}{4(x-1)} - \frac{1}{4(x+1)} - \frac{1}{2(x^2+1)},$$

which gives

$$\int \frac{dx}{x^4-1} = \frac{1}{4} \log\left(\frac{x-1}{x+1}\right) - \frac{1}{2} \operatorname{arc\,tan} x.$$

Note. The preceding method, though absolutely general, is not always the simplest. The work may often be shortened by using a suitable device. Let us consider, for example, the integral

$$\int \frac{dx}{(x^2 - 1)^n}.$$

If $n > 1$, we may either break up the integrand into partial fractions by means of the roots $+1$ and -1, or we may use a reduction formula similar to that for I_n. But the most elegant method is to make the substitution $x = (1 + z)/(1 - z)$, which gives

$$x^2 - 1 = \frac{4z}{(1 - z)^2}, \quad dx = \frac{2\,dz}{(1 - z)^2},$$

$$\int \frac{dx}{(x^2 - 1)^n} = \frac{2}{4^n} \int \frac{(1 - z)^{2n - 2}}{z^n}\,dz.$$

Developing $(1 - z)^{2n - 2}$ by the binomial theorem, it only remains to integrate terms of the form Az^μ, where μ may be positive or negative.

104. Hermite's method. We have heretofore supposed that the fraction to be integrated was broken up into partial fractions, which presumes a knowledge of the roots of the denominator. The following method, due to Hermite, enables us to find the algebraic part of the integral without knowing these roots, and it involves only elementary operations, that is to say, additions, multiplications, and divisions of polynomials.

Let $f(x)/F(x)$ be the rational fraction which is to be integrated. We may assume that $f(x)$ and $F(x)$ are prime to each other, and we may suppose, according to the theory of equal roots, that the polynomial $F(x)$ is written in the form

$$F(x) = X_1 X_2^2 X_3^3 \cdots X_p^p,$$

where $X_1, X_2, \cdots, X_p$ are polynomials none of which have multiple roots and no two of which have any common factor. We may now break up the given fraction into partial fractions whose denominators are $X_1, X_2^2, \cdots, X_p^p$:

$$\frac{f(x)}{F(x)} = \frac{A_1}{X_1} + \frac{A_2}{X_2^2} + \cdots + \frac{A_p}{X_p^p},$$

where A_i is a polynomial prime to X_i. For, by the theory of highest common divisor, if X and Y are any two polynomials which are prime to each other, and Z any third polynomial, two other polynomials A and B may always be found such that

$$BX + AY = Z.$$

Let us set $X = X_1$, $Y = X_2^2 \cdots X_p^p$, and $Z = f(x)$. Then this identity becomes

$$BX_1 + AX_2^2 \cdots X_p^p = f(x),$$

or, dividing by $F(x)$,

$$\frac{f(x)}{F(x)} = \frac{A}{X_1} + \frac{B}{X_2^2 \cdots X_p^p}.$$

It also follows from the preceding identity that if $f(x)$ is prime to $F(x)$, A is prime to X_1 and B is prime to $X_2^2 \cdots X_p^p$. Repeating the process upon the fraction

$$\frac{B}{X_2^2 \cdots X_p^p},$$

and so on, we finally reach the form given above.

It is therefore sufficient to show how to obtain the rational part of an integral of the form

$$\int \frac{A\,dx}{\phi^n},$$

where $\phi(x)$ is a polynomial which is prime to its derivative. Then, by the theorem mentioned above, we can find two polynomials B and C such that

$$B\phi(x) + C\phi'(x) = A,$$

and hence the preceding integral may be written in the form

$$\int \frac{A\,dx}{\phi^n} = \int \frac{B\phi + C\phi'}{\phi^n}\,dx = \int \frac{B\,dx}{\phi^{n-1}} + \int C\,\frac{\phi'dx}{\phi^n}.$$

If n is greater than unity, taking

$$u = C, \quad v = \frac{-1}{(n-1)\phi^{n-1}},$$

and integrating by parts, we get

$$\int C\frac{\phi'dx}{\phi^n} = -\frac{C}{(n-1)\phi^{n-1}} + \frac{1}{n-1}\int \frac{C'}{\phi^{n-1}}\,dx,$$

whence, substituting in the preceding equation, we find the formula

$$\int \frac{A\,dx}{\phi^n} = -\frac{C}{(n-1)\phi^{n-1}} + \int \frac{A_1\,dx}{\phi^{n-1}},$$

where A_1 is a new polynomial. If $n > 2$, we may apply the same process to the new integral, and so on : the process may always be continued until the exponent of ϕ in the denominator is equal to one, and we shall then have an expression of the form

$$\int \frac{A\,dx}{\phi^n} = R(x) + \int \frac{\psi\,dx}{\phi},$$

where $R(x)$ is a rational function of x, and ψ is a polynomial whose degree we may always suppose to be less than that of ϕ, but which is not necessarily prime to ϕ. To integrate the latter form we must know the roots of ϕ, but the evaluation of this integral will introduce no new rational terms, for the decomposition of the fraction ψ/ϕ leads only to terms of the two types

$$\frac{A}{x-a}, \quad \frac{Mx+N}{(x-\alpha)^2+\beta^2},$$

each of which has an integral which is a transcendental function.

This method enables us, in particular, to determine whether the integral of a given rational function is itself a rational function. The necessary and sufficient condition that this should be true is that each of the polynomials like ψ should vanish when the process has been carried out as far as possible.

It will be noticed that the method used in obtaining the reduction formula for I_n is essentially only a special case of the preceding method. Let us now consider the more general integral

$$\int \frac{dx}{(Ax^2 + 2Bx + C)^n}, \quad A \neq 0, \quad B^2 - AC \neq 0.$$

From the identity

$$A(Ax^2 + 2Bx + C) - (Ax + B)^2 = AC - B^2$$

it is evident that we may write

$$\int \frac{dx}{(Ax^2 + 2Bx + C)^n} = \frac{A}{AC - B^2} \int \frac{dx}{(Ax^2 + 2Bx + C)^{n-1}}$$
$$- \frac{1}{AC - B^2} \int (Ax + B) \frac{(Ax + B)\,dx}{(Ax^2 + 2Bx + C)^n}.$$

Integrating the last integral by parts, we find

$$\int (Ax + B) \frac{Ax + B}{(Ax^2 + 2Bx + C)^n}\,dx = - \frac{Ax + B}{2(n-1)(Ax^2 + 2Bx + C)^{n-1}}$$
$$+ \frac{A}{2n - 2} \int \frac{dx}{(Ax^2 + 2Bx + C)^{n-1}},$$

whence the preceding relation becomes

$$\int \frac{dx}{(Ax^2 + 2Bx + C)^n} = \frac{Ax + B}{2(n-1)(AC - B^2)(Ax^2 + 2Bx + C)^{n-1}}$$
$$+ \frac{2n - 3}{2n - 2} \frac{A}{AC - B^2} \int \frac{dx}{(Ax^2 + 2Bx + C)^{n-1}}.$$

Continuing the same process, we are led eventually to the integral

$$\int \frac{dx}{Ax^2 + 2Bx + C},$$

which is a logarithm if $B^2 - AC > 0$, and an arctangent if $B^2 - AC < 0$.

As another example, consider the integral

$$\int \frac{5x^3 + 3x - 1}{(x^3 + 3x + 1)^3} \, dx.$$

From the identity

$$5x^3 + 3x - 1 = 6x(x^2 + 1) - (x^3 + 3x + 1)$$

it is evident that we may write

$$\int \frac{5x^3 + 3x - 1}{(x^3 + 3x + 1)^3} \, dx = \int \frac{6x(x^2 + 1)}{(x^3 + 3x + 1)^3} \, dx - \int \frac{dx}{(x^3 + 3x + 1)^2}.$$

Integrating the first integral on the right by parts, we find

$$\int x \, \frac{6(x^2 + 1) \, dx}{(x^3 + 3x + 1)^3} = \frac{-x}{(x^3 + 3x + 1)^2} + \int \frac{dx}{(x^3 + 3x + 1)^2},$$

whence the value of the given integral is seen to be

$$\int \frac{5x^3 + 3x - 1}{(x^3 + 3x + 1)^3} \, dx = \frac{-x}{(x^3 + 3x + 1)^2}.$$

Note. In applying Hermite's method it becomes necessary to solve the following problem: *given three polynomials A, B, C, of degrees m, n, p, respectively, two of which, A and B, are prime to each other, find two other polynomials u and v such that the relation $Au + Bv = C$ is identically satisfied.*

In order to determine two polynomials u and v of the least possible degree which solve the problem, let us first suppose that p is at most equal to $m + n - 1$. Then we may take for u and v two polynomials of degrees $n - 1$ and $m - 1$, respectively. The $m + n$ unknown coefficients are then given by the system of $m + n$ linear non-homogeneous equations found by equating the coefficients. For the determinant of these equations cannot vanish, since, if it did, we could find two polynomials u and v of degrees $n - 1$ and $m - 1$ or less which satisfy the identity $Au + Bv = 0$, and this can be true only when A and B have a common factor.

If the degree of C is equal to or greater than $m + n$, we may divide C by AB and obtain a remainder C' whose degree is less than $m + n$. Then $C = ABQ + C'$, and, making the substitution $u - BQ = u_1$, the relation $Au + Bv = C$ reduces to $Au_1 + Bv = C'$. This is a problem under the first case.

105. Integrals of the type $\int R\left(x, \sqrt{Ax^2 + 2Bx + C}\right) dx$. After the integrals of rational functions it is natural to consider the integrals of irrational functions. We shall commence with the case in which the integrand is a rational function of x and the square root of a polynomial of the second degree. In this case a simple substitution eliminates the radical and reduces the integral to the preceding case. This substitution is self-evident in case the expression under the radical is of the first degree, say $ax + b$. If we set $ax + b = t^2$, the integral becomes

$$\int R\left(x, \sqrt{ax + b}\right) dx = \int R\left(\frac{t^2 - b}{a}, t\right) \frac{2t\, dt}{a},$$

and the integrand of the transformed integral is a rational function.

If the expression under the radical is of the second degree and has two real roots a and b, we may write

$$\sqrt{A(x - a)(x - b)} = (x - b)\sqrt{A\frac{x - a}{x - b}},$$

and the substitution

$$\sqrt{A\frac{x - a}{x - b}} = t, \quad \text{or} \quad x = \frac{Aa - bt^2}{A - t^2},$$

actually removes the radical.

If the expression under the radical sign has imaginary roots, the above process would introduce imaginaries. In order to get to the bottom of the matter, let y denote the radical $\sqrt{Ax^2 + 2Bx + C}$. Then x and y are the coördinates of a point of the curve whose equation is

$$(1) \qquad y^2 = Ax^2 + 2Bx + C,$$

and it is evident that the whole problem amounts to expressing the coördinates of a point upon a conic by means of rational functions of a parameter. It can be seen geometrically that this is possible. For, if a secant

$$y - \beta = t(x - \alpha)$$

be drawn through any point (α, β) on the conic, the coördinates of the second point of intersection of the secant with the conic are given by equations of the first degree, and are therefore rational functions of t.

If the trinomial $Ax^2 + 2Bx + C$ has imaginary roots, the coefficient A must be positive, for if it is not, the trinomial will be negative for all real values of x. In this case the conic (1) is an hyperbola. A straight line parallel to one of the asymptotes of this hyperbola,

$$y = x \sqrt{A} + t,$$

cuts the hyperbola in a point whose coördinates are

$$x = \frac{C - t^2}{2t \sqrt{A} - 2B}, \qquad y = t + \sqrt{A} \, \frac{C - t^2}{2t \sqrt{A} - 2B}.$$

If $A < 0$, the conic is an ellipse, and the trinomial $Ax^2 + 2Bx + C$ must have two real roots a and b, or else the trinomial is negative for all real values of x. The change of variable given above is precisely that which we should obtain by cutting this conic by the moving secant

$$y = t(x - a).$$

As an example let us take the integral

$$\int \frac{dx}{(x^2 + k) \sqrt{x^2 + k}}.$$

The auxiliary conic $y^2 = x^2 + k$ is an hyperbola, and the straight line $x + y = t$, which is parallel to one of the asymptotes, cuts the hyperbola in a point whose coördinates are

$$x = \frac{1}{2}\left(t - \frac{k}{t}\right), \qquad y = \sqrt{x^2 + k} = \frac{1}{2}\left(t + \frac{k}{t}\right).$$

Making the substitution indicated by these equations, we find

$$dx = \frac{dt}{2}\left(\frac{t^2 + k}{t^2}\right), \qquad \int \frac{dx}{y^3} = \int \frac{4t \, dt}{(t^2 + k)^2} = -\frac{2}{t^2 + k},$$

or, returning to the variable x,

$$\int \frac{dx}{(x^2 + k)^{\frac{3}{2}}} = \frac{x - \sqrt{x^2 + k}}{k \sqrt{x^2 + k}} = \frac{x}{k \sqrt{x^2 + k}} - \frac{1}{k},$$

where the right-hand side is determined save for a constant term. In general, if $AC - B^2$ is not zero, we have the formula

$$\int \frac{dx}{(Ax^2 + 2Bx + C)^{\frac{3}{2}}} = \frac{1}{AC - B^2} \frac{Ax + B}{\sqrt{Ax^2 + 2Bx + C}}.$$

In some cases it is easier to evaluate the integral directly without removing the radical. Consider, for example, the integral

$$\int \frac{dx}{\sqrt{Ax^2 + 2Bx + C}}.$$

If the coefficient A is positive, the integral may be written

$$\int \frac{\sqrt{A}\,dx}{\sqrt{A^2x^2 + 2ABx + AC}} = \int \frac{\sqrt{A}\,dx}{\sqrt{(Ax + B)^2 + AC - B^2}},$$

or setting $Ax + B = t$,

$$\frac{1}{\sqrt{A}} \int \frac{dt}{\sqrt{t^2 + AC - B^2}} = \frac{1}{\sqrt{A}} \log\left(t + \sqrt{t^2 + AC - B^2}\right).$$

Returning to the variable x, we have the formula

$$\int \frac{dx}{\sqrt{Ax^2 + 2Bx + C}} = \frac{1}{\sqrt{A}} \log\left(Ax + B + \sqrt{A}\,\sqrt{Ax^2 + 2Bx + C}\right).$$

If the coefficient of x^2 is negative, the integral may be written in the form

$$\int \frac{dx}{\sqrt{-Ax^2 + 2Bx + C}} = \int \frac{\sqrt{A}\,dx}{\sqrt{AC + B^2 - (Ax - B)^2}}, \qquad A > 0.$$

The quantity $AC + B^2$ is necessarily positive. Hence, making the substitution

$$Ax - B = t\sqrt{AC + B^2},$$

the given integral becomes

$$\frac{1}{\sqrt{A}} \int \frac{dt}{\sqrt{1 - t^2}} = \frac{1}{\sqrt{A}} \text{ arc sin } t.$$

Hence the formula in this case is

$$\int \frac{dx}{\sqrt{-Ax^2 + 2Bx + C}} = \frac{1}{\sqrt{A}} \text{ arc sin } \frac{Ax - B}{\sqrt{AC + B^2}}.$$

It is easy to show that the argument of the arcsine varies from -1 to $+1$ as x varies between the two roots of the trinomial.

In the intermediate case when $A = 0$ and $B \neq 0$, the integral is algebraic:

$$\int \frac{dx}{\sqrt{2Bx + C}} = \frac{1}{B}\sqrt{2Bx + C}.$$

Integrals of the type

$$\int \frac{dx}{(x - a)\sqrt{Ax^2 + 2Bx + C}}$$

reduce to the preceding type by means of the substitution $x = a + 1/y$. We find, in fact, the formula

$$\int \frac{dx}{(x - a)\sqrt{Ax^2 + 2Bx + C}} = -\int \frac{dy}{\sqrt{A_1 y^2 + 2B_1 y + C_1}},$$

where
$$A_1 = Aa^2 + 2Ba + C, \qquad B_1 = Aa + B, \qquad C_1 = A.$$

It should be noticed that this integral is algebraic if and only if the quantity a is a root of the trinomial under the radical.

Let us now consider the integrals of the type $\int \sqrt{x^2 + A}\, dx$. Integrating by parts, we find

$$\int \sqrt{x^2 + A}\, dx = x\sqrt{x^2 + A} - \int \frac{x^2\, dx}{\sqrt{x^2 + A}}.$$

On the other hand we have

$$\int \frac{x^2\, dx}{\sqrt{x^2 + A}} = \int \sqrt{x^2 + A}\, dx - \int \frac{A\, dx}{\sqrt{x^2 + A}}$$

$$= \int \sqrt{x^2 + A}\, dx - A\log\left(x + \sqrt{x^2 + A}\right).$$

From these two relations it is easy to obtain the formulæ

$$(2) \quad \int \sqrt{x^2 + A}\, dx = \frac{x}{2}\sqrt{x^2 + A} + \frac{A}{2}\log\left(x + \sqrt{x^2 + A}\right),$$

$$(3) \quad \int \frac{x^2\, dx}{\sqrt{x^2 + A}} = \frac{x}{2}\sqrt{x^2 + A} - \frac{A}{2}\log\left(x + \sqrt{x^2 + A}\right).$$

The following formulæ may be derived in like manner:

$$(4) \quad \int \sqrt{a^2 - x^2}\, dx = \frac{x}{2}\sqrt{a^2 - x^2} + \frac{a^2}{2}\arcsin\frac{x}{a},$$

$$(5) \quad \int \frac{x^2\, dx}{\sqrt{a^2 - x^2}} = -\frac{x}{2}\sqrt{a^2 - x^2} + \frac{a^2}{2}\arcsin\frac{x}{a}.$$

106. Area of the hyperbola. The preceding integrals occur in the evaluation of the area of a sector of an ellipse or an hyperbola. Let us consider, for example, the hyperbola

$$\frac{x^2}{a^2} - \frac{y^2}{b^2} = 1,$$

and let us try to find the area of a segment AMP bounded by the arc AM, the x axis, and the ordinate MP. This area is equal to the definite integral

$$\int_a^x \frac{b}{a}\sqrt{x^2-a^2}\,dx,$$

that is, by the formula (2),

$$\frac{1}{2}\frac{b}{a}\left[x\sqrt{x^2-a^2} - a^2\log\left(\frac{x+\sqrt{x^2-a^2}}{a}\right)\right].$$

But $MP = y = (b/a)\sqrt{x^2-a^2}$, and the term $(b/2a)x\sqrt{x^2-a^2}$ is precisely the area of the triangle OMP. Hence the area S of the sector OAM, bounded by the arc AM and the radii vectores OA and OM, is

$$S = \frac{1}{2}ab\log\left(\frac{x+\sqrt{x^2-a^2}}{a}\right)$$
$$= \frac{1}{2}ab\log\left(\frac{x}{a}+\frac{y}{b}\right).$$

This formula enables us to express the coördinates x and y of a point M of the hyperbola in terms of the area S. In fact, from the above and from the equation of the hyperbola, it is easy to show that

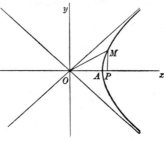

Fig. 21

$$\frac{x}{a}+\frac{y}{b}=e^{\frac{2S}{ab}}, \qquad \frac{x}{a}-\frac{y}{b}=e^{-\frac{2S}{ab}},$$

or

$$x=\frac{a}{2}\left(e^{\frac{2S}{ab}}+e^{-\frac{2S}{ab}}\right), \qquad y=\frac{b}{2}\left(e^{\frac{2S}{ab}}-e^{-\frac{2S}{ab}}\right).$$

The functions which occur on the right-hand side are called the *hyperbolic cosine and sine*:

$$\cosh x = \frac{e^x+e^{-x}}{2}, \qquad \sinh x = \frac{e^x-e^{-x}}{2}.$$

The above equations may therefore be written in the form

$$x = a\cosh\frac{2S}{ab}, \qquad y = b\sinh\frac{2S}{ab}.$$

These hyperbolic functions possess properties analogous to those of the trigonometric functions.* It is easy to deduce, for instance, the following formulæ:

$$\cosh^2 x - \sinh^2 x = 1,$$
$$\cosh(x+y) = \cosh x\cosh y + \sinh x\sinh y,$$
$$\sinh(x+y) = \sinh x\cosh y + \sinh y\cosh x.$$

---

* A table of the logarithms of these functions for positive values of the argument is to be found in Houël's *Recueil des formules numériques*.

It may be shown in like manner that the coördinates of a point on an ellipse may be expressed in terms of the area of the corresponding sector, as follows:

$$x = a \cos \frac{2S}{ab}, \qquad y = b \sin \frac{2S}{ab}.$$

In the case of a circle of unit radius, and in the case of an equilateral hyperbola whose semiaxis is one, these formulæ become, respectively,

$$x = \cos 2S, \qquad y = \sin 2S;$$
$$x = \cosh 2S, \qquad y = \sinh 2S.$$

It is evident that the hyperbolic functions bear the same relations to the equilateral hyperbola as do the trigonometric functions to the circle.

107. Rectification of the parabola. Let us try to find the length of the arc of a parabola $2py = x^2$ between the vertex O and any point M. The general formula gives

$$\text{arc } OM = \int_0^x \sqrt{1 + \left(\frac{dy}{dx}\right)^2}\, dx = \int_0^x \frac{\sqrt{x^2 + p^2}}{p}\, dx,$$

or, applying the formula (2),

$$\text{arc } OM = \frac{x\sqrt{x^2 + p^2}}{2p} + \frac{p}{2} \log\left(\frac{x + \sqrt{x^2 + p^2}}{p}\right).$$

The algebraic term in this result is precisely the length MT of the tangent, for we know that $OT = x/2$, and hence

$$MT^2 = y^2 + \frac{x^2}{4} = \frac{x^4}{4p^2} + \frac{x^2}{4} = \frac{x^2(x^2 + p^2)}{4p^2}.$$

If we draw the straight line connecting T to the focus F, the angle MTF will be a right angle. Hence we have

$$FT = \sqrt{\frac{p^2}{4} + \frac{x^2}{4}} = \frac{1}{2}\sqrt{p^2 + x^2},$$

whence we may deduce a curious property of the parabola.

Suppose that the parabola rolls without slipping on the x axis, and let us try to find the locus of the focus, which is supposed rigidly connected to the parabola. When the parabola

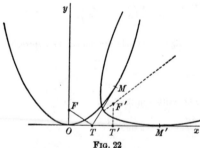

Fig. 22

is tangent at M' to the x axis, $OM' = \text{arc } OM$. The point T has come into a position T' such that $M'T' = MT$, and the focus F is at a point F' which is found by laying off $T'F' = TF$ on a line parallel to the y axis. The coördinates X and Y of the point F' are then

$$X = \text{arc } OM - MT = \frac{p}{2} \log\left(\frac{x + \sqrt{x^2 + p^2}}{p}\right),$$
$$Y = TF = \frac{1}{2}\sqrt{p^2 + x^2},$$

and the equation of the locus is given by eliminating x between these two equations.   From the first we find

$$x + \sqrt{x^2 + p^2} = p e^{\frac{2X}{p}},$$

to which we may add the equation

$$x - \sqrt{x^2 + p^2} = - p e^{-\frac{2X}{p}},$$

since the product of the two left-hand sides is equal to $- p^2$.   Subtracting these two equations, we find

$$\sqrt{x^2 + p^2} = \frac{p}{2} \left(e^{\frac{2X}{p}} + e^{-\frac{2X}{p}} \right),$$

and the desired equation of the locus is

$$Y = \frac{p}{4} \left(e^{\frac{2X}{p}} + e^{-\frac{2X}{p}} \right) = \frac{p}{2} \cosh \frac{2X}{p}.$$

This curve, which is called the *catenary*, is quite easy to construct.   Its form is somewhat similar to that of the parabola.

108. Unicursal curves. Let us now consider, in general, the integrals of algebraic functions.   Let

(6) $$F(x, y) = 0$$

be the equation of an algebraic curve, and let $R(x, y)$ be a rational function of   and y.   If we suppose y replaced by one of the roots of the equation (6) in $R(x, y)$, the result is a function of the single variable x, and the integral

$$\int R(x, y)\, dx$$

is called *an Abelian integral* with respect to the curve (6).   When the given curve and the function $R(x, y)$ are arbitrary these integrals are transcendental functions.   But in the particular case where the curve is unicursal, i.e. when the coördinates of a point on the curve can be expressed as rational functions of a variable parameter t, the Abelian integrals attached to the curve can be reduced at once to integrals of rational functions.   For, let

$$x = f(t), \qquad y = \phi(t)$$

be the equations of the curve in terms of the parameter t.   Taking t as the new independent variable, the integral becomes

$$\int R(x, y)\, dx = \int R[f(t), \phi(t)] f'(t)\, dt,$$

and the new integrand is evidently rational.

It is shown in treatises on Analytic Geometry [*] that every uni-cursal curve of degree n has $(n-1)(n-2)/2$ double points, and, conversely, that every curve of degree n which has this number of double points is unicursal. I shall merely recall the process for obtaining the expressions for the coördinates in terms of the param-eter. Given a curve C_n of degree n, which has $\delta = (n-1)(n-2)/2$ double points, let us pass a one-parameter family of curves of degree $n-2$ through these δ double points and through $n-3$ ordinary points on C_n. These points actually determine such a family, for

$$\frac{(n-1)(n-2)}{2} + n - 3 = \frac{(n-2)(n+1)}{2} - 1,$$

whereas $(n-2)(n+1)/2$ points are necessary to determine uniquely a curve of order $n-2$. Let $P(x, y) + tQ(x, y) = 0$ be the equation of this family, where t is an arbitrary parameter. Each curve of the family meets the curve C_n in $n(n-2)$ points, of which a certain num-ber are independent of t, namely the $n-3$ ordinary points chosen above and the δ double points, each of which counts as two points of intersection. But we have

$$n - 3 + 2\delta = n - 3 + (n-1)(n-2) = n(n-2) - 1,$$

and there remains just one point of intersection which varies with t. The coördinates of this point are the solutions of certain linear equa-tions whose coefficients are integral polynomials in t, and hence they are themselves rational functions of t. Instead of the preceding we might have employed a family of curves of degree $n-1$ through the $(n-1)(n-2)/2$ double points and $2n-3$ ordinary points chosen at pleasure on C_n.

If $n = 2$, $(n-1)(n-2)/2 = 0$, — every curve of the second degree is therefore unicursal, as we have seen above. If $n = 3$, $(n-1)(n-2)/2 = 1$, — the unicursal curves of the third degree are those which have one double point. Taking the double point as origin, the equation of the cubic is of the form

$$\phi_3(x, y) + \phi_2(x, y) = 0,$$

where ϕ_3 and ϕ_2 are homogeneous polynomials of the degree of their indices. A secant $y = tx$ through the double point meets the cubic in a single variable point whose coördinates are

$$x = -\frac{\phi_2(1, t)}{\phi_3(1, t)}, \qquad y = -\frac{t\phi_2(1, t)}{\phi_3(1, t)}.$$

---

[*] See, e.g., Niewenglowski, *Cours de Géométrie analytique*, Vol. II, pp. 99–114.

A unicursal curve of the fourth degree has three double points. In order to find the coördinates of a point on it, we should pass a family of conics through the three double points and through another point chosen at pleasure on the curve. Every conic of this family would meet the quartic in just one point which varies with the parameter. The equation which gives the abscissæ of the points of intersection, for instance, would reduce to an equation of the first degree when the factors corresponding to the double points had been removed, and would give x as a rational function of the parameter. We should proceed to find y in a similar manner.

As an example let us consider the lemniscate

$$(x^2 + y^2)^2 = a^2(x^2 - y^2),$$

which has a double point at the origin and two others at the imaginary circular points. A circle through the origin tangent to one of the branches of the lemniscate,

$$x^2 + y^2 = t(x - y),$$

meets the curve in a single variable point. Combining these two equations, we find

$$t^2(x - y)^2 = a^2(x^2 - y^2),$$

or, dividing by $x - y$,

$$t^2(x - y) = a^2(y + x).$$

This last equation represents a straight line through the origin which cuts the circle in a point not the origin, whose coördinates are

$$x = \frac{a^2 t(t^2 + a^2)}{t^4 + a^4}, \qquad y = \frac{a^2 t(t^2 - a^2)}{t^4 + a^4}.$$

These results may be obtained more easily by the following process, which is at once applicable to any unicursal curve of the fourth degree one of whose double points is known. The secant $y = \lambda x$ cuts the lemniscate in two points whose coördinates are

$$x = \frac{\pm a\sqrt{1 - \lambda^2}}{1 + \lambda^2}, \qquad y = \lambda x.$$

The expression under the radical is of the second degree. Hence, by § 105, the substitution $(1 - \lambda)/(1 + \lambda) = (a/t)^2$ removes the radical. It is easy to show that this substitution leads to the expressions just found.

Note. When a plane curve has singular points of higher order, it can be shown that each of them is equivalent to a certain number of isolated double points. In order that a curve be unicursal, it is sufficient that its singular points should be equivalent to $(n-1)(n-2)/2$ isolated double points. For example, a curve of order n which has a multiple point of order $n-1$ is unicursal, for a secant through the multiple point meets the curve in only one variable point.

109. Integrals of binomial differentials. Among the other integrals in which the radicals can be removed may be mentioned the following types:

$$\int R\Big[x, \, (ax+b)^{\frac{1}{q}}\Big]dx, \qquad \int R(x, \, \sqrt{ax+b}, \, \sqrt{cx+d})\,dx,$$

$$\int R(x^{\alpha}, \, x^{\alpha'}, \, x^{\alpha''}, \, \cdots)\,dx,$$

where R denotes a rational function and where the exponents $\alpha, \, \alpha', \, \alpha'', \, \cdots$ are commensurable numbers. For the first type it is sufficient to set $ax+b=t^q$. In the second type the substitution $ax+b=t^2$ leaves merely a square root of an expression of the second degree, which can then be removed by a second substitution. Finally, in the third type we may set $x=t^D$, where D is a common denominator of the fractions $\alpha, \, \alpha', \, \alpha'', \, \cdots$.

In connection with the third type we may consider a class of differentials of the form

$$x^m(ax^n+b)^p\,dx,$$

which are called *binomial differentials*. Let us suppose that the three exponents $m, \, n, \, p$ are *commensurable*. If p is an integer, the expression may be made rational by means of the substitution $x=t^D$, as we have just seen. In order to discover further cases of integrability, let us try the substitution $ax^n+b=t$. This gives

$$x=\left(\frac{t-b}{a}\right)^{\frac{1}{n}}, \qquad dx=\frac{1}{na}\left(\frac{t-b}{a}\right)^{\frac{1}{n}-1}dt,$$

$$\int x^m(ax^n+b)^p\,dx=\frac{1}{na}\int t^p\left(\frac{t-b}{a}\right)^{\frac{m+1}{n}-1}dt.$$

The transformed integral is of the same form as the original, and the exponent which takes the place of p is $(m+1)/n-1$. Hence the integration can be performed if $(m+1)/n$ is an integer.

On the other hand, the integral may be written in the form

$$\int x^{m+np}(a + bx^{-n})^p\, dx,$$

whence it is clear that another case of integrability is that in which $(m + np + 1)/n = (m + 1)/n + p$ is an integer. To sum up, the integration can be performed *whenever one of the three numbers p, $(m + 1)/n$, $(m + 1)/n + p$ is an integer.* In no other case can the integral be expressed by means of a finite number of elementary functional symbols when m, n, and p are rational.

In these cases it is convenient to reduce the integral to a simpler form in which only two exponents occur. Setting $ax^n = bt$, we find

$$x = \left(\frac{b}{a}\right)^{\frac{1}{n}} t^{\frac{1}{n}}, \qquad dx = \frac{1}{n}\left(\frac{b}{a}\right)^{\frac{1}{n}} t^{\frac{1}{n}-1} dt,$$

$$\int x^m (ax^n + b)^p\, dx = \frac{b^p}{n}\left(\frac{b}{a}\right)^{\frac{m+1}{n}} \int t^{\frac{m+1}{n}-1}(1 + t)^p\, dt.$$

Neglecting the constant factor and setting $q = (m + 1)/n - 1$, we are led to the integral

$$\int t^q (1 + t)^p\, dt.$$

The cases of integrability are those in which *one of the three numbers p, q, $p + q$ is an integer.* If p is an integer and $q = r/s$, we should set $t = u^s$. If q is an integer and $p = r/s$, we should set $1 + t = u^s$. Finally, if $p + q$ is an integer, the integral may be written in the form

$$\int t^{p+q}\left(\frac{1 + t}{t}\right)^p dt,$$

and the substitution $1 + t = tu^s$, where $p = r/s$, removes the radical.

As an example consider the integral

$$\int x\sqrt[3]{1 + x^3}\, dx.$$

Here $m = 1$, $n = 3$, $p = 1/3$, and $(m + 1)/n + p = 1$. Hence this is an integrable case. Setting $x^3 = t$, the integral becomes

$$\frac{1}{3}\int \sqrt[3]{\frac{1 + t}{t}}\, dt,$$

and a second substitution $1 + t = tu^3$ removes the radical.

II. ELLIPTIC AND HYPERELLIPTIC INTEGRALS

110. Reduction of integrals. Let $P(x)$ be an integral polynomial of degree p which is prime to its derivative. The integral

$$\int R\big[x,\ \sqrt{P(x)}\big]\,dx,$$

where R denotes a rational function of x and the radical $y = \sqrt{P(x)}$, cannot be expressed in terms of elementary functions, in general, when p is greater than 2. Such integrals, which are particular cases of general Abelian integrals, can be split up into portions which result in algebraic and logarithmic functions and a certain number of other integrals which give rise to new transcendental functions which cannot be expressed by means of a finite number of elementary functional symbols. We proceed to consider this reduction.

The rational function $R(x, y)$ is the quotient of two integral polynomials in x and y. Replacing any even power of y, such as y^{2q}, by $[P(x)]^q$, and any odd power, such as y^{2q+1}, by $y\,[P(x)]^q$, we may evidently suppose the numerator and denominator of this fraction to be of the first degree in y,

$$R(x,\ y) = \frac{A + By}{C + Dy},$$

where A, B, C, D are integral polynomials in x. Multiplying the numerator and the denominator each by $C - Dy$, and replacing y^2 by $P(x)$, we may write this in the form

$$R(x,\ y) = \frac{F + Gy}{K},$$

where F, G, and K are polynomials. The integral is now broken up into two parts, of which the first $\int F/K\,dx$ is the integral of a rational function. For this reason we shall consider only the second integral $\int Gy/K\,dx$, which may also be written in the form

$$\int \frac{M\,dx}{N\,\sqrt{P(x)}},$$

where M and N are integral polynomials in x. The rational fraction M/N may be decomposed into an integral part $E(x)$ and a sum of partial fractions

$$\frac{M}{N} = E(x) + \frac{A_1}{X_1} + \frac{A_2}{X_2^2} + \cdots + \frac{A_p}{X_p^p},$$

where each of the polynomials X_i is prime to its derivative. We shall therefore have to consider two types of integrals,

$$Y_m = \int \frac{x^m \, dx}{\sqrt{P(x)}}, \qquad Z_n = \int \frac{A \, dx}{X^n \sqrt{P(x)}}.$$

If the degree of $P(x)$ is p, all the integrals Y_m may be expressed in terms of the first $p - 1$ of them, $Y_0, Y_1, \cdots, Y_{p-2}$, and certain algebraic expressions.

For, let us write
$$P(x) = a_0 x^p + a_1 x^{p-1} + \cdots.$$

It follows that

$$\begin{aligned}
\frac{d}{dx}\left(x^m \sqrt{P(x)}\right) &= m x^{m-1} \sqrt{P(x)} + \frac{x^m P'(x)}{2 \sqrt{P(x)}} \\
&= \frac{2m x^{m-1} P(x) + x^m P'(x)}{2 \sqrt{P(x)}}.
\end{aligned}$$

The numerator of this expression is of degree $m + p - 1$, and its highest term is $(2m + p) a_0 x^{m+p-1}$. Integrating both sides of the above equation, we find

$$2x^m \sqrt{P(x)} = (2m + p) a_0 Y_{m+p-1} + \cdots,$$

where the terms not written down contain integrals of the type Y whose indices are less than $m + p - 1$. Setting $m = 0, 1, 2, \cdots$, successively, we can calculate the integrals $Y_{p-1}, Y_p, \cdots$ successively in terms of algebraic expressions and the $p - 1$ integrals $Y_0, Y_1, \cdots, Y_{p-2}$.

With respect to the integrals of the second type we shall distinguish the two cases where X is or is not prime to $P(x)$.

1) *If X is prime to $P(x)$, the integral Z_n reduces to the sum of an algebraic term, a number of integrals of the type Y_k, and a new integral*

$$\int \frac{B \, dx}{X \sqrt{P(x)}},$$

where B is a polynomial whose degree is less than that of X.

Since X is prime to its derivative X' and also to $P(x)$, X^n is prime to PX'. Hence two polynomials λ and μ can be found such that $\lambda X^n + \mu X' P = A$, and the integral in question breaks up into two parts:

$$\int \frac{A \, dx}{X^n \sqrt{P(x)}} = \int \frac{\lambda \, dx}{\sqrt{P(x)}} + \int \frac{\mu \sqrt{P} X'}{X^n} \, dx.$$

The first part is a sum of integrals of the type Y. In the second integral, when $n > 1$, let us integrate by parts, taking

$$\mu \sqrt{P} = u, \quad v = \frac{-1}{(n-1)\,X^{n-1}},$$

which gives

$$\int \frac{\mu \sqrt{P}\,X'\,dx}{X^n} = \frac{-\mu \sqrt{P}}{(n-1)\,X^{n-1}} + \frac{1}{n-1} \int \frac{2\mu' P + \mu P'}{2 X^{n-1} \sqrt{P(x)}}\,dx.$$

The new integral obtained is of the same form as the first, except that the exponent of X is diminished by one. Repeating this process as often as possible, i.e. as long as the exponent of X is greater than unity, we finally obtain a result of the form

$$\int \frac{A\,dx}{X^n \sqrt{P(x)}} = \int \frac{B\,dx}{X \sqrt{P}} + \int \frac{C\,dx}{\sqrt{P}} + \frac{D \sqrt{P}}{X^{n-1}},$$

where B, C, D are all polynomials, and where the degree of B may always be supposed to be less than that of X.

2) If X and P have a common divisor D, we shall have $X = YD$, $P = SD$, where the polynomials D, S, and Y are all prime to each other. Hence two polynomials λ and μ may be found such that $A = \lambda D^n + \mu Y^n$, and the integral may be written in the form

$$\int \frac{A\,dx}{X^n \sqrt{P}} = \int \frac{\lambda\,dx}{Y^n \sqrt{P}} + \int \frac{\mu\,dx}{D^n \sqrt{P}}.$$

The first of the new integrals is of the type just considered. *The second integral,*

$$\int \frac{\mu\,dx}{D^n \sqrt{P}},$$

where D is a factor of P, reduces to the sum of an algebraic term and a number of integrals of the type Y.

For, since D^n is prime to the product $D'S$, we can find two polynomials λ_1 and μ_1 such that $\lambda_1 D^n + \mu_1 D'S = \mu$. Hence we may write

$$\int \frac{\mu\,dx}{D^n \sqrt{P}} = \int \frac{\lambda_1\,dx}{\sqrt{P}} + \int \frac{\mu_1 SD'}{D^n \sqrt{P}}\,dx.$$

Replacing P by DS, let us write the second of these integrals in the form

$$\int \mu_1 \sqrt{S}\,\frac{D'}{D^{n+\frac{1}{2}}}\,dx,$$

and then integrate it by parts, taking

$$u = \mu_1 \sqrt{S}, \qquad v = \frac{-1}{n - \frac{1}{2}} \frac{1}{D^{n-\frac{1}{2}}},$$

which gives

$$\int \frac{\mu \, dx}{D^n \sqrt{P}} = \int \frac{\lambda_1 \, dx}{\sqrt{P}} - \frac{\mu_1 \sqrt{S}}{(n - \frac{1}{2}) D^{n-\frac{1}{2}}} + \frac{1}{2n - 1} \int \frac{2\mu_1' S + \mu_1 S'}{D^{n-1} \sqrt{P}} \, dx.$$

This is again a reduction formula; but in this case, since the exponent $n - 1/2$ is fractional, the reduction may be performed even when D occurs only to the first power in the denominator, and we finally obtain an expression of the form

$$\int \frac{\mu \, dx}{D^n \sqrt{P}} = \frac{K \sqrt{P}}{D^n} + \int \frac{H \, dx}{\sqrt{P}},$$

where H and K are polynomials.

To sum up our results, we see that the integral

$$\int \frac{M \, dx}{N \sqrt{P}}$$

can always be reduced to a sum of algebraic terms and a number of integrals of the two types

$$\int \frac{x^m \, dx}{\sqrt{P}}, \qquad \int \frac{X_1 \, dx}{X \sqrt{P}},$$

where m is less than or equal to $p - 2$, where X is prime to its derivative X' and also to P, and where the degree of X_1 is less than that of X. *This reduction involves only the operations of addition, multiplication, and division of polynomials.*

If the roots of the equation $X = 0$ are known, each of the rational fractions X_1 / X can be broken up into a sum of partial fractions of the two forms

$$\frac{A}{x - a}, \qquad \frac{Bx + C}{(x - \alpha)^2 + \beta^2},$$

where A, B, and C are constants. This leads to the two new types

$$\int \frac{dx}{(x - a) \sqrt{P(x)}}, \qquad \int \frac{(Bx + C) \, dx}{[(x - \alpha)^2 + \beta^2] \sqrt{P(x)}},$$

which reduce to a single type, namely the first of these, if we agree to allow a to have imaginary values. Integrals of this sort are called *integrals of the third kind*. Integrals of the type Y_m are called *integrals of the first kind* when m is less than $p/2 - 1$, and are called *integrals of the second kind* when m is equal to or greater than $p/2 - 1$. Integrals of the first kind have a characteristic property, — they remain finite when the upper limit increases indefinitely, and also when the upper limit is a root of $P(x)$ (§§ 89, 90); but the essential distinction between the integrals of the second and third kinds must be accepted provisionally at this time without proof. The real distinction between them will be pointed out later.

Note. Up to the present we have made no assumption about the degree p of the polynomial $P(x)$. If p is an odd number, it may always be increased by unity. For, suppose that $P(x)$ is a polynomial of degree $2q - 1$:

$$P(x) = A_0 x^{2q-1} + A_1 x^{2q-2} + \cdots + A_{2q-1}.$$

Then let us set $x = a + 1/y$, where a is not a root of $P(x)$. This gives

$$P(x) = P(a) + P'(a) \frac{1}{y} + \cdots + \frac{P^{(2q-1)}(a)}{(2q-1)!} \frac{1}{y^{2q-1}} = \frac{P_1(y)}{y^{2q}},$$

where $P_1(y)$ is a polynomial of degree $2q$. Hence we have

$$\sqrt{P(x)} = \frac{\sqrt{P_1(y)}}{y^q},$$

and any integral of a rational function of x and $\sqrt{P(x)}$ is transformed into an integral of a rational function of y and $\sqrt{P_1(y)}$.

Conversely, if the degree of the polynomial $P(x)$ under the radical is an even number $2q$, it may be reduced by unity *provided a root of $P(x)$ is known*. For, if a is a root of $P(x)$, let us set $x = a + 1/y$. This gives

$$P(x) = P'(a) \frac{1}{y} + \cdots + \frac{P^{(2q)}(a)}{(2q)!} \frac{1}{y^{2q}} = \frac{P_1(y)}{y^{2q}},$$

where $P_1(y)$ is of degree $2q - 1$, and we shall have

$$\sqrt{P(x)} = \frac{\sqrt{P_1(y)}}{y^q}.$$

Hence the integrand of the transformed integral will contain no other radical than $\sqrt{P_1(y)}$.

111. Case of integration in algebraic terms. We have just seen that an integral of the form

$$\int R[x,\ \sqrt{P(x)}]\,dx$$

can always be reduced by means of elementary operations to the sum of an integral of a rational fraction, an algebraic expression of the form $G\sqrt{P(x)}/L$, and a number of integrals of the first, second, and third kinds. Since we can also find by elementary operations the rational part of the integral of a rational fraction, it is evident that the given integral can always be reduced to the form

$$\int R[x,\ \sqrt{P(x)}]\,dx = F[x,\ \sqrt{P(x)}] + T,$$

where F is a rational function of x and $\sqrt{P(x)}$, and where T is a sum of integrals of the three kinds and an integral $\int X_1/X\,dx$, X being prime to its derivative and of higher degree than X_1. Liouville showed that if the given integral is integrable in algebraic terms, it is equal to $F[x,\ \sqrt{P(x)}]$. We should therefore have, identically,

$$R[x,\ \sqrt{P(x)}] = \frac{d}{dx}\{F[x,\ \sqrt{P(x)}]\},$$

and hence $T = 0$.

Hence we can discover by means of multiplications and divisions of polynomials whether a given integral is integrable in algebraic terms or not, and in case it is, the same process gives the value of the integral.

112. Elliptic integrals. If the polynomial $P(x)$ is of the second degree, the integration of a rational function of x and $P(x)$ can be reduced, by the general process just studied, to the calculation of the integrals

$$\int \frac{dx}{\sqrt{P(x)}}, \qquad \int \frac{dx}{(x-a)\sqrt{P(x)}},$$

which we know how to evaluate directly (§ 105).

The next simplest case is that of elliptic integrals, for which $P(x)$ is of the third or fourth degree. Either of these cases can be reduced to the other, as we have seen just above. Let $P(x)$ be a polynomial of the fourth degree whose coefficients are all real and whose linear factors are all distinct. We proceed to show that a *real* substitution can always be found which carries $P(x)$ into a polynomial each of whose terms is of even degree.

Let a, b, c, d be the four roots of $P(x)$. Then there exists an involutory relation of the form

$$(7) \qquad\qquad Lx'x'' + M(x'+x'') + N = 0,$$

which is satisfied by $x' = a$, $x'' = b$, and by $x' = c$, $x'' = d$.   For the coefficients L, M, N need merely satisfy the two relations

$$Lab + M(a + b) + N = 0,$$
$$Lcd + M(c + d) + N = 0,$$

which are evidently satisfied if we take

$$L = a + b - c - d, \quad M = cd - ab, \quad N = ab(c + d) - cd(a + b).$$

Let α and β be the two double points of this involution, i.e. the roots of the equation

$$Lu^2 + 2Mu + N = 0.$$

These roots will both be real if

$$(cd - ab)^2 - (a + b - c - d)[ab(c + d) - cd(a + b)] > 0,$$

that is, if

$$(8) \qquad (a - c)(a - d)(b - c)(b - d) > 0.$$

The roots of $P(x)$ can always be arranged in such a way that this condition is satisfied.   If all four roots are real, we need merely choose a and b as the two largest.   Then each factor in (8) is positive. If only two of the roots are real, we should choose a and b as the real roots, and c and d as the two conjugate imaginary roots.   Then the two factors $a - c$ and $a - d$ are conjugate imaginary, and so are the other two, $b - c$ and $b - d$.   Finally, if all four roots are imaginary, we may take a and b as one pair and c and d as the other pair of conjugate imaginary roots.   In this case also the factors in (8) are conjugate imaginary by pairs.   It should also be noticed that these methods of selection make the corresponding values of L, M, N real.

The equation (7) may now be written in the form

$$(9) \qquad \frac{x' - \alpha}{x' - \beta} + \frac{x'' - \alpha}{x'' - \beta} = 0.$$

If we set $(x - \alpha)/(x - \beta) = y$, or $x = (\beta y - \alpha)/(y - 1)$, we find

$$P(x) = \frac{P_1(y)}{(y - 1)^4},$$

where $P_1(y)$ is a new polynomial of the fourth degree with real coefficients whose roots are

$$\frac{a - \alpha}{a - \beta}, \quad \frac{b - \alpha}{b - \beta}, \quad \frac{c - \alpha}{c - \beta}, \quad \frac{d - \alpha}{d - \beta}.$$

It is evident from (9) that these four roots satisfy the equation

$y' + y'' = 0$ by pairs; hence the polynomial $P_1(y)$ contains no term of odd degree.

If the four roots a, b, c, d satisfy the equation $a + b = c + d$, we shall have $L = 0$, and one of the double points of the involution lies at infinity. Setting $\alpha = - N/2M$, the equation (7) takes the form

$$x' - \alpha + x'' - \alpha = 0,$$

and we need merely set $x = \alpha + y$ in order to obtain a polynomial which contains no term of odd degree.

We may therefore suppose $P(x)$ reduced to the canonical form

$$P(x) = A_0 x^4 + A_1 x^2 + A_2.$$

It follows that any elliptic integral, neglecting an algebraic term and an integral of a rational function, may be reduced to the sum of integrals of the forms

$$\int \frac{dx}{\sqrt{A_0 x^4 + A_1 x^2 + A_2}}, \quad \int \frac{x\,dx}{\sqrt{A_0 x^4 + A_1 x^2 + A_2}}, \quad \int \frac{x^2\,dx}{\sqrt{A_0 x^4 + A_1 x^2 + A_2}},$$

and integrals of the form

$$\int \frac{dx}{(x - a)\sqrt{A_0 x^4 + A_1 x^2 + A_2}}.$$

The integral

$$u = \int_{x_0}^x \frac{dx}{\sqrt{A_0 x^4 + A_1 x^2 + A_2}}$$

is the elliptic integral of the *first kind*. If we consider x, on the other hand, as a function of u, this *inverse function* is called an *elliptic function*. The second of the above integrals reduces to an elementary integral by means of the substitution $x^2 = u$. The third integral

$$\int \frac{x^2\,dx}{\sqrt{A_0 x^4 + A_1 x^2 + A_2}}$$

is Legendre's integral of the *second kind*. Finally, we have the identity

$$\int \frac{dx}{(x - a)\sqrt{P(x)}} = \int \frac{x\,dx}{(x^2 - a^2)\sqrt{P(x)}} + a \int \frac{dx}{(x^2 - a^2)\sqrt{P(x)}}.$$

The integral

$$\int \frac{dx}{(x^2 + h)\sqrt{A_0 x^4 + A_1 x^2 + A_2}}$$

is Legendre's integral of the *third kind*.

These elliptic integrals were so named because they were first met with in the problem of rectifying the ellipse. Let

$$x = a \cos \phi, \qquad y = b \sin \phi$$

be the coördinates of a point of an ellipse. Then we shall have

$$ds^2 = dx^2 + dy^2 = (a^2 \sin^2 \phi + b^2 \cos^2 \phi) \, d\phi^2,$$

or, setting $a^2 - b^2 = e^2 a^2$,

$$ds = a \sqrt{1 - e^2 \cos^2 \phi} \, d\phi.$$

Hence the integral which gives an arc of the ellipse, after the substitution $\cos \phi = t$, takes the form

$$s = a \int \frac{\sqrt{1 - e^2 t^2}}{\sqrt{1 - t^2}} \, dt = a \int \frac{1 - e^2 t^2}{\sqrt{(1 - t^2)(1 - e^2 t^2)}} \, dt.$$

It follows that the arc of an ellipse is equal to the sum of an integral of the first kind and an integral of the second kind.

Again, consider the lemniscate defined by the equations

$$x = a^2 \frac{t(t^2 + a^2)}{t^4 + a^4}, \qquad y = a^2 \frac{t(t^2 - a^2)}{t^4 + a^4}.$$

An easy calculation gives the element of length in the form

$$ds^2 = dx^2 + dy^2 = \frac{2a^4}{t^4 + a^4} \, dt^2.$$

Hence the arc of the lemniscate is given by an elliptic integral of the first kind.*

113. Pseudo-elliptic integrals. It sometimes happens that an integral of the form $\int F[x, \sqrt{P(x)}] \, dx$, where $P(x)$ is a polynomial of the third or fourth degree, can be expressed in terms of algebraic functions and a sum of a finite number of logarithms of algebraic functions. Such integrals are called *pseudo-elliptic*. This happens in the following general case. *Let*

$$(10) \qquad Lx'x'' + M(x' + x'') + N = 0$$

be an involutory relation which establishes a correspondence between two pairs of the four roots of the quartic equation $P(x) = 0$. If the function $f(x)$ be such that the relation

$$(11) \qquad f(x) + f\left(-\frac{Mx + N}{Lx + M}\right) = 0$$

is identically satisfied, the integral $\int [f(x)/\sqrt{P(x)}] \, dx$ is pseudo-elliptic.

---

* This is a common property of a whole class of curves discovered by Serret (*Cours de Calcul différentiel et intégral*, Vol. II, p. 264).

Let α and β be the double points of the involution. As we have already seen, the equation (10) may be written in the form

$$(12) \qquad \frac{x' - \alpha}{x' - \beta} + \frac{x'' - \alpha}{x'' - \beta} = 0.$$

Let us now make the substitution $(x - \alpha)/(x - \beta) = y$. This gives

$$dx = \frac{(\alpha - \beta)\,dy}{(1 - y)^2}, \qquad P(x) = \frac{P_1(y)}{(1 - y)^4},$$

and consequently

$$\frac{dx}{\sqrt{P(x)}} = \frac{(\alpha - \beta)\,dy}{\sqrt{P_1(y)}},$$

where $P_1(y)$ is a polynomial of the fourth degree which contains no odd powers of y (§ 112). On the other hand, the rational fraction $f(x)$ goes over into a rational fraction $\phi(y)$, which satisfies the identity $\phi(y) + \phi(-y) = 0$. For if two values of x correspond by means of (12), they are transformed into two values of y, say y' and y'', which satisfy the equation $y' + y'' = 0$. It is evident that $\phi(y)$ is of the form $y\,\psi(y^2)$, where ψ is a rational function of y^2. Hence the integral under discussion takes the form

$$\int \frac{y\,\psi(y^2)\,dy}{\sqrt{A_0 y^4 + A_1 y^2 + A_2}},$$

and we need merely set $y^2 = z$ in order to reduce it to an elementary integral. Thus the proposition is proved, and it merely remains actually to carry out the reduction.

The theorem remains true when the polynomial $P(x)$ is of the third degree, provided that we think of one of its roots as infinite. The demonstration is exactly similar to the preceding.

If, for example, the equation $P(x) = 0$ is a reciprocal equation, one of the involutory relations which interchanges the roots by pairs is $x'x'' = 1$. Hence, if $f(x)$ be a rational function which satisfies the relation $f(x) + f(1/x) = 0$, the integral $\int [f(x)/\sqrt{P(x)}]\,dx$ is pseudo-elliptic, and the two substitutions $(x - 1)/(x + 1) = y,\ y^2 = z$, performed in order, transform it into an elementary integral.

Again, suppose that $P(x)$ is a polynomial of the third degree,

$$P(x) = x\,(x - 1)\left(x - \frac{1}{k^2}\right).$$

Let us set $a = \infty$, $b = 0$, $c = 1$, $d = 1/k^2$. There exist three involutory relations which interchange these roots by pairs:

$$x' = \frac{1}{k^2 x''}, \qquad x' = \frac{1 - k^2 x''}{k^2(1 - x'')}, \qquad x' = \frac{1 - x''}{1 - k^2 x''}.$$

Hence, if $f(x)$ be a rational function which satisfies one of the identities

$$f(x) + f\left(\frac{1}{k^2 x}\right) = 0, \qquad f(x) + f\left[\frac{1 - k^2 x}{k^2(1 - x)}\right] = 0, \qquad f(x) + f\left(\frac{1 - x}{1 - k^2 x}\right) = 0,$$

the integral

$$\int \frac{f(x)\,dx}{\sqrt{x(1-x)(1-k^2x)}}$$

is pseudo-elliptic. From this others may be derived. For instance, if we set $x = z^2$, the preceding integral becomes

$$\int \frac{2f(z^2)\,dz}{\sqrt{(1-z^2)(1-k^2z^2)}},$$

whence it follows that this new integral is also pseudo-elliptic if $f(z^2)$ satisfies one of the identities

$$f(z^2) + f\left(\frac{1}{k^2z^2}\right) = 0, \qquad f(z^2) + f\left[\frac{1-k^2z^2}{k^2(1-z^2)}\right] = 0,$$

$$f(z^2) + f\left(\frac{1-z^2}{1-k^2z^2}\right) = 0.$$

The first of these cases was noticed by Euler.*

III. INTEGRATION OF TRANSCENDENTAL FUNCTIONS

114. Integration of rational functions of sin x and cos x. It is well known that $\sin x$ and $\cos x$ may be expressed rationally in terms of $\tan x/2 = t$. Hence this change of variable reduces an integral of the form

$$\int R(\sin x,\ \cos x)\,dx$$

to the integral of a rational function of t. For we have

$$x = 2 \arctan t, \qquad dx = \frac{2\,dt}{1+t^2}, \qquad \sin x = \frac{2t}{1+t^2}, \qquad \cos x = \frac{1-t^2}{1+t^2},$$

and the given integral becomes

$$\int R\left(\frac{2t}{1+t^2},\ \frac{1-t^2}{1+t^2}\right)\frac{2\,dt}{1+t^2} = \int \Phi(t)\,dt,$$

where $\Phi(t)$ is a rational function. For example,

$$\int \frac{dx}{\sin x} = \int \frac{dt}{t} = \log t\,;$$

hence

$$\int \frac{dx}{\sin x} = \log \tan \frac{x}{2}.$$

---

* See Hermite's lithographed *Cours*, 4th ed., pp. 25–28.

The integral $\int [1/\cos x]\, dx$ reduces to the preceding by means of the substitution $x = \pi/2 - y$, which gives

$$\int \frac{dx}{\cos x} = - \log \tan \left(\frac{\pi}{4} - \frac{x}{2} \right) = \log \tan \left(\frac{\pi}{4} + \frac{x}{2} \right).$$

The preceding method has the advantage of generality, but it is often possible to find a simpler substitution which is equally successful. Thus, if the function $f(\sin x, \cos x)$ has the period π, it is a rational function of $\tan x$, $F(\tan x)$. The substitution $\tan x = t$ therefore reduces the integral to the form

$$\int F(\tan x)\, dx = \int \frac{F(t)\, dt}{1 + t^2}.$$

As an example let us consider the integral

$$\int \frac{dx}{A \cos^2 x + B \sin x \cos x + C \sin^2 x + D},$$

where A, B, C, D are any constants. The integrand evidently has the period π; and, setting $\tan x = t$, we find

$$\cos^2 x = \frac{1}{1 + t^2}, \qquad \sin x \cos x = \frac{t}{1 + t^2}, \qquad \sin^2 x = \frac{t^2}{1 + t^2}$$

Hence the given integral becomes

$$\int \frac{dt}{A + Bt + Ct^2 + D(1 + t^2)}.$$

The form of the result will depend upon the nature of the roots of the denominator. Taking certain three of the coefficients zero, we find the formulæ

$$\int \frac{dx}{\cos^2 x} = \tan x, \qquad \int \frac{dx}{\sin x \cos x} = \log \tan x,$$

$$\int \frac{dx}{\sin^2 x} = - \cot x.$$

When the integrand is of the form $R(\sin x) \cos x$, or of the form $R(\cos x) \sin x$, the proper change of variable is apparent. In the first case we should set $\sin x = t$; in the second case, $\cos x = t$.

It is sometimes advantageous to make a first substitution in order to simplify the integral before proceeding with the general method. For example, let us consider the integral

$$\int \frac{dx}{a \cos x + b \sin x + c},$$

where a, b, c are any three constants. If ρ is a positive number and ϕ an angle determined by the equations

$$a = \rho \cos \phi, \qquad b = \rho \sin \phi,$$

we shall have

$$\rho = \sqrt{a^2 + b^2}, \qquad \cos \phi = \frac{a}{\sqrt{a^2 + b^2}}, \qquad \sin \phi = \frac{b}{\sqrt{a^2 + b^2}},$$

and the given integral may be written in the form

$$\int \frac{dx}{\rho \cos (x - \phi) + c} = \int \frac{dy}{\rho \cos y + c},$$

where $x - \phi = y$. Let us now apply the general method, setting $\tan y/2 = t$. Then the integral becomes

$$\int \frac{2\, dt}{\rho + c + (c - \rho)\, t^2},$$

and the rest of the calculation presents no difficulty. Two different forms will be found for the result, according as $\rho^2 - c^2 = a^2 + b^2 - c^2$ is positive or negative.

The integral

$$\int \frac{m \cos x + n \sin x + p}{a \cos x + b \sin x + c}\, dx$$

may be reduced to the preceding. For, let $u = a \cos x + b \sin x + c$, and let us determine three constants λ, μ, and ν such that the equation

$$m \cos x + n \sin x + p = \lambda u + \mu \frac{du}{dx} + \nu$$

is identically satisfied. The equations which determine these numbers are

$$m = \lambda a + \mu b, \qquad n = \lambda b - \mu a, \qquad p = \lambda c + \nu,$$

the first two of which determine λ and μ. The three constants having been selected in this way, the given integral may be written in the form

$$\int \frac{\lambda u + \mu \dfrac{du}{dx} + \nu}{u}\, dx = \lambda x + \mu \log u + \nu \int \frac{dx}{a \cos x + b \sin x + c}.$$

Example. Let us try to evaluate the definite integral

$$\int_0^\pi \frac{dx}{1 + e \cos x}, \qquad \text{where} \qquad |e| < 1.$$

Considering it first as an indefinite integral, we find successively

$$\int \frac{dx}{1+e\cos x} = 2\int \frac{dt}{1+e+(1-e)t^2} = \frac{2}{\sqrt{1-e^2}}\int \frac{du}{1+u^2},$$

by means of the successive substitutions $\tan x/2 = t$, $t = u\sqrt{(1+e)/(1-e)}$. Hence the indefinite integral is equal to

$$\frac{2}{\sqrt{1-e^2}}\arctan\left(\sqrt{\frac{1-e}{1+e}}\tan\frac{x}{2}\right).$$

As x varies from 0 to π, $\sqrt{(1-e)/(1+e)}\tan x/2$ increases from 0 to $+\infty$, and the arctangent varies from 0 to $\pi/2$. Hence the given definite integral is equal to $\pi/\sqrt{(1-e^2)}$.

115. Reduction formulæ. There are also certain classes of integrals for which reduction formulæ exist. For instance, the formula for the derivative of $\tan^{n-1}x$ may be written

$$\frac{d}{dx}(\tan^{n-1}x) = (n-1)\tan^{n-2}x(1+\tan^2 x),$$

whence we find

$$\int \tan^n x\, dx = \frac{\tan^{n-1}x}{n-1} - \int \tan^{n-2}x\, dx.$$

The exponent of $\tan x$ in the integrand is diminished by two units. Repeated applications of this formula lead to one or the other of the two integrals

$$\int dx = x, \qquad \int \tan x\, dx = -\log\cos x.$$

The analogous formula for integrals of the type $\int\cot^n x\, dx$ is

$$\int \cot^n x\, dx = -\frac{\cot^{n-1}x}{n-1} - \int \cot^{n-2}x\, dx.$$

In general, consider the integral

$$\int \sin^m x \cos^n x\, dx,$$

where m and n are any positive or negative integers. When one of these integers is odd it is best to use the change of variable given above. If, for instance, $n = 2p+1$, we should set $\sin x = t$, which reduces the integral to the form $\int t^m(1-t^2)^p\, dt$.

Let us, therefore, restrict ourselves to the case where m and n are both even, that is, to integrals of the type

$$I_{m,n} = \int \sin^{2m}x \cos^{2n}x\, dx,$$

which may be written in the form

$$I_{m,n} = \int \sin^{2m-1}x \cos^{2n}x \sin x \, dx.$$

Taking $\cos^{2n}x \sin x \, dx$ as the differential of $[-1/(2n+1)]\cos^{2n+1}x$, an integration by parts gives

$$I_{m,n} = -\sin^{2m-1}x \frac{\cos^{2n+1}x}{2n+1} + \frac{2m-1}{2n+1}\int \sin^{2m-2}x \cos^{2n}x \,(1-\sin^2 x)\, dx,$$

which may be written in the form

$$\text{(A)} \quad I_{m,n} = -\frac{\sin^{2m-1}x \cos^{2n+1}x}{2(m+n)} + \frac{2m-1}{2(m+n)} \ I_{m-1,n}.$$

This formula enables us to diminish the exponent m without altering the second exponent. If m is negative, an analogous formula may be obtained by solving the equation (A) with respect to $I_{m-1,n}$ and replacing m by $1-m$:

$$\text{(B)} \quad I_{-m,n} = \frac{\sin^{1-2m}x \cos^{2n+1}x}{1-2m} + \frac{2(n-m+1)}{1-2m} I_{1-m,n}.$$

The following analogous formulæ, which are easily derived, enable us to reduce the exponent of $\cos x$:

$$\text{(C)} \quad I_{m,n} = \frac{\sin^{2m+1}x \cos^{2n-1}x}{2(m+n)} + \frac{2n-1}{2(m+n)} \ I_{m,n-1},$$

$$\text{(D)} \quad I_{m,-n} = -\frac{\sin^{2m+1}x \cos^{1-2n}x}{1-2n} + \frac{2(m+1-n)}{1-2n} I_{m,-n+1}.$$

Repeated applications of these formulæ reduce each of the numbers m and n to zero. The only case in which we should be unable to proceed is that in which we obtain an integral $I_{m,n}$, where $m+n=0$. But such an integral is of one of the types for which reduction formulæ were derived at the beginning of this article.

116. Wallis' formulæ. There exist reduction formulæ whether the exponents m and n are even or odd.

As an example let us try to evaluate the definite integral

$$I_m = \int_0^{\frac{\pi}{2}} \sin^m x \, dx,$$

where m is a positive integer. An integration by parts gives

$$\int_0^{\frac{\pi}{2}} \sin^{m-1}x \sin x \, dx = -\left[\cos x \sin^{m-1}x\right]_0^{\frac{\pi}{2}} + (m-1)\int_0^{\frac{\pi}{2}} \sin^{m-2}x \cos^2 x \, dx,$$

whence, noting that $\cos x \sin^{m-1} x$ vanishes at both limits, we find the formula

$$I_m = (m-1)\int_0^{\frac{\pi}{2}} \sin^{m-2} x\,(1-\sin^2 x)\,dx = (m-1)(I_{m-2} - I_m),$$

which leads to the recurrent formula

$$(13) \qquad\qquad I_m = \frac{m-1}{m} I_{m-2}.$$

Repeated applications of this formula reduce the given integral to $I_0 = \pi/2$ if m is even, or to $I_1 = 1$ if m is odd. In the former case, taking $m = 2p$ and replacing m successively by $2, 4, 6, \cdots, 2p$, we find

$$I_2 = \frac{1}{2} I_0, \qquad I_4 = \frac{3}{4} I_2, \qquad \cdots, \qquad I_{2p} = \frac{2p-1}{2p} I_{2p-2},$$

or, multiplying these equations together,

$$I_{2p} = \frac{1 \cdot 3 \cdot 5 \cdots (2p-1)}{2 \cdot 4 \cdot 6 \cdots 2p} \frac{\pi}{2}.$$

Similarly, we find the formula

$$I_{2p+1} = \frac{2 \cdot 4 \cdot 6 \cdots 2p}{1 \cdot 3 \cdot 5 \cdots (2p+1)}.$$

A curious result due to Wallis may be deduced from these formulæ. It is evident that the value of I_m diminishes as m increases, for $\sin^{m+1} x$ is less than $\sin^m x$. Hence

$$I_{2p+1} < I_{2p} < I_{2p-1},$$

and if we replace I_{2p+1}, I_{2p}, I_{2p-1} by their values from the formulæ above, we find the new inequalities

$$H_p > \frac{\pi}{2} > H_p \frac{2p}{2p+1},$$

where we have set, for brevity,

$$H_p = \frac{2}{1} \cdot \frac{2}{3} \cdot \frac{4}{3} \cdot \frac{4}{5} \cdots \frac{2p-2}{2p-1} \cdot \frac{2p}{2p-1}.$$

It is evident that the ratio $\pi/2H_p$ approaches the limit one as p increases indefinitely. It follows that $\pi/2$ is the limit of the product H_p as the number of factors increases indefinitely. The law of formation of the successive factors is apparent.

117. The integral $\int \cos(ax+b)\cos(a'x+b')\cdots dx$. Let us consider a product of any number of factors of the form $\cos(ax+b)$, where a and b are constants, and where the same factor may occur several times. The formula

$$\cos u \cos v = \frac{\cos(u+v)}{2} + \frac{\cos(u-v)}{2}$$

enables us to replace the product of two factors of this sort by the sum of two cosines of linear functions of x; hence also the product of n factors by the sum of two products of $n-1$ factors each. Repeated applications of this formula finally reduce the given integral to a sum of the form $\Sigma H \cos(Ax + B)$, each term of which is immediately integrable. If A is not zero, we have

$$\int \cos(Ax + B)\, dx = \frac{\sin(Ax + B)}{A} + C,$$

while, in the particular case when $A = 0$, $\int \cos B\, dx = x \cos B + C$.

This transformation applies in the special case of products of the form

$$\cos^m x \sin^n x,$$

where m and n are both positive integers. For this product may be written

$$\cos^m x \cos^n\left(\frac{\pi}{2} - x\right),$$

and, applying the preceding process, we are led to a sum of sines and cosines of multiples of the angle, each term of which is immediately integrable.

As an example let us try to calculate the area of the curve

$$\left(\frac{x}{a}\right)^{\frac{2}{3}} + \left(\frac{y}{b}\right)^{\frac{2}{3}} = 1,$$

which we may suppose given in the parametric form $x = a \cos^3\theta$, $y = b \sin^3\theta$, where θ varies from 0 to 2π for the whole curve. The formula for the area of a closed curve,

$$\mathsf{A} = \frac{1}{2}\int_{(C)} x\, dy - y\, dx,$$

gives

$$\mathsf{A} = \int_0^{2\pi} \frac{3ab}{2} \sin^2\theta \cos^2\theta\, d\theta.$$

But we have the formula

$$(\sin\theta \cos\theta)^2 = \frac{1}{4}\sin^2 2\theta = \frac{1}{8}(1 - \cos 4\theta).$$

Hence the area of the given curve is

$$\mathsf{A} = \frac{3ab}{16}\left[\theta - \frac{\sin 4\theta}{4}\right]^{2\pi} = \frac{3\pi ab}{8}.$$

It is now easy to deduce the following formulæ :

$$\int \sin^2 x \, dx = \int \frac{1 - \cos 2x}{2} \, dx \qquad = \frac{x}{2} - \frac{\sin 2x}{4} + C,$$

$$\int \sin^3 x \, dx = \int \frac{3 \sin x - \sin 3x}{4} \, dx \qquad = -\frac{3 \cos x}{4} + \frac{\cos 3x}{12} + C,$$

$$\int \sin^4 x \, dx = \int \frac{3 - 4 \cos 2x + \cos 4x}{8} \, dx = \frac{3x}{8} - \frac{\sin 2x}{4} + \frac{\sin 4x}{32} + C,$$

$$\cdots \cdots \cdots \cdots \cdots \cdots \cdots \cdots ,$$

$$\int \cos^2 x \, dx = \int \frac{1 + \cos 2x}{2} \, dx \qquad = \frac{x}{2} + \frac{\sin 2x}{4} + C,$$

$$\int \cos^3 x \, dx = \int \frac{3 \cos x + \cos 3x}{4} \, dx \qquad = \frac{3 \sin x}{4} + \frac{\sin 3x}{12} + C,$$

$$\int \cos^4 x \, dx = \int \frac{3 + 4 \cos 2x + \cos 4x}{8} \, dx = \frac{3x}{8} + \frac{\sin 2x}{4} + \frac{\sin 4x}{32} + C,$$

$$\cdots \cdots \cdots \cdots \cdots \cdots \cdots \cdots$$

A general law may be noticed in these formulæ. The integrals $F(x) = \int_0^x \sin^n x \, dx$ and $\Phi(x) = \int_0^x \cos^n x \, dx$ have the period 2π when n is odd. On the other hand, when n is even, these integrals increase by a positive constant when x increases by 2π. It is evident *a priori* that these statements hold in general. For we have

$$F(x + 2\pi) = \int_0^{2\pi} \sin^n x \, dx + \int_{2\pi}^{2\pi + x} \sin^n x \, dx,$$

or

$$F(x + 2\pi) = \int_0^{2\pi} \sin^n x \, dx + \int_0^x \sin^n x \, dx = F(x) + \int_0^{2\pi} \sin^n x \, dx,$$

since $\sin x$ has the period 2π. If n is even, it is evident that the integral $\int_0^{2\pi} \sin^n x \, dx$ is a positive quantity. If n is odd, the same integral vanishes, since $\sin (x + \pi) = - \sin x$.

Note. On account of the great variety of transformations applicable to trigonometric functions it is often convenient to introduce them in the calculation of other integrals. Consider, for example, the integral $\int [1/(1 + x^2)^{\frac{3}{2}}] \, dx$. Setting $x = \tan \phi$, this integral becomes $\int \cos \phi \, d\phi = \sin \phi + C$. Hence, returning to the variable x,

$$\int \frac{dx}{(1 + x^2)^{\frac{3}{2}}} = \frac{x}{\sqrt{1 + x^2}} + C,$$

which is the result already found in § 105.

118. The integral $\int R(x)\,e^{\omega x}dx$. Let us now consider an integral of the form $\int R(x)\,e^{\omega x}dx$, where $R(x)$ is a rational function of x. Let us suppose the function $R(x)$ broken up, as we have done several times, into a sum of the form

$$R(x) = E(x) + \frac{A_1}{X_1} + \frac{A_2}{X_2^2} + \cdots + \frac{A_p}{X_p^p},$$

where $E(x)$, A_1, A_2, $\cdots$, A_p, X_1, $\cdots$, X_p are polynomials, and X_i is prime to its derivative. The given integral is then equal to the sum of the integral $\int E(x)\,e^{\omega x}dx$, which we learned to integrate in § 85 by a suite of integrations by parts, and a number of integrals of the form

$$\int \frac{A\,e^{\omega x}dx}{X^n}.$$

There exists a reduction formula for the case when n is greater than unity. For, since X is prime to its derivative, we can determine two polynomials λ and μ which satisfy the identity $A = \lambda X + \mu X'$. Hence we have

$$\int \frac{A\,e^{\omega x}dx}{X^n} = \int \frac{\lambda\,e^{\omega x}dx}{X^{n-1}} + \int \frac{\mu X'\,e^{\omega x}}{X^n}\,dx,$$

and an integration by parts gives the formula

$$\int \mu\,e^{\omega x}\,\frac{X'dx}{X^n} = -\frac{1}{n-1}\frac{\mu\,e^{\omega x}}{X^{n-1}} + \frac{1}{n-1}\int \frac{e^{\omega x}(\mu' + \mu\omega)}{X^{n-1}}\,dx.$$

Uniting these two formulæ, the integral under consideration is reduced to an integral of the same type, where the exponent n is reduced by unity. Repeated applications of this process lead to the integral

$$\int \frac{B\,e^{\omega x}}{X}\,dx,$$

where the polynomial B may always be supposed to be prime to and of less degree than X. The reduction formula cannot be applied to this integral, but if the roots of X be known, it can always be reduced to a single new type of transcendental function. For definiteness suppose that all the roots are real. Then the integral in question can be broken up into several integrals of the form

$$\int \frac{\alpha\,e^{\omega x}}{x-a}\,dx.$$

Neglecting a constant factor, the substitutions $x = a + y/\omega$, $u = e^y$ enable us to write this integral in either of the following forms:

$$\int \frac{e^y\,dy}{y}, \qquad \int \frac{du}{\log u}.$$

The latter integral $\int [1/\log u]\,du$ is a transcendental function which is called *the integral logarithm*.

119. Miscellaneous integrals. Let us consider an integral of the form

$$\int e^{ax} f(\sin x,\ \cos x)\,dx,$$

where f is an *integral* function of $\sin x$ and $\cos x$. **Any term of** this integral is of the form

$$\int e^{ax} \sin^m x \cos^n x\,dx,$$

where m and n are positive integers. We have seen above that the product $\sin^m x \cos^n x$ may be replaced by a sum of sines and cosines of multiples of x. Hence it only remains to study the following two types:

$$\int e^{ax} \cos bx\,dx, \qquad \int e^{ax} \sin bx\,dx.$$

Integrating each of these by parts, we find the formulæ

$$\int e^{ax} \cos bx\,dx = \frac{e^{ax} \sin bx}{b} - \frac{a}{b} \int e^{ax} \sin bx\,dx,$$

$$\int e^{ax} \sin bx\,dx = -\frac{e^{ax} \cos bx}{b} + \frac{a}{b} \int e^{ax} \cos bx\,dx.$$

Hence the values of the integrals under consideration are

$$\int e^{ax} \cos bx\,dx = \frac{e^{ax}(a \cos bx + b \sin bx)}{a^2 + b^2},$$

$$\int e^{ax} \sin bx\,dx = \frac{e^{ax}(a \sin bx - b \cos bx)}{a^2 + b^2}.$$

Among the integrals which may be reduced to the preceding types we may mention the following cases:

$$\int f(\log x)\, x^m\,dx, \qquad \int f(\arcsin x)\,dx,$$

$$\int f(x) \arcsin x\,dx, \qquad \int f(x) \arctan x\,dx,$$

where f denotes any integral function. In the first two cases we should take $\log x$ or $\arcsin x$ as the new variable. In the last two we should integrate by parts, taking $f(x)\,dx$ as the differential of another polynomial $F(x)$, which would lead to types of integrals already considered.

EXERCISES

1. Evaluate the indefinite integrals of each of the following functions:

$$\frac{1}{(x^4+1)^2}, \qquad \frac{1}{x\,(x^3+1)^3}, \qquad \frac{x^4-x^3-3x^2-x}{(x^2+1)^3}, \qquad \frac{1+\sqrt{1+x}}{1-\sqrt{x}},$$

$$\frac{1}{1+x+\sqrt{1+x^2}}, \qquad \frac{1+\sqrt[3]{1+x}}{1-\sqrt[3]{1+x}}, \qquad \frac{1}{\sqrt{x}+\sqrt{x+1}+\sqrt{x\,(x+1)}}, \qquad \frac{x}{\cos^2 x},$$

$$xe^x\cos x, \qquad \frac{x^{\frac{n}{2}}}{\sqrt{a+x^{n+2}}}, \qquad x^{\frac{p}{q}}\tan x.$$

2. Find the area of the loop of the folium of Descartes:

$$x^3 + y^3 - 3axy = 0.$$

3. Evaluate the integral $\int y\,dx$, where x and y satisfy one of the following identities:

$$(x^2-a^2)^2 - ay^2\,(2y+3a) = 0, \qquad y^2\,(a-x) = x^3, \qquad y\,(x^2+y^2) = a\,(y^2-x^2).$$

4. Derive the formulæ

$$\int \sin^{n-1}x \cos(n+1)x\,dx = \frac{\sin^n x \cos nx}{n} + C,$$

$$\int \sin^{n-1}x \sin(n+1)x\,dx = \frac{\sin^n x \sin nx}{n} + C,$$

$$\int \cos^{n-1}x \cos(n+1)x\,dx = \frac{\cos^n x \sin nx}{n} + C,$$

$$\int \cos^{n-1}x \sin(n+1)x\,dx = -\frac{\cos^n x \cos nx}{n} + C.$$

[EULER.]

5. Evaluate each of the following pseudo-elliptic integrals:

$$\int \frac{(1+x^2)\,dx}{(1-x^2)\sqrt{1+x^4}}, \qquad \int \frac{(1-x^2)\,dx}{(1+x^2)\sqrt{1+x^4}}.$$

6. Reduce the following integrals to elliptic integrals:

$$\int \frac{R(x)\,dx}{\sqrt{a\,(1+x^6)+bx\,(1+x^4)+cx^2\,(1+x^2)+dx^3}},$$

$$\int \frac{R(x)\,dx}{\sqrt{a\,(1+x^8)+bx^2\,(1+x^4)+cx^4}},$$

where $R(x)$ denotes a rational function.

7*. Let a, b, c, d be the roots of an equation of the fourth degree $P(x) = 0$. Then there exist three involutory relations of the form

$$x' = -\frac{M_i x'' + N_i}{L_i x'' + M_i}, \qquad i = 1, \ 2, \ 3,$$

which interchange the roots by pairs. If the rational function $f(x)$ satisfies the identity

$$f(x) + \sum_{i=1}^{3} f\left(-\frac{M_i x + N_i}{L_i x + M_i}\right) = 0,$$

the integral $\int [f(x)/\sqrt{P(x)}] \, dx$ is pseudo-elliptic (see *Bulletin de la Société mathématique*, Vol. XV, p. 106).

8. The rectification of a curve of the type $y = A x^\mu$ leads to an integral of a binomial differential. Discuss the cases of integrability.

9. If $a > 1$, show that

$$\int_{-1}^{+1} \frac{dx}{(a-x)\sqrt{1-x^2}} = \frac{\pi}{\sqrt{a^2-1}}.$$

Hence deduce the formula

$$\int_{-1}^{+1} \frac{x^{2n} \, dx}{\sqrt{1-x^2}} = \frac{1 \cdot 3 \cdot 5 \cdots (2n-1)}{2 \cdot 4 \cdot 6 \cdots 2n} \pi.$$

10. If $AC - B^2 > 0$, show that

$$\int_{-\infty}^{+\infty} \frac{dx}{(Ax^2 + 2Bx + C)^n} = \frac{1 \cdot 3 \cdot 5 \cdots (2n-3)}{2 \cdot 4 \cdot 6 \cdots (2n-2)} \pi \frac{A^{n-1}}{(AC-B^2)^{n+\frac{1}{2}}}.$$

[Apply the reduction formula of § 104.]

11. Evaluate the definite integral

$$\int_0^\pi \frac{\sin^2 x \, dx}{1 + 2a \cos x + a^2}.$$

12. Derive the following formulæ:

$$\int_{-1}^{+1} \frac{dx}{\sqrt{1 - 2\alpha x + \alpha^2} \sqrt{1 - 2\beta x + \beta^2}} = \frac{1}{\sqrt{\alpha\beta}} \log\left(\frac{1 + \sqrt{\alpha\beta}}{1 - \sqrt{\alpha\beta}}\right), \qquad \alpha\beta > 0.$$

$$\int_{-1}^{+1} \frac{(1 - \alpha x)(1 - \beta x) \, dx}{(1 - 2\alpha x + \alpha^2)(1 - 2\beta x + \beta^2)\sqrt{1-x^2}} = \frac{\pi}{2} \frac{2 - \alpha\beta}{1 - \alpha\beta}.$$

13*. Derive the formula

$$\int_0^{+\infty} \frac{x^{m-1} \, dx}{1 + x^n} = \frac{\pi}{n \sin \dfrac{m\pi}{n}},$$

where m and n are positive integers ($m < n$). [Break up the integrand into partial fractions.]

14. From the preceding exercise deduce the formula

$$\int_0^{+\infty} \frac{x^{a-1}dx}{1+x} = \frac{\pi}{\sin a\pi}, \qquad 0 < a < 1.$$

15. Setting $I_{p,q} = \int t^q (t+1)^p \, dt$, deduce the following reduction formulæ :

$$(p+q+1) I_{p,q} = t^{q+1}(t+1)^p + p I_{p-1,q},$$
$$(p-1) I_{-p,q} = t^{q+1}(t+1)^{1-p} - (2+q-p) I_{-p+1,q},$$

and two analogous formulæ for reducing the exponent q.

16. Derive formulæ of reduction for the integrals

$$I_n = \int \frac{x^n \, dx}{\sqrt{Ax^2 + 2Bx + C}}, \qquad Z_m = \int \frac{dx}{(x-a)^m \sqrt{Ax^2 + 2Bx + C}}.$$

17*. Derive a reduction formula for the integral

$$\int_0^1 \frac{x^n \, dx}{\sqrt{1-x^4}}.$$

Hence deduce a formula analogous to that of Wallis for the definite integral

$$\int_0^1 \frac{dx}{\sqrt{1-x^4}}.$$

18. Has the definite integral

$$\int_0^{+\infty} \frac{dx}{1 + x^4 \sin^2 x}$$

a finite value ?

19. Show that the area of a sector of an ellipse bounded by the focal axis and a radius vector through the focus is

$$\mathsf{A} = \frac{p^2}{2} \int_0^\omega \frac{d\omega}{(1 + e \cos \omega)^2},$$

where p denotes the parameter b^2/a and e the eccentricity. Applying the general method, make the substitutions $\tan \omega/2 = t$, $t = u \sqrt{(1+e)/(1-e)}$ successively, and show that the area in question is

$$\mathsf{A} = ab \left(\arctan u - e \, \frac{u}{1+u^2} \right).$$

Also show that this expression may be written in the form

$$\mathsf{A} = \frac{ab}{2} (\phi - e \sin \phi),$$

where ϕ is the eccentric anomaly. See p. 406.

20. Find the curves for which the distance NT, or the area of the triangle MNT, is constant (Fig. 3, p. 31). Construct the two branches of the curve.

[*Licence*, Paris, 1880 ; Toulouse, 1882.]

21*. Setting

$$A_n = \frac{x^{2n+1}}{2 \cdot 4 \cdot 6 \cdots 2n} \int_0^1 (1 - z^2)^n \cos xz \, dz,$$

derive the recurrent formula

$$A_{n+1} = (2n+1) A_n - x \frac{dA_n}{dx}.$$

From this deduce the formulæ

$$A_{2p} = U_{2p} \sin x + V_{2p} \cos x,$$
$$A_{2p+1} = U_{2p+1} \sin x + V_{2p+1} \cos x,$$

where U_{2p}, V_{2p}, U_{2p+1}, V_{2p+1} are polynomials with integral coefficients, and where U_{2p} and U_{2p+1} contain no odd powers of x. It is readily shown that these formulæ hold when $n = 1$, and the general case follows from the above recurrent formula.

The formula for A_{2p} enables us to show that π^2 is incommensurable. For if we assume that $\pi^2/4 = b/a$, and then replace x by $\pi/2$ in A_{2p}, we obtain a relation of the form

$$H_1 = a^p \sqrt{\frac{b}{a}} \frac{\left(\dfrac{b}{a}\right)^{2p}}{2 \cdot 4 \cdot 6 \cdots 4p} \int_0^1 (1 - z^2)^{2p} \cos \frac{\pi z}{2} \, dz,$$

where H_1 is an integer. Such an equation, however, is impossible, for the right-hand side approaches zero as p increases indefinitely.

CHAPTER VI

DOUBLE INTEGRALS

I. DOUBLE INTEGRALS   METHODS OF EVALUATION GREEN'S THEOREM

120. Continuous functions of two variables. Let $z = f(x, y)$ be a function of the two independent variables x and y which is continuous inside a region A of the plane which is bounded by a closed contour C, and also upon the contour itself. A number of propositions analogous to those proved in § 70 for a continuous function of a single variable can be shown to hold for this function. For instance, *given any positive number ϵ, the region A can be divided into subregions in such a way that the difference between the values of z at any two points (x, y), (x', y') in the same subregion is less than ϵ.*

We shall always proceed by means of successive subdivisions as follows: Suppose the region A divided into subregions by drawing

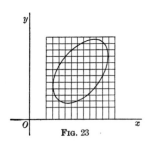

parallels to the two axes at equal distances δ from each other. The corresponding subdivisions of A are either squares of side δ lying entirely inside C, or else portions of squares bounded in part by an arc of C. Then, if the proposition were untrue for the whole region A, it would also be untrue for at least one of the subdivisions, say A_1. Subdividing the subregion A_1 in the same manner and continuing the process indefinitely, we would obtain a sequence of squares or portions of squares $A, A_1, \cdots, A_n, \cdots$, for which the proposition would be untrue. The region A_n lies between the two lines $x = a_n$ and $x = b_n$, which are parallel to the y axis, and the two lines $y = c_n$, $y = d_n$, which are parallel to the x axis. As n increases indefinitely a_n and b_n approach a common limit λ, and c_n and d_n approach a common limit μ, for the numbers a_n, for example, never decrease and always remain less than a fixed number. It follows that all the points of A_n approach a limiting point (λ, μ) which lies within or upon the contour C. The rest of the reasoning is similar to that in § 70; if the theorem stated were untrue, the function $f(x, y)$ could be shown to be discontinuous at the point (λ, μ), which is contrary to hypothesis.

Corollary. Suppose that the parallel lines have been chosen so near together that the difference of any two values of z in any one subregion is less than $\epsilon/2$, and let η be the distance between the successive parallels. Let (x, y) and (x', y') be two points inside or upon the contour C, the distance between which is less than η. These two points will lie either in the same subregion or else in two different subregions which have one vertex in common. In either case the absolute value of the difference

$$f(x, y) - f(x', y')$$

cannot exceed $2\epsilon/2 = \epsilon$. Hence, *given any positive number ϵ, another positive number η can be found such that*

$$|f(x, y) - f(x', y')| < \epsilon$$

whenever the distance between the two points (x, y) and (x', y'), which lie in A or on the contour C, is less than η. In other words, any function which is continuous in A and on its boundary C is *uniformly continuous.*

From the preceding theorem it can be shown, as in § 70, that every function which is continuous in A (inclusive of its boundary) is necessarily *finite* in A. If M be the upper limit and m the lower limit of the function in A, the difference $M - m$ is called the *oscillation.* The method of successive subdivisions also enables us to show that the function actually attains each of the values m and M at least once inside or upon the contour C. Let a be a point for which $z = m$ and b a point for which $z = M$, and let us join a and b by a broken line which lies entirely inside C. As the point (x, y) describes this line, z is a continuous function of the distance of the point (x, y) from the point a. Hence z assumes every value μ between m and M at least once upon this line (§ 70). Since a and b can be joined by an infinite number of different broken lines, it follows that the function $f(x, y)$ assumes every value between m and M at an infinite number of points which lie inside of C.

A finite region A of the plane is said to be less than l in all its dimensions if a circle of radius l can be found which entirely encloses A. A variable region of the plane is said to be infinitesimal in all its dimensions if a circle whose radius is arbitrarily preassigned can be found which eventually contains the region entirely within it. For example, a square whose side approaches zero or an ellipse both of whose axes approach zero is infinitesimal in all its dimensions. On the other hand, a rectangle of which only one side approaches zero or an ellipse only one of whose axes approaches zero is not infinitesimal in all its dimensions.

121. Double integrals. Let the region A of the plane be divided into subregions $a_1, a_2, \cdots, a_n$ in any manner, and let ω_i be the area of the subregion a_i, and M_i and m_i the limits of $f(x, y)$ in a_i. Consider the two sums

$$S = \sum_{i=1}^{n} \omega_i M_i, \qquad s = \sum_{i=1}^{n} \omega_i m_i,$$

each of which has a definite value for any particular subdivision of A. None of the sums S are less than $m\Omega$,* where Ω is the area of the region A of the plane, and where m is the lower limit of $f(x, y)$ in the region A; hence these sums have a lower limit I. Likewise, none of the sums s are greater than $M\Omega$, where M is the upper limit of $f(x, y)$ in the region A; hence these sums have an upper limit I'. Moreover it can be shown, as in § 71, that any of the sums S is greater than or equal to any one of the sums s; hence it follows that

$$I \geqq I'.$$

If the function $f(x, y)$ is continuous, the sums S and s approach a common limit as each of the subregions approaches zero in all its dimensions. For, suppose that η is a positive number such that the oscillation of the function is less than ϵ in any portion of A which is less in all its dimensions than η. If each of the subregions $a_1, a_2, \cdots, a_n$ be less in all its dimensions than η, each of the differences $M_i - m_i$ will be less than ϵ, and hence the difference $S - s$ will be less than $\epsilon\Omega$, where Ω denotes the total area of A. But we have

$$S - s = S - I + I - I' + I' - s,$$

where none of the quantities $S - I$, $I - I'$, $I' - s$ can be negative. Hence, in particular, $I - I' < \epsilon\Omega$; and since ϵ is an arbitrary positive number, it follows that $I = I'$. Moreover each of the numbers $S - I$ and $I - s$ can be made less than any preassigned number by

---

*If $f(x, y)$ is a constant k, $M = m = M_i = m_i = k$, and $S = s = m\Omega = M\Omega$. — TRANS.

a proper choice of ϵ. Hence the sums S and s have a common limit I, which is called the *double integral* of the function $f(x, y)$ extended over the region A. It is denoted by the symbol

$$I = \iint_{(A)} f(x, y)\, dx\, dy \,,$$

and the region A is called the *field of integration*.

If (ξ_i, η_i) be any point inside or on the boundary of the sub-region a_i, it is evident that the sum $\Sigma f(\xi_i, \eta_i)\, \omega_i$ lies between the two sums S and s or is equal to one of them. It therefore also approaches the double integral as its limit whatever be the method of choice of the point (ξ_i, η_i).

The first theorem of the mean may be extended without difficulty to double integrals. Let $f(x, y)$ be a function which is continuous in A, and let $\phi(x, y)$ be another function which is continuous and which has the same sign throughout A. For definiteness we shall suppose that $\phi(x, y)$ is positive in A. If M and m are the limits of $f(x, y)$ in A, it is evident that *

$$M\phi(\xi_i, \eta_i)\, \omega_i > f(\xi_i, \eta_i)\, \phi(\xi_i, \eta_i)\, \omega_i > m\phi(\xi_i, \eta_i)\, \omega_i.$$

Adding all these inequalities and passing to the limit, we find the formula

$$\iint_{(A)} f(x, y)\, \phi(x, y)\, dx\, dy = \mu \iint_{(A)} \phi(x, y)\, dx\, dy \,,$$

where μ lies *between* M and m. Since the function $f(x, y)$ assumes the value μ at a point (ξ, η) *inside* of the contour C, we may write this in the form

$$(1) \qquad \iint_{(A)} f(x, y)\, \phi(x, y)\, dx\, dy = f(\xi, \eta) \iint_{(A)} \phi(x, y)\, dx\, dy,$$

which constitutes the law of the mean for double integrals. If $\phi(x, y) = 1$, for example, the integral on the right, $\iint dx\, dy$, extended over the region A, is evidently equal to the area Ω of that region. In this case the formula (1) becomes

$$(2) \qquad \iint_{(A)} f(x, y)\, dx\, dy = \Omega f(\xi, \eta).$$

---

* If $f(x, y)$ is a constant k, we shall have $M = m = k$, and these inequalities become equations. The following formula holds, however, with $\mu = k$. — TRANS.

122. Volume. To the analytic notion of a double integral corresponds the important geometric notion of volume. Let $f(x, y)$ be a function which is continuous inside and upon a closed contour C. We shall further suppose for definiteness that this function is positive. Let S be the portion of the surface represented by the equation $z = f(x, y)$ which is bounded by a curve Γ whose projection upon the xy plane is the contour C. We shall denote by E the portion of space bounded by the xy plane, the surface S, and the cylinder whose right section is C. The region A of the xy plane which is bounded by the contour C being subdivided in any manner, let a_i be one of the subregions bounded by a contour c_i, and ω_i the area of this subregion. The cylinder whose right section is the curve c_i cuts out of the surface S a portion s_i bounded by a curve γ_i. Let p_i and P_i be the points of s_i whose distances from the xy plane are a minimum and a maximum, respectively. If planes be drawn through these two points parallel to the xy plane, two right cylinders are obtained which have the same base ω_i, and whose altitudes are the limits M_i and m_i of the function $f(x, y)$ inside the contour c_i, respectively. The volumes V_i and v_i of these cylinders are, respectively, $\omega_i M_i$ and $\omega_i m_i$.* The sums S and s considered above therefore represent, respectively, the sums ΣV_i and Σv_i of these two types of cylinders. We shall call the common limit of these two sums the *volume* of the portion E of space. It may be noted, as was done in the case of area (§ 78), that this definition agrees with the ordinary conception of what is meant by volume.

If the surface S lies partly beneath the xy plane, the double integral will still represent a volume if we agree to attach the sign $-$ to the volumes of portions of space below the xy plane. It appears then that every double integral represents an algebraic sum of volumes, just as a simple integral represents an algebraic sum of areas. The limits of integration in the case of a simple integral are replaced in the case of a double integral by the contour which encloses the field of integration.

123. Evaluation of double integrals. The evaluation of a double integral can be reduced to the successive evaluations of two simple integrals. Let us first consider the case where the field of integration

---

* By the *volume of a right cylinder* we shall understand the limit approached by the volume of a right prism of the same height, whose base is a polygon inscribed in a right section of the cylinder, as each of the sides of this polygon approaches zero. [This definition is not necessary for the argument, but is useful in showing that the definition of volume in general agrees with our ordinary conceptions. — TRANS.]

is a rectangle R bounded by the straight lines $x = x_0$, $x = X$, $y = y_0$, $y = Y$, where $x_0 < X$ and $y_0 < Y$. Suppose this rectangle to be subdivided by parallels to the two axes $x = x_i$, $y = y_k$ $(i = 1, 2, \cdots, n; \ k = 1, 2, \cdots, m)$. The area of the small rectangle R_{ik} bounded by the lines $x = x_{i-1}$, $x = x_i$, $y = y_{k-1}$, $y = y_k$ is

$$(x_i - x_{i-1})(y_k - y_{k-1}).$$

Hence the double integral is the limit of the sum

$$(3) \qquad S = \sum_{i=1}^{n} \sum_{k=1}^{m} f(\xi_{ik}, \eta_{ik})(x_i - x_{i-1})(y_k - y_{k-1}),$$

where (ξ_{ik}, η_{ik}) is any point inside or upon one of the sides of R_{ik}.

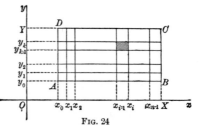

Fig. 24

We shall employ the indetermination of the points (ξ_{ik}, η_{ik}) in order to simplify the calculation. Let us remark first of all that if $f(x)$ is a continuous function in the interval (a, b), and if the interval (a, b) be subdivided in any manner, a value ξ_i can be found in each subinterval (x_{i-1}, x_i) such that

$$(4) \qquad \int_a^b f(x)\, dx = f(\xi_1)(x_1 - a) + f(\xi_2)(x_2 - x_1) + \cdots + f(\xi_n)(b - x_{n-1}).$$

For we need merely apply the law of the mean for integrals to each of the subintervals $(a, x_1), (x_1, x_2), \cdots, (x_{n-1}, b)$ to find these values of ξ_i.

Now the portion of the sum S which arises from the row of rectangles between the lines $x = x_{i-1}$ and $x = x_i$ is

$$(x_i - x_{i-1})[f(\xi_{i1}, \eta_{i1})(y_1 - y_0) + f(\xi_{i2}, \eta_{i2})(y_2 - y_1) + \cdots$$
$$+ f(\xi_{ik}, \eta_{ik})(y_k - y_{k-1}) + \cdots].$$

Let us take $\xi_{i1} = \xi_{i2} = \cdots = \xi_{im} = x_{i-1}$, and then choose $\eta_{i1}, \eta_{i2}, \cdots$ in such a way that the sum

$$f(x_{i-1}, \eta_{i1})(y_1 - y_0) + f(x_{i-1}, \eta_{i2})(y_2 - y_1) + \cdots$$

is equal to the integral $\int_{y_0}^{Y} f(x_{i-1}, y)\, dy$, where the integral is to be evaluated under the assumption that x_{i-1} is a constant. If we proceed in the same way for each of the rows of rectangles bounded by two consecutive parallels to the y axis, we finally find the equation

$$(5) \quad S = \Phi(x_0)(x_1 - x_0) + \Phi(x_1)(x_2 - x_1) + \cdots + \Phi(x_{i-1})(x_i - x_{i-1}) + \cdots,$$

where we have set for brevity

$$\Phi(x) = \int_{y_0}^{Y} f(x, y)\, dy.$$

This function $\Phi(x)$, defined by a definite integral, where x is considered as a parameter, is a continuous function of x. As all the intervals $x_i - x_{i-1}$ approach zero, the formula (5) shows that S approaches the definite integral

$$\int_{x_0}^{X} \Phi(x)\, dx.$$

Hence the double integral in question is given by the formula

$$(6) \qquad \iint_{(R)} f(x, y)\, dx\, dy = \int_{x_0}^{X} dx \int_{y_0}^{Y} f(x, y)\, dy.$$

In other words, in order to evaluate the double integral, *the function $f(x, y)$ should first be integrated between the limits y_0 and Y, regarding x as a constant and y as a variable; and then the resulting function, which is a function of x alone, should be integrated again between the limits x_0 and X.*

If we proceed in the reverse order, i.e. first evaluate the portion of S which comes from a row of rectangles which lie between two consecutive parallels to the x axis, we find the analogous formula

$$\iint_{(R)} f(x, y)\, dx\, dy = \int_{y_0}^{Y} dy \int_{x_0}^{X} f(x, y)\, dx.$$

A comparison of these two formulæ gives the new formula

$$\int_{x_0}^{X} dx \int_{y_0}^{Y} f(x, y)\, dy = \int_{y_0}^{Y} dy \int_{x_0}^{X} f(x, y)\, dx,$$

which is called the formula for *integration under the integral sign.* An essential presupposition in the proof is that the limits x_0, X, y_0, Y are constants, and that the function $f(x, y)$ is continuous throughout the field of integration.

Example. Let $z = xy/a$. Then the general formula gives

$$\iint_{(R)} \frac{xy}{a}\, dx\, dy = \int_{x_0}^{X} dx \int_{y_0}^{Y} \frac{xy}{a}\, dy$$

$$= \int_{x_0}^{X} \frac{x}{2a} (Y^2 - y_0^2)\, dx = \frac{1}{4a} (X^2 - x_0^2)(Y^2 - y_0^2).$$

In general, if the function $f(x, y)$ is the product of a function of x alone by a function of y alone, we shall have

$$\iint_{(R)} \phi(x)\psi(y)\, dx\, dy = \int_{x_0}^{X} \phi(x)\, dx \times \int_{y_0}^{Y} \psi(y)\, dy.$$

The two integrals on the right are absolutely independent of each other.

Franklin * has deduced from this remark a very simple demonstration of certain interesting theorems of Tchebycheff. Let $\phi(x)$ and $\psi(x)$ be two functions which are continuous in an interval (a, b), where $a < b$. Then the double integral

$$\iint [\phi(x) - \phi(y)][\psi(x) - \psi(y)]\, dx\, dy$$

extended over the square bounded by the lines $x = a$, $x = b$, $y = a$, $y = b$ is equal to the difference

$$2(b - a)\int_{a}^{b} \phi(x)\psi(x)\, dx - 2\int_{a}^{b} \phi(x)\, dx \times \int_{a}^{b} \psi(x)\, dx.$$

But all the elements of the above double integral have the same sign if the two functions $\phi(x)$ and $\psi(x)$ always increase or decrease simultaneously, or if one of them always increases when the other decreases. In the first case the two functions $\phi(x) - \phi(y)$ and $\psi(x) - \psi(y)$ always have the same sign, whereas they have opposite signs in the second case. Hence we shall have

$$(b - a)\int_{a}^{b} \phi(x)\psi(x)\, dx > \int_{a}^{b} \phi(x)\, dx \times \int_{a}^{b} \psi(x)\, dx$$

whenever the two functions $\phi(x)$ and $\psi(x)$ both increase or both decrease throughout the interval (a, b). On the other hand, we shall have

$$(b - a)\int_{a}^{b} \phi(x)\psi(x)\, dx < \int_{a}^{b} \phi(x)\, dx \times \int_{a}^{b} \psi(x)\, dx$$

whenever one of the functions increases and the other decreases throughout the interval.

The sign of the double integral is also definitely determined in case $\phi(x) = \psi(x)$, for then the integrand becomes a perfect square. In this case we shall have

$$(b - a)\int_{a}^{b} \cdot [\phi(x)]^2\, dx \geqq \left[\int_{a}^{b} \phi(x)\, dx\right]^2,$$

whatever be the function $\phi(x)$, where the sign of equality can hold only when $\phi(x)$ is a constant.

The solution of an interesting problem of the calculus of variations may be deduced from this result. Let P and Q be two fixed points in a plane whose coördinates are (a, A) and (b, B), respectively. Let $y = f(x)$ be the equation of any curve joining these two points, where $f(x)$, together with its first derivative

$f'(x)$, is supposed to be continuous in the interval (a, b). The problem is to find that one of the curves $y = f(x)$ for which the integral $\int_a^b y'^2 dx$ is a minimum. But by the formula just found, replacing $\phi(x)$ by y' and noting that $f(a) = A$ and $f(b) = B$ by hypothesis, we have

$$(b - a) \int_a^b y'^2 dx \geqq (B - A)^2.$$

The minimum value of the integral is therefore $(B - A)^2/(b - a)$, and that value is actually assumed when y' is a constant, i.e. when the curve joining the two fixed points reduces to the straight line PQ.

124. Let us now pass to the case where the field of integration is bounded by a contour of any form whatever. We shall first suppose that this contour is met in at most two points by any parallel to the y axis. We may then suppose that it is composed of two straight

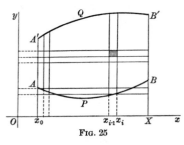

FIG. 25

lines $x = a$ and $x = b$ $(a < b)$ and two arcs of curves APB and $A'QB'$ whose equations are $Y_1 = \phi_1(x)$ and $Y_2 = \phi_2(x)$, respectively, where the functions ϕ_1 and ϕ_2 are continuous between a and b. It may happen that the points A and A' coincide, or that B and B' coincide, or both. This occurs, for instance, if the contour is a convex curve like an ellipse. Let us again subdivide the field of integration R by means of parallels to the axes. Then we shall have two classes of subregions: *regular* if they are rectangles which lie wholly within the contour, *irregular* if they are portions of rectangles bounded in part by arcs of the contour. Then it remains to find the limit of the sum

$$S = \Sigma f(\xi, \eta) \omega,$$

where ω is the area of any one of the subregions and (ξ, η) is a point in that subregion.

Let us first evaluate the portion of S which arises from the row of subregions between the consecutive parallels $x = x_{i-1}$, $x = x_i$. These subregions will consist of several regular ones, beginning with a vertex whose ordinate is $y' \geqq Y_1$ and going to a vertex whose ordinate is $y'' \leqq Y_2$, and several irregular ones. Choosing a suitable point (ξ, η) in each rectangle, it is clear, as above, that the portion of S which comes from these regular rectangles may be written in the form

$$(x_i - x_{i-1}) \int_{y'}^{y''} f(x_{i-1}, y)\, dy.$$

Suppose that the oscillation of each of the functions $\phi_1(x)$ and $\phi_2(x)$ in each of the intervals (x_{i-1}, x_i) is less than δ, and that each of the differences $y_k - y_{k-1}$ is also less than δ. Then it is easily seen that the total area of the irregular subregions between $x = x_{i-1}$ and $x = x_i$ is less than $4\delta(x_i - x_{i-1})$, and that the portion of S which arises from these regions is less than $4H\delta(x_i - x_{i-1})$ in absolute value, where H is the upper limit of the absolute value of $f(x, y)$ in the whole field of integration. On the other hand, we have

$$\int_{y'}^{y''} f(x_{i-1},\ y)\, dy = \int_{Y_1}^{Y_2} f(x_{i-1},\ y)\, dy + \int_{y'}^{Y_1} + \int_{Y_2}^{y''},$$

and since $|Y_1 - y'|$ and $|Y_2 - y''|$ are each less than 2δ, we may write

$$\int_{y'}^{y''} f(x_{i-1},\ y)\, dy = \int_{Y_1}^{Y_2} f(x_{i-1},\ y)\, dy + 4H\lambda\delta, \qquad |\lambda| < 1.$$

The portion of S which arises from the row of subregions under consideration may therefore be written in the form

$$(x_i - x_{i-1}) \left[\int_{Y_1}^{Y_2} f(x_{i-1},\ y)\, dy + 8H\theta_i\delta \right],$$

where θ_i lies between -1 and $+1$. The sum $8H\delta\Sigma\theta_i(x_i - x_{i-1})$ is less than $8H\delta(b - a)$ in absolute value, and approaches zero with δ, which may be taken as small as we please. The double integral is therefore the limit of the sum

$$\Phi(a)(x_1 - a) + \cdots + \Phi(x_{i-1})(x_i - x_{i-1}) + \cdots,$$

where

$$\Phi(x) = \int_{Y_1}^{Y_2} f(x, y)\, dy.$$

Hence we have the formula

$$(7) \qquad \iint_{(R)} f(x, y)\, dx\, dy = \int_a^b dx \int_{Y_1}^{Y_2} f(x, y)\, dy.$$

In the first integration x is to be regarded as a constant, but the limits Y_1 and Y_2 are themselves functions of x and not constants.

Example. Let us try to evaluate the double integral of the function xy/a over the interior of a quarter circle bounded by the axes and the circumference

$$x^2 + y^2 - R^2 = 0 \, .$$

The limits for x are 0 and R, and if x is constant, y may vary from 0 to $\sqrt{R^2 - x^2}$. Hence the integral is

$$\int_0^R dx \int_0^{\sqrt{R^2-x^2}} \frac{xy}{a} \, dy = \int_0^R \frac{x}{2a} \left[y^2 \right]_0^{\sqrt{R^2-x^2}} dx = \int_0^R \frac{x(R^2 - x^2)}{2a} \, dx \, .$$

The value of the latter integral is easily shown to be $R^4/8a$.

When the field of integration is bounded by a contour of any form whatever, it may be divided into several parts in such a way that the boundary of each part is met in at most two points by a parallel to the y axis. We might also divide it into parts in such a way that the boundary of each part would be met in at most two points by any line parallel to the x axis, and begin by integrating with respect to x. Let us consider, for example, a convex closed curve which lies inside the rectangle formed by the lines $x = a$, $x = b$, $y = c$, $y = d$, upon which lie the four points A, B, C, D, respectively, for which x or y is a minimum or a maximum.* Let $y_1 = \phi_1(x)$ and $y_2 = \phi_2(x)$ be the equations of the two arcs ACB and ADB, respectively, and let $x_1 = \psi_1(y)$ and $x_2 = \psi_2(y)$ be the equations of the two arcs CAD and CBD, respectively. The functions $\phi_1(x)$ and $\phi_2(x)$ are continuous between a and b, and $\psi_1(y)$ and $\psi_2(y)$ are continuous between c and d. The double integral of a function $f(x, y)$, which is continuous inside this contour, may be evaluated in two ways. Equating the values found, we obtain the formula

$$(8) \qquad \int_a^b dx \int_{y_1}^{y_2} f(x, y) \, dy = \int_c^d dy \int_{x_1}^{x_2} f(x, y) \, dx \, .$$

It is clear that the limits are entirely different in the two integrals. Every convex closed contour leads to a formula of this sort. For example, taking the triangle bounded by the lines $y = 0$, $x = a$, $y = x$ as the field of integration, we obtain the following formula, which is due to Lejeune Dirichlet:

$$\int_0^a dx \int_0^x f(x, y) \, dy = \int_0^a dy \int_y^a f(x, y) \, dx \, .$$

---

* The reader is advised to draw the figure.

125. Analogies to simple integrals. The integral $\int_a^x f(t) \, dt$, considered as a function of x, has the derivative $f(x)$. There exists an analogous theorem for double integrals. Let $f(x, y)$ be a function which is continuous inside a rectangle bounded by the straight lines $x = a$, $x = A$, $y = b$, $y = B$, $(a < A, b < B)$. The double integral of $f(x, y)$ extended over a rectangle bounded by the lines $x = a$, $x = X$, $y = b$, $y = Y$, $(a < X < A, b < Y < B)$, is a function of the coördinates X and Y of the variable corner, that is,

$$F(X, Y) = \int_a^X dx \int_b^Y f(x, y) \, dy.$$

Setting $\Phi(x) = \int_b^Y f(x, y) \, dy$, a first differentiation with respect to X gives

$$\frac{\partial F}{\partial X} = \Phi(X) = \int_b^Y f(X, y) \, dy.$$

A second differentiation with respect to Y leads to the formula

(9) $$\frac{\partial^2 F}{\partial X \, \partial Y} = f(X, Y).$$

The most general function $u(X, Y)$ which satisfies the equation (9) is evidently obtained by adding to $F(X, Y)$ a function z whose second derivative $\partial^2 z/\partial X \, \partial Y$ is zero. It is therefore of the form

(10) $$u(X, Y) = \int_a^X dx \int_b^Y f(x, y) \, dy + \phi(X) + \psi(Y),$$

where $\phi(X)$ and $\psi(Y)$ are two arbitrary functions (see § 38). The two arbitrary functions may be determined in such a way that $u(X, Y)$ reduces to a given function $V(Y)$ when $X = a$, and to another given function $U(X)$ when $Y = b$. Setting $X = a$ and then $Y = b$ in the preceding equation, we obtain the two conditions

$$V(Y) = \phi(a) + \psi(Y), \qquad U(X) = \phi(X) + \psi(b),$$

whence we find

$$\psi(Y) = V(Y) - \phi(a), \qquad \psi(b) = V(b) - \phi(a), \qquad \phi(X) = U(X) - V(b) + \phi(a),$$

and the formula (10) takes the form

(11) $$u(X, Y) = \int_a^X dx \int_b^Y f(x, y) \, dy + U(X) + V(Y) - V(b).$$

Conversely, if, by any means whatever, a function $u(X, Y)$ has been found which satisfies the equation (9), it is easy to show by methods similar to the above that the value of the double integral is given by the formula

(12) $$\int_a^X dx \int_b^Y f(x, y) \, dy = u(X, Y) - u(X, b) - u(a, Y) + u(a, b).$$

This formula is analogous to the fundamental formula (6) on page 155.

The following formula is in a sense analogous to the formula for integration by parts. Let A be a finite region of the plane bounded by one or more curves of any form. A function $f(x, y)$ which is continuous in A varies between its minimum v_0 and its maximum V. Imagine the *contour lines* $f(x, y) = v$ drawn where v lies between v_0 and V, and suppose that we are able to find the area of the portion of A for which $f(x, y)$ lies between v_0 and v. This area is a function $F(v)$ which increases with v, and the area between two neighboring contour lines is $F(v + \Delta v) - F(v) = \Delta v F'(v + \theta \Delta v)$. If this area be divided into infinitesimal portions by lines joining the two contour lines, a point (ξ, η) may be found in each of them such that $f(\xi, \eta) = v + \theta \Delta v$. Hence the sum of the elements of the double integral $\int \int f \, dx \, dy$ which arise from this region is

$$(v + \theta \Delta v) F'(v + \theta \Delta v) \Delta v.$$

It follows that the double integral is equal to the limit of the sum

$$\Sigma (v + \theta \Delta v) F'(v + \theta \Delta v) \Delta v,$$

that is to say, to the simple integral

$$\int_{v_0}^{V} v F'(v) \, dv = V F(V) - \int_{v_0}^{V} F(v) \, dv.$$

This method is especially convenient when the field of integration is bounded by two contour lines

$$f(x, y) = v_0, \qquad f(x, y) = V.$$

For example, consider the double integral $\int \int \sqrt{1 + x^2 + y^2} \, dx \, dy$ extended over the interior of the circle $x^2 + y^2 = 1$. If we set $v = \sqrt{1 + x^2 + y^2}$, the field of integration is bounded by the two contour lines $v = 1$ and $v = \sqrt{2}$, and the function $F(v)$, which is the area of the circle of radius $\sqrt{v^2 - 1}$, is equal to $\pi (v^2 - 1)$. Hence the given double integral has the value

$$\int_{1}^{\sqrt{2}} 2 \pi v^2 \, dv = \frac{2\pi}{3} (2 \sqrt{2} - 1). \; *$$

The preceding formula is readily extended to the double integral

$$\int \int f(x, y) \, \phi(x, y) \, dx \, dy,$$

where $F(v)$ now denotes the double integral $\int \int \phi(x, y) \, dx \, dy$ extended over that portion of the field of integration bounded by the contour line $v = f(x, y)$.

126. Green's theorem. If the function $f(x, y)$ is the partial derivative of a known function with respect to either x or y, one of the integrations may be performed at once, leaving only one indicated integration. This very simple remark leads to a very important formula which is known as *Green's theorem*.

---

* Numerous applications of this method are to be found in a memoir by Catalan (*Journal de Liouville*, 1st series, Vol. IV, p. 233).

Let us consider first a double integral $\iint \partial P/\partial y \, dx \, dy$ extended over a region of the plane bounded by a contour C, which is met in at most two points by any line parallel to the y axis (see Fig. 15, p. 188).

Let A and B be the points of C at which x is a minimum and a maximum, respectively. A parallel to the y axis between Aa and Bb meets C in two points m_1 and m_2 whose ordinates are y_1 and y_2, respectively. Then the double integral after integration with respect to y may be written

$$\iint \frac{\partial P}{\partial y} \, dx \, dy = \int_a^b dx \int_{y_1}^{y_2} \frac{\partial P}{\partial y} \, dy = \int_a^b [P(x, \, y_2) - P(x, \, y_1)] \, dx.$$

But the two integrals $\int_a^b P(x, \, y_1) \, dx$ and $\int_a^b P(x, \, y_2) \, dx$ are line integrals taken along the arcs Am_1B and Am_2B, respectively; hence the preceding formula may be written in the form

$$(13) \qquad \iint \frac{\partial P}{\partial y} \, dx \, dy = - \int_{(C)} P \, dx,$$

where the line integral is to be taken along the contour C in the direction indicated by the arrows, that is to say in the positive sense, if the axes are chosen as in the figure. In order to extend the formula to an area bounded by any contour we should proceed as above (§ 94), dividing the given region into several parts for each of which the preceding conditions are satisfied, and applying the formula to each of them. In a similar manner the following analogous form is easily derived:

$$(14) \qquad \iint \frac{\partial Q}{\partial x} \, dx \, dy = \int_{(C)} Q \, dy,$$

where the line integral is always taken in the same sense. Subtracting the equations (13) and (14), we find the formula

$$(15) \qquad \int_{(C)} P \, dx + Q \, dy = \iint \left(\frac{\partial Q}{\partial x} - \frac{\partial P}{\partial y} \right) dx \, dy,$$

where the double integral is extended over the region bounded by C. This is Green's formula; its applications are very important. Just now we shall merely point out that the substitution $Q = x$ and $P = - y$ gives the formula obtained above (§ 94) for the area of a closed curve as a line integral.

II. CHANGE OF VARIABLES   AREA OF A SURFACE

In the evaluation of double integrals we have supposed up to the present that the field of integration was subdivided into infinitesimal rectangles by parallels to the two coördinate axes. We are now going to suppose the field of integration subdivided by any two systems of curves whatever.

127. Preliminary formula. Let u and v be the coördinates of a point with respect to a set of rectangular axes in a plane, x and y the coördinates of another point with respect to a similarly chosen set of rectangular axes in that or in some other plane. The formulæ

$$(16) \qquad x = f(u, v), \qquad y = \phi(u, v)$$

establish a certain correspondence between the points of the two planes. We shall suppose 1) that the functions $f(u, v)$ and $\phi(u, v)$, together with their first partial derivatives, are continuous for all points (u, v) of the uv plane which lie within or on the boundary of a region A_1 bounded by a contour C_1; 2) that the equations (16) transform the region A_1 of the uv plane into a region A of the xy plane bounded by a contour C, and that a *one-to-one* correspondence exists between the two regions and between the two contours in such a way that one and only one point of A_1 corresponds to any point of A; 3) that the functional determinant $\Delta = D(f, \phi)/D(u, v)$ does not change sign inside of C_1, though it may vanish at certain points of A_1.

Two cases may arise. When the point (u, v) describes the contour C_1 in the positive sense the point (x, y) describes the contour C either in the positive or else in the negative sense without ever reversing the sense of its motion. We shall say that the correspondence is direct or inverse, respectively, in the two cases.

The area Ω of the region A is given by the line integral

$$\Omega = \int_{(C)} x \, dy$$

taken along the contour C in the positive sense. In terms of the new variables u and v defined by (16) this becomes

$$\Omega = \pm \int_{(C_1)} f(u, v) \, d\phi(u, v),$$

where the new integral is to be taken along the contour C_1 in the positive sense, and where the sign $+$ or the sign $-$ should be taken according as the correspondence is direct or inverse. Applying Green's theorem to the new integral with $x = u$, $v = y$, $P = f\, \partial\phi/\partial u$, $Q = f\, \partial\phi/\partial v$, we find

$$\frac{\partial Q}{\partial u} - \frac{\partial P}{\partial v} = \Delta = \frac{D(f,\ \phi)}{D(u,\ v)},$$

whence

$$\Omega = \pm \iint_{(A_1)} \frac{D(f,\ \phi)}{D(u,\ v)}\, du\, dv,$$

or, applying the law of the mean to the double integral,

$$(17) \qquad\qquad \Omega = \pm\, \Omega_1 \frac{D(f,\ \phi)}{D(\xi,\ \eta)},$$

where (ξ, η) is a point inside the contour C_1, and Ω_1 is the area of the region A_1 in the uv plane. It is clear that the sign $+$ or the sign $-$ should be taken according as Δ itself is positive or negative. Hence *the correspondence is direct or inverse according as Δ is positive or negative.*

The formula (17) moreover establishes an analogy between functional determinants and ordinary derivatives. For, suppose that the region A_1 approaches zero in all its dimensions, all its points approaching a limiting point (u, v). Then the region A will do the same, and the ratio of the two areas Ω and Ω_1 approaches as its limit the absolute value of the determinant Δ. Just as the ordinary derivative is the limit of the ratio of two linear infinitesimals, the functional determinant is thus seen to be the limit of the ratio of two infinitesimal areas. From this point of view the formula (17) is the analogon of the law of the mean for derivatives.

Remarks. The hypotheses which we have made concerning the correspondence between A and A_1 are not all independent. Thus, in order that the correspondence should be one-to-one, it is necessary that Δ should not change sign in the region A_1 of the uv plane. For, suppose that Δ vanishes along a curve γ_1 which divides the portion of A_1 where Δ is positive from the portion where Δ is negative. Let us consider a small arc $m_1 n_1$ of γ_1 and a small portion of A_1 which contains the arc $m_1 n_1$. This portion is composed of two regions a_1 and a_1' which are separated by $m_1 n_1$ (Fig. 26).

When the point (u, v) describes the region a_1, where Δ is positive, the point

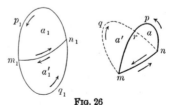

FIG. 26

(x, y) describes a region a bounded by a contour $mnpm$, and the two contours $m_1 n_1 p_1 m_1$ and $mnpm$ are described simultaneously in the positive sense. When the point (u, v) describes the region a_1', where Δ is negative, the point (x, y)

describes a region α' whose contour $nmqr$ is described in the negative sense as $n_1 m_1 q_1 n_1$ is described in the positive sense. The region α' must therefore cover a part of the region α. Hence to any point (x, y) in the common part nrm correspond two points in the uv plane which lie on either side of the line $m_1 n_1$.

As an example consider the transformation $X = x$, $Y = y^2$, for which $\Delta = 2y$. If the point (x, y) describes a closed region which encloses a segment ab of the x axis, it is evident that the point (X, Y) describes two regions both of which lie above the X axis and both of which are bounded by the same segment AB of that axis. A sheet of paper folded together along a straight line drawn upon it gives a clear idea of the nature of the region described by the point (X, Y).

The condition that Δ should preserve the same sign throughout A_1 is not sufficient for one-to-one correspondence. In the example $X = x^2 - y^2$, $Y = 2xy$, the Jacobian $\Delta = 4(x^2 + y^2)$ is always positive. But if (r, θ) and (R, ω) are the polar coördinates of the points (x, y) and (X, Y), respectively, the formulæ of transformation may be written in the form $R = r^2$, $\omega = 2\theta$. As r varies from a to b $(a < b)$ and θ varies from 0 to $\pi + \alpha$ $(0 < \alpha < \pi/2)$, the point (R, ω) describes a circular ring bounded by two circles of radii a^2 and b^2. But to every value of the angle ω between 0 and 2α correspond two values of θ, one of which lies between 0 and α, the other between π and $\pi + \alpha$. The region described by the point (X, Y) may be realized by forming a circular ring of paper which partially overlaps itself.

128. Transformation of double integrals. First method. Retaining the hypotheses made above concerning the regions A and A_1 and the formulæ (16), let us consider a function $F(x, y)$ which is continuous in the region A. To any subdivision of the region A_1 into subregions $\alpha_1, \alpha_2, \cdots, \alpha_n$ corresponds a subdivision of the region A into subregions $a_1, a_2, \cdots, a_n$. Let ω_i and σ_i be the areas of the two corresponding subregions a_i and α_i, respectively. Then, by formula (17),

$$\omega_i = \sigma_i \left| \frac{D(f, \phi)}{D(u_i, v_i)} \right|,$$

where u_i and v_i are the coördinates of some point in the region α_i. To this point (u_i, v_i) corresponds a point $x_i = f(u_i, v_i)$, $y_i = \phi(u_i, v_i)$ of the region a_i. Hence, setting $\Phi(u, v) = F[f(u, v), \phi(u, v)]$, we may write

$$\sum_{i=1}^{n} F(x_i, y_i) \omega_i = \sum_{i=1}^{n} \Phi(u_i, v_i) \left| \frac{D(f, \phi)}{D(u_i, v_i)} \right| \sigma_i,$$

whence, passing to the limit, we obtain the formula

$$(18) \quad \iint_{(A)} F(x, y) \, dx \, dy = \iint_{(A_1)} F[f(u, v), \phi(u, v)] \left| \frac{D(f, \phi)}{D(u, v)} \right| du \, dv.$$

Hence *to perform a transformation in a double integral x and y should be replaced by their values as functions of the new variables u and v, and dx dy should be replaced by* $|\Delta|\,du\,dv$. We have seen already how the new field of integration is determined.

In order to find the limits between which the integrations should be performed in the calculation of the new double integral, it is in general unnecessary to construct the contour C_1 of the new field of integration A_1. For, let us consider u and v as a system of curvilinear coördinates, and let one of the variables u and v in the formulæ (16) be kept constant while the other varies. We obtain in this way two systems of curves $u = $ const. and $v = $ const. By the hypotheses made above, one and only one curve of each of these families passes through any given point of the region A.

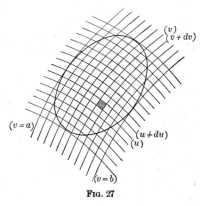

FIG. 27

Let us suppose for definiteness that a curve of the family $v = $ const. meets the contour C in at most two points M_1 and M_2 which correspond to values u_1 and u_2 of u $(u_1 < u_2)$, and that each of the (v) curves which meets the contour C lies between the two curves $v = a$ and $v = b$ $(a < b)$. In this case we should integrate first with regard to u, keeping v constant and letting u vary from u_1 to u_2, where u_1 and u_2 are in general functions of v, and then integrate this result between the limits a and b.

The double integral is therefore equal to the expression

$$\int_a^b dv \int_{u_1}^{u_2} F[f(u, v),\ \phi(u, v)]\,|\Delta|\,du.$$

A change of variables amounts essentially to a subdivision of the field of integration by means of the two systems of curves (u) and (v). Let ω be the area of the curvilinear quadrilateral bounded by the curves (u), $(u + du)$, (v), $(v + dv)$, where du and dv are positive. To this quadrilateral corresponds in the uv plane a rectangle whose sides are du and dv. Then, by formula (17), $\omega = |\Delta(\xi, \eta)|\,du\,dv$, where ξ lies between u and $u + du$, and η between v and $v + dv$. The expression $|\Delta(u,\ v)|\,du\,dv$ is called the *element of area* in the system of coördinates (u, v). The exact value of ω is $\omega = \{|\Delta(u, v)| + \epsilon\}\,du\,dv$, where ϵ approaches zero with du and dv. This infinitesimal may be neglected in finding the limit of the sum $\Sigma F(x, y)\,\omega$, for since $\Delta(u, v)$ is continuous, we may suppose the two (u) curves and the two (v) curves taken so close together that each of the ϵ's is less in absolute value than any preassigned positive number. Hence the absolute value of the sum $\Sigma F(x, y)\epsilon\,du\,dv$ itself may be made less than any preassigned positive number.

129. Examples. 1) *Polar coördinates.* Let us pass from rectangular to polar coördinates by means of the transformation $x = \rho \cos \omega$, $y = \rho \sin \omega$. We obtain all the points of the xy plane as ρ varies from zero to $+\infty$ and ω from zero to 2π. Here $\Delta = \rho$; hence the element of area is $\rho\,d\omega\,d\rho$, which is also evident geometrically. Let us try first to evaluate a double integral extended over a portion of the plane bounded by an arc AB which intersects a radius vector in at most one point, and by the two straight lines OA and OB which make angles ω_1 and ω_2 with the x axis (Fig. 17, p. 189). Let $R = \phi(\omega)$ be the equation of the arc AB. In the field of integration ω varies from ω_1 to ω_2 and ρ from zero to R. Hence the double integral of a function $f(x, y)$ has the value

$$\int_{\omega_1}^{\omega_2} d\omega \int_0^R f(\rho \cos \omega, \rho \sin \omega)\,\rho\,d\rho.$$

If the arc AB is a closed curve enclosing the origin, we should take the limits $\omega_1 = 0$ and $\omega_2 = 2\pi$. Any field of integration can be divided into portions of the preceding types. Suppose, for instance, that the origin lies outside of the contour C of a given convex closed curve. Let OA and OB be the two tangents from the origin to this curve, and let $R_1 = f_1(\omega)$ and $R_2 = f_2(\omega)$ be the equations of the two arcs ANB and AMB, respectively. For a given value of ω between ω_1 and ω_2, ρ varies from R_1 to R_2, and the value of the double integral is

$$\int_{\omega_1}^{\omega_2} d\omega \int_{R_1}^{R_2} f(\rho \cos \omega, \rho \sin \omega)\,\rho\,d\rho.$$

2) *Elliptic coördinates.* Let us consider a family of confocal conics

(19) $$\frac{x^2}{\lambda} + \frac{y^2}{\lambda - c^2} = 1,$$

where λ denotes an arbitrary parameter. Through every point of the plane pass two conics of this family, — an ellipse and an hyperbola, — for the equation (19)

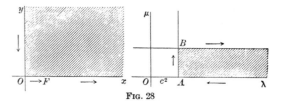

FIG. 28

has one root λ greater than c^2, and another positive root μ less than c^2, for any values of x and y. From (19) and from the analogous equation where λ is replaced by μ we find

$$(20) \qquad x = \frac{\sqrt{\lambda\mu}}{c}, \qquad y = \frac{\sqrt{(\lambda - c^2)(c^2 - \mu)}}{c}, \qquad 0 \leqq \mu \leqq c^2 \leqq \lambda.$$

To avoid ambiguity, we shall consider only the first quadrant in the xy plane. This region corresponds point for point in a one-to-one manner to the region of the $\lambda\mu$ plane which is bounded by the straight lines

$$\lambda = c^2, \qquad \mu = 0, \qquad \mu = c^2.$$

It is evident from the formulæ (20) that when the point (λ, μ) describes the boundary of this region in the direction indicated by the arrows, the point (x, y) describes the two axes Ox and Oy in the sense indicated by the arrows. The transformation is therefore inverse, which is verified by calculating Δ :

$$\Delta = \frac{D(x, y)}{D(\lambda, \mu)} = -\frac{1}{4} \frac{\lambda - \mu}{\sqrt{\lambda\mu(\lambda - c^2)(c^2 - \mu)}}.$$

130. Transformation of double integrals. Second method. We shall now derive the general formula (18) by another method which depends solely upon the rule for calculating a double integral. We shall retain, however, the hypotheses made above concerning the correspondence between the points of the two regions A and A_1. If the formula is correct for two particular transformations

$$\begin{cases} x = f(u, v), \\ y = \phi(u, v), \end{cases} \qquad \begin{cases} u = f_1(u', v'), \\ v = \phi_1(u', v'), \end{cases}$$

it is evident that it is also correct for the transformation obtained by carrying out the two transformations in succession. This follows at once from the fundamental property of functional determinants (§ 30)

$$\frac{D(x, y)}{D(u', v')} = \frac{D(x, y)}{D(u, v)} \cdot \frac{D(u, v)}{D(u', v')}.$$

Similarly, if the formula holds for several regions A, B, C, $\cdots$, L, to which correspond the regions A_1, B_1, C_1, $\cdots$, L_1, it also holds for the region $A + B + C + \cdots + L$. Finally, the formula holds if the transformation is a change of axes:

$$x = x_0 + x' \cos \alpha - y' \sin \alpha, \qquad y = y_0 + x' \sin \alpha + y' \cos \alpha.$$

Here $\Delta = 1$, and the equation

$$\iint_{(A)} F(x, y)\, dx\, dy$$
$$= \iint_{(A')} F(x_0 + x' \cos \alpha - y' \sin \alpha,\ y_0 + x' \sin \alpha + y' \cos \alpha)\, dx'\, dy'$$

is satisfied, since the two integrals represent the same volume.

We shall proceed to prove the formula for the particular transformation

(21) $x = \phi(x', y'), \qquad y = y',$

which carries the region A into a region A' which is included between the same parallels to the x axis, $y = y_0$ and $y = y_1$. We shall suppose that just one point of A corresponds to any given point of A' and conversely. If a parallel to the x axis meets the boundary C of the region A in at most two points, the same will be true for the boundary C' of the region A'. To any pair of points m_0 and m_1 on C whose ordinates are each y correspond two points m'_0

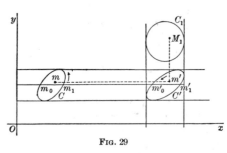

Fig. 29

and m'_1 of the contour C'. But the correspondence may be direct or inverse. To distinguish the two cases, let us remark that if $\partial\phi/\partial x'$ is positive, x increases with x', and the points m_0 and m_1 and m'_0 and m'_1 lie as shown in Fig. 29; hence the correspondence is direct. On the other hand, if $\partial\phi/\partial x'$ is negative, the correspondence is inverse.

Let us consider the first case, and let x_0, x_1, x'_0, x'_1 be the abscissæ of the points m_0, m_1, m'_0, m'_1, respectively. Then, applying the formula for change of variable in a simple integral, we find

$$\int_{x_0}^{x_1} F(x, y)\, dx = \int_{x'_0}^{x'_1} F[\phi(x', y'), y'] \frac{\partial\phi}{\partial x'}\, dx',$$

where y and y' are treated as constants. A single integration gives the formula

$$\int_{y_0}^{y_1} dy \int_{x_0}^{x_1} F(x, y)\, dx = \int_{y_0}^{y_1} dy' \int_{x_0'}^{x_1'} F[\phi(x', y'), y']\, \frac{\partial \phi}{\partial x'}\, dx'.$$

But the Jacobian Δ reduces in this case to $\partial \phi / \partial x'$, and hence the preceding formula may be written in the form

$$\iint_{(A)} F(x, y)\, dx\, dy = \iint_{(A')} F[\phi(x', y'), y']\,|\,\Delta\,|\, dx'dy'.$$

This formula can be established in the same manner if $\partial \phi / \partial x'$ is negative, and evidently holds for a region of any form whatever.

In an exactly similar manner it can be shown that the transformation

(22) $$x = x', \qquad y = \psi(x', y')$$

leads to the formula

$$\iint_{(A)} F(x, y)\, dx\, dy = \iint_{(A')} F[x', \psi(x', y')]\,|\,\Delta\,|\, dx'dy',$$

where the new field of integration A' corresponds point for point to the region A.

Let us now consider the general formulæ of transformation

(23) $$x = f(x_1, y_1), \qquad y = f_1(x_1, y_1),$$

where for the sake of simplicity (x, y) and (x_1, y_1) denote the coördinates of two corresponding points m and M_1 with respect to the same system of axes. Let A and A_1 be the two corresponding regions bounded by contours C and C_1, respectively. Then a third point m', whose coördinates are given in terms of those of m and M_1 by the relations $x' = x_1$, $y' = y$, will describe an auxiliary region A', which for the moment we shall assume corresponds point for point to each of the two regions A and A_1. The six quantities x, y, x_1, y_1, x', y' satisfy the four equations

$$x = f(x_1, y_1), \qquad y = f_1(x_1, y_1), \qquad x' = x_1, \qquad y' = y,$$

whence we obtain the relations

(24) $$x' = x_1, \qquad y' = f_1(x_1, y_1),$$

which define a transformation of the type (22). From the equation $y' = f_1(x', y_1)$ we find a relation of the form $y_1 = \pi(x', y')$; hence we may write

(25) $$x = f(x', y_1) = \phi(x', y'), \qquad y = y'.$$

The given transformation (23) amounts to a combination of the two transformations (24) and (25), for each of which the general formula holds. Therefore the same formula holds for the transformation (23).

Remark. We assumed above that the region described by the point m' corresponds point for point to each of the regions A and A_1. At least, this can always be brought about. For, let us consider the curves of the region A_1 which correspond to the straight lines parallel to the x axis in A. If these curves meet a parallel to the y axis in just one point, it is evident that just one point m' of A' will correspond to any given point m of A. Hence we need merely divide the region A_1 into parts so small that this condition is satisfied in each of them. If these curves were parallels to the y axis, we should begin by making a change of axes.

131. Area of a curved surface. Let S be a region of a curved surface free from singular points and bounded by a contour Γ. Let S be subdivided in any way whatever, let s_i be one of the subregions bounded by a contour γ_i, and let m_i be a point of s_i. Draw the tangent plane to the surface S at the point m_i, and suppose s_i taken so small that it is met in at most one point by any perpendicular to this plane. The contour γ_i projects into a curve γ_i' upon this plane; we shall denote the area of the region of the tangent plane bounded by γ_i' by σ_i. As the number of subdivisions is increased indefinitely in such a way that each of them is infinitesimal in all its dimensions, the sum $\Sigma\sigma_i$ approaches a limit, and this limit is called *the area of the region S of the given surface.*

Let the rectangular coördinates x, y, z of a point of S be given in terms of two variable parameters u and v by means of the equations

$$(26) \qquad x = f(u, v), \qquad y = \phi(u, v), \qquad z = \psi(u, v),$$

in such a way that the region S of the surface corresponds point for point to a region R of the uv plane bounded by a closed contour C. We shall assume that the functions f, ϕ, and ψ, together with their first partial derivatives, are continuous in this region. Let R be subdivided, let r_i be one of the subdivisions bounded by a contour c_i, and let ω_i be the area of r_i. To r_i corresponds on S a subdivision s_i bounded by a contour γ_i. Let σ_i be the corresponding area upon the tangent plane defined as above, and let us try to find an expression for the ratio σ_i/ω_i.

Let α_i, β_i, γ_i be the direction cosines of the normal to the surface S at a point $m_i(x_i, y_i, z_i)$ of s_i which corresponds to a point (u_i, v_i)

of r_i. Let us take the point m_i as a new origin, and as the new axes the normal at m_i and two perpendicular lines $m_i X$ and $m_i Y$ in the tangent plane whose direction cosines with respect to the old axes are α', β', γ' and α'', β'', γ'', respectively. Let X, Y, Z be the coördinates of a point on the surface S with respect to the new axes. Then, by the well-known formulæ for transformation of coördinates, we shall have

$$X = \alpha' (x - x_i) + \beta' (y - y_i) + \gamma' (z - z_i),$$
$$Y = \alpha''(x - x_i) + \beta''(y - y_i) + \gamma''(z - z_i),$$
$$Z = \alpha_i (x - x_i) + \beta_i (y - y_i) + \gamma_i (z - z_i).$$

The area σ_i is the area of that portion of the XY plane which is bounded by the closed curve which the point (X, Y) describes, as the point (u, v) describes the contour c_i. Hence, by § 127,

$$\sigma_i = \omega_i \left| \frac{D(X, Y)}{D(u_i', v_i')} \right|,$$

where u_i' and v_i' are the coördinates of some point inside of o_i. An easy calculation now leads us to the form

$$\frac{D(X, Y)}{D(u_i', v_i')} = (\beta'\gamma'' - \gamma'\beta'') \frac{D(y, z)}{D(u_i', v_i')}$$
$$+ (\gamma'\alpha'' - \alpha'\gamma'') \frac{D(z, x)}{D(u_i', v_i')} + (\alpha'\beta'' - \beta'\alpha'') \frac{D(x, y)}{D(u_i', v_i')},$$

or, by the well-known relations between the nine direction cosines,

$$\frac{D(X, Y)}{D(u_i', v_i')} = \pm \left\{ \alpha_i \frac{D(y, z)}{D(u_i', v_i')} + \beta_i \frac{D(z, x)}{D(u_i', v_i')} + \gamma_i \frac{D(x, y)}{D(u_i', v_i')} \right\}.$$

Applying the general formula (17), we therefore obtain the equation

$$\sigma_i = \omega_i \left| \alpha_i \frac{D(y, z)}{D(u_i', v_i')} + \beta_i \frac{D(z, x)}{D(u_i', v_i')} + \gamma_i \frac{D(x, y)}{D(u_i', v_i')} \right|,$$

where u_i' and v_i' are the coördinates of a point of the region r_i in the uv plane. If this region is very small, the point (u_i', v_i') is very near the point (u_i, v_i), and we may write

$$\frac{D(y, z)}{D(u_i', v_i')} = \frac{D(y, z)}{D(u_i, v_i)} + \epsilon_i, \qquad \frac{D(z, x)}{D(u_i', v_i')} = \frac{D(z, x)}{D(u_i, v_i)} + \epsilon_i', \qquad \cdots,$$

$$\Sigma\sigma_i = \Sigma\omega_i \left| \alpha_i \frac{D(y, z)}{D(u_i, v_i)} + \cdots \right| + \theta\Sigma\omega_i |\alpha_i \epsilon_i + \beta_i \epsilon_i' + \gamma_i \epsilon_i''|,$$

where the absolute value of θ does not exceed unity. Since the derivatives of the functions f, ϕ, and ψ are continuous in the region R, we may assume that the regions r_i have been taken so small that each of the quantities ϵ_i, ϵ_i', ϵ_i'' is less than an arbitrarily preassigned number η. Then the supplementary term will certainly be less in absolute value than $3\eta\Omega$, where Ω is the area of the region R. Hence that term approaches zero as the regions s_i (and r_i) all approach zero in the manner described above, and the sum $\Sigma\sigma_i$ approaches the double integral

$$\iint_{(R)} \left| \alpha \frac{D(y, z)}{D(u, v)} + \beta \frac{D(z, x)}{D(u, v)} + \gamma \frac{D(x, y)}{D(u, v)} \right| du\, dv,$$

where α, β, γ are the direction cosines of the normal to the surface S at the point (u, v).

Let us calculate these direction cosines. The equation of the tangent plane (§ 39) is

$$(X - x) \frac{D(y, z)}{D(u, v)} + (Y - y) \frac{D(z, x)}{D(u, v)} + (Z - z) \frac{D(x, y)}{D(u, v)} = 0,$$

whence

$$\frac{\alpha}{\dfrac{D(y, z)}{D(u, v)}} = \frac{\beta}{\dfrac{D(z, x)}{D(u, v)}} = \frac{\gamma}{\dfrac{D(x, y)}{D(u, v)}} = \frac{\pm 1}{\sqrt{\left[\dfrac{D(y, z)}{D(u, v)}\right]^2 + \cdots}}$$

Choosing the positive sign in the last ratio, we obtain the formula

$$\alpha \frac{D(y, z)}{D(u, v)} + \beta \frac{D(z, x)}{D(u, v)} + \gamma \frac{D(x, y)}{D(u, v)}$$
$$= \sqrt{\left[\frac{D(y, z)}{D(u, v)}\right]^2 + \left[\frac{D(z, x)}{D(u, v)}\right]^2 + \left[\frac{D(x, y)}{D(u, v)}\right]^2}.$$

The well-known identity

$$(ab' - ba')^2 + (bc' - cb')^2 + (ca' - ac')^2$$
$$= (a^2 + b^2 + c^2)(a'^2 + b'^2 + c'^2) - (aa' + bb' + cc')^2,$$

which was employed by Lagrange, enables us to write the quantity under the radical in the form $EG - F^2$, where

$$(27) \quad E = S\left(\frac{\partial x}{\partial u}\right)^2, \quad F = S\frac{\partial x}{\partial u}\frac{\partial x}{\partial v}, \quad G = S\left(\frac{\partial x}{\partial v}\right)^2,$$

the symbol S indicating that x is to be replaced by y and z successively and the three resulting terms added. It follows that the area of the surface S is given by the double integral

$$(28) \quad A = \iint_{(R)} \sqrt{EG - F^2}\, du\, dv.$$

The functions E, F, and G play an important part in the theory of surfaces. Squaring the expressions for dx, dy, and dz and adding the results, we find

$$(29) \qquad ds^2 = dx^2 + dy^2 + dz^2 = E\,du^2 + 2F\,du\,dv + G\,dv^2.$$

It is clear that these quantities E, F, and G do not depend upon the choice of axes, but solely upon the surface S itself and the independent variables u and v. If the variables u and v and the surface S are all real, it is evident that $EG - F^2$ must be positive.

132. Surface element. The expression $\sqrt{EG - F^2}\,du\,dv$ is called *the element of area* of the surface S in the system of coördinates (u, v). The precise value of the area of a small portion of the surface bounded by the curves (u), $(u + du)$, (v), $(v + dv)$ is $(\sqrt{EG - F^2} + \epsilon)\,du\,dv$, where ϵ approaches zero with du and dv. It is evident, as above, that the term $\epsilon\,du\,dv$ is negligible.

Certain considerations of differential geometry confirm this result. For, if the portion of the surface in question be thought of as a small curvilinear parallelogram on the tangent plane to S at the point (u, v), its area will be equal, approximately, to the product of the lengths of its sides times the sine of the angle between the two curves (u) and (v). If we further replace the increment of arc by the differential ds, the lengths of the sides, by formula (29), are $\sqrt{E}\,du$ and $\sqrt{G}\,dv$, if du and dv are taken positive. The direction parameters of the tangents to the two curves (u) and (v) are $\partial x/\partial u$, $\partial y/\partial u$, $\partial z/\partial u$ and $\partial x/\partial v$, $\partial y/\partial v$, $\partial z/\partial v$, respectively. Hence the angle α between them is given by the formula

$$\cos \alpha = \frac{S\dfrac{\partial x}{\partial u}\dfrac{\partial x}{\partial v}}{\sqrt{S\left(\dfrac{\partial x}{\partial u}\right)^2}\sqrt{S\left(\dfrac{\partial x}{\partial v}\right)^2}} = \frac{F}{\sqrt{EG}},$$

whence $\sin \alpha = \sqrt{EG - F^2}/\sqrt{EG}$. Forming the product mentioned, we find the same expression as that given above for the element of area. The formula for $\cos \alpha$ shows that $F = 0$ when and only when the two families of curves (u) and (v) are orthogonal to each other.

When the surface S reduces to a plane, the formulæ just found *reduce to the formulæ found in* § 128. For, if we set $\psi(u, v) = 0$, we find

$$E = \left(\frac{\partial x}{\partial u}\right)^2 + \left(\frac{\partial y}{\partial u}\right)^2, \qquad F = \frac{\partial x}{\partial u}\frac{\partial x}{\partial v} + \frac{\partial y}{\partial u}\frac{\partial y}{\partial v}, \qquad G = \left(\frac{\partial x}{\partial v}\right)^2 + \left(\frac{\partial y}{\partial v}\right)^2,$$

whence, by the rule for squaring a determinant,

$$\Delta^2 = \left\{ \left| \begin{array}{cc} \dfrac{\partial x}{\partial u} & \dfrac{\partial x}{\partial v} \\[2ex] \dfrac{\partial y}{\partial u} & \dfrac{\partial y}{\partial v} \end{array} \right| \right\}^2 = \left| \begin{array}{cc} E & F \\ F & G \end{array} \right| = EG - F^2.$$

Hence $\sqrt{EG - F^2}$ reduces to $|\Delta|$.

Examples. 1) *To find the area of a region of a surface whose equation is $z = f(x, y)$ which projects on the xy plane into a region R in which the function $f(x, y)$, together with its derivatives $p = \partial f/\partial x$ and $q = \partial f/\partial y$, is continuous.* Taking x and y as the independent variables, we find $E = 1 + p^2$, $F = pq$, $G = 1 + q^2$, and the area in question is given by the double integral

$$(30) \qquad \mathsf{A} = \iint_{(R)} \sqrt{1 + p^2 + q^2}\, dx\, dy = \iint_{(R)} \frac{dx\, dy}{\cos \gamma},$$

where γ is the acute angle between the z axis and the normal to the surface.

2) *To calculate the area of the region of a surface of revolution between two plane sections perpendicular to the axis of revolution.* Let the axis of revolution be taken as the z axis, and let $z = f(x)$ be the equation of the generating curve in the xz plane. Then the coördinates of a point on the surface are given by the equations

$$x = \rho \cos \omega, \qquad y = \rho \sin \omega, \qquad z = f(\rho),$$

where the independent variables ρ and ω are the polar coördinates of the projection of the point on the xy plane. In this case we have

$$ds^2 = d\rho^2 [1 + f'^2(\rho)] + \rho^2 d\omega^2,$$
$$E = 1 + f'^2(\rho), \qquad F = 0, \qquad G = \rho^2.$$

To find the area of the portion of the surface bounded by two plane sections perpendicular to the axis of revolution whose radii are ρ_1 and ρ_2, respectively, ρ should be allowed to vary from ρ_1 to ρ_2 ($\rho_1 < \rho_2$) and ω from zero to 2π. Hence the required area is given by the integral

$$\mathsf{A} = \int_{\rho_1}^{\rho_2} d\rho \int_0^{2\pi} \rho \sqrt{1 + f'^2(\rho)}\, d\omega = 2\pi \int_{\rho_1}^{\rho_2} \rho \sqrt{1 + f'^2(\rho)}\, d\rho,$$

and can therefore be evaluated by a single quadrature. If s denote the arc of the generating curve, we have

$$ds^2 = d\rho^2 + dz^2 = d\rho^2 [1 + f'^2(\rho)],$$

and the preceding formula may be written in the form

$$A = \int_{\rho_1}^{\rho_2} 2\pi\rho \, ds.$$

The geometrical interpretation of this result is easy: $2\pi\rho \, ds$ is the lateral area of a frustum of a cone whose slant height is ds and whose mean radius is ρ. Replacing the area between two sections whose distance from each other is infinitesimal by the lateral area of such a frustum of a cone, we should obtain precisely the above formula for A.

For example, on the paraboloid of revolution generated by revolving the parabola $x^2 = 2pz$ about the z axis the area of the section between the vertex and the circular plane section whose radius is r is

$$A = 2\pi \int_0^r \frac{\rho}{p} \sqrt{\rho^2 + p^2} \, d\rho = \frac{2\pi}{3p} \left[(r^2 + p^2)^{\frac{3}{2}} - p^3 \right].$$

III. GENERALIZATIONS OF DOUBLE INTEGRALS
IMPROPER INTEGRALS   SURFACE INTEGRALS

133. Improper integrals. Let $f(x, y)$ be a function which is continuous in the whole region of the plane which lies outside a closed contour Γ. The double integral of $f(x, y)$ extended over the region between Γ and another closed curve C outside of Γ has a finite value. If this integral approaches one and the same limit no matter how C varies, provided merely that the distance from the origin to the nearest point of C becomes infinite, this limit is defined to be the value of the double integral extended over the whole region outside Γ.

Let us assume for the moment that the function $f(x, y)$ has a constant sign, say positive, outside Γ. In this case the limit of the double integral is independent of the form of the curves C. For, let $C_1, C_2, \cdots, C_n, \cdots$ be a sequence of closed curves each of which encloses the preceding in such a way that the distance to the nearest point of C_n becomes infinite with n. If the double integral I_n extended over the region between Γ and C_n approaches a limit I, the same will be true for any other sequence of curves $C_1', C_2', \cdots, C_m', \cdots$ which satisfy the same conditions. For, if I_m' be the value of the double integral extended over the region between Γ and C_m', n may be chosen so large that the curve C_n entirely encloses C_m', and we shall have $I_m' < I_n < I$. Moreover I_m' increases with m. Hence I_m'

has a limit $I' \leqq I$. It follows in the same manner that $I \leqq I'$. Hence $I' = I$, i.e. the two limits are equal.

As an example let us consider a function $f(x, y)$, which outside a circle of radius r about the origin as center is of the form

$$f(x, y) = \frac{\psi(x, y)}{(x^2 + y^2)^\alpha},$$

where the value of the numerator $\psi(x, y)$ remains between two positive numbers m and M. Choosing for the curves C the circles concentric to the above, the value of the double integral extended over the circular ring between the two circles of radii r and R is given by the definite integral

$$\int_0^{2\pi} d\omega \int_r^R \frac{\psi(\rho \cos \omega, \rho \sin \omega)\rho \, d\rho}{\rho^{2\alpha}}.$$

It therefore lies between the values of the two expressions

$$2\pi m \int_r^R \frac{d\rho}{\rho^{2\alpha-1}}, \qquad 2\pi M \int_r^R \frac{d\rho}{\rho^{2\alpha-1}}.$$

By § 90, the simple integral involved approaches a limit as R increases indefinitely, provided that $2\alpha - 1 > 1$ or $\alpha > 1$. But it becomes infinite with R if $\alpha \leqq 1$.

If no closed curve can be found outside which the function $f(x, y)$ has a constant sign, it can be shown, as in § 89, that the integral $\int\int f(x, y) \, dx \, dy$ approaches a limit if the integral $\int\int |f(x, y)| \, dx \, dy$ itself approaches a limit. But if the latter integral becomes infinite, the former integral is indeterminate. The following example, due to Cayley, is interesting. Let $f(x, y) = \sin(x^2 + y^2)$, and let us integrate this function first over a square of side a formed by the axes and the two lines $x = a$, $y = a$. The value of this integral is

$$\int_0^a dx \int_0^a \sin(x^2 + y^2) \, dy$$
$$= \int_0^a \sin x^2 dx \times \int_0^a \cos y^2 dy + \int_0^a \cos x^2 dx \times \int_0^a \sin y^2 dy.$$

As a increases indefinitely, each of the integrals on the right has a limit, by § 91. This limit can be shown to be $\sqrt{\pi/2}$ in each case; hence the limit of the whole right-hand side is π. On the other hand, the double integral of the same function extended over the quarter circle bounded by the axes and the circle $x^2 + y^2 = R^2$ is equal to the expression

$$\int_0^{\frac{\pi}{2}} d\omega \int_0^R \rho \sin \rho^2 \, d\rho = -\frac{\pi}{4} \big[\cos \rho^2 \big]_0^R = \frac{\pi}{4} \big[1 - \cos R^2 \big],$$

which, as R becomes infinite, oscillates between zero and $\pi/2$ and does not approach any limit whatever.

We should define in a similar manner the double integral of a function $f(x, y)$ which becomes infinite at a point or all along a line. First, we should remove the point (or the line) from the field of integration by surrounding it by a small contour (or by a contour very close to the line) which we should let diminish indefinitely. For example, if the function $f(x, y)$ can be written in the form

$$f(x, y) = \frac{\psi(x, y)}{[(x-a)^2 + (y-b)^2]^{\alpha}}$$

in the neighborhood of the point (a, b), where $\psi(x, y)$ lies between two positive numbers m and M, the double integral of $f(x, y)$ extended over a region about the point (a, b) which contains no other point of discontinuity has a finite value if and only if α is less than unity.

134. The function B(p, q). We have assumed above that the contour C_n recedes indefinitely in every direction. But it is evident that we may also suppose that only a certain portion recedes to infinity. This is the case in the above example of Cayley's and also in the following example. Let us take the function

$$f(x, y) = 4x^{2p-1} y^{2q-1} e^{-x^2-y^2},$$

where p and q are each positive. This function is continuous and positive in the first quadrant. Integrating first over the square of side a bounded by the axes and the lines $x = a$ and $y = a$, we find, for the value of the double integral,

$$\int_0^a 2x^{2p-1} e^{-x^2} dx \times \int_0^a 2y^{2q-1} e^{-y^2} dy.$$

Each of these integrals approaches a limit as a becomes infinite. For, by the definition of the function $\Gamma(p)$ in § 92,

$$\Gamma(p) = \int_0^{+\infty} t^{p-1} e^{-t} dt,$$

whence, setting $t = x^2$, we find

(31) $$\Gamma(p) = \int_0^{+\infty} 2x^{2p-1} e^{-x^2} dx.$$

Hence the double integral approaches the limit $\Gamma(p)\,\Gamma(q)$ as a becomes infinite.

Let us now integrate over the quarter circle bounded by the axes and the circle $x^2 + y^2 = R^2$. The value of the double integral in polar coördinates is

$$\int_0^R 2\rho^{2(p+q)-1} e^{-\rho^2} d\rho \times \int_0^{\frac{\pi}{2}} 2 \cos^{2p-1}\phi \sin^{2q-1}\phi \, d\phi.$$

As R becomes infinite this product approaches the limit

$$\Gamma(p + q)\, B(p,\ q),$$

where we have set

(32) $$B(p,\ q) = \int_0^{\frac{\pi}{2}} 2 \cos^{2p-1}\phi \sin^{2q-1}\phi\, d\phi.$$

Expressing the fact that these two limits must be the same, we find the equation

(33) $$\Gamma(p)\, \Gamma(q) = \Gamma(p + q)\, B(p,\ q).$$

The integral $B(p, q)$ is called Euler's integral *of the first kind.* Setting $t = \sin^2\phi$, it may be written in the form

(34) $$B(p,\ q) = \int_0^1 t^{q-1}(1 - t)^{p-1}\, dt.$$

The formula (33) reduces the calculation of the function $B(p, q)$ to the calculation of the function Γ. For example, setting $p = q = 1/2$, we find

$$\left[\Gamma\!\left(\frac{1}{2}\right)\right]^2 = \Gamma(1) \int_0^{\frac{\pi}{2}} 2\, d\phi = \pi,$$

whence $\Gamma(1/2) = \sqrt{\pi}$. Hence the formula (31) gives

$$\int_0^{+\infty} e^{-x^2}\, dx = \frac{\sqrt{\pi}}{2}.$$

In general, setting $q = 1 - p$ and taking p between 0 and 1, we find

$$\Gamma(p)\, \Gamma(1 - p) = B(p,\ 1 - p) = \int_0^1 \left(\frac{1 - t}{t}\right)^{p-1} \frac{dt}{t}$$

We shall see later that the value of this integral is $\pi/\sin p\pi$.

135. Surface integrals. The definition of *surface integrals* is analogous to that of line integrals. Let S be a region of a surface bounded by one or more curves Γ. We shall assume that the surface has two distinct sides in such a way that if one side be painted red and the other blue, for instance, it will be impossible to pass from the red side to the blue side along a continuous path which lies on the surface and which does not cross one of the bounding curves.* Let us think of S as a material surface having a certain thickness, and let m and m' be two points near each other on opposite sides of the surface. At m let us draw that half of the normal mn to the surface which does not pierce the surface. The direction thus defined upon the normal will be said, for brevity, to correspond to that side of the surface on which m lies. The direction of the normal which corresponds to the other side of the surface at the point m' will be opposite to the direction just defined.

Let $z = \phi(x, y)$ be the equation of the given surface, and let S be a region of this surface bounded by a contour Γ. We shall assume that the surface is met in at most one point by any parallel to the z axis, and that the function $\phi(x, y)$

---

* It is very easy to form a surface which does not satisfy this condition. We need only deform a rectangular sheet of paper $ABCD$ by pasting the side BC to the side AD in such a way that the point C coincides with A and the point B with D.

is continuous inside the region A of the xy plane which is bounded by the curve C into which Γ projects. It is evident that this surface has two sides for which the corresponding directions of the normal make, respectively, acute and obtuse angles with the positive direction of the z axis. We shall call that side whose corresponding normal makes an acute angle with the positive z axis the *upper side*. Now let $P(x, y, z)$ be a function of the three variables x, y, and z which is continuous in a certain region of space which contains the region S of the surface. If z be replaced in this function by $\phi(x, y)$, there results a certain function $P[x, y, \phi(x, y)]$ of x and y alone; and it is natural by analogy with line integrals to call the double integral of this function extended over the region A,

$$(35) \qquad \iint_{(A)} P[x, y, \phi(x, y)]\, dx\, dy,$$

the *surface integral* of the function $P(x, y, z)$ taken over the region S of the given surface. Suppose the coördinates x, y, and z of a point of S given in terms of two auxiliary variables u and v in such a way that the portion S of the surface corresponds point for point in a one-to-one manner to a region R of the uv plane. Let $d\sigma$ be the surface element of the surface S, and γ the acute angle between the positive z axis and the normal to the upper side of S. Then the preceding double integral, by §§ 131–132, is equal to the double integral

$$(36) \qquad \iint_{(R)} P(x, y, z) \cos \gamma\, d\sigma,$$

where x, y, and z are to be expressed in terms of u and v. This new expression is, however, more general than the former, for $\cos \gamma$ may take on either of two values according to which side of the surface is chosen. When the acute angle γ is chosen, as above, the double integral (35) or (36) is called the surface integral

$$(37) \qquad \iint P(x, y, z)\, dx\, dy$$

extended over the *upper side* of the surface S. But if γ be taken as the obtuse angle, every element of the double integral will be changed in sign, and the new double integral would be called the surface integral $\iint P\, dx\, dy$ extended over the *lower side* of S. In general, the surface integral $\iint P\, dx\, dy$ is equal to $\pm$ the double integral (35) according as it is extended over the upper or the lower side of S.

This definition enables us to complete the analogy between simple and double integrals. Thus a simple integral changes sign when the limits are interchanged, while nothing similar has been developed for double integrals. With the generalized definition of double integrals, we may say that the integral $\iint f(x, y)\, dx\, dy$ previously considered is the surface integral extended over the upper side of the xy plane, while the same integral with its sign changed represents the surface integral taken over the under side. The two senses of motion for a simple integral thus correspond to the two sides of the xy plane for a double integral.

The expression (36) for a surface integral evidently does not require that the surface should be met in at most one point by any parallel to the z axis. In the same manner we might define the surface integrals

$$\iint Q(x, y, z)\, dy\, dz, \qquad \iint R(x, y, z)\, dz\, dx,$$

and the more general integral

$$\int\int P(x, y, z)\,dx\,dy + Q(x, y, z)\,dy\,dz + R(x, y, z)\,dz\,dx.$$

This latter integral may also be written in the form

$$\int\int [P\cos\gamma + Q\cos\alpha + R\cos\beta]\,d\sigma,$$

where α, β, γ are the direction angles of the direction of the normal which corresponds to the side of the surface selected.

Surface integrals are especially important in Mathematical Physics.

136. Stokes' theorem. Let L be a skew curve along which the functions $P(x, y, z)$, $Q(x, y, z)$, $R(x, y, z)$ are continuous. Then the definition of the line integral

$$\int_{(L)} P\,dx + Q\,dy + R\,dz$$

taken along the line L is similar to that given in § 93 for a line integral taken along a plane curve, and we shall not go into the matter in detail. If the curve L is closed, the integral evidently may be broken up into the sum of three line integrals taken over closed plane curves. Applying Green's theorem to each of these, it is evident that we may replace the line integral by the sum of three double integrals. The introduction of surface integrals enables us to state this result in very compact form.

Let us consider a two-sided piece S of a surface which we shall suppose for definiteness to be bounded by a single curve Γ. To each side of the surface corresponds a definite sense of direct motion along the contour Γ. We shall assume the following convention: At any point M of the contour let us draw that half of the normal Mn which corresponds to the side of the surface under consideration, and let us imagine an observer with his head at n and his feet at M;

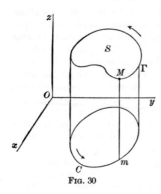

FIG. 30

we shall say that that is the positive sense of motion which the observer must take in order to have the region S at his left hand. Thus to the two sides of the surface correspond two opposite senses of motion along the contour Γ.

Let us first consider a region S of a surface which is met in at most one point by any parallel to the z axis, and let us suppose the trihedron $Oxyz$ placed as in Fig. 30, where the plane of the paper is the yz plane and the x axis extends toward the observer. To the boundary Γ of S will correspond a closed contour C in the xy plane; and these two curves are described simultaneously in the sense indicated by the arrows. Let $z = f(x, y)$ be the equation of the given surface, and let $P(x, y, z)$ be a function which is continuous in a region of space which contains S. Then the line integral $\int_{(\Gamma)} P(x, y, z)\,dx$ is identical with the line integral

$$\int_{(C)} P[x, y, \phi(x, y)] \, dx$$

taken along the plane curve C. Let us apply Green's theorem (§ 126) to this latter integral. Setting

$$\overline{P(x, y)} = P[x, y, \phi(x, y)]$$

for definiteness, we find

$$\frac{\partial \overline{P(x, y)}}{\partial y} = \frac{\partial P}{\partial y} + \frac{\partial P}{\partial z} \frac{\partial \phi}{\partial y} = \frac{\partial P}{\partial y} - \frac{\partial P}{\partial z} \frac{\cos \beta}{\cos \gamma},$$

where α, β, γ are the direction angles of the normal to the upper side of S. Hence, by Green's theorem,

$$\int_{(C)} \overline{P(x, y)} \, dx = \iint_{(A)} \left(\frac{\partial P}{\partial z} \cos \beta - \frac{\partial P}{\partial y} \cos \gamma \right) \frac{dx \, dy}{\cos \gamma},$$

where the double integral is to be taken over the region A of the xy plane bounded by the contour C. But the right-hand side is simply the surface integral

$$\iint \left(\frac{\partial P}{\partial z} \cos \beta - \frac{\partial P}{\partial y} \cos \gamma \right) d\sigma$$

extended over the upper side of S; and hence we may write

$$\int_{(\Gamma)} P(x, y, z) \, dx = \iint_{(S)} \frac{\partial P}{\partial z} \, dz \, dx - \frac{\partial P}{\partial y} \, dx \, dy.$$

This formula evidently holds also when the surface integral is taken over the other side of S, if the line integral is taken in the other direction along Γ. And it also holds, as does Green's theorem, no matter what the form of the surface may be. By cyclic permutation of x, y, and z we obtain the following analogous formulæ:

$$\int_{(\Gamma)} Q(x, y, z) \, dy = \iint_{(S)} \frac{\partial Q}{\partial x} \, dx \, dy - \frac{\partial Q}{\partial z} \, dy \, dz,$$

$$\int_{(\Gamma)} R(x, y, z) \, dz = \iint_{(S)} \frac{\partial R}{\partial y} \, dy \, dz - \frac{\partial R}{\partial x} \, dz \, dx.$$

Adding the three, we obtain *Stokes' theorem in its general form*:

$$(38) \quad \begin{cases} \int_{(\Gamma)} P(x, y, z) \, dx + Q(x, y, z) \, dy + R(x, y, z) \, dz \\ = \iint_{(S)} \left(\frac{\partial Q}{\partial x} - \frac{\partial P}{\partial y} \right) dx \, dy + \left(\frac{\partial R}{\partial y} - \frac{\partial Q}{\partial z} \right) dy \, dz + \left(\frac{\partial P}{\partial z} - \frac{\partial R}{\partial x} \right) dz \, dx. \end{cases}$$

The sense in which Γ is described and the side of the surface over which the double integral is taken correspond according to the convention made above.

IV. ANALYTICAL AND GEOMETRICAL APPLICATIONS

137. Volumes. Let us consider, as above, a region of space bounded by the xy plane, a surface S above that plane, and a cylinder whose generators are parallel to the z axis. We shall suppose that the section of the cylinder by the plane $z = 0$ is a contour similar to that drawn in Fig. 25, composed of two parallels to the y axis and two curvilinear arcs APB and $A'QB'$. If $z = f(x, y)$ is the equation of the surface S, the volume in question is given, by § 124, by the integral

$$V = \int_a^b dx \int_{y_1}^{y_2} f(x, y) \, dy.$$

Now the integral $\int_{y_1}^{y_2} f(x, y) \, dy$ represents the area A of a section of this volume by a plane parallel to the yz plane. Hence the preceding formula may be written in the form

$$(39) \qquad\qquad V = \int_a^b \mathsf{A} \, dx.$$

The volume of a solid bounded in any way whatever is equal to the algebraic sum of several volumes bounded as above. For instance, to find the volume of a solid bounded by a convex closed surface we should circumscribe the solid by a cylinder whose generators are parallel to the z axis and then find the difference between two volumes like the preceding. Hence the formula (39) holds for any volume which lies between two parallel planes $x = a$ and $x = b$ $(a < b)$ and which is bounded by any surface whatever, where A denotes the area of a section made by a plane parallel to the two given planes. Let us suppose the interval (a, b) subdivided by the points $a, x_1, x_2, \cdots, x_{n-1}, b$, and let $\mathsf{A}_0, \mathsf{A}_1, \cdots, \mathsf{A}_i, \cdots$ be the areas of the sections made by the planes $x = a, x = x_1, \cdots$, respectively. Then the definite integral $\int_a^b \mathsf{A} \, dx$ is the limit of the sum

$$\mathsf{A}_0(x_1 - a) + \mathsf{A}_1(x_2 - x_1) + \cdots + \mathsf{A}_{i-1}(x_i - x_{i-1}) \cdots.$$

The geometrical meaning of this result is apparent. For $\mathsf{A}_{i-1}(x_i - x_{i-1})$, for instance, represents the volume of a right cylinder whose base is the section of the given solid by the plane $x = x_{i-1}$ and whose height is the distance between two consecutive sections. Hence the volume of the given solid is the limit of the sum of such infinitesimal cylinders. This fact is in conformity with the ordinary crude notion of volume.

If the value of the area A be known as a function of x, the volume to be evaluated may be found by a single quadrature. As an example let us try to find the volume of a portion of a solid of revolution between two planes perpendicular to the axis of revolution. Let this axis be the x axis and let $z = f(x)$ be the equation of the generating curve in the xz plane. The section made by a plane parallel to the yz plane is a circle of radius $f(x)$. Hence the required volume is given by the integral $\pi \int_a^b [f(x)]^2 dx$.

Again, let us try to find the volume of the portion of the ellipsoid

$$\frac{x^2}{a^2} + \frac{y^2}{b^2} + \frac{z^2}{c^2} = 1$$

bounded by the two planes $x = x_0$, $x = X$. The section made by a plane parallel to the plane $x = 0$ is an ellipse whose semiaxes are $b\sqrt{1 - x^2/a^2}$ and $c\sqrt{1 - x^2/a^2}$. Hence the volume sought is

$$V = \int_{x_0}^X \pi bc \left(1 - \frac{x^2}{a^2} \right) dx = \pi bc \left(X - x_0 - \frac{X^3 - x_0^3}{3a^2} \right).$$

To find the total volume we should set $x = -a$ and $X = a$, which gives the value $\tfrac{4}{3}\pi abc$.

138. Ruled surface. Prismoidal formula. When the area A is an integral function of the second degree in x, the volume may be expressed very simply in terms of the areas B and B' of the bounding sections, the area b of the mean section, and the distance h between the two bounding sections. If the mean section be the plane of yz, we have

$$V = \int_{-a}^{+a} (lx^2 + 2mx + n) \, dx = 2l\frac{a^3}{3} + 2na.$$

But we also have

$$h = 2a, \qquad b = n, \qquad B = la^2 + 2ma + n, \qquad B' = la^2 - 2ma + n,$$

whence $n = b$, $a = h/2$, $2la^2 = B + B' - 2b$. These equations lead to the formula

(40) $$V = \frac{h}{6}[B + B' + 4b],$$

which is called the *prismoidal formula*.

This formula holds *in particular* for any solid bounded by a ruled surface and two parallel planes, including as a special case the so-called prismoid.* For, let $y = ax + p$ and $z = bx + q$ be the equations of a variable straight line, where a, b, p, and q are continuous functions of a variable parameter t which resume their initial values when t increases from t_0 to T. This straight line describes

---

* A prismoid is a solid bounded by any number of *planes*, two of which are parallel and contain all the vertices. — TRANS.

a ruled surface, and the area of the section made by a plane parallel to the plane $x = 0$ is given, by § 94, by the integral

$$\mathsf{A} = \int_{t_0}^{T} (ax + p)(b'x + q')\,dt,$$

where a', b', c', d' denote the derivatives of a, b, c, d with respect to t. These derivatives may even be discontinuous for a finite number of values between t_0 and T, which will be the case when the lateral boundary consists of portions of several ruled surfaces. The expression for A may be written in the form

$$\mathsf{A} = x^2 \int_{t_0}^{T} ab'\,dt + x \int_{t_0}^{T} (aq' + pb')\,dt + \int_{t_0}^{T} pq'\,dt,$$

where the integrals on the right are evidently independent of x. Hence the formula (40) holds for the volume of the given solid. It is worthy of notice that *the same formula also gives the volumes of most of the solids of elementary geometry.*

139. Viviani's problem. Let C be a circle described with a radius OA $(= R)$ of a given sphere as diameter, and let us try to find the volume of the portion of the sphere inside a circular cylinder whose right section is the circle C. Taking the origin at the center of the sphere, one fourth the required volume is given by the double integral

$$\frac{V}{4} = \int\int \sqrt{R^2 - x^2 - y^2}\,dx\,dy$$

extended over a semicircle described on OA as diameter. Passing to polar coördinates ρ and ω, the angle ω varies from 0 to $\pi/2$, and ρ from 0 to $R\cos\omega$. Hence we find

$$\frac{V}{4} = \int_0^{\frac{\pi}{2}} d\omega \int_0^{R\cos\omega} \rho \sqrt{R^2 - \rho^2}\,d\rho = -\int_0^{\frac{\pi}{2}} \frac{1}{3}\Big[(R^2 - \rho^2)^{\frac{3}{2}}\Big]_0^{R\cos\omega} d\omega,$$

or

$$\frac{V}{4} = \frac{1}{3}\int_0^{\frac{\pi}{2}}(R^3 - R^3\sin^3\omega)\,d\omega = \frac{R^3}{3}\left(\frac{\pi}{2} - \frac{2}{3}\right).$$

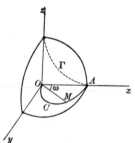

FIG. 31

If this volume and the volume inside the cylinder which is symmetrical to this one with respect to the z axis be subtracted from the volume of the whole sphere, the remainder is

$$\frac{4}{3}\pi R^3 - \frac{8R^3}{3}\left(\frac{\pi}{2} - \frac{2}{3}\right) = \frac{16}{9} R^3.$$

Again, the *area* Ω of the portion of the surface of the sphere inside the given cylinder is

$$\Omega = 4 \int\int \sqrt{1 + p^2 + q^2}\,dx\,dy.$$

Replacing p and q by their values $-x/z$ and $-y/z$, respectively, and passing to polar coördinates, we find

$$\Omega = 4\int_0^{\frac{\pi}{2}} d\omega \int_0^{R\cos\omega} \frac{R\rho\, d\rho}{\sqrt{R^2 - \rho^2}} = 4\int_0^{\frac{\pi}{2}} - R\left(\sqrt{R^2 - \rho^2}\right)_0^{R\cos\omega} d\omega,$$

or

$$\Omega = 4R^2 \int_0^{\frac{\pi}{2}} (1 - \sin\omega)\, d\omega = 4R^2\left(\frac{\pi}{2} - 1\right).$$

Subtracting the area enclosed by the two cylinders from the whole area of the sphere, the remainder is

$$4\pi R^2 - 8R^2\left(\frac{\pi}{2} - 1\right) = 8R^2.$$

140. Evaluation of particular definite integrals. The theorems established above, in particular the theorem regarding differentiation under the integral sign, sometimes enable us to evaluate certain definite integrals without knowing the corresponding indefinite integrals We proceed to give a few examples.

Setting

$$A = F(\alpha) = \int_0^{\alpha} \frac{\log(1 + \alpha x)}{1 + x^2}\, dx,$$

the formula for differentiation under the integral sign gives

$$\frac{dA}{d\alpha} = \frac{\log(1 + \alpha^2)}{1 + \alpha^2} + \int_0^{\alpha} \frac{x\, dx}{(1 + \alpha x)(1 + x^2)}.$$

Breaking up this integrand into partial fractions, we find

$$\frac{x}{(1 + \alpha x)(1 + x^2)} = \frac{1}{1 + \alpha^2}\left(\frac{x + \alpha}{1 + x^2} - \frac{\alpha}{1 + \alpha x}\right),$$

whence

$$\int_0^{\alpha} \frac{x\, dx}{(1 + \alpha x)(1 + x^2)} = -\frac{\log(1 + \alpha^2)}{2(1 + \alpha^2)} + \frac{\alpha}{1 + \alpha^2}\text{ arc tan }\alpha.$$

It follows that

$$\frac{dA}{d\alpha} = \frac{\alpha}{1 + \alpha^2}\text{ arc tan }\alpha + \frac{\log(1 + \alpha^2)}{2(1 + \alpha^2)},$$

whence, observing that A vanishes when $\alpha = 0$, we may write

$$A = \int_0^{\alpha} \frac{\log(1 + \alpha^2)}{2(1 + \alpha^2)}\, d\alpha + \int_0^{\alpha} \frac{\alpha}{1 + \alpha^2}\text{ arc tan }\alpha\, d\alpha.$$

Integrating the first of these integrals by parts, we finally find

$$A = \frac{1}{2}\text{ arc tan }\alpha \log(1 + \alpha^2).$$

Again, consider the function x^y. This function is continuous when x lies between 0 and 1 and y between any two positive numbers a and b. Hence, by the general formula of § 123,

$$\int_0^1 dx \int_a^b x^y\, dy = \int_a^b dy \int_0^1 x^y\, dx.$$

But

$$\int_0^1 x^y\, dx = \left[\frac{x^{y+1}}{y+1}\right]_0^1 = \frac{1}{y+1};$$

hence the value of the right-hand side of the previous equation is

$$\int_a^b \frac{dy}{y+1} = \log\left(\frac{b+1}{a+1}\right).$$

On the other hand, we have

$$\int_a^b x^y\, dy = \left[\frac{x^y}{\log x}\right]_a^b = \frac{x^b - x^a}{\log x},$$

whence

$$\int_0^1 \frac{x^b - x^a}{\log x}\, dx = \log\left(\frac{b+1}{a+1}\right).$$

In general, suppose that $P(x, y)$ and $Q(x, y)$ are two functions which satisfy the relation $\partial P/\partial y = \partial Q/\partial x$, and that x_0, x_1, y_0, y_1 are given constants. Then, by the general formula for integration under the integral sign, we shall have

$$\int_{x_0}^{x_1} dx \int_{y_0}^{y_1} \frac{\partial P}{\partial y}\, dy = \int_{y_0}^{y_1} dy \int_{x_0}^{x_1} \frac{\partial Q}{\partial x}\, dx,$$

or

$$(41) \quad \int_{x_0}^{x_1} [P(x, y_1) - P(x, y_0)]\, dx = \int_{y_0}^{y_1} [Q(x_1, y) - Q(x_0, y)]\, dy.$$

Cauchy deduced the values of a large number of definite integrals from this formula. It is also closely and simply related to Green's theorem, of which it is essentially only a special case. For it may be derived by applying Green's theorem to the line integral $\int P\, dx + Q\, dy$ taken along the boundary of the rectangle formed by the lines $x = x_0$, $x = x_1$, $y = y_0$, $y = y_1$.

In the following example the definite integral is evaluated by a special device. The integral

$$F(\alpha) = \int_0^\pi \log(1 - 2\alpha \cos x + \alpha^2)\, dx$$

has a finite value if $|\alpha|$ is different from unity. This function $F(\alpha)$ has the following properties.

1) $F(-\alpha) = F(\alpha)$. For

$$F(-\alpha) = \int_0^\pi \log\left(1 + 2\alpha \cos x + \alpha^2\right) dx,$$

or, making the substitution $x = \pi - y$,

$$F(-\alpha) = \int_0^\pi \log\left(1 - 2\alpha \cos y + \alpha^2\right) dy = F(\alpha).$$

2) $F(\alpha^2) = 2F(\alpha)$. For we may set

$$2F(\alpha) = F(\alpha) + F(-\alpha),$$

whence

$$2F(\alpha) = \int_0^\pi \left[\log\left(1 - 2\alpha \cos x + \alpha^2\right) + \log\left(1 + 2\alpha \cos x + \alpha^2\right)\right] dx$$

$$= \int_0^\pi \log\left(1 - 2\alpha^2 \cos 2x + \alpha^4\right) dx.$$

If we now make the substitution $2x = y$, this becomes

$$2F(\alpha) = \frac{1}{2} \int_0^\pi \log\left(1 - 2\alpha^2 \cos y + \alpha^4\right) dy$$

$$+ \frac{1}{2} \int_\pi^{2\pi} \log\left(1 - 2\alpha^2 \cos y + \alpha^4\right) dy.$$

Making a second substitution $y = 2\pi - z$ in the last integral, we find

$$\int_\pi^{2\pi} \log\left(1 - 2\alpha^2 \cos y + \alpha^4\right) dy = \int_0^\pi \log\left(1 - 2\alpha^2 \cos z + \alpha^4\right) dz,$$

which leads to the formula

$$2F(\alpha) = \frac{1}{2} F(\alpha^2) + \frac{1}{2} F(\alpha^2) = F(\alpha^2).$$

From this result we have, successively,

$$F(\alpha) = \frac{1}{2} F(\alpha^2) = \frac{1}{4} F(\alpha^4) = \cdots = \frac{1}{2^n} F\left(\alpha^{2^n}\right).$$

If $|\alpha|$ is less than unity, α^{2^n} approaches zero as n becomes infinite. The same is true of $F(\alpha^{2^n})$, for the logarithm approaches zero. Hence, if $|\alpha| < 1$, we have $F(\alpha) = 0$.

If $|\alpha|$ is greater than unity, let us set $\alpha = 1/\beta$. Then we find

$$F(\alpha) = \int_0^\pi \log\left(1 - \frac{2\cos x}{\beta} + \frac{1}{\beta^2}\right) dx$$

$$= \int_0^\pi \log\left(1 - 2\beta\cos x + \beta^2\right) dx - \pi \log \beta^2,$$

where $|\beta|$ is less than unity.   Hence we have in this case

$$F(\alpha) = -\pi \log \beta^2 = \pi \log \alpha^2.$$

Finally, it can be shown by the aid of Ex. 6, p. 205, that $F(\pm 1) = 0$; hence $F(\alpha)$ is continuous for all values of α.

141. Approximate value of $\log \Gamma(n+1)$. A great variety of devices may be employed to find either the exact or at least an approximate value of a definite integral. We proceed to give an example. We have, by definition,

$$\Gamma(n+1) = \int_0^{+\infty} x^n e^{-x}\, dx.$$

The function $x^n e^{-x}$ assumes its maximum value $n^n e^{-n}$ for $x = n$. As x increases from zero to n, $x^n e^{-x}$ increases from zero to $n^n e^{-n}$ $(n>0)$, and when x increases from n to $+\infty$, $x^n e^{-x}$ decreases from $n^n e^{-n}$ to zero. Likewise, the function $n^n e^{-n} e^{-t^2}$ increases from zero to $n^n e^{-n}$ as t increases from $-\infty$ to zero, and decreases from $n^n e^{-n}$ to zero as t increases from zero to $+\infty$. Hence, by the substitution

$$(42) \qquad x^n e^{-x} = n^n e^{-n} e^{-t^2},$$

the values of x and t correspond in such a way that as t increases from $-\infty$ to $+\infty$, x increases from zero to $+\infty$.

It remains to calculate dx/dt. Taking the logarithmic derivative of each side of (42), we find

$$\frac{dx}{dt} = \frac{2tx}{x-n}.$$

We have also, by (42), the equation

$$t^2 = x - n - n \log\left(\frac{x}{n}\right).$$

For simplicity let us set $x = n + z$, and then develop $\log(1 + z/n)$ by Taylor's theorem with a remainder after two terms. Substituting this expansion in the value for t^2, we find

$$t^2 = z - n\left[\frac{z}{n} - \frac{z^2}{2n^2\left(1 + \theta\frac{z}{n}\right)^2}\right] = \frac{nz^2}{2(n+\theta z)^2},$$

where θ lies between zero and unity. From this we find, successively,

$$\frac{n}{z} + \theta = \frac{1}{t}\sqrt{\frac{n}{2}},$$

$$\frac{2tx}{x-n} = 2t\left(\frac{n}{z} + 1\right) = 2\left[\sqrt{\frac{n}{2}} + (1-\theta)t\right],$$

whence, applying the formula for change of variable,

$$\Gamma(n + 1) = 2n^n e^{-n} \sqrt{\frac{n}{2}} \int_{-\infty}^{+\infty} e^{-t^2} \, dt + 2n^n e^{-n} \int_{-\infty}^{+\infty} e^{-t^2} (1 - \theta) t \, dt.$$

The first integral is

$$\int_{-\infty}^{+\infty} e^{-t^2} \, dt = 2 \int_{0}^{+\infty} e^{-t^2} \, dt = \sqrt{\pi}.$$

As for the second integral, though we cannot evaluate it exactly, since we do not know θ, we can at least locate its value between certain fixed limits. For all its elements are negative between $-\infty$ and zero, and they are all positive between zero and $+\infty$. Moreover each of the integrals $\int_{-\infty}^{0}, \int_{0}^{+\infty}$ is less in absolute value than $\int_{0}^{+\infty} te^{-t^2} \, dt = 1/2$. It follows that

$$(43) \qquad \Gamma(n + 1) = \sqrt{2n} \, n^n e^{-n} \left(\sqrt{\pi} + \frac{\omega}{\sqrt{2n}} \right),$$

where ω lies between -1 and $+1$.

If n is very large, $\omega/\sqrt{2n}$ is very small. Hence, if we take

$$\Gamma(n + 1) = n^n e^{-n} \sqrt{2n\pi}$$

as an approximate value of $\Gamma(n + 1)$, our error is relatively small, though the actual error may be considerable. Taking the logarithm of each side of (43), we find the formula

$$(44) \qquad \log \Gamma(n + 1) = \left(n + \frac{1}{2} \right) \log n - n + \frac{1}{2} \log(2\pi) + \epsilon,$$

where ϵ is very small when n is very large. Neglecting ϵ, we have an expression which is called the *asymptotic value* of $\log \Gamma(n + 1)$. This formula is interesting as giving us an idea of the order of magnitude of a factorial.

142. D'Alembert's theorem. The formula for integration under the integral sign applies to any function $f(x, y)$ which is continuous in the rectangle of integration. Hence, if two different results are obtained by two different methods of integrating the function $f(x, y)$, we may conclude that the function $f(x, y)$ is discontinuous for at least one point in the field of integration. Gauss deduced from this fact an elegant demonstration of d'Alembert's theorem.

Let $F(z)$ be an integral polynomial of degree m in z. We shall assume for definiteness that all its coefficients are real. Replacing z by $\rho(\cos \omega + i \sin \omega)$, and separating the real and the imaginary parts, we have

$$F(z) = P + iQ,$$

where

$$P = A_0 \rho^m \cos m\omega + A_1 \rho^{m-1} \cos(m - 1)\omega + \cdots + A_m,$$
$$Q = A_0 \rho^m \sin m\omega + A_1 \rho^{m-1} \sin(m - 1)\omega + \cdots + A_{m-1} \rho \sin \omega.$$

If we set $V = \arctan(P/Q)$, we shall have

$$\frac{\partial V}{\partial \rho} = \frac{Q \dfrac{\partial P}{\partial \rho} - P \dfrac{\partial Q}{\partial \rho}}{P^2 + Q^2}, \qquad \frac{\partial V}{\partial \omega} = \frac{Q \dfrac{\partial P}{\partial \omega} - P \dfrac{\partial Q}{\partial \omega}}{P^2 + Q^2},$$

and it is evident, without actually carrying out the calculation, that the second derivative is of the form

$$\frac{\partial^2 V}{\partial \rho \, \partial \omega} = \frac{M}{(P^2 + Q^2)^2},$$

where M is a continuous function of ρ and ω. This second derivative can only be discontinuous for values of ρ and ω for which P and Q vanish simultaneously, that is to say, for the roots of the equation $F(z) = 0$. Hence, if we can show that the two integrals

$$(45) \qquad \int_0^{2\pi} d\omega \int_0^R \frac{\partial^2 V}{\partial\rho\,\partial\omega}\,d\rho, \qquad \int_0^R d\rho \int_0^{2\pi} \frac{\partial^2 V}{\partial\rho\,\partial\omega}\,d\omega$$

are unequal for a given value of R, we may conclude that the equation $F(z) = 0$ has at least one root whose absolute value is less than R. But the second integral is always zero, for

$$\int_0^{2\pi} \frac{\partial^2 V}{\partial\rho\,\partial\omega}\,d\omega = \left[\frac{\partial V}{\partial\rho}\right]_{\omega=0}^{\omega=2\pi},$$

and $\partial V/\partial\rho$ is a periodic function of ω, of period 2π. Calculating the first integral in a similar manner, we find

$$\int_0^R \frac{\partial^2 V}{\partial\rho\,\partial\omega}\,d\rho = \left[\frac{\partial V}{\partial\omega}\right]_{\rho=0}^{\rho=R},$$

and it is easy to show that $\partial V/\partial\omega$ is of the form

$$\frac{\partial V}{\partial\omega} = \frac{-mA_0^2\,\rho^{2m}+\cdots}{A_0^2\,\rho^{2m}+\cdots},$$

where the degree of the terms not written down is less than $2m$ in ρ, and where the numerator contains no term which does not involve ρ. As ρ increases indefinitely, the right-hand side approaches $-m$. Hence R may be chosen so large that the value of $\partial V/\partial\omega$, for $\rho = R$, is equal to $-m + \epsilon$, where ϵ is less than m in absolute value. The integral $\int_0^{2\pi}(-m+\epsilon)\,d\omega$ is evidently negative, and hence the first of the integrals (45) cannot be zero.

EXERCISES

1. At any point of the catenary defined in rectangular coördinates by the equation

$$y = \frac{a}{2}\left(e^{\frac{x}{a}} + e^{-\frac{x}{a}}\right)$$

let us draw the tangent and extend it until it meets the x axis at a point T. Revolving the whole figure about the x axis, find the difference between the areas described by the arc AM of the catenary, where A is the vertex of the catenary, and that described by the tangent MT (1) as a function of the abscissa of the point M, (2) as a function of the abscissa of the point T.

[*Licence*, Paris, 1889.]

2. Using the usual system of trirectangular coördinates, let a ruled surface be formed as follows: The plane zOA revolves about the x axis, while the generating line D, which lies in this plane, makes with the z axis a constant angle whose tangent is λ and cuts off on OA an intercept OC equal to $\lambda a\theta$, where a is a given length and θ is the angle between the two planes zOx and zOA.

1) Find the volume of the solid bounded by the ruled surface and the planes xOy, zOx, and zOA, where the angle θ between the last two is less than 2π.

2) Find the area of the portion of the surface bounded by the planes xOy, zOx, zOA.

[*Licence*, Paris, July, 1882.]

3. Find the volume of the solid bounded by the xy plane, the cylinder $b^2x^2 + a^2y^2 = a^2b^2$, and the elliptic paraboloid whose equation in rectangular coördinates is

$$\frac{2z}{c} = \frac{x^2}{p^2} + \frac{y^2}{q^2}.$$

[*Licence*, Paris, 1882.]

4. Find the area of the curvilinear quadrilateral bounded by the four confocal conics of the family

$$\frac{x^2}{\lambda} + \frac{y^2}{\lambda - c^2} = 1,$$

which are determined by giving λ the values $c^2/3$, $2c^2/3$, $4c^2/3$, $5c^2/3$, respectively.

[*Licence*, Besançon, 1885.]

5. Consider the curve

$$y = \sqrt{2}\,(\sin x - \cos x),$$

where x and y are the rectangular coördinates of a point, and where x varies from $\pi/4$ to $5\pi/4$.   Find:

1) the area between this curve and the x axis;

2) the volume of the solid generated by revolving the curve about the x axis;

3) the lateral area of the same solid.

[*Licence*, Montpellier, 1898.]

6. In an ordinary rectangular coördinate plane let A and B be any two points on the y axis, and let AMB be any curve joining A and B which, together with the line AB, forms the boundary of a region $AMBA$ whose area is a preassigned quantity S.   Find the value of the following definite integral taken over the curve AMB:

$$\int \left[\phi(y)e^x - my\right] dx + \left[\phi'(y)e^x - m\right] dy,$$

where m is a constant, and where the function $\phi(y)$, together with its derivative $\phi'(y)$, is continuous.

[*Licence*, Nancy, 1895.]

7. By calculating the double integral

$$\int_0^{+\infty} \int_0^{+\infty} e^{-xy} \sin ax\, dy\, dx$$

in two different ways, show that, provided that a is not zero,

$$\int_0^{+\infty} \frac{\sin ax}{x}\, dx = \pm \frac{\pi}{2}.$$

8. Find the area of the lateral surface of the portion of an ellipsoid of revolution or of an hyperboloid of revolution which is bounded by two planes perpendicular to the axis of revolution.

9*. To find the area of an ellipsoid with three unequal axes. Half of the total area A is given by the double integral

$$\frac{\mathsf{A}}{2} = \iint \sqrt{\frac{1 - \dfrac{a^2 - c^2}{a^4} x^2 - \dfrac{b^2 - c^2}{b^4} y^2}{1 - \dfrac{x^2}{a^2} - \dfrac{y^2}{b^2}}} \; dx \, dy$$

extended over the interior of the ellipse $b^2 x^2 + a^2 y^2 = a^2 b^2$. Among the methods employed to reduce this double integral to elliptic integrals, one of the simplest, due to Catalan, consists in the transformation used in § 125. Denoting the integrand of the double integral by v, and letting v vary from 1 to $+\infty$, it is easy to show that the double integral is equal to the limit, as l becomes infinite, of the difference

$$\frac{\pi a b l (l^2 - 1)}{\sqrt{\left(l^2 - 1 + \dfrac{c^2}{a^2}\right)\left(l^2 - 1 + \dfrac{c^2}{b^2}\right)}} - \pi a b \int_1^l \frac{(v^2 - 1)\, dv}{\sqrt{\left(v^2 - 1 + \dfrac{c^2}{a^2}\right)\left(v^2 - 1 + \dfrac{c^2}{b^2}\right)}}.$$

This expression is an undetermined form; but we may write

$$\int_1^l \frac{v^2\, dv}{\sqrt{\left(v^2 - 1 + \dfrac{c^2}{a^2}\right)\left(v^2 - 1 + \dfrac{c^2}{b^2}\right)}} = \left[\frac{\sqrt{\left(v^2 - 1 + \dfrac{c^2}{a^2}\right)\left(v^2 - 1 + \dfrac{c^2}{b^2}\right)}}{v} \right]_1^l$$

$$+ \int_1^l \frac{\left(1 - \dfrac{c^2}{a^2}\right)\left(1 - \dfrac{c^2}{b^2}\right) dv}{v^2 \sqrt{\left(v^2 - 1 + \dfrac{c^2}{a^2}\right)\left(v^2 - 1 + \dfrac{c^2}{b^2}\right)}},$$

and hence the limit considered above is readily seen to be

$$\pi a b \left[\frac{c^2}{ab} + \int_1^{+\infty} \frac{dv}{\sqrt{\left(v^2 - 1 + \dfrac{c^2}{a^2}\right)\left(v^2 - 1 + \dfrac{c^2}{b^2}\right)}} \right.$$

$$\left. - \left(1 - \dfrac{c^2}{a^2}\right)\left(1 - \dfrac{c^2}{b^2}\right) \int_1^{+\infty} \frac{dv}{v^2 \sqrt{\left(v^2 - 1 + \dfrac{c^2}{a^2}\right)\left(v^2 - 1 + \dfrac{c^2}{b^2}\right)}} \right]$$

10*. If from the center of an ellipsoid whose semiaxes are a, b, c a perpendicular be let fall upon the tangent plane to the ellipsoid, the area of the surface which is the locus of the foot of the perpendicular is equal to the area of an ellipsoid whose semiaxes are bc/a, ac/b, ab/c.

[WILLIAM ROBERTS, *Journal de Liouville*, Vol. XI, 1st series, p. 81.]

11. Evaluate the double integral of the expression

$$(x - y)^n f(y)$$

extended over the interior of the triangle bounded by the straight lines $y = x_0$, $y = x$, and $x = X$ in two different ways, and thereby establish the formula

$$\int_{x_0}^{X} dx \int_{x_0}^{x} (x - y)^n f(y)\, dy = \int_{x_0}^{X} \frac{(X - y)^{n+1}}{n + 1} f(y)\, dy.$$

From this result deduce the relation

$$\int_{x_0}^{x} dx \int_{x_0}^{x} dx \cdots \int_{x_0}^{x} f(x)\, dx = \frac{1}{(n-1)!} \int_{x_0}^{x} (x - y)^n f(y)\, dy.$$

In a similar manner derive the formula

$$\int_{x_0}^{x} x\, dx \int_{x_0}^{x} x\, dx \cdots \int_{x_0}^{x} x\, dx \int_{x_0}^{x} f(x)\, dx = \frac{1}{2 \cdot 4 \cdot 6 \cdots 2n} \int_{x_0}^{x} (x^2 - y^2)^n f(y)\, dy,$$

and verify these formulæ by means of the law for differentiation under the integral sign.

CHAPTER VII

MULTIPLE INTEGRALS
INTEGRATION OF TOTAL DIFFERENTIALS

I. MULTIPLE INTEGRALS   CHANGE OF VARIABLES

143. Triple integrals. Let $F(x, y, z)$ be a function of the three variables x, y, z which is continuous for all points M, whose rectangular coördinates are (x, y, z), in a finite region of space (E) bounded by one or more closed surfaces. Let this region be subdivided into a number of subregions (e_1), (e_2), $\cdots$, (e_n), whose volumes are v_1, v_2, $\cdots$, v_n, and let (ξ_i, η_i, ζ_i) be the coördinates of any point m_i of the subregion (e_i). Then the sum

$$(1) \qquad \sum_{i=1}^{n} F(\xi_i, \eta_i, \zeta_i) v_i$$

approaches a limit as the number of the subregions (e_i) is increased indefinitely in such a way that the maximum diameter of each of them approaches zero. This limit is called the triple integral of the function $F(x, y, z)$ extended throughout the region (E), and is represented by the symbol

$$(2) \qquad \iiint_{(E)} F(x, y, z)\, dx\, dy\, dz.$$

The proof that this limit exists is practically a repetition of the proof given above in the case of double integrals.

Triple integrals arise in various problems of Mechanics, for instance in finding the mass or the center of gravity of a solid body. Suppose the region (E) filled with a heterogeneous substance, and let $\mu(x, y, z)$ be the density at any point, that is to say, the limit of the ratio of the mass inside an infinitesimal sphere about the point (x, y, z) as center to the volume of the sphere. If μ_1 and μ_2 are the maximum and the minimum value of μ in the subregion (e_i), it is evident that the mass inside that subregion lies between $\mu_1 v_i$ and $\mu_2 v_i$; hence it is equal to $v_i \mu(\xi_i, \eta_i, \zeta_i)$, where (ξ_i, η_i, ζ_i) is a suitably chosen point of the subregion (e_i). It follows that the total mass is equal to the triple integral $\iiint \mu \, dx \, dy \, dz$ extended throughout the region (E).

The evaluation of a triple integral may be reduced to the successive evaluation of three simple integrals. Let us suppose first that the region (E) is a rectangular parallelopiped bounded by the six planes $x = x_0$, $x = X$, $y = y_0$, $y = Y$, $z = z_0$, $z = Z$. Let (E) be divided into smaller parallelopipeds by planes parallel to the three coördinate planes. The volume of one of the latter is $(x_i - x_{i-1})(y_k - y_{k-1})(z_l - z_{l-1})$, and we have to find the limit of the sum

$$(3) \quad S = \sum_i \sum_k \sum_l F(\xi_{ikl}, \eta_{ikl}, \zeta_{ikl})(x_i - x_{i-1})(y_k - y_{k-1})(z_l - z_{l-1}),$$

where the point $(\xi_{ikl}, \eta_{ikl}, \zeta_{ikl})$ is any point inside the corresponding parallelopiped. Let us evaluate first that part of S which arises from the column of elements bounded by the four planes

$$x = x_{i-1}, \qquad x = x_i, \qquad y = y_{k-1}, \qquad y = y_k,$$

taking all the points $(\xi_{ikl}, \eta_{ikl}, \zeta_{ikl})$ upon the straight line $x = x_{i-1}$, $y = y_{k-1}$. This column of parallelopipeds gives rise to the sum

$$(x_i - x_{i-1})(y_k - y_{k-1})[F(x_{i-1}, y_{k-1}, \zeta_1)(z_1 - z_0) + \cdots],$$

and, as in § 123, the ζ's may be chosen in such a way that the quantity inside the bracket will be equal to the simple integral

$$\Phi(x_{i-1}, y_{k-1}) = \int_{z_0}^{Z} F(x_{i-1}, y_{k-1}, z) \, dz.$$

It only remains to find the limit of the sum

$$\sum_i \sum_k (x_i - x_{i-1})(y_k - y_{k-1}) \Phi(x_{i-1}, y_{k-1}).$$

But this limit is precisely the double integral

$$\iint \Phi(x, y) \, dx \, dy$$

extended over the rectangle formed by the lines $x = x_0$, $x = X$, $y = y_0$, $y = Y$. Hence the triple integral is equal to

$$\int_{x_0}^{X} dx \int_{y_0}^{Y} \Phi(x, y) \, dy,$$

or, replacing $\Phi(x, y)$ by its value,

$$(4) \quad \int_{x_0}^{X} dx \int_{y_0}^{Y} dy \int_{z_0}^{Z} F(x, y, z) \, dz.$$

The meaning of this symbol is perfectly obvious. During the first integration x and y are to be regarded as constants. The result will be a function of x and y, which is then to be integrated between the limits y_0 and Y, x being regarded as a constant and y as a variable. The result of this second integration is a function of x alone, and the last step is the integration of this function between the limits x_0 and X.

There are evidently as many ways of performing this evaluation as there are permutations on three letters, that is, six. For instance, the triple integral is equivalent to

$$\int_{z_0}^{Z} dz \int_{x_0}^{X} dx \int_{y_0}^{Y} F(x,\, y,\, z)\, dy = \int_{z_0}^{Z} \Psi(z)\, dz,$$

where $\Psi(z)$ denotes the double integral of $F(x, y, z)$ extended over the rectangle formed by the lines $x = x_0$, $x = X$, $y = y_0$, $y = Y$. We might rediscover this formula by commencing with the part of the sum S which arises from the layer of parallelopipeds bounded by the two planes $z = z_{l-1}$, $z = z_l$. Choosing the points (ξ, η, ζ) suitably, the part of S which arises from this layer is

$$\Psi(z_{l-1})(z_l - z_{l-1}),$$

and the rest of the reasoning is similar to that above.

144. Let us now consider a region of space bounded in any manner whatever, and let us divide it into subregions such that any

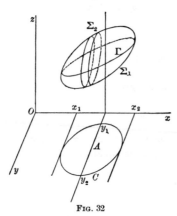

line parallel to a suitably chosen fixed line meets the surface which bounds any subregion in at most two points. We may evidently restrict ourselves without loss of generality to the case in which a line parallel to the z axis meets the surface in at most two points. The points upon the bounding surface project upon the xy plane into the points of a region A bounded by a closed contour C. To every point (x, y) inside C correspond two points on the bounding surface whose coördinates are

Fig. 32

$z_1 = \phi_1(x, y)$ and $z_2 = \phi_2(x, y)$. We shall suppose that the functions ϕ_1 and ϕ_2 are continuous inside C, and that $\phi_1 < \phi_2$. Let us now divide the region under consideration by planes parallel to the coördinate planes. Some of the subdivisions will be portions of parallelopipeds. The part of the sum (1) which arises from the column of elements bounded by the four planes $x = x_{i-1}$, $x = x_i$, $y = y_{k-1}$, $y = y_k$ is equal, by § 124, to the expression

$$(x_i - x_{i-1})(y_k - y_{k-1}) \left[\int_{z_1}^{z_2} F(x_{i-1}, y_{k-1}, z) \, dz + \epsilon_{ik} \right],$$

where the absolute value of ϵ_{ik} may be made less than any preassigned number ϵ by choosing the parallel planes sufficiently near together. The sum

$$\sum_i \sum_k \epsilon_{ik} (x_i - x_{i-1})(y_k - y_{k-1})$$

approaches zero as a limit, and the triple integral in question is therefore equal to the double integral

$$\iint_{(A)} \Phi(x, y) \, dx \, dy$$

extended over the region (A) bounded by the contour C, where the function $\Phi(x, y)$ is defined by the equation

$$\Phi(x, y) = \int_{z_1}^{z_2} F(x, y, z) \, dz.$$

If a line parallel to the y axis meets the contour C in at most two points whose coördinates are $y = \psi_1(x)$ and $y = \psi_2(x)$, respectively, while x varies from x_1 to x_2, the triple integral may also be written in the form

$$(5) \qquad \int_{x_1}^{x_2} dx \int_{y_1}^{y_2} dy \int_{z_1}^{z_2} F(x, y, z) \, dz.$$

The limits z_1 and z_2 depend upon both x and y, the limits y_1 and y_2 are functions of x alone, and finally the limits x_1 and x_2 are constants.

We may invert the order of the integrations as for double integrals, but the limits are in general totally different for different orders of integration.

Note. If $\Psi(x)$ be the function of x given by the double integral

$$\Psi(x) = \int_{y_1}^{y_2} dy \int_{z_1}^{z_2} F(x, y, z) \, dz$$

extended over the section of the given region by a plane parallel to the yz plane whose abscissa is x, the formula (5) may be written

$$\int_{x_1}^{x_2} \Psi(x)\, dx.$$

This is the result we should have obtained by starting with the layer of subregions bounded by the two planes $x = x_{i-1}$, $x = x_i$. Choosing the points (ξ, η, ζ) suitably, this layer contributes to the total sum the quantity

$$\Psi(x_{i-1})(x_i - x_{i-1}).$$

Example. Let us evaluate the triple integral $\int\int\int z\,dx\,dy\,dz$ extended throughout that eighth of the sphere $x^2 + y^2 + z^2 = R^2$ which lies in the first octant. If we integrate first with regard to z, then with regard to y, and finally with regard to x, the limits are as follows: x and y being given, z may vary from zero to $\sqrt{R^2 - x^2 - y^2}$; x being given, y may vary from zero to $\sqrt{R^2 - x^2}$; and x itself may vary from zero to R. Hence the integral in question has the value

$$\int\int\int z\,dx\,dy\,dz = \int_0^R dx \int_0^{\sqrt{R^2-x^2}} dy \int_0^{\sqrt{R^2-x^2-y^2}} z\,dz,$$

whence we find successively

$$\int_0^{\sqrt{R^2-x^2-y^2}} z\,dz = \frac{1}{2}(R^2 - x^2 - y^2),$$

$$\frac{1}{2}\int_0^{\sqrt{R^2-x^2}}(R^2 - x^2 - y^2)\,dy = \left[\frac{1}{2}(R^2 - x^2)y - \frac{1}{6}y^3\right]_0^{\sqrt{R^2-x^2}} = \frac{1}{3}(R^2 - x^2)^{\frac{3}{2}},$$

and it merely remains to calculate the definite integral $\frac{1}{3}\int_0^R (R^2 - x^2)^{\frac{3}{2}}\,dx$, which, by the substitution $x = R\cos\phi$, takes the form

$$\frac{1}{3}\int_0^{\frac{\pi}{2}} R^4 \sin^4\phi\, d\phi.$$

Hence the value of the given triple integral is, by § 116, $\pi R^4 / 16$.

145. Change of variables. Let

$$(6) \qquad \begin{cases} x = f(u, v, w), \\ y = \phi(u, v, w), \\ z = \psi(u, v, w), \end{cases}$$

be formulæ of transformation which establish a one-to-one correspondence between the points of the region (E) and those of another region (E_1). We shall think of u, v, and w as the rectangular coördinates of a point with respect to another system of rectangular coördinates, in general different from the first. If $F(x, y, z)$ is a continuous function throughout the region (E), we shall always have

(7)
$$
\begin{cases}
\iiint_{(E)} F(x, y, z)\, dx\, dy\, dz \\
\quad = \iiint_{(E_1)} F[f(u, v, w), \cdots] \left| \dfrac{D(f, \phi, \psi)}{D(u, v, w)} \right| du\, dv\, dw,
\end{cases}
$$

where the two integrals are extended throughout the regions (E) and (E_1), respectively. This is the formula for change of variables in triple integrals.

In order to show that the formula (7) always holds, we shall commence by remarking that if it holds for two or more particular transformations, it will hold also for the transformation obtained by carrying out these transformations in succession, by the well-known properties of the functional determinant (§ 29). If it is applicable to several regions of space, it is also applicable to the region obtained by combining them. We shall now proceed to show, as we did for double integrals, that the formula holds for a transformation which leaves all but one of the independent variables unchanged, — for example, for a transformation of the form

(8) $\qquad x = x', \qquad y = y', \qquad z = \psi(x', y', z').$

We shall suppose that the two points $M(x, y, z)$ and $M'(x', y', z')$ are referred to the same system of rectangular axes, and that a parallel to the z axis meets the surface which bounds the region (E) in at most two points. The formulæ (8) establish a correspondence between this surface and another surface which bounds the region (E'). The cylinder circumscribed about the two surfaces with its generators parallel to the z axis cuts the plane $z = 0$ along a closed curve C. Every point m of the region A inside the contour C is the projection of two points m_1 and m_2 of the first surface,

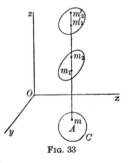

Fig. 33

whose coördinates are z_1 and z_2, respectively, and also of two points m'_1 and m'_2 of the second surface, whose coördinates are z'_1 and z'_2, respectively. Let us choose the notation in such a way that $z_1 < z_2$, and $z'_1 < z'_2$. The formulæ (8) transform the point m_1 into the point m'_1, or else into the point m'_2. To distinguish the two cases, we need merely consider the sign of $\partial\psi/\partial z'$. If $\partial\psi/\partial z'$ is

positive, z increases with z', and the points m_1 and m_2 go into the
points m_1' and m_2', respectively. On the other hand, if $\partial\psi/\partial z'$ is
negative, z decreases as z' increases, and m_1 and m_2 go into m_2' and
m_1', respectively. In the previous case we shall have

$$\int_{z_1}^{z} F(x, y, z)\, dz = \int_{z_1'}^{z_2'} F[x, y, \psi(x, y, z')] \frac{\partial\psi}{\partial z'}\, dz',$$

whereas in the second case

$$\int_{z_1}^{z_2} F(x, y, z)\, dz = -\int_{z_1'}^{z_2'} F[x, y, \psi(x, y, z')] \frac{\partial\psi}{\partial z'}\, dz'.$$

In either case we may write

$$(9) \quad \int_{z_1}^{z_2} F(x, y, z)\, dz = \int_{z_1'}^{z_2'} F[x, y, \psi(x, y, z')] \left|\frac{\partial\psi}{\partial z'}\right| dz'.$$

If we now consider the double integrals of the two sides of this
equation over the region A, the double integral of the left-hand side,

$$\iint_{(A)} dx\, dy \int_{z_1}^{z_2} F(x, y, z)\, dz,$$

is precisely the triple integral $\iiint F(x,y,z)\, dx\, dy\, dz$ extended throughout the region (E). Likewise, the double integral of the right-hand
side of (9) is equal to the triple integral of

$$F[x', y', \psi(x', y', z')] \left|\frac{\partial\psi}{\partial z'}\right|$$

extended throughout the region (E'), which readily follows when
x and y are replaced by x' and y', respectively. Hence we have in
this particular case

$$\iiint_{(E)} F(x, y, z)\, dx\, dy\, dz$$
$$= \iiint_{(E')} F[x', y', \psi(x', y', z')] \left|\frac{\partial\psi}{\partial z'}\right| dx'\, dy'\, dz'.$$

But in this case the determinant $D(x, y, z)/D(x', y', z')$ reduces to
$\partial\psi/\partial z'$. Hence the formula (7) holds for the transformation (8).

Again, the general formula (7) holds for a transformation of the
type

$$(10) \quad x = f(x', y', z'), \qquad y = \phi(x', y', z'), \qquad z = z',$$

where the variable z remains unchanged. We shall suppose that the formulæ (10) establish a one-to-one correspondence between the points of two regions (E) and (E'), and in particular that the sections R and R' made in (E) and (E'), respectively, by any plane parallel to the xy plane correspond in a one-to-one manner. Then by the formulæ for transformation of double integrals we shall have

$$
(11) \quad
\begin{cases}
\displaystyle \iint_{(R)} F(x,\,y,\,z)\,dx\,dy \\[2mm]
\displaystyle \qquad = \iint_{(R')} F[f(x',\,y',\,z'),\,\phi(x',\,y',\,z'),\,z']\left|\frac{D(f,\,\phi)}{D(x',\,y')}\right|dx'\,dy'.
\end{cases}
$$

The two members of this equation are functions of the variable $z = z'$ alone. Integrating both sides again between the limits z_1 and z_2, between which z can vary in the region (E), we find the formula

$$
(12) \quad
\begin{cases}
\displaystyle \iiint_{(E)} F(x,\,y,\,z)\,dx\,dy\,dz \\[2mm]
\displaystyle \qquad = \iiint_{(E')} F[f(x',y',z'),\,\phi(x',y',z'),z']\left|\frac{D(f,\,\phi)}{D(x',y')}\right|dx'\,dy'\,dz'.
\end{cases}
$$

But in this case $D(x, y, z)/D(x', y', z') = D(x, y)/D(x', y')$. Hence the formula (7) holds for the transformation (10) also.

We shall now show that any change of variables whatever

$$(13) \quad x = f(x_1,\,y_1,\,z_1), \qquad y = \phi(x_1,\,y_1,\,z_1), \qquad z = \psi(x_1,\,y_1,\,z_1)$$

may be obtained by a combination of the preceding transformations. For, let us set $x' = x_1, y' = y_1, z' = z$. Then the last equation of (13) may be written $z' = \psi(x', y', z_1)$, whence $z_1 = \pi(x', y', z')$. Hence the equations (13) may be replaced by the six equations

$$(14) \quad x = f[x', y', \pi(x', y', z')], \qquad y = \phi[x', y', \pi(x', y', z')], \qquad z = z',$$

$$(15) \quad x' = x_1, \qquad y' = y_1, \qquad z' = \psi(x_1,\,y_1,\,z_1).$$

The general formula (7) holds, as we have seen, for each of the transformations (14) and (15). Hence it holds for the transformation (13) also.

We might have replaced the general transformation (13), as the reader can easily show, by a sequence of three transformations of the type (8).

146. Element of volume. Setting $F(x, y, z) = 1$ in the formula (7), we find

$$\iiint_{(E)} dx\, dy\, dz = \iiint_{(E_1)} \left| \frac{D(x, y, z)}{D(u, v, w)} \right| du\, dv\, dw.$$

The left-hand side of this equation is the volume of the region (E). Applying the law of the mean to the integral on the right, we find the relation

$$(16) \qquad V = V_1 \left| \frac{D(f, \phi, \psi)}{D(u, v, w)} \right|_{(\xi, \eta, \zeta)},$$

where V_1 is the volume of (E_1), and ξ, η, ζ are the coördinates of some point in (E_1). This formula is exactly analogous to formula (17), Chapter VI. It shows that the functional determinant is the limit of the ratio of two corresponding infinitesimal volumes.

If one of the variables u, v, w in (6) be assigned a constant value, while the others are allowed to vary, we obtain three families of surfaces, $u = $ const., $v = $ const., $w = $ const., by means of which the region (E) may be divided into subregions analogous to the parallelopipeds used above, each of which is bounded by six curved faces. The volume of one of these subregions bounded by the surfaces (u), $(u + du)$, (v), $(v + dv)$, (w), $(w + dw)$ is, by (16),

$$\Delta V = \left\{ \left| \frac{D(f, \phi, \psi)}{D(u, v, w)} \right| + \epsilon \right\} du\, dv\, dw,$$

where du, dv, and dw are positive increments, and where ϵ is infinitesimal with du, dv, and dw. The term $\epsilon\, du\, dv\, dw$ may be neglected, as has been explained several times (§ 128). The product

$$(17) \qquad dV = \left| \frac{D(f, \phi, \psi)}{D(u, v, w)} \right| du\, dv\, dw$$

is the principal part of the infinitesimal ΔV, and is called the *element of volume* in the system of curvilinear coördinates (u, v, w).

Let ds^2 be the square of the linear element in the same system of coördinates. Then, from (6),

$$dx = \frac{\partial f}{\partial u} du + \frac{\partial f}{\partial v} dv + \frac{\partial f}{\partial w} dw, \quad dy = \frac{\partial \phi}{\partial u} du + \cdots, \quad dz = \frac{\partial \psi}{\partial u} du + \cdots,$$

whence, squaring and adding, we find

$$(18) \quad \begin{cases} ds^2 = dx^2 + dy^2 + dz^2 \\ \quad = H_1 du^2 + H_2 dv^2 + H_3 dw^2 + 2F_1 dv\, dw + 2F_2 du\, dw + 2F_3 du\, dv, \end{cases}$$

the notation employed being

$$(19) \quad \begin{cases} H_1 = S\left(\frac{\partial x}{\partial u}\right)^2, & H_2 = S\left(\frac{\partial x}{\partial v}\right)^2, & H_3 = S\left(\frac{\partial x}{\partial w}\right)^2, \\ F_1 = S\frac{\partial x}{\partial v}\frac{\partial x}{\partial w}, & F_2 = S\frac{\partial x}{\partial u}\frac{\partial x}{\partial w}, & F_3 = S\frac{\partial x}{\partial u}\frac{\partial x}{\partial v}, \end{cases}$$

where the symbol S means, as usual, that x is to be replaced by y and z successively and the resulting terms then added.

The formula for dV is easily deduced from this formula for ds^2. For, squaring the functional determinant by the usual rule, we find

$$\begin{vmatrix} \dfrac{\partial x}{\partial u} & \dfrac{\partial y}{\partial u} & \dfrac{\partial z}{\partial u} \\[2mm] \dfrac{\partial x}{\partial v} & \dfrac{\partial y}{\partial v} & \dfrac{\partial z}{\partial v} \\[2mm] \dfrac{\partial x}{\partial w} & \dfrac{\partial y}{\partial w} & \dfrac{\partial z}{\partial w} \end{vmatrix}^2 = \begin{vmatrix} H_1 & F_3 & F_2 \\ F_3 & H_2 & F_1 \\ F_2 & F_1 & H_3 \end{vmatrix} = M,$$

whence the element of volume is equal to $\sqrt{M}\,du\,dv\,dw$.

Let us consider in particular the very important case in which the coördinate surfaces (u), (v), (w) form a triply orthogonal system, that is to say, in which the three surfaces which pass through any point in space intersect in pairs at right angles. The tangents to the three curves in which the surfaces intersect in pairs form a trirectangular trihedron. It follows that we must have $F_1 = 0$, $F_2 = 0$, $F_3 = 0$; and these conditions are also sufficient. The formulæ for dV and ds^2 then take the simple forms

$$(20) \quad ds^2 = H_1\,du^2 + H_2\,dv^2 + H_3\,dw^2, \quad dV = \sqrt{H_1 H_2 H_3}\,du\,dv\,dw.$$

These formulæ may also be derived from certain considerations of infinitesimal geometry. Let us suppose du, dv, and dw very small, and let us substitute in place of the small subregion defined above a small parallelopiped with plane faces. Neglecting infinitesimals of higher order, the three adjacent edges of the parallelopiped may be taken to be $\sqrt{H_1}\,du$, $\sqrt{H_2}\,dv$, and $\sqrt{H_3}\,dw$, respectively. The formulæ (20) express the fact that the linear element and the element of volume are equal to the diagonal and the volume of this parallelopiped, respectively. The area $\sqrt{H_1 H_2}\,du\,dv$ of one of the faces represents in a similar manner the element of area of the surface (w).

As an example consider the transformation to polar coördinates

$$(21) \quad x = \rho\sin\theta\cos\phi, \qquad y = \rho\sin\theta\sin\phi, \qquad z = \rho\cos\theta,$$

where ρ denotes the distance of the point $M(x, y, z)$ from the origin, θ the angle between OM and the positive z axis, and ϕ the angle which the projection of OM on the xy plane makes with the positive x axis.   In order to reach all points in space, it is sufficient to let ρ vary from zero to $+\infty$, θ from zero to π, and ϕ from zero to 2π. From (21) we find

$$(22) \qquad ds^2 = d\rho^2 + \rho^2\, d\theta^2 + \rho^2 \sin^2\theta\, d\phi^2,$$

whence

$$(23) \qquad dV = \rho^2 \sin\theta\, d\rho\, d\theta\, d\phi.$$

These formulæ may be derived without any calculation, however. The three families of surfaces (ρ), (θ), (ϕ) are concentric spheres

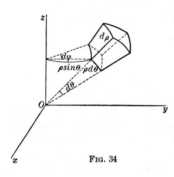

FIG. 34

about the origin, cones of revolution about the z axis with their vertices at the origin, and planes through the z axis, respectively.   These surfaces evidently form a triply orthogonal system, and the dimensions of the elementary subregion are seen from the figure to be $d\rho$, $\rho\, d\theta$, $\rho \sin\theta\, d\phi$; the formulæ (22) and (23) now follow immediately.

To calculate in terms of the variables ρ, θ, and ϕ a triple integral extended throughout a region bounded by a closed surface S, which contains the origin and which is met in at most one point by a radius vector through the origin, ρ should be allowed to vary from zero to R, where $R = f(\theta, \phi)$ is the equation of the surface; θ from zero to π; and ϕ from zero to 2π.   For example, the volume of such a surface is

$$V = \int_0^{2\pi} d\phi \int_0^{\pi} d\theta \int_0^{R} \rho^2 \sin\theta\, d\rho.$$

The first integration can always be performed, and we may write

$$V = \int_0^{2\pi} d\phi \int_0^{\pi} \frac{R^3 \sin\theta}{3}\, d\theta.$$

Occasional use is made of cylindrical coördinates r, ω, and z defined by the equations $x = r \cos\omega$, $y = r \sin\omega$, $z = z$.   It is evident that

$$ds^2 = dr^2 + r^2\, d\omega^2 + dz^2,$$

and

$$dV = r\, d\omega\, dr\, dz.$$

147. Elliptic coördinates. The surfaces represented by the equation

$$(24) \qquad \frac{x^2}{\lambda - a} + \frac{y^2}{\lambda - b} + \frac{z^2}{\lambda - c} - 1 = 0,$$

where λ is a variable parameter and $a > b > c > 0$, form a family of confocal conics. Through every point in space there pass three surfaces of this family, — an ellipsoid, a parted hyperboloid, and an unparted hyperboloid. For the equation (24) always has one root λ_1 which lies between b and c, another root λ_2 between a and b, and a third root λ_3 greater than a. These three roots $\lambda_1, \lambda_2, \lambda_3$ are called the *elliptic coördinates* of the point whose rectangular coördinates are (x, y, z). Any two surfaces of the family intersect at right angles: if λ be given the values λ_1 and λ_2, for instance, in (24), and the resulting equations be subtracted, a division by $\lambda_1 - \lambda_2$ gives

$$(25) \qquad \frac{x^2}{(\lambda_1 - a)(\lambda_2 - a)} + \frac{y^2}{(\lambda_1 - b)(\lambda_2 - b)} + \frac{z^2}{(\lambda_1 - c)(\lambda_2 - c)} = 0,$$

which shows that the two surfaces (λ_1) and (λ_2) are orthogonal.

In order to obtain x, y, and z as functions of $\lambda_1, \lambda_2, \lambda_3$, we may note that the relation

$$(\lambda - a)(\lambda - b)(\lambda - c) - x^2(\lambda - b)(\lambda - c) - y^2(\lambda - c)(\lambda - a) - z^2(\lambda - a)(\lambda - b)$$
$$= (\lambda - \lambda_1)(\lambda - \lambda_2)(\lambda - \lambda_3)$$

is identically satisfied. Setting $\lambda = a$, $\lambda = b$, $\lambda = c$, successively, in this equation, we obtain the values

$$(26) \qquad \begin{cases} x^2 = \dfrac{(\lambda_3 - a)(a - \lambda_1)(a - \lambda_2)}{(a - b)(a - c)}, \\[2ex] y^2 = \dfrac{(\lambda_3 - b)(\lambda_2 - b)(b - \lambda_1)}{(a - b)(b - c)}, \\[2ex] z^2 = \dfrac{(\lambda_3 - c)(\lambda_2 - c)(\lambda_1 - c)}{(a - c)(b - c)}, \end{cases}$$

whence, taking the logarithmic derivatives,

$$dx = \frac{x}{2}\left(\frac{d\lambda_1}{\lambda_1 - a} + \frac{d\lambda_2}{\lambda_2 - a} + \frac{d\lambda_3}{\lambda_3 - a}\right),$$

$$dy = \frac{y}{2}\left(\frac{d\lambda_1}{\lambda_1 - b} + \frac{d\lambda_2}{\lambda_2 - b} + \frac{d\lambda_3}{\lambda_3 - b}\right),$$

$$dz = \frac{z}{2}\left(\frac{d\lambda_1}{\lambda_1 - c} + \frac{d\lambda_2}{\lambda_2 - c} + \frac{d\lambda_3}{\lambda_3 - c}\right).$$

Forming the sum of the squares, the terms in $d\lambda_1 \, d\lambda_2$, $d\lambda_2 \, d\lambda_3$, $d\lambda_3 \, d\lambda_1$ must disappear by means of (25) and similar relations. Hence the coefficient of $d\lambda_1^2$ is

$$M_1 = \frac{1}{4}\left[\frac{x^2}{(\lambda_1 - a)^2} + \frac{y^2}{(\lambda_1 - b)^2} + \frac{z^2}{(\lambda_1 - c)^2}\right],$$

or, replacing x, y, z by their values and simplifying,

$$(27) \qquad M_1 = \frac{1}{4}\frac{(\lambda_3 - \lambda_1)(\lambda_2 - \lambda_1)}{(\lambda_1 - a)(\lambda_1 - b)(\lambda_1 - c)}.$$

The coefficients M_2 and M_3 of $d\lambda_2^2$ and $d\lambda_3^2$, respectively, may be obtained from this expression by cyclic permutation of the letters. The element of volume is therefore $\sqrt{M_1 M_2 M_3}\; d\lambda_1\, d\lambda_2\, d\lambda_3$.

148. Dirichlet's integrals. Consider the triple integral

$$\int\int\int x^p y^q z^r (1 - x - y - z)^s\, dx\, dy\, dz$$

taken throughout the interior of the tetrahedron formed by the four planes $x = 0$, $y = 0$, $z = 0$, $x + y + z = 1$. Let us set

$$x + y + z = \xi, \qquad y + z = \xi\eta, \qquad z = \xi\eta\zeta,$$

where ξ, η, ζ are three new variables. These formulæ may be written in the form

$$\xi = x + y + z, \qquad \eta = \frac{y + z}{x + y + z}, \qquad \zeta = \frac{z}{y + z},$$

and the inverse transformation is

$$x = \xi(1 - \eta), \qquad y = \xi\eta(1 - \zeta), \qquad z = \xi\eta\zeta.$$

When x, y, and z are all positive and $x + y + z$ is less than unity, ξ, η, and ζ all lie between zero and unity. Conversely, if ξ, η, and ζ all lie between zero and unity, x, y, and z are all positive and $x + y + z$ is less than unity. The tetrahedron therefore goes over into a cube.

In order to calculate the functional determinant, let us introduce the auxiliary transformation $X = \xi$, $Y = \xi\eta$, $Z = \xi\eta\zeta$, which gives $x = X - Y$, $y = Y - Z$, $z = Z$. Hence the functional determinant has the value

$$\frac{D(x,\, y,\, z)}{D(\xi,\, \eta,\, \zeta)} = \frac{D(x,\, y,\, z)}{D(X,\, Y,\, Z)} \cdot \frac{D(X,\, Y,\, Z)}{D(\xi,\, \eta,\, \zeta)} = \xi^2\eta,$$

and the given triple integral becomes

$$\int_0^1 d\xi \int_0^1 d\eta \int_0^1 \xi^{p+q+r+2}(1 - \xi)^s \eta^{q+r+1}(1 - \eta)^p \zeta^r (1 - \zeta)^q d\zeta.$$

The integrand is the product of a function of ξ, a function of η, and a function of ζ. Hence the triple integral may be written in the form

$$\int_0^1 \xi^{p+q+r+2}(1 - \xi)^s d\xi \times \int_0^1 \eta^{q+r+1}(1 - \eta)^p d\eta \times \int_0^1 \zeta^r (1 - \zeta)^q d\zeta,$$

or, introducing Γ functions (see (33), p. 280),

$$\frac{\Gamma(p + q + r + 3)\Gamma(s + 1)}{\Gamma(p + q + r + s + 4)} \times \frac{\Gamma(q + r + 2)\Gamma(p + 1)}{\Gamma(p + q + r + 3)} \times \frac{\Gamma(r + 1)\Gamma(q + 1)}{\Gamma(q + r + 2)}.$$

Canceling the common factors, the value of the given triple integral is finally found to be

$$(28) \qquad \frac{\Gamma(p + 1)\Gamma(q + 1)\Gamma(r + 1)\Gamma(s + 1)}{\Gamma(p + q + r + s + 4)}.$$

149. Green's theorem.* A formula entirely analogous to (15), § 126, may be derived for triple integrals. Let us first consider a closed surface S which is met in at most two points by a parallel to the z axis, and a function $R(x, y, z)$ which, together with $\partial R/\partial z$, is continuous throughout the interior of this surface. All the points of the surface S project into points of a region A of the xy plane which is bounded by a closed contour C. To every point of A inside C correspond two points of S whose coördinates are $z_1 = \phi_1(x, y)$ and $z_2 = \phi_2(x, y)$. The surface S is thus divided into two distinct portions S_1 and S_2. We shall suppose that z_1 is less than z_2.

Let us now consider the triple integral

$$\iiint \frac{\partial R}{\partial z}\, dx\, dy\, dz$$

taken throughout the region bounded by the closed surface S. A first integration may be performed with regard to z between the limits z_1 and z_2 (§ 144), which gives $R(x, y, z_2) - R(x, y, z_1)$. The given triple integral is therefore equal to the double integral

$$\iint [R(x, y, z_2) - R(x, y, z_1)]\, dx\, dy$$

over the region A. But the double integral $\iint R(x, y, z_2)\, dx\, dy$ is equal to the surface integral (§ 135)

$$\iint_{(S_2)} R(x, y, z)\, dx\, dy$$

taken over the upper side of the surface S_2. Likewise, the double integral of $R(x, y, z_1)$ with its sign changed is the surface integral

$$\iint_{(S_1)} R(x, y, z)\, dx\, dy$$

taken over the lower side of S_1. Adding these two integrals, we may write

$$\iiint \frac{\partial R}{\partial z}\, dx\, dy\, dz = \iint_{(S)} R(x, y, z)\, dx\, dy,$$

where the surface integral is to be extended over the whole *exterior* of the surface S.

By the methods already used several times in similar cases this formula may be extended to the case of a region bounded by a surface of any form whatever. Again, permuting the letters x, y, and z, we obtain the analogous formulæ

$$\iiint \frac{\partial P}{\partial x}\, dx\, dy\, dz = \iint_{(S)} P(x, y, z)\, dy\, dz,$$

$$\iiint \frac{\partial Q}{\partial y}\, dx\, dy\, dz = \iint_{(S)} Q(x, y, z)\, dz\, dx.$$

---

* Occasionally called *Ostrogradsky's theorem*. The theorem of § 126 is sometimes called *Riemann's theorem*. But the title *Green's theorem* is more clearly established and seems to be the more fitting. See *Ency. der Math. Wiss.*, II, A, 7, b and c. — TRANS.

Adding these three formulæ, we finally find the general Green's theorem for triple integrals :

$$(29) \quad \begin{cases} \iiint \left(\frac{\partial P}{\partial x} + \frac{\partial Q}{\partial y} + \frac{\partial R}{\partial z} \right) dx\,dy\,dz \\ \qquad = \iint_{(S)} P(x, y, z)\,dy\,dz + Q(x, y, z)\,dz\,dx + R(x, y, z)\,dx\,dy, \end{cases}$$

where the surface integrals are to be taken, as before, over the exterior of the bounding surface.

If, for example, we set $P = x$, $Q = R = 0$ or $Q = y$, $P = R = 0$ or $R = z$, $P = Q = 0$, it is evident that the volume of the solid bounded by S is equal to any one of the surface integrals

$$(29') \qquad \iint_{(S)} x\,dy\,dz, \qquad \iint_{(S)} y\,dz\,dx, \qquad \iint_{(S)} z\,dx\,dy.$$

150. Multiple integrals. The purely analytical definitions which have been given for double and triple integrals may be extended to any number of variables. We shall restrict ourselves to a sketch of the general process.

Let x_1, x_2, $\cdots$, x_n be n independent variables. We shall say for brevity that a system of values x_1^0, x_2^0, $\cdots$, x_n^0 of these variables represents *a point* in space of n dimensions. Any equation $F(x_1, x_2, \cdots, x_n) = 0$, whose first member is a continuous function, will be said to represent a *surface;* and if F is of the first degree, the equation will be said to represent a *plane.* Let us consider the totality of all points whose coördinates satisfy certain inequalities of the form

$$(30) \qquad \psi_i(x_1, x_2, \cdots, x_n) \leqq 0, \qquad i = 1, 2, \cdots, k.$$

We shall say that the totality of these points forms a *domain D* in space of n dimensions. If for all the points of this domain the absolute value of each of the coördinates x_i is less than a fixed number, we shall say that the domain D is finite. If the inequalities which define D are of the form

$$(31) \qquad x_1^0 \leqq x_1 \leqq x_1^1, \qquad x_2^0 \leqq x_2 \leqq x_2^1, \qquad \cdots, \qquad x_n^0 \leqq x_n \leqq x_n^1,$$

we shall call the domain a *prismoid,* and we shall say that the n positive quantities $x_i^1 - x_i^0$ are the *dimensions* of this prismoid. Finally, we shall say that a point of the domain D lies on the *frontier* of the domain if at least one of the functions ψ_i in (30) vanishes at that point.

Now let D be a finite domain, and let $f(x_1, x_2, \cdots, x_n)$ be a function which is continuous in that domain. Suppose D divided into subdomains by planes parallel to the planes $x_i = 0$ ($i = 1, 2, \cdots, n$), and consider any one of the prismoids determined by these planes which lies entirely inside the domain D. Let Δx_1, Δx_2, $\cdots$, Δx_n be the dimensions of this prismoid, and let ξ_1, ξ_2, $\cdots$, ξ_n be the coördinates of some point of the prismoid. Then the sum

$$(32) \qquad S = \Sigma f(\xi_1, \xi_2, \cdots, \xi_n)\, \Delta x_1 \Delta x_2 \cdots \Delta x_n,$$

formed for all the prismoids which lie entirely inside the domain D, approaches a limit I as the number of the prismoids is increased indefinitely in such a way that all of the dimensions of each of them approach zero. We shall call this limit I the n-tuple integral of $f(x_1, x_2, \cdots, x_n)$ taken in the domain D and shall denote it by the symbol

$$I = \int \int \cdots \int f(x_1, x_2, \cdots, x_n)\, dx_1 dx_2 \cdots dx_n.$$

The evaluation of an n-tuple integral may be reduced to the evaluation of n successive simple integrals. In order to show this in general, we need only show that if it is true for an $(n-1)$-tuple integral, it will also be true for an n-tuple integral. For this purpose let us consider any point $(x_1, x_2, \cdots, x_n)$ of D. Discarding the variable x_n for the moment, the point $(x_1, x_2, \cdots, x_{n-1})$ evidently describes a domain D' in space of $(n-1)$ dimensions. We shall suppose that to any point $(x_1, x_2, \cdots, x_{n-1})$ inside of D' there correspond just two points on the frontier of D, whose coördinates are $(x_1, x_2, \cdots, x_{n-1}; x_n^{(1)})$ and $(x_1, x_2, \cdots, x_{n-1}; x_n^{(2)})$, where the coördinates $x_n^{(1)}$ and $x_n^{(2)}$ are continuous functions of the $n-1$ variables $x_1, x_2, \cdots, x_{n-1}$ inside the domain D'. If this condition were not satisfied, we should divide the domain D into domains so small that the condition would be met by each of the partial domains. Let us now consider the column of prismoids of the domain D which correspond to the same point $(x_1, x_2, \cdots, x_{n-1})$. It is easy to show, as we did in the similar case treated in § 124, that the part of S which arises from this column of prismoids is

$$\Delta x_1 \Delta x_2 \cdots \Delta x_{n-1} \left[\int_{x_n^{(1)}}^{x_n^{(2)}} f(x_1, x_2, \cdots, x_n)\, dx_n + \epsilon \right],$$

where $|\epsilon|$ may be made smaller than any positive number whatever by choosing the quantities Δx_i sufficiently small. If we now set

$$(33) \qquad \Phi(x_1, x_2, \cdots, x_{n-1}) = \int_{x_n^{(1)}}^{x_n^{(2)}} f(x_1, x_2, \cdots, x_n)\, dx_n,$$

it is clear that the integral I will be equal to the limit of the sum

$$\Sigma \Phi(x_1, x_2, \cdots, x_{n-1})\, \Delta x_1 \Delta x_2 \cdots \Delta x_{n-1},$$

that is, to the $(n-1)$-tuple integral

$$(34) \qquad I = \int \int \int \cdots \int \Phi(x_1, x_2, \cdots, x_{n-1})\, dx_1 \cdots dx_{n-1},$$

in the domain D'. The law having been supposed to hold for an $(n-1)$-tuple integral, it is evident, by mathematical induction, that it holds in general.

We might have proceeded differently. Consider the totality of points $(x_1, x_2, \cdots, x_n)$ for which the coördinate x_n has a fixed value. Then the point $(x_1, x_2, \cdots, x_{n-1})$ describes a domain δ in space of $(n-1)$ dimensions, and it is easy to show that the n-tuple integral I is also equal to the expression

$$(35) \qquad I = \int_{x_n^{(1)}}^{x_n^{(2)}} \theta(x_n)\, dx_n,$$

where $\theta(x_n)$ is the $(n-1)$-tuple integral $\int \int \int \cdots \int f\, dx_1 \cdots dx_{n-1}$ extended throughout the domain δ. Whatever be the method of carrying out the process, the limits for the various integrations depend upon the nature of the domain D, and vary in general for different orders of integration. An exception exists in case D is a prismoid defined by inequalities of the form

$$x_1^0 \leqq x_1 \leqq X_1, \qquad \cdots, \qquad x_i^0 \leqq x_i \leqq X_i, \qquad \cdots .$$

The multiple integral is then of the form

$$I = \int_{x_1^0}^{X_1} dx_1 \int_{x_2^0}^{X_2} dx_2 \cdots \int_{x_n^0}^{X_n} f \, dx_n,$$

and the order in which the integrations are performed may be permuted in any way whatever without altering the limits which correspond to each of the variables.

The formula for change of variables also may be extended to n-tuple integrals. Let

$$(36) \qquad x_i = \phi_i(x_1', x_2', \cdots, x_n'), \qquad i = 1, 2, \cdots, n,$$

be formulæ of transformation which establish a one-to-one correspondence between the points $(x_1', x_2', \cdots, x_n')$ of a domain D' and the points $(x_1, x_2, \cdots, x_n)$ of a domain D. Then we shall have

$$(37) \quad \begin{cases} \displaystyle\int\int \cdots \int_{(D)} F(x_1, x_2, \cdots, x_n) \, dx_1 \cdots dx_n \\ \displaystyle = \int\int \cdots \int_{(D')} F(\phi_1, \cdots, \phi_n) \left| \frac{D(\phi_1, \cdots, \phi_n)}{D(x_1', \cdots, x_n')} \right| dx_1' \cdots dx_n'. \end{cases}$$

The proof is similar to that given in analogous cases above. A sketch of the argument is all that we shall attempt here.

1) If (37) holds for each of two transformations, it also holds for the transformation obtained by carrying out the two in succession.

2) Any change of variables may be obtained by combining two transformations of the following types:

$$(38) \quad x_1 = x_1', \quad x_2 = x_2', \quad \cdots, \quad x_{n-1} = x_{n-1}', \quad x_n = \phi_n(x_1', x_2', \cdots, x_n'),$$

$$(39) \quad x_1 = \psi_1(x_1', \cdots, x_n'), \quad \cdots, \quad x_{n-1} = \psi_{n-1}(x_1', \cdots, x_n'), \quad x_n = x_n'.$$

3) The formula (37) holds for a transformation of the type (38), since the given n-tuple integral may be written in the form (34). It also holds for any transformation of the form (39), by the second form (35) in which the multiple integral may be written. These conclusions are based on the assumption that (37) holds for an $(n-1)$-tuple integral. The usual reasoning by mathematical induction establishes the formula in general.

As an example let us try to evaluate the definite integral

$$I = \int\int \cdots \int x_1^{\alpha_1} x_2^{\alpha_2} \cdots x_n^{\alpha_n} (1 - x_1 - x_2 - \cdots - x_n)^\beta \, dx_1 \, dx_2 \cdots dx_n,$$

where $\alpha_1, \alpha_2, \cdots, \alpha_n, \beta$ are certain positive constants, and the integral is to be extended throughout the domain D defined by the inequalities

$$0 \leqq x_1, \qquad 0 \leqq x_2, \qquad \cdots, \qquad 0 \leqq x_n, \qquad x_1 + x_2 + \cdots + x_n \leqq 1.$$

The transformation

$$x_1 + x_2 + \cdots + x_n = \xi_1, \qquad x_2 + \cdots + x_n = \xi_1 \xi_2, \qquad \cdots, \qquad x_n = \xi_1 \xi_2 \cdots \xi_n$$

carries D into a new domain D' defined by the inequalities

$$0 \leqq \xi_1 \leqq 1, \qquad 0 \leqq \xi_2 \leqq 1, \qquad \cdots, \qquad 0 \leqq \xi_n \leqq 1,$$

and it is easy to show as in § 148 that the value of the functional determinant is

$$\frac{D(x_1, x_2, \cdots, x_n)}{D(\xi_1, \xi_2, \cdots, \xi_n)} = \xi_1^{n-1} \xi_2^{n-2} \cdots \xi_{n-1}.$$

The new integrand is therefore of the form

$$\xi_1^{\alpha_1 + \cdots + \alpha_n + n - 1} \xi_2^{\alpha_2 + \cdots + \alpha_n + n - 2} \cdots \xi_n^{\alpha_n} (1 - \xi_1)^\beta (1 - \xi_2)^{\alpha_1} \cdots (1 - \xi_n)^{\alpha_{n-1}},$$

and the given integral may be expressed, as before, in terms of Γ functions:

$$(40) \qquad I = \frac{\Gamma(\alpha_1 + 1) \Gamma(\alpha_2 + 1) \cdots \Gamma(\alpha_n + 1) \Gamma(\beta + 1)}{\Gamma(\alpha_1 + \alpha_2 + \cdots + \alpha_n + \beta + n + 1)}.$$

II. INTEGRATION OF TOTAL DIFFERENTIALS

151. General method. Let $P(x, y)$ and $Q(x, y)$ be two functions of the two independent variables x and y. Then the expression

$$P\,dx + Q\,dy$$

is not in general the total differential of a single function of the two variables x and y. For we have seen that the equation

$$(41) \qquad du = P\,dx + Q\,dy$$

is equivalent to the two distinct equations

$$(42) \qquad \frac{\partial u}{\partial x} = P(x, y), \qquad \frac{\partial u}{\partial y} = Q(x, y).$$

Differentiating the first of these equations with respect to y and the second with respect to x, it appears that $u(x, y)$ must satisfy each of the equations

$$\frac{\partial^2 u}{\partial x\,\partial y} = \frac{\partial P(x, y)}{\partial y}, \qquad \frac{\partial^2 u}{\partial y\,\partial x} = \frac{\partial Q(x, y)}{\partial x}.$$

A *necessary* condition that a function $u(x, y)$ should exist which satisfies these requirements is that the equation

$$(43) \qquad \frac{\partial P}{\partial y} = \frac{\partial Q}{\partial x}$$

should be identically satisfied.

This condition is also *sufficient*. For there exist an infinite number of functions $u(x, y)$ for which the first of equations (42) is satisfied. All these functions are given by the formula

$$u = \int_{x_0}^{x} P(x, y)\,dx + Y,$$

where x_0 is an arbitrary constant and Y is an arbitrary function of y. In order that this function $u(x, y)$ should satisfy the equation (41), it is necessary and sufficient that its partial derivative with respect to x should be equal to $Q(x, y)$, that is, that the equation

$$\int_{x_0}^x \frac{\partial P}{\partial y} dx + \frac{dY}{dy} = Q(x, y)$$

should be satisfied. But by the assumed relation (43) we have

$$\int_{x_0}^x \frac{\partial P}{\partial y} dx = \int_{x_0}^x \frac{\partial Q}{\partial x} dx = Q(x, y) - Q(x_0, y),$$

whence the preceding relation reduces to

$$\frac{dY}{dy} = Q(x_0, y).$$

The right-hand side of this equation is independent of x. Hence there are an infinite number of functions of y which satisfy the equation, and they are all given by the formula

$$Y = \int_{y_0}^y Q(x_0, y) \, dy + C,$$

where y_0 is an arbitrary value of y, and C is an arbitrary constant. It follows that there are an infinite number of functions $u(x, y)$ which satisfy the equation (41). They are all given by the formula

$$(44) \qquad u = \int_{x_0}^x P(x, y) \, dx + \int_{y_0}^y Q(x_0, y) \, dy + C,$$

and differ from each other only by the additive constant C.

Consider, for example, the pair of functions

$$P = \frac{x + my}{x^2 + y^2}, \qquad Q = \frac{y - mx}{x^2 + y^2},$$

which satisfy the condition (43). Setting $x_0 = 0$ and $y_0 = 1$, the formula for u gives

$$u = \int_0^x \frac{x + my}{x^2 + y^2} \, dx + \int_1^y \frac{dy}{y} + C,$$

whence, performing the indicated integrations, we find

$$u = \frac{1}{2} \left[\log(x^2 + y^2) \right]_0^x + m \left[\text{ arc tan} \frac{x}{y} \right]_0^x + \log y + C,$$

or, simplifying,

$$u = \frac{1}{2} \log(x^2 + y^2) + m \text{ arc tan} \frac{x}{y} + C.$$

The preceding method may be extended to any number of independent variables. We shall give the reasoning for three variables. Let P, Q, and R be three functions of x, y, and z. Then the total differential equation

$$(45) \qquad du = P\,dx + Q\,dy + R\,dz$$

is equivalent to the three distinct equations

$$(46) \qquad \frac{\partial u}{\partial x} = P, \qquad \frac{\partial u}{\partial y} = Q, \qquad \frac{\partial u}{\partial z} = R.$$

Calculating the three derivatives $\partial^2 u/\partial x\,\partial y$, $\partial^2 u/\partial y\,\partial z$, $\partial^2 u/\partial z\,\partial x$ in two different ways, we find the three following equations as necessary conditions for the existence of the function u:

$$(47) \qquad \frac{\partial P}{\partial y} = \frac{\partial Q}{\partial x}, \qquad \frac{\partial Q}{\partial z} = \frac{\partial R}{\partial y}, \qquad \frac{\partial R}{\partial x} = \frac{\partial P}{\partial z}.$$

Conversely, let us suppose these equations satisfied. Then, by the first, there exist an infinite number of functions $u(x, y, z)$ whose partial derivatives with respect to x and y are equal to P and Q, respectively, and they are all given by the formula

$$u = \int_{x_0}^{x} P(x, y, z)\,dx + \int_{y_0}^{y} Q(x_0, y, z)\,dy + Z,$$

where Z denotes an arbitrary function of z. In order that the derivative $\partial u/\partial z$ should be equal to R, it is necessary and sufficient that the equation

$$\int_{x_0}^{x} \frac{\partial P}{\partial z}\,dx + \int_{y_0}^{y} \frac{\partial Q(x_0, y, z)}{\partial z}\,dy + \frac{dZ}{dz} = R$$

should be satisfied. Making use of the relations (47), which were assumed to hold, this condition reduces to the equation

$$R(x, y, z) - R(x_0, y, z) + R(x_0, y, z) - R(x_0, y_0, z) + \frac{dZ}{dz} = R(x, y, z),$$

or

$$\frac{dZ}{dz} = R(x_0, y_0, z).$$

It follows that an infinite number of functions $u(x, y, z)$ exist which satisfy the equation (45). They are all given by the formula

$$(48) \quad u = \int_{x_0}^{x} P(x, y, z)\,dx + \int_{y_0}^{y} Q(x_0, y, z)\,dy + \int_{z_0}^{z} R(x_0, y_0, z)\,dz + C,$$

where x_0, y_0, z_0 are three arbitrary numerical values, and C is an arbitrary constant.

152. The integral $\int_{(x_0, y_0)}^{(x, y)} P\,dx + Q\,dy$. The same subject may be
treated from a different point of view, which gives deeper insight
into the question and leads to new results. Let $P(x, y)$ and $Q(x, y)$
be two functions which, together with their first derivatives, are
continuous in a region A bounded by a single closed contour C.
It may happen that the region A embraces the whole plane, in
which case the contour C would be supposed to have receded to
infinity. The line integral

$$\int P\,dx + Q\,dy$$

taken along any path D which lies in A will depend in general upon
the path of integration. Let us first try to find the conditions under
which this integral depends only upon the coördinates of the extremities (x_0, y_0) and (x_1, y_1) of the path. Let M and N be any two points
of region A, and let L and L' be any two paths which connect these
two points without intersecting each other between the extremities.
Taken together they form a closed contour. In order that the values
of the line integral taken along these two paths L and L' should be
equal, it is evidently necessary and sufficient that the integral taken
around the closed contour formed by the two curves, proceeding
always in the same sense, should be zero. Hence the question at
issue is exactly equivalent to the following : *What are the conditions
under which the line integral*

$$\int P\,dx + Q\,dy$$

*taken around any closed contour whatever which lies in the region A
should vanish?*

The answer to this question is an immediate result of Green's
theorem :

$$(49) \qquad \int_{(C)} P\,dx + Q\,dy = \int\int \left(\frac{\partial Q}{\partial x} - \frac{\partial P}{\partial y}\right) dx\,dy,$$

where C is any closed contour which lies in A, and where the double
integral is to be extended over the whole interior of C. It is clear
that if the functions P and Q satisfy the equation

$$(43') \qquad \frac{\partial P}{\partial y} = \frac{\partial Q}{\partial x},$$

the line integral on the left will always vanish. This condition is
also necessary. For, if $\partial P/\partial y - \partial Q/\partial x$ were not identically zero

in the region A, since it is a continuous function, it would surely be possible to find a region a so small that its sign would be constant inside of a. But in that case the line integral taken around the boundary of a would not be zero, by (49).

If the condition (43') is identically satisfied, the values of the integral taken along two paths L and L' between the same two points M and N are equal provided the two paths do not intersect between M and N. It is easy to see that the same thing is true even when the two paths intersect any number of times between M and N. For in that case it would be necessary only to compare the values of the integral taken along the paths L and L' with its value taken along a third path L'', which intersects neither of the preceding except at M and N.

Let us now suppose that one of the extremities of the path of integration is a fixed point (x_0, y_0), while the other extremity is a variable point (x, y) of A. Then the integral

$$(50) \qquad F(x, y) = \int_{(x_0, y_0)}^{(x, y)} P\, dx + Q\, dy$$

taken along an arbitrary path depends only upon the coördinates (x, y) of the variable extremity. The partial derivatives of this function are precisely $P(x, y)$ and $Q(x, y)$. For example, we have

$$F(x + \Delta x, y) = F(x, y) + \int_{(x, y)}^{(x + \Delta x, y)} P(x, y)\, dx,$$

for we may suppose that the path of integration goes from (x_0, y_0) to (x, y), and then from (x, y) to $(x + \Delta x, y)$ along a line parallel to the x axis, along which $dy = 0$. Applying the law of the mean, we may write

$$\frac{F(x + \Delta x, y) - F(x, y)}{\Delta x} = P(x + \theta \Delta x, y), \qquad 0 < \theta < 1.$$

Taking the limit when Δx approaches zero, this gives $F_x = P$. Similarly, $F_y = Q$. The line integral $F(x, y)$, therefore, satisfies the total differential equation (41), and the general integral of this equation is given by adding to $F(x, y)$ an arbitrary constant.

This new formula is more general than the formula (44) in that the path of integration is still arbitrary. It is easy to deduce (44) from the new form. To avoid ambiguity, let (x_0, y_0) and (x_1, y_1) be the coördinates of the two extremities, and let the path of integration be the two straight lines $x = x_0$, $y = y_1$. Along the former,

$x = x_0$, $dx = 0$, and y varies from y_0 to y_1. Along the second, $y = y_1$, $dy = 0$, and x varies from x_0 to x_1. Hence the integral (50) is equal to

$$\int_{y_0}^{y_1} Q(x_0, y)\, dy + \int_{x_0}^{x_1} P(x, y_1)\, dx,$$

which differs from (44) only in notation.

But it might be more advantageous to consider another path of integration. Let $x = f(t)$, $y = \phi(t)$ be the equations of a curve joining (x_0, y_0) and (x_1, y_1), and let t be supposed to vary continuously from t_0 to t_1 as the point (x, y) describes the curve between its two extremities. Then we shall have

$$\int_{(x_0, y_0)}^{(x_1, y_1)} P\, dx + Q\, dy = \int_{t_0}^{t_1} \left[P(x, y) f'(t) + Q(x, y) \phi'(t) \right] dt,$$

where there remains but a single quadrature. If the path be a straight line, for example, we should set $x = x_0 + t(x_1 - x_0)$, $y = y_0 + t(y_1 - y_0)$, and we should let t vary from 0 to 1.

Conversely, if a particular integral $\Phi(x, y)$ of the equation (41) be known, the line integral is given by the formula

$$\int_{(x_0, y_0)}^{(x, y)} P\, dx + Q\, dy = \Phi(x, y) - \Phi(x_0, y_0),$$

which is analogous to the equation (6) of Chapter IV.

153. Periods. More general cases may be investigated. In the first place, Green's theorem applies to regions bounded by several contours. Let us consider for definiteness a region A bounded by an exterior contour C and two contours C' and C'' which lie inside the first (Fig. 35). Let P and Q be two functions which, together with their first derivatives, are continuous in this region. (The regions inside the contours C' and C'' should not be considered as parts of the region A, and no hypothesis whatever is made regarding P and Q inside these regions.)

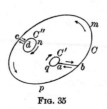

Fig. 35

Let the contours C' and C'' be joined to the contour C by transversals ab and cd. We thus obtain a closed contour $abmcdndcpbaqa$, or Γ, which may be described at one stroke. Applying Green's theorem to the region bounded by this contour, the line integrals which arise from the transversals ab and cd cancel out, since each of them is described twice in opposite directions. It follows that

$$\int P\,dx + Q\,dy = \int\int \left(\frac{\partial Q}{\partial x} - \frac{\partial P}{\partial y}\right) dx\,dy,$$

where the line integral is to be taken along the whole boundary of the region A, i.e. along the three contours C, C', and C'', in the senses indicated by the arrows, respectively, these being such that the region A always lies on the left.

If the functions P and Q satisfy the relation $\partial Q/\partial x = \partial P/\partial y$ in the region A, the double integral vanishes, and we may write the resulting relation in the form

$$(51) \quad \int_{(C)} P\,dx + Q\,dy = \int_{(C')} P\,dx + Q\,dy + \int_{(C'')} P\,dx + Q\,dy,$$

where each of the line integrals is to be taken in the sense designated above.

Let us now return to the region A bounded by a single contour C, and let P and Q be two functions which satisfy the equation $\partial P/\partial y = \partial Q/\partial x$, and which, together with their first derivatives, are continuous except at a finite number of points of A, at which at least one of the functions P or Q is discontinuous. We shall suppose for definiteness that there are three points of discontinuity a, b, c in A. Let us surround each of these points by a small circle, and then join each of these circles to the contour C by a cross cut (Fig. 36). Then the integral $\int P\,dx + Q\,dy$ taken from a fixed point (x_0, y_0) to a variable point (x, y) along a curve which does not cross any

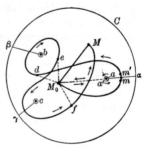

FIG. 36

of these cuts has a definite value at every point. For the contour C, the circles and the cuts form a single contour which may be described at one stroke, just as in the case discussed above. We shall call such a path *direct*, and shall denote the value of the line integral taken along it from $M_0(x_0, y_0)$ to $M(x, y)$ by $\overline{F(x, y)}$.

We shall call the path composed of the straight line from M_0 to a point a', whose distance from a is infinitesimal, the circumference of the circle of radius aa' about a, and the straight line $a'M_0$, a *loop-circuit*. The line integral $\int P\,dx + Q\,dy$ taken along a loop-circuit reduces to the line integral taken along the circumference of the circle. This latter integral is not zero, in general, if one of the functions P or Q is infinite at the point a, but it is independent of the radius of the circle. It is a certain constant $\pm \mathsf{A}$, the double sign corresponding to the two senses in which the circumference may be described. Similarly, we shall denote by $\pm \mathsf{B}$ and $\pm \mathsf{C}$ the values of the integral taken along loop-circuits drawn about the two singular points b and c, respectively.

Any path whatever joining M_0 and M may now be reduced to a combination of loop-circuits followed by a direct path from M_0 to M. For example, the path $M_0 mdefM$ may be reduced to a combination of the paths $M_0 mdM_0$, $M_0 deM_0$, $M_0 efM_0$, and $M_0 fM$. The path $M_0 mdM_0$ may then be reduced to a loop-circuit about the singular point a, and similarly for the other two. Finally, the path $M_0 fM$ is equivalent to a direct path. It follows that, whatever be the path of integration, the value of the line integral will be of the form

$$(52) \qquad F(x, y) = \overline{F(x, y)} + m\mathsf{A} + n\mathsf{B} + p\mathsf{C},$$

where m, n, and p may be any positive or negative integers. The quantities A, B, C are called the *periods* of the line integral. That integral is evidently a function of the variables x and y which admits of an infinite number of different determinations, and the origin of this indetermination is apparent.

Remark. The function $\overline{F(x, y)}$ is a definitely defined function in the whole region A when the cuts $a\alpha$, $b\beta$, $c\gamma$ have been traced. But it should be noticed that the difference $\overline{F(m)} - \overline{F(m')}$ between the values of the function at two points m and m' which lie on opposite sides of a cut does not necessarily vanish. For we have

$$\mathsf{A} = \int_{M_0}^{m} + \int_{m}^{m'} + \int_{m'}^{M_0},$$

which may be written

$$\int_{M_0}^{m} = \int_{M_0}^{m'} + \mathsf{A} + \int_{m'}^{m}.$$

But $\int_{m'}^{m}$ is zero; hence

$$\overline{F(m)} - \overline{F(m')} = \mathsf{A}.$$

It follows that the difference $F(m) - F(m')$ is constant and equal to A all along $a\alpha$. The analogous proposition holds for each of the cuts.

Example. The line integral

$$\int_{(1,\,0)}^{(x,\,y)} \frac{x\,dy - y\,dx}{x^2 + y^2}$$

has a single critical point, the origin. In order to find the corresponding period, let us integrate along the circle $x^2 + y^2 = \rho^2$. Along this circle we have

$$x = \rho \cos \omega, \qquad y = \rho \sin \omega, \qquad x\,dy - y\,dx = \rho^2 d\omega,$$

whence the period is equal to $\int_0^{2\pi} d\omega = 2\pi$. It is easy to verify this, for the integrand is the total differential of arc tan y/x.

154. Common roots of two equations. Let X and Y be two functions of the variables x and y which, together with their first partial derivatives, are continuous in a region A bounded by a single closed contour C. Then the expression $(X\,dY - Y\,dX)/(X^2 + Y^2)$ satisfies the condition of integrability, for it is the derivative of arc tan Y/X. Hence the line integral

$$(53) \qquad \int_{(C)} \frac{X\,dY - Y\,dX}{X^2 + Y^2}$$

taken along the contour C in the positive sense vanishes provided the coefficients of dx and dy in the integrand remain continuous inside C, i.e. if the two curves $X = 0$, $Y = 0$ have no common point inside that contour. But if these two curves have a certain number of common points a, b, c, $\cdots$ inside C, the value of the integral will be equal to the sum of the values of the same integral taken along the circumferences of small circles described about the points a, b, c, $\cdots$ as centers. Let (α, β) be the coördinates of one of the common points. We shall suppose that the functional determinant $D(X, Y)/D(x, y)$ is not zero, i.e. that the two curves $X = 0$ and $Y = 0$ are not tangent at the point. Then it is possible to draw about the point (α, β) as center a circle c whose radius is so small that the point (X, Y) describes a small plane region about the point $(0, 0)$ which is bounded by a contour γ and which corresponds point for point to the circle c (§§ 25 and 127).

As the point (x, y) describes the circumference of the circle c in the positive sense, the point (X, Y) describes the contour γ in the positive or in the negative sense, according as the sign of the functional determinant inside the circle c is positive or negative. But the definite integral along the circumference of c is equal to the change in arc tan Y/X in one revolution, that is, $\pm 2\pi$. Similar reasoning for all of the roots shows that

$$(54) \qquad \int_{(C)} \frac{X\,dY - Y\,dX}{X^2 + Y^2} = 2\pi(P - N),$$

where P denotes the number of points common to the two curves at which $D(X, Y)/D(x, y)$ is positive, and N the number of common points at which the determinant is negative.

The definite integral on the left is also equal to the variation in arc tan Y/X in going around c, that is, to the index of the function Y/X as the point (x, y) describes the contour C. If the functions X and Y are polynomials, and if the contour C is composed of a finite number of arcs of unicursal curves, we are led to calculate the index of one or more rational functions, which involves only elementary operations (§ 77). Moreover, whatever be the functions X and Y, we can always evaluate the definite integral (54) approximately, with an error less than π, which is all that is necessary, since the right-hand side is always a multiple of 2π.

The formula (54) does not give the exact number of points common to the two curves unless the functional determinant has a constant sign inside of C. Picard's recent work has completed the results of this investigation.*

155. Generalization of the preceding. The results of the preceding paragraphs may be extended without essential alteration to line integrals in space. Let P, Q, and R be three functions which, together with their first partial derivatives, are continuous in a region (E) of space bounded by a single closed surface S. Let us seek first to determine the conditions under which the line integral

$$(55) \qquad U = \int_{(x_0, y_0, z_0)}^{(x, y, z)} P\,dx + Q\,dy + R\,dz$$

depends only upon the extremities (x_0, y_0, z_0) and (x, y, z) of the path of integration. This amounts to inquiring under what conditions the same integral vanishes when taken along any closed path Γ. But by Stokes' theorem (§ 136) the above line integral is equal to the surface integral

$$\iint \left(\frac{\partial Q}{\partial x} - \frac{\partial P}{\partial y} \right) dx\,dy + \left(\frac{\partial R}{\partial y} - \frac{\partial Q}{\partial z} \right) dy\,dz + \left(\frac{\partial P}{\partial z} - \frac{\partial R}{\partial x} \right) dz\,dx$$

extended over a surface Σ which is bounded by the contour Γ. In order that this surface integral should be zero, it is evidently necessary and sufficient that the equations

$$(56) \qquad \frac{\partial P}{\partial y} = \frac{\partial Q}{\partial x}, \qquad \frac{\partial Q}{\partial z} = \frac{\partial R}{\partial y}, \qquad \frac{\partial R}{\partial x} = \frac{\partial P}{\partial z}$$

should be satisfied. If these conditions are satisfied, U is a function of the variables x, y, and z whose total differential is $P\,dx + Q\,dy + R\,dz$, and which is single valued in the region (E). In order to find the value of U at any point, the path of integration may be chosen arbitrarily.

If the functions P, Q, and R satisfy the equations (56), but at least one of them becomes infinite at all the points of one or more curves in (E), results analogous to those of § 153 may be derived.

If, for example, one of the functions P, Q, R becomes infinite at all the points of a closed curve γ, the integral U will admit a period equal to the value of the line integral taken along a closed contour which pierces once and only once a surface σ bounded by γ.

We may also consider questions relating to surface integrals which are exactly analogous to the questions proposed above for line integrals. Let A, B, and C be three functions which, together with their first partial derivatives, are

---

* *Traité d'Analyse*, Vol. II.

continuous in a region (E) of space bounded by a single closed surface S. Let Σ be a surface inside of (E) bounded by a contour Γ of any form whatever. Then the surface integral

$$(57) \qquad I = \iint_{(\Sigma)} A\,dy\,dz + B\,dz\,dx + C\,dx\,dy$$

depends in general upon the surface Σ as well as upon the contour Γ. In order that the integral should depend only upon Γ, it is evidently necessary and sufficient that its value when taken over any closed surface in (E) should vanish. Green's theorem (§ 149) gives at once the conditions under which this is true. For we know that the given double integral extended over any closed surface is equal to the triple integral

$$\iiint \left(\frac{\partial A}{\partial x} + \frac{\partial B}{\partial y} + \frac{\partial C}{\partial z} \right) dx\,dy\,dz$$

extended throughout the region bounded by the surface. In order that this latter integral should vanish for any region inside (E), it is evidently necessary that the functions A, B, and C should satisfy the equation

$$(58) \qquad \frac{\partial A}{\partial x} + \frac{\partial B}{\partial y} + \frac{\partial C}{\partial z} = 0.$$

This condition is also sufficient.

Stokes' theorem affords an easy verification of this fact. For if A, B, and C are three functions which satisfy the equation (58), it is always possible to determine in an infinite number of ways three other functions P, Q, and R such that

$$(59) \qquad \frac{\partial R}{\partial y} - \frac{\partial Q}{\partial z} = A, \qquad \frac{\partial P}{\partial z} - \frac{\partial R}{\partial x} = B, \qquad \frac{\partial Q}{\partial x} - \frac{\partial P}{\partial y} = C.$$

In the first place, if these equations admit solutions, they admit an infinite number, for they remain unchanged if P, Q, and R be replaced by

$$P + \frac{\partial \lambda}{\partial x}, \qquad Q + \frac{\partial \lambda}{\partial y}, \qquad R + \frac{\partial \lambda}{\partial z},$$

respectively, where λ is an arbitrary function of x, y, and z. Again, setting $R = 0$, the first two of equations (59) give

$$P = \int_{z_0}^{z} B(x,\,y,\,z)\,dz + \phi(x,\,y), \qquad Q = -\int_{z_0}^{z} A(x,\,y,\,z)\,dz + \psi(x,\,y),$$

where $\phi(x,\,y)$ and $\psi(x,\,y)$ are arbitrary functions of x and y. Substituting these values in the last of equations (59), we find

$$- \int_{z_0}^{z} \left(\frac{\partial A}{\partial x} + \frac{\partial B}{\partial y} \right) dz + \frac{\partial \psi}{\partial x} - \frac{\partial \phi}{\partial y} = C(x,\,y,\,z),$$

or, making use of (58),

$$\frac{\partial \psi}{\partial x} - \frac{\partial \phi}{\partial y} = C(x,\,y,\,z_0).$$

One of the functions ϕ or ψ may still be chosen at random.

The functions P, Q, and R having been determined, the surface integral, by Stokes' theorem, is equal to the line integral $\int_{(\Gamma)} P\,dx + Q\,dy + R\,dz$, which evidently depends only upon the contour Γ.

EXERCISES

1. Find the value of the triple integral

$$\int\int\int [5\,(x - y)^2 + 3az - 4a^2]\,dx\,dy\,dz$$

extended throughout the region of space defined by the inequalities

$$x^2 + y^2 - az < 0, \qquad x^2 + y^2 + z^2 - 2a^2 < 0.$$

[Licence, Montpellier, 1895.]

2. Find the area of the surface

$$x^2 + y^2 + z^2 = \frac{a^2 b^2 (x^2 + y^2)\,z}{a^2 x^2 + b^2 y^2},$$

and the volume of the solid bounded by the same surface.

3. Investigate the properties of the function

$$F(X,\,Y,\,Z) = \int_{x_0}^{X} dx \int_{y_0}^{Y} dy \int_{z_0}^{Z} f(x,\,y,\,z)\,dz$$

considered as a function of X, Y, and Z.   Generalize the results of § 125.

4. Find the volume of the portion of the solid bounded by the surface

$$(x^2 + y^2 + z^2)^3 = 3a^3 xyz$$

which lies in the first octant.

5. Reduce to a simple integral the multiple integral

$$\int\int \cdots \int x_1^{\alpha_1} x_2^{\alpha_2} \cdots x_n^{\alpha_n} F(x_1 + x_2 + \cdots + x_n)\,dx_1\,dx_2 \cdots dx_n$$

extended throughout the domain D defined by the inequalities

$$0 \leqq x_1, \qquad 0 \leqq x_2, \qquad \cdots, \qquad 0 \leqq x_n, \qquad x_1 + x_2 + \cdots + x_n \leqq a.$$

[Proceed as in § 148.]

6. Reduce to a simple integral the multiple integral

$$\int\int \cdots \int x_1^{\alpha_1} x_2^{\alpha_2} \cdots x_n^{\alpha_n} F\left[\left(\frac{x_1}{a_1}\right)^{p_1} + \cdots + \left(\frac{x_n}{a_n}\right)^{p_n} \right] dx_1\,dx_2 \cdots dx_n$$

extended throughout the domain D defined by the inequalities

$$0 \leqq x_1, \qquad 0 \leqq x_2, \qquad \cdots, \qquad 0 \leqq x_n, \qquad \left(\frac{x_1}{a_1}\right)^{p_1} + \cdots + \left(\frac{x_n}{a_n}\right)^{p_n} \leqq 1.$$

7*. Derive the formula

$$\int\int\int \cdots \int dx_1\,dx_2 \cdots dx_n = \frac{\pi^{\frac{n}{2}}}{\Gamma\left(\frac{n}{2} + 1\right)},$$

where the multiple integral is extended throughout the domain D defined by the inequality

$$x_1^2 + x_2^2 + \cdots + x_n^2 < 1.$$

8*. Derive the formula

$$\int_0^\pi d\theta \int_0^{2\pi} F(a\cos\theta + b\sin\theta\cos\phi + c\sin\theta\sin\phi)\sin\theta\,d\phi = 2\pi\int_{-1}^{+1} F(uR)\,du,$$

where a, b, and c are three arbitrary constants, and where $R = \sqrt{a^2 + b^2 + c^2}$.

[POISSON.]

[First observe that the given double integral is equal to a certain surface integral taken over the surface of the sphere $x^2 + y^2 + z^2 = 1$. Then take the plane $ax + by + cz = 0$ as the plane of xy in a new system of coördinates.]

9*. Let $\rho = F(\theta, \phi)$ be the equation in polar coördinates of a closed surface. Show that the volume of the solid bounded by the surface is equal to the double integral

(α)
$$\frac{1}{3}\int\int \rho\cos\gamma\,d\sigma$$

extended over the whole surface, where $d\sigma$ represents the element of area, and γ the angle which the radius vector makes with the exterior normal.

10*. Let us consider an ellipsoid whose equation is

$$\frac{x^2}{\mu^2} + \frac{y^2}{\mu^2 - b^2} + \frac{z^2}{\mu^2 - c^2} = 1,$$

and let us define the positions of any point on its surface by the elliptic coördinates ν and ρ, that is, by the roots which the above equation would have if μ were regarded as unknown (cf. § 147). The application of the formulæ (29) to the volume of this ellipsoid leads to the equation

$$\int_0^b d\rho \int_b^c \frac{(\nu^2 - \rho^2)\sqrt{(c^2 - \rho^2)(c^2 - \nu^2)}}{\sqrt{(b^2 - \rho^2)(\nu^2 - b^2)}}\,d\nu = \frac{1}{b}\pi c^2(c^2 - b^2).$$

Likewise, the formula (α) gives

$$\int_0^b d\rho \int_b^c \frac{(\nu^2 - \rho^2)\,d\nu}{\sqrt{(b^2 - \rho^2)(c^2 - \rho^2)(\nu^2 - b^2)(c^2 - \nu^2)}} = \frac{\pi}{2}.$$

[LAMÉ.]

11. Determine the functions $P(x, y)$ and $Q(x, y)$ which, together with their partial derivatives, are continuous, and for which the line integral

$$\int P(x + \alpha, y + \beta)\,dx + Q(x + \alpha, y + \beta)\,dy$$

taken along any closed contour whatever is independent of the constants α and β and depends only upon the contour itself.

[*Licence*, Paris, July, 1900.]

12*. Consider the point transformation defined by the equations

$$\begin{cases} x = f(x', y', z'), \\ y = \phi(x', y', z'), \\ z = \psi(x', y', z'). \end{cases}$$

As the point (x', y', z') describes a surface S', the point (x, y, z) describes a surface S. Let α, β, γ be the direction angles of the normal to S; α', β', γ' the direction angles of the corresponding normal to the surface S'; and $d\sigma$ and $d\sigma'$ the corresponding surface elements of the two surfaces. Prove the formula

$$\cos \gamma \, d\sigma = \pm \, d\sigma' \left\{ \frac{D(x, y)}{D(y', z')} \cos \alpha' + \frac{D(x, y)}{D(z', x')} \cos \beta' + \frac{D(x, y)}{D(x', y')} \cos \gamma' \right\}.$$

13*. Derive the formula (16) on page 304 directly.

[The volume V may be expressed by the surface integral

$$V = \int_{(S)} z \cos \gamma \, d\sigma,$$

and we may then make use of the identity

$$\frac{D(f, \phi, \psi)}{D(x', y', z')} = \frac{\partial}{\partial x'} \left\{ \psi \, \frac{D(f, \phi)}{D(y', z')} \right\} + \frac{\partial}{\partial y'} \left\{ \psi \, \frac{D(f, \phi)}{D(z', x')} \right\} + \frac{\partial}{\partial z'} \left\{ \psi \, \frac{D(f, \phi)}{D(x', y')} \right\},$$

which is easily verified.]

CHAPTER VIII

INFINITE SERIES

I. SERIES OF REAL CONSTANT TERMS
GENERAL PROPERTIES   TESTS FOR CONVERGENCE

156. **Definitions and general principles. Sequences.** The elementary properties of series are discussed in all texts on College Algebra and on Elementary Calculus. We shall review rapidly the principal points of these elementary discussions.

First of all, let us consider an infinite *sequence* of quantities

$$(1) \qquad\qquad s_0, \quad s_1, \quad s_2, \quad \cdots, \quad s_n, \quad \cdots$$

in which each quantity has a definite place, the order of precedence being *fixed*. Such a sequence is said to be *convergent* if s_n approaches a limit as the index n becomes infinite. Every sequence which is not convergent is said to be *divergent*. This may happen in either of two ways: s_n may finally become and remain larger than any preassigned quantity, or s_n may approach no limit even though it does not become infinite.

In order that a sequence should be convergent, it is necessary and sufficient that, corresponding to any preassigned positive number ϵ, a positive integer n should exist such that the difference $s_{n+p} - s_n$ is less than ϵ in absolute value for any positive integer p.

In the first place, the condition is necessary. For if s_n approaches a limit s as n becomes infinite, a number n always exists for which each of the differences $s - s_n, s - s_{n+1}, \cdots, s - s_{n+p}, \cdots$ is less than $\epsilon/2$ in absolute value. It follows that the absolute value of $s_{n+p} - s_n$ will be less than $2\,\epsilon/2 = \epsilon$ for any value of p.

In order to prove the converse, we shall introduce a very important idea due to Cauchy. Suppose that the absolute value of each of the terms of the sequence (1) is less than a positive number N. Then all the numbers between $-N$ and $+N$ may be separated into two classes as follows. We shall say that a number belongs to the class A if there exist an infinite number of terms of the sequence (1)

which are greater than the given number.   A number belongs to
the class B if there are only a finite number of terms of the
sequence (1) which are greater than the given number.   It is
evident that every number between $-N$ and $+N$ belongs to one
of the two classes, and that every number of the class A is less
than any number of the class B.   Let S be the upper limit of the
numbers of the class A, which is obviously the same as the lower
limit of the numbers of the class B.   Cauchy called this number the
greatest limit (*la plus grande des limites*) of the terms of the
sequence (1).*   This number S should be carefully distinguished
from the upper limit of the terms of the sequence (1) (§ 68).   For
instance, for the sequence

$$1, \quad \frac{1}{2}, \quad \frac{1}{3}, \quad \cdots, \quad \frac{1}{n}, \quad \cdots$$

the upper limit of the terms of the sequence is 1, while the greatest
limit is 0.

The name given by Cauchy is readily justified.   There always
exist an infinite number of terms of the sequence (1) which lie
between $S - \epsilon$ and $S + \epsilon$, however small ϵ be chosen.   Let us then
consider a decreasing sequence of positive numbers ϵ_1, ϵ_2, $\cdots$,
ϵ_n, $\cdots$, where the general term ϵ_n approaches zero.   To each number ϵ_i of the sequence let us assign a number α_i of the sequence (1)
which lies between $S - \epsilon_i$ and $S + \epsilon_i$.   We shall thus obtain a
suite of numbers α_1, α_2, $\cdots$, α_n, $\cdots$ belonging to the sequence (1)
which approach S as their limit.   On the other hand, it is clear
from the very definition of S that no partial sequence of the kind just
mentioned can be picked out of the sequence (1) which approaches
a limit greater than S.   Whenever the sequence is convergent its
limit is evidently the number S itself.

Let us now suppose that the difference $s_{n+p} - s_n$ of two terms of
the sequence (1) can be made smaller than any positive number ϵ
for any value of p by a proper choice of n.   Then all the terms of
the sequence past s_n lie between $s_n - \epsilon$ and $s_n + \epsilon$.   Let S be the
greatest limit of the terms of the sequence.   By the reasoning just
given it is possible to pick a partial sequence out of the sequence (1)
which approaches S as its limit.   Since each term of the partial
sequence, after a certain one, lies between $s_n - \epsilon$ and $s_n + \epsilon$, it is

---

* *Résumés analytiques de Turin*, 1833 (*Collected Works*, 2d series, Vol. X, p. 49).
The definition may be extended to any assemblage of numbers which has an upper
limit.

clear that the absolute value of $S - s_n$ is at most equal to ϵ. Now let s_m be any term of the sequence (1) whose index m is greater than n. Then we may write

$$s_m - S = (s_m - s_n) + (s_n - S),$$

and the value of the right-hand side is surely less than 2ϵ. Since ϵ is an arbitrarily preassigned positive number, it follows that the general term s_m approaches S as its limit as the index m increases indefinitely.

Note. If S is the greatest limit of the terms of the sequence (1), every number greater than S belongs to the class B, and every number less than S belongs to the class A. The number S itself may belong to either class.

157. Passage from sequences to series. Given any infinite sequence

$$u_0, \quad u_1, \quad u_2, \quad \cdots, \quad u_n, \quad \cdots,$$

the *series* formed from the terms of this sequence,

$$(2) \qquad u_0 + u_1 + u_2 + \cdots + u_n + \cdots,$$

is said to be *convergent* if the sequence of the successive sums

$$S_0 = u_0, \quad S_1 = u_0 + u_1, \quad \cdots, \quad S_n = u_0 + u_1 + \cdots + u_n, \quad \cdots$$

is convergent. Let S be the limit of the latter sequence, i.e. the limit which the sum S_n approaches as n increases indefinitely:

$$S = \lim_{n=\infty} S_n = \lim_{n=\infty} \sum_{\nu=0}^{\nu=n} u_\nu.$$

Then S is called *the sum of the preceding series*, and this relation is indicated by writing the symbolic equation

$$S = u_0 + u_1 + \cdots + u_n + \cdots = \sum_{\nu=0}^{+\infty} u_\nu.$$

A series which is not convergent is said to be *divergent*.

It is evident that the problem of determining whether the series is convergent or divergent is equivalent to the problem of determining whether the sequence of the successive sums $S_0, S_1, S_2, \cdots$ is convergent or divergent. Conversely, the sequence

$$s_0, \quad s_1, \quad s_2, \quad \cdots, \quad s_n, \quad \cdots$$

will be convergent or divergent according as the series

$$s_0 + (s_1 - s_0) + (s_2 - s_1) + \cdots + (s_n - s_{n-1}) + \cdots$$

is convergent or divergent. For the sum S_n of the first $n + 1$ terms of this series is precisely equal to the general term s_n of the given sequence. We shall apply this remark frequently.

The series (2) converges or diverges with the series

$$(3) \qquad u_p + u_{p+1} + \cdots + u_{p+q} + \cdots,$$

obtained by omitting the first p terms of (2). For, if $S_n (n > p)$ denote the sum of the first $n + 1$ terms of the series (2), and Σ_{n-p} the sum of the $n - p + 1$ first terms of the series (3), i.e.

$$\Sigma_{n-p} = u_p + u_{p+1} + \cdots + u_n,$$

the difference $S_n - \Sigma_{n-p} = u_0 + u_1 + \cdots + u_{p-1}$ is independent of n. Hence the sum Σ_{n-p} approaches a limit if S_n approaches a limit, and conversely. It follows that in determining whether the series converges or diverges we may neglect as many of the terms at the beginning of a series as we wish.

Let S be the sum of a convergent series, S_n the sum of the first $n + 1$ terms, and R_n the sum of the series obtained by omitting the first $n + 1$ terms,

$$R_n = u_{n+1} + u_{n+2} + \cdots + u_{n+p} + \cdots.$$

It is evident that we shall always have

$$S = S_n + R_n.$$

It is not possible, in general, to find the sum S of a convergent series. If we take the sum S of the first $n + 1$ terms as an approximate value of S, the error made is equal to R_n. Since S_n approaches S as n becomes infinite, the error R_n approaches zero, and hence the number of terms may always be taken so large — at least theoretically — that the error made in replacing S by S_n is less than any preassigned number. In order to have an idea of the degree of approximation obtained, it is sufficient to know an upper limit of R_n. It is evident that the only series which lend themselves readily to numerical calculation in practice are those for which the remainder R_n approaches zero rather rapidly.

A number of properties result directly from the definition of convergence. We shall content ourselves with stating a few of them.

1) *If each of the terms of a given series be multiplied by a constant k different from zero, the new series obtained will converge or diverge with the given series; if the given series converges to a sum S, the sum of the second series is kS.*

2) *If there be given two convergent series*

$$u_0 + u_1 + u_2 + \cdots + u_n + \cdots,$$

$$v_0 + v_1 + v_2 + \cdots + v_n + \cdots,$$

whose sums are S and S', respectively, the new series obtained by adding the given series term by term, namely,

$$(u_0 + v_0) + (u_1 + v_1) + \cdots + (u_n + v_n) + \cdots,$$

converges, and its sum is S + S'. The analogous theorem holds for the term-by-term addition of p convergent series.

3) *The convergence or divergence of a series is not affected if the values of a finite number of the terms be changed.* For such a change would merely increase or decrease all of the sums S_n after a certain one by a constant amount.

4) The test for convergence of any infinite sequence, applied to series, gives Cauchy's general test for convergence : *

In order that a series be convergent it is necessary and sufficient that, corresponding to any preassigned positive number ϵ, an integer n should exist, such that the sum of any number of terms whatever, starting with u_{n+1}, is less than ϵ in absolute value. For $S_{n+p} - S_n = u_{n+1} + u_{n+2} + \cdots + u_{n+p}.$

In particular, the general term $u_{n+1} = S_{n+1} - S_n$ must approach zero as n becomes infinite.

Cauchy's test is absolutely general, but it is often difficult to apply it in practice. It is essentially a development of the very notion of a limit. We shall proceed to recall the practical rules most frequently used for testing series for convergence and divergence. None of these rules can be applied in all cases, but together they suffice for the treatment of the majority of cases which actually arise.

158. Series of positive terms. We shall commence by investigating a very important class of series, — those whose terms are all positive. In such a series the sum S_n increases with n. Hence in order that the series converge it is sufficient that the sum S_n should remain less than some fixed number for all values of n. The most general test for the convergence of such a series is based upon comparisons of the given series with others previously studied. The following propositions are fundamental for this process :

---

* *Exercices de Mathématiques*, 1827. (*Collected Works*, Vol. VII, 2d series, p. 267.)

1) *If each of the terms of a given series of positive terms is less than or at most equal to the corresponding term of a known convergent series of positive terms, the given series is convergent.* For the sum S_n of the first n terms of the given series is evidently less than the sum S' of the second series. Hence S_n approaches a limit S which is less than S'.

2) *If each of the terms of a given series of positive terms is greater than or equal to the corresponding term of a known divergent series of positive terms, the given series diverges.* For the sum of the first n terms of the given series is not less than the sum of the first n terms of the second series, and hence it increases indefinitely with n.

We may compare two series also by means of the following lemma. *Let*

$$(U) \qquad u_0 + u_1 + u_2 + \cdots + u_n + \cdots,$$

$$(V) \qquad v_0 + v_1 + v_2 + \cdots + v_n + \cdots$$

be two series of positive terms. If the series (U) converges, and if, after a certain term, we always have $v_{n+1}/v_n \leqq u_{n+1}/u_n$, the series (V) also converges. If the series (U) diverges, and if, after a certain term, we always have $u_{n+1}/u_n \leqq v_{n+1}/v_n$, the series (V) also diverges.

In order to prove the first statement, let us suppose that $v_{n+1}/v_n \leqq u_{n+1}/u_n$ whenever $n \geqq p$. Since the convergence of a series is not affected by multiplying each term by the same constant, and since the ratio of two consecutive terms also remains unchanged, we may suppose that $v_p < u_p$, and it is evident that we should have $v_{p+1} \leqq u_{p+1}$, $v_{p+2} \leqq u_{p+2}$, etc. Hence the series (V) must converge. The proof of the second statement is similar.

Given a series of positive terms which is known to converge or to diverge, we may make use of either set of propositions in order to determine in a given case whether a second series of positive terms converges or diverges. For we may compare the terms of the two series themselves, or we may compare the ratios of two consecutive terms.

159. Cauchy's test and d'Alembert's test. The simplest series which can be used for purposes of comparison is a geometrical progression whose ratio is r. It converges if $r < 1$, and diverges if $r \geqq 1$. The comparison of a given series of positive terms with a geometrical progression leads to the following test, which is due to Cauchy:

If the nth root $\sqrt[n]{u_n}$ of the general term u_n of a series of positive terms after a certain term is constantly less than a fixed number less than unity, the series converges. If $\sqrt[n]{u_n}$ after a certain term is constantly greater than unity, the series diverges.

For in the first case $\sqrt[n]{u_n} < k < 1$, whence $u_n < k^n$. Hence each of the terms of the series after a certain one is less than the corresponding term of a certain geometrical progression whose ratio is less than unity. In the second case, on the other hand, $\sqrt[n]{u_n} > 1$, whence $u_n > 1$. Hence in this case the general term does not approach zero.

This test is applicable whenever $\sqrt[n]{u_n}$ approaches a limit. In fact, the following proposition may be stated:

If $\sqrt[n]{u_n}$ approaches a limit l as n becomes infinite, the series will converge if l is less than unity, and it will diverge if l is greater than unity.

A doubt remains if $l = 1$, except when $\sqrt[n]{u_n}$ remains greater than unity as it approaches unity, in which case the series surely diverges.

Comparing the ratio of two consecutive terms of a given series of positive terms with the ratio of two consecutive terms of a geometrical progression, we obtain d'Alembert's test:

If in a given series of positive terms the ratio of any term to the preceding after a certain term remains less than a fixed number less than unity, the series converges. If that ratio after a certain term remains greater than unity, the series diverges.

From this theorem we may deduce the following corollary:

If the ratio u_{n+1}/u_n approaches a limit l as n becomes infinite, the series converges if $l < 1$, and diverges if $l > 1$.

The only doubtful case is that in which $l = 1$; even then, if u_{n+1}/u_n remains greater than unity as it approaches unity, the series is divergent.

General commentary. Cauchy's test is more general than d'Alembert's. For suppose that the terms of a given series, after a certain one, are each less than the corresponding terms of a decreasing geometrical progression, i.e. that the general term u_n is less than Ar^n for all values of n greater than a fixed integer p, where A is a certain constant and r is less than unity. Hence $\sqrt[n]{u_n} < rA^{1/n}$, and the second member of this inequality approaches unity as n becomes infinite. Hence, denoting by k a fixed number between r and 1, we shall have after a certain term $\sqrt[n]{u_n} < k$. Hence Cauchy's test is applicable in any such case. But it may happen that the ratio u_{n+1}/u_n assumes values greater than unity, however far out in the series we may go. For example, consider the series

$$1 + r\,|\sin \alpha\,| + r^2\,|\sin 2\alpha\,| + \cdots + r^n\,|\sin n\alpha\,| + \cdots,$$

where $r<1$ and where α is an arbitrary constant. In this case $\sqrt[n]{u_n} = r \sqrt[n]{|\sin n\alpha|} < r$, whereas the ratio

$$\frac{u_{n+1}}{u_n} = r \left| \frac{\sin (n+1)\alpha}{\sin n\alpha} \right|$$

may assume, in general, an infinite number of values greater than unity as n increases indefinitely.

Nevertheless, it is advantageous to retain d'Alembert's test, for it is more convenient in many cases.   For instance, for the series

$$1 + \frac{x}{1} + \frac{x^2}{1 \cdot 2} + \frac{x^3}{1 \cdot 2 \cdot 3} + \cdots + \frac{x^n}{1 \cdot 2 \cdots n} + \cdots$$

the ratio of any term to the preceding is $x/(n+1)$, which approaches zero as n becomes infinite; whereas some consideration is necessary to determine independently what happens to $\sqrt[n]{u_n} = x/\sqrt[n]{1 \cdot 2 \cdots n}$ as n becomes infinite.

After we have shown by the application of one of the preceding tests that each of the terms of a given series is less than the corresponding term of a decreasing geometrical progression A, Ar, Ar^2, $\cdots$, Ar^n, $\cdots$, it is easy to find an upper limit of the error made when the sum of the first m terms is taken in place of the sum of the series.   For this error is certainly less than the sum of the geometrical progression

$$Ar^m + Ar^{m+1} + Ar^{m+2} + \cdots = \frac{Ar^m}{1-r}.$$

When each of the two expressions $\sqrt[n]{u_n}$ and u_{n+1}/u_n approaches a limit, the two limits are necessarily the same.   For, let us consider the auxiliary series

$$(4) \qquad u_0 + u_1 x + u_2 x^2 + \cdots + u_n x^n + \cdots,$$

where x is positive.   In this series the ratio of any term to the preceding approaches the limit lx, where l is the limit of the ratio u_{n+1}/u_n.   Hence the series (4) converges when $x < 1/l$, and diverges when $x > 1/l$.   Denoting the limit of $\sqrt[n]{u_n}$ by l', the expression $\sqrt[n]{u_n x^n}$ also approaches a limit $l'x$, and the series (4) converges if $x < 1/l'$, and diverges if $x > 1/l'$.   In order that the two tests should not give contradictory results, it is evidently necessary that l and l' should be equal.   If, for instance, l were greater than l', the series (4) would be convergent, by Cauchy's test, for any number x between $1/l$ and $1/l'$, whereas the same series, for the same value of x, would be divergent by d'Alembert's test.

Still more generally, if u_{n+1}/u_n approaches a limit l, $\sqrt[n]{u_n}$ approaches the same limit.[*]   For suppose that, after a certain term, each of the ratios

$$\frac{u_{n+1}}{u_n}, \qquad \frac{u_{n+2}}{u_{n+1}}, \qquad \cdots, \qquad \frac{u_{n+p}}{u_{n+p-1}}$$

lies between $l - \epsilon$ and $l + \epsilon$, where ϵ is a positive number which may be taken as small as we please by taking n sufficiently large.   Then we shall have

$$(l-\epsilon)^p < \frac{u_{n+p}}{u_n} < (l+\epsilon)^p,$$

or

$$u_n^{\frac{1}{n+p}} (l-\epsilon)^{\frac{p}{n+p}} < \sqrt[n+p]{u_{n+p}} < u_n^{\frac{1}{n+p}} (l+\epsilon)^{\frac{p}{n+p}}.$$

---

* Cauchy, *Cours d'Analyse.*

As the number p increases indefinitely, while n remains fixed, the two terms on the extreme right and left of this double inequality approach $l + \epsilon$ and $l - \epsilon$, respectively. Hence for all values of m greater than a suitably chosen number we shall have

$$l - 2\epsilon < \sqrt[m]{u_m} < l + 2\epsilon,$$

and, since ϵ is an arbitrarily assigned number, it follows that $\sqrt[m]{u_m}$ approaches the number l as its limit.

It should be noted that the converse is not true. Consider, for example, the sequence

$$1, \quad a, \quad ab, \quad a^2 b, \quad a^2 b^2, \quad \cdots, \quad a^n b^{n-1}, \quad a^n b^n, \quad \cdots,$$

where a and b are two different numbers. The ratio of any term to the preceding is alternately a and b, whereas the expression $\sqrt[n]{u_n}$ approaches the limit $\sqrt{ab}$ as n becomes infinite.

The preceding proposition may be employed to determine the limits of certain expressions which occur in undetermined forms. Thus it is evident that the expression $\sqrt[n]{1 \cdot 2 \cdots n}$ increases indefinitely with n, since the ratio $n!/(n-1)!$ increases indefinitely with n. In a similar manner it may be shown that each of the expressions $\sqrt[n]{n}$ and $\sqrt[n]{\log n}$ approaches the limit unity as n becomes infinite.

160. Application of the greatest limit. Cauchy formulated the preceding test in a more general manner. Let a_n be the general term of a series of positive terms. Consider the sequence

$$(5) \qquad\qquad a_1, \quad a_2^{\frac{1}{2}}, \quad a_3^{\frac{1}{3}}, \quad \cdots, \quad a_n^{\frac{1}{n}}, \quad \cdots.$$

If the terms of this sequence have no upper limit, the general term a_n will not approach zero, and the given series will be divergent. If all the terms of the sequence (5) are less than a fixed number, let ω be the greatest limit of the terms of the sequence.

The series Σa_n is convergent if ω is less than unity, and divergent if ω is greater than unity.

In order to prove the first part of the theorem, let $1 - \alpha$ be a number between ω and 1. Then, by the definition of the greatest limit, there exist but a finite number of terms of the sequence (5) which are greater than $1 - \alpha$. It follows that a positive integer p may be found such that $\sqrt[n]{a_n} < 1 - \alpha$ for all values of n greater than p. Hence the series Σa_n converges. On the other hand, if $\omega > 1$, let $1 + \alpha$ be a number between 1 and ω. Then there are an infinite number of terms of the sequence (5) which are greater than $1 + \alpha$, and hence there are an infinite number of values of n for which a_n is greater than unity. It follows that the series Σa_n is divergent in this case. The case in which $\omega = 1$ remains in doubt.

161. Cauchy's theorem. In case u_{n+1}/u_n and $\sqrt[n]{u_n}$ both approach unity without remaining constantly greater than unity, neither d'Alembert's test nor Cauchy's test enables us to decide whether the series is convergent or divergent. We must then take as a comparison series some series which has the same characteristic

but which is known to be convergent or divergent.   The following
proposition, which Cauchy discovered in studying definite integrals,
often enables us to decide whether a given series is convergent or
divergent when the preceding rules fail.

Let $\phi(x)$ be a function which is positive for values of x greater
than a certain number a, and which constantly decreases as x
increases past $x = a$, approaching zero as x increases indefinitely.
Then the x axis is an asymptote to the curve $y = \phi(x)$, and the
definite integral

$$\int_a^l \phi(x)\,dx$$

may or may not approach a finite limit as l increases indefinitely.

The series

(6) $\phi(a) + \phi(a+1) + \cdots + \phi(a+n) + \cdots$

*converges if the preceding integral approaches a limit, and diverges if
it does not.*

For, let us consider the set of rectangles whose bases are each
unity and whose altitudes are $\phi(a)$, $\phi(a+1)$, $\cdots$, $\phi(a+n)$, respectively.   Since each of these rectangles extends beyond the curve
$y = \phi(x)$, the sum of their areas is evidently greater than the area
between the x axis, the curve $y = \phi(x)$, and the two ordinates $x = a$,
$x = a + n$, that is,

$$\phi(a) + \phi(a+1) + \cdots + \phi(a+n) > \int_a^{a+n} \phi(x)\,dx.$$

On the other hand, if we consider the rectangles constructed
inside the curve, with a common base equal to *unity* and with the
altitudes $\phi(a+1)$, $\phi(a+2)$, $\cdots$, $\phi(a+n)$, respectively, the sum of
the areas of these rectangles is evidently less than the area under
the curve, and we may write

$$\phi(a) + \phi(a+1) + \cdots + \phi(a+n) < \phi(a) + \int_a^{a+n} \phi(x)\,dx.$$

Hence, if the integral $\int_a^l \phi(x)\,dx$ approaches a limit L as l increases
indefinitely, the sum $\phi(a) + \cdots + \phi(a+n)$ always remains less than
$\phi(a) + L$.   It follows that the sum in question approaches a limit;
hence the series (6) is convergent.   On the other hand, if the integral $\int_a^{a+n} \phi(x)\,dx$ increases beyond all limit as n increases indefinitely,
the same is true of the sum

$$\phi(a) + \phi(a+1) + \cdots + \phi(a+n),$$

as is seen from the first of the above inequalities. Hence in this case the series (6) diverges.

Let us consider, for example, the function $\phi(x) = 1/x^\mu$, where μ is positive and $a = 1$. This function satisfies all the requirements of the theorem, and the integral $\int_1^l [1/x^\mu] \, dx$ approaches a limit as l increases indefinitely if and only if μ is greater than unity. It follows that the series

$$\frac{1}{1^\mu} + \frac{1}{2^\mu} + \frac{1}{3^\mu} + \cdots + \frac{1}{n^\mu} + \cdots$$

converges if μ is greater than unity, and diverges if $\mu \leqq 1$.

Again, consider the function $\phi(x) = 1/[x(\log x)^\mu]$, where $\log x$ denotes the natural logarithm, μ is a positive number, and $a = 2$. Then, if $\mu \neq 1$, we shall have

$$\int_2^n \frac{dx}{x(\log x)^\mu} = \frac{-1}{\mu - 1} \big[(\log n)^{1-\mu} - (\log 2)^{1-\mu} \big].$$

The second member approaches a limit if $\mu > 1$, and increases indefinitely with n if $\mu < 1$. In the particular case when $\mu = 1$ it is easy to show in a similar manner that the integral increases beyond all limit. Hence the series

$$\frac{1}{2(\log 2)^\mu} + \frac{1}{3(\log 3)^\mu} + \cdots + \frac{1}{n(\log n)^\mu} + \cdots$$

converges if $\mu > 1$, and diverges if $\mu \leqq 1$.

More generally the series whose general term is

$$\frac{1}{n \log n \log^2 n \log^3 n \cdots \log^{p-1} n (\log^p n)^\mu}$$

converges if $\mu > 1$, and diverges if $\mu \leqq 1$. In this expression $\log^2 n$ denotes $\log \log n$, $\log^3 n$ denotes $\log \log \log n$, etc. It is understood, of course, that the integer n is given only values so large that $\log n$, $\log^2 n$, $\log^3 n$, $\cdots$, $\log^p n$ are positive. The missing terms in the series considered are then to be supplied by zeros. The theorem may be proved easily in a manner similar to the demonstrations given above. If, for instance, $\mu \neq 1$, the function

$$\frac{1}{x \log x \log^2 x \cdots (\log^p x)^\mu}$$

is the derivative of $(\log^p x)^{1-\mu}/(1 - \mu)$, and this latter function approaches a finite limit if and only if $\mu > 1$.

Cauchy's theorem admits of applications of another sort. Let us suppose that the function $\phi(x)$ satisfies the conditions imposed above, and let us consider the sum

$$\phi(n) + \phi(n+1) + \cdots + \phi(n+p),$$

where n and p are two integers which are to be allowed to become infinite. If the series whose general term is $\phi(n)$ is convergent, the preceding sum approaches zero as a limit, since it is the difference between the two sums S_{n+p+1} and S_n, each of which approaches the sum of the series. But if this series is divergent, no conclusion can be drawn. Returning to the geometrical interpretation given above, we find the double inequality

$$\int_n^{n+p} \phi(x)\,dx < \phi(n) + \phi(n+1) + \cdots + \phi(n+p) < \phi(n) + \int_n^{n+p} \phi(x)\,dx.$$

Since $\phi(n)$ approaches zero as n becomes infinite, it is evident that the limit of the sum in question is the same as that of the definite integral $\int_n^{n+p}\phi(x)\,dx$, and this depends upon the manner in which n and p become infinite.

For example, the limit of the sum

$$\frac{1}{n} + \frac{1}{n+1} + \cdots + \frac{1}{n+p}$$

is the same as that of the definite integral $\int_n^{n+p}[1/x]\,dx = \log(1 + p/n)$. It is clear that this integral approaches a limit if and only if the ratio p/n approaches a limit. If α is the limit of this ratio, the preceding sum approaches $\log(1 + \alpha)$ as its limit, as we have already seen in § 49.

Finally, the limit of the sum

$$\frac{1}{\sqrt{n}} + \frac{1}{\sqrt{n+1}} + \cdots + \frac{1}{\sqrt{n+p}}$$

is the same as that of the definite integral

$$\int_n^{n+p} \frac{dx}{\sqrt{x}} = 2\left(\sqrt{n+p} - \sqrt{n}\right).$$

In order that this expression should approach a limit, it is necessary that the ratio $p/\sqrt{n}$ should approach a limit α. Then the preceding expression may be written in the form

$$2\,\frac{p}{\sqrt{n+p} + \sqrt{n}} = 2\,\frac{\dfrac{p}{\sqrt{n}}}{1 + \sqrt{1 + \dfrac{p}{n}}},$$

and it is evident that the limit of this expression is α.

162. Logarithmic criteria. Taking the series

$$\frac{1}{1^\mu} + \frac{1}{2^\mu} + \cdots + \frac{1}{n^\mu} + \cdots$$

as a comparison series, Cauchy deduced a new test for convergence which is entirely analogous to that which involves $\sqrt[n]{u_n}$.

If after a certain term the expression $\log(1/u_n)/\log n$ *is always greater than a fixed number which is greater than unity, the series converges. If after a certain term* $\log(1/u_n)/\log n$ *is always less than unity, the series diverges.*

If $\log(1/u_n)/\log n$ *approaches a limit* l *as* n *increases indefinitely, the series converges if* $l > 1$, *and diverges if* $l < 1$. *The case in which* $l = 1$ *remains in doubt.*

In order to prove the first part of the theorem, we will remark that the inequality

$$\log \frac{1}{u_n} > k \log n$$

is equivalent to the inequality

$$\frac{1}{u_n} > n^k \quad \text{or} \quad u_n < \frac{1}{n^k};$$

since $k > 1$, the series surely converges.

Likewise, if

$$\log \frac{1}{u_n} < \log n,$$

we shall have $u_n > 1/n$, whence the series surely diverges.

This test enables us to determine whether a given series converges or diverges whenever the terms of the series, after a certain one, are each less, respectively, than the corresponding terms of the series

$$\frac{A}{1^\mu} + \frac{A}{2^\mu} + \cdots + \frac{A}{n^\mu} + \cdots,$$

where A is a constant factor and $\mu > 1$. For, if

$$u_n < \frac{A}{n^\mu},$$

we shall have $\log u_n + \mu \log n < \log A$ or

$$\frac{\log \dfrac{1}{u_n}}{\log n} > \mu - \frac{\log A}{\log n},$$

and the right-hand side approaches the limit μ as n increases indefinitely. If K denotes a number between *unity* and μ, we shall have, after a certain term,

$$\frac{\log \dfrac{1}{u_n}}{\log n} > K.$$

Similarly, taking the series

$$\sum \frac{1}{n(\log n)^{\mu}}, \qquad \sum \frac{1}{n \log n (\log^2 n)^{\mu}}, \qquad \cdots$$

as comparison series, we obtain an infinite suite of tests for convergence which may be obtained mechanically from the preceding by replacing the expression $\log(1/u_n)/\log n$ by $\log[1/(nu_n)]/\log^2 n$, then by

$$\frac{\log \dfrac{1}{nu_n \log n}}{\log^3 n},$$

and so forth, in the statement of the preceding tests.* These tests apply in more and more general cases. Indeed, it is easy to show that if the convergence or divergence of a series can be established by means of any one of them, the same will be true of any of those which follow. It may happen that no matter how far we proceed with these trial tests, no one of them will enable us to determine whether the series converges or diverges. Du Bois-Reymond † and Pringsheim ‡ have in fact actually given examples of both convergent and divergent series for which none of these logarithmic tests determines whether the series converge or diverge. This result is of great theoretical importance, but convergent series of this type evidently converge very slowly, and it scarcely appears possible that they should ever have any practical application whatever in problems which involve numerical calculation.§

163. Raabe's or Duhamel's test. Retaining the same comparison series, but comparing the ratios of two consecutive terms instead of comparing the terms themselves, we are led to new tests which are, to be sure, less general than the preceding, but which are often easier to apply in practice. For example, consider the series of positive terms

$$(7) \qquad u_0 + u_1 + u_2 + \cdots + u_n + \cdots,$$

---

* See Bertrand, *Traité de Calcul différentiel et intégral*, Vol. I, p. 238; *Journal de Liouville*, 1st series, Vol. VII, p. 35.

† *Ueber Convergenz von Reihen* . . . (*Crelle's Journal*, Vol. LXXVI, p. 85, 1873).

‡ *Allgemeine Theorie der Divergenz* . . . (*Mathematische Annalen*, Vol. XXXV, 1890).

§ In an example of a certain convergent series due to du Bois-Reymond it would be necessary, according to the author, to take a number of terms equal *to the volume of the earth expressed in cubic millimeters* in order to obtain merely half the sum of the series.

in which the ratio u_{n+1}/u_n approaches unity, remaining constantly less than unity. Then we may write

$$\frac{u_{n+1}}{u_n} = \frac{1}{1+\alpha_n},$$

where α_n approaches zero as n becomes infinite. The comparison of this ratio with $[n/(n+1)]^\mu$ leads to the following rule, discovered first by Raabe* and then by Duhamel.†

If after a certain term the product $n\alpha_n$ is always greater than a fixed number which is greater than unity, the series converges. If after a certain term the same product is always less than unity, the series diverges.

The second part of the theorem follows immediately. For, since $n\alpha_n < 1$ after a certain term, it follows that

$$\frac{1}{1+\alpha_n} > \frac{n}{n+1},$$

and the ratio u_{n+1}/u_n is greater than the ratio of two consecutive terms of the harmonic series. Hence the series diverges.

In order to prove the first part, let us suppose that after a certain term we always have $n\alpha_n > k > 1$. Let μ be a number which lies between 1 and k, $1 < \mu < k$. Then the series surely converges if after a certain term the ratio u_{n+1}/u_n is less than the ratio $[n/(n+1)]^\mu$ of two consecutive terms of the series whose general term is $n^{-\mu}$. The necessary condition that this should be true is that

(8)
$$\frac{1}{1+\alpha_n} < \frac{1}{\left(1+\frac{1}{n}\right)^\mu},$$

or, developing $(1+1/n)^\mu$ by Taylor's theorem limited to the term in $1/n^2$,

$$1 + \frac{\mu}{n} + \frac{\lambda_n}{n^2} < 1 + \alpha_n,$$

where λ_n always remains less than a fixed number as n becomes infinite. Simplifying this inequality, we may write it in the form

$$\mu + \frac{\lambda_n}{n} < n\alpha_n.$$

---

* *Zeitschrift für Mathematik und Physik*, Vol. **X**, 1832.
† *Journal de Liouville*, Vol. **IV**, 1838.

The left-hand side of this inequality approaches μ as its limit as n becomes infinite. Hence, after a sufficiently large value of n, the left-hand side will be less than $n\alpha_n$, which proves the inequality (8). It follows that the series is convergent.

If the product $n\alpha_n$ approaches a limit l as n becomes infinite, we may apply the preceding rule. The series is convergent if $l > 1$, and divergent if $l < 1$. A doubt exists if $l = 1$, except when $n\alpha_n$ approaches unity remaining constantly less than unity: in that case the series diverges.

If the product $n\alpha_n$ approaches unity as its limit, we may compare the ratio u_{n+1}/u_n with the ratio of two consecutive terms of the series

$$\frac{1}{2(\log 2)^\mu} + \cdots + \frac{1}{n(\log n)^\mu} + \cdots,$$

which converges if $\mu > 1$, and diverges if $\mu \leq 1$. The ratio of two consecutive terms of the given series may be written in the form

$$\frac{u_{n+1}}{u_n} = \frac{1}{1 + \frac{1}{n} + \frac{\beta_n}{n}},$$

where β_n approaches zero as n becomes infinite. *If after a certain term the product $\beta_n \log n$ is always greater than a fixed number which is greater than unity, the series converges. If after a certain term the same product is always less than unity, the series diverges.*

In order to prove the first part of the theorem, let us suppose that $\beta_n \log n > k > 1$. Let μ be a number between 1 and k. Then the series will surely converge if after a certain term we have

(9)
$$\frac{u_{n+1}}{u_n} < \frac{n}{n+1} \left[\frac{\log n}{\log(n+1)} \right]^\mu,$$

which may be written in the form

$$1 + \frac{1}{n} + \frac{\beta_n}{n} > \left(1 + \frac{1}{n}\right) \left[1 + \frac{\log\left(1 + \frac{1}{n}\right)}{\log n} \right]^\mu,$$

or, applying Taylor's theorem to the right-hand side,

$$1 + \frac{1}{n} + \frac{\beta_n}{n} > \left(1 + \frac{1}{n}\right) \left\{ 1 + \frac{\mu \log\left(1 + \frac{1}{n}\right)}{\log n} + \lambda_n \left[\frac{\log\left(1 + \frac{1}{n}\right)}{\log n} \right]^2 \right\},$$

where λ_n always remains less than a fixed number as n becomes infinite. Simplifying this inequality, it becomes

$$\beta_n \log n > \mu(n+1) \log\left(1 + \frac{1}{n}\right) + \frac{\lambda_n (n+1)\left[\log\left(1 + \frac{1}{n}\right)\right]^2}{\log n}.$$

The product $(n + 1) \log(1 + 1/n)$ approaches unity as n becomes infinite, for it may be written, by Taylor's theorem, in the form

$$(10) \qquad (n + 1) \log\left(1 + \frac{1}{n}\right) = 1 + \frac{1}{2n}(1 + \epsilon),$$

where ϵ approaches zero. The right-hand side of the above inequality therefore approaches μ as its limit, and the truth of the inequality is established for sufficiently large values of n, since the left-hand side is greater than k, which is itself greater than μ.

The second part of the theorem may be proved by comparing the ratio u_{n+1}/u_n with the ratio of two consecutive terms of the series whose general term is $1/(n \log n)$. For the inequality

$$\frac{u_{n+1}}{u_n} > \frac{n}{n+1} \frac{\log n}{\log(n+1)},$$

which is to be proved, may be written in the form

$$1 + \frac{1}{n} + \frac{\beta_n}{n} < \left(1 + \frac{1}{n}\right)\left[1 + \frac{\log\left(1 + \frac{1}{n}\right).}{\log n}\right],$$

or

$$\beta_n \log n < (n + 1) \log\left(1 + \frac{1}{n}\right).$$

The right-hand side approaches unity through values which are greater than unity, as is seen from the equation (10). The truth of the inequality is therefore established for sufficiently large values of n, for the left-hand side cannot exceed unity.

From the above proposition it may be shown, as a corollary, that if the product $\beta_n \log n$ approaches a limit l as n becomes infinite, the series converges if $l > 1$, and diverges if $l < 1$. The case in which $l = 1$ remains in doubt, unless $\beta_n \log n$ is always less than unity. In that case the series surely diverges.

If $\beta_n \log n$ approaches unity through values which are greater than unity, we may write, in like manner,

$$\frac{u_{n+1}}{u_n} = \frac{1}{1 + \dfrac{1}{n} + \dfrac{1 + \gamma_n}{n \log n}},$$

where γ_n approaches zero as n becomes infinite. It would then be possible to prove theorems exactly analogous to the above by considering the product $\gamma_n \log^2 n$, and so forth.

Corollary. If in a series of positive terms the ratio of any term to the preceding can be written in the form

$$\frac{u_{n+1}}{u_n} = 1 - \frac{r}{n} + \frac{H_n}{n^{1+\mu}},$$

where μ is a positive number, r a constant, and H_n a quantity whose absolute value remains less than a fixed number as n increases indefinitely, *the series converges if r is greater than unity, and diverges in all other cases.*

For if we set

$$\frac{u_{n+1}}{u_n} = \frac{1}{1 + \alpha_n},$$

we shall have

$$n\alpha_n = \frac{r - \dfrac{H_n}{n^\mu}}{1 - \dfrac{r}{n} + \dfrac{H_n}{n^{1+\mu}}},$$

and hence $\lim n\alpha_n = r$. It follows that the series converges if $r > 1$, and diverges if $r < 1$. The only case which remains in doubt is that in which $r = 1$. In order to decide this case, let us set

$$\frac{u_{n+1}}{u_n} = \frac{1}{1 + \dfrac{1}{n} + \dfrac{\beta_n}{n}}.$$

From this we find

$$\beta_n \log n = \frac{\dfrac{\log n}{n} - \dfrac{n+1}{n} H_n \dfrac{\log n}{n^\mu}}{1 - \dfrac{1}{n} + \dfrac{H_n}{n^{1+\mu}}},$$

and the right-hand side approaches zero as n becomes infinite, no matter how small the number μ may be. Hence the series diverges.

Suppose, for example, that u_{n+1}/u_n is a rational function of n which approaches unity as n increases indefinitely:

$$\frac{u_{n+1}}{u_n} = \frac{n^p + a_1 n^{p-1} + a_2 n^{p-2} + \cdots}{n^p + b_1 n^{p-1} + b_2 n^{p-2} + \cdots}.$$

Then, performing the division indicated and stopping with the term in $1/n^2$, we may write

$$\frac{u_{n+1}}{u_n} = 1 + \frac{a_1 - b_1}{n} + \frac{\phi(n)}{n^2},$$

where $\phi(n)$ is a rational function of n which approaches a limit as n becomes infinite. By the preceding theorem, *the necessary and sufficient condition that the series should converge is that*

$$b_1 > a_1 + 1.$$

This theorem is due to Gauss, who proved it directly.* It was one of the first general tests for convergence.

164. Absolute convergence. We shall now proceed to study series whose terms may be either positive or negative. If after a certain term all the terms have the same sign, the discussion reduces to the previous case. Hence we may restrict ourselves to series which contain an infinite number of positive terms and an infinite

---

* (*Collected Works*, Vol. III, p. 138.) *Disquisitiones generales circa seriem infinitam*

$$1 + \frac{\alpha \cdot \beta}{1 \cdot \gamma} x + \cdots.$$

number of negative terms. We shall prove first of all the following fundamental theorem:

Any series whatever is convergent if the series formed of the absolute values of the terms of the given series converges.

Let

(11) $$u_0 + u_1 + \cdots + u_n + \cdots$$

be a series of positive and negative terms, and let

(12) $$U_0 + U_1 + \cdots + U_n + \cdots$$

be the series of the absolute values of the terms of the given series, where $U_n = |u_n|$. If the series (12) converges, the series (11) likewise converges. This is a consequence of the general theorem of § 157. For we have

$$|u_n + u_{n+1} + \cdots + u_{n+p}| < U_n + U_{n+1} + \cdots + U_{n+p},$$

and the right-hand side may be made less than any preassigned number by choosing n sufficiently large, for any subsequent choice of p. Hence the same is true for the left-hand side, and the series (11) surely converges.

The theorem may also be proved as follows: Let us write

$$u_n = (u_n + U_n) - U_n,$$

and then consider the auxiliary series whose general term is $u_n + U_n$,

(13) $$(u_0 + U_0) + (u_1 + U_1) + \cdots + (u_n + U_n) + \cdots.$$

Let S_n, S_n', and S_n'' denote the sums of the first n terms of the series (11), (12), and (13), respectively. Then we shall have

$$S_n = S_n'' - S_n'.$$

The series (12) converges by hypothesis. Hence the series (13) also converges, since none of its terms is negative and its general term cannot exceed $2U_n$. It follows that each of the sums S_n' and S_n'', and hence also the sum S_n, approaches a limit as n increases indefinitely. Hence the given series (11) converges. It is evident that the given series may be thought of as arising from the subtraction of two convergent series of positive terms.

Any series is said to be *absolutely convergent* if the series of the absolute values of its terms converges. *In such a series the order of the terms may be changed in any way whatever without altering the*

sum of the series.   Let us first consider a convergent series of positive terms,

(14) $a_0 + a_1 + \cdots + a_n + \cdots,$

whose sum is S, and let

(15) $b_0 + b_1 + \cdots + b_n + \cdots$

be a series whose terms are the same as those of the first series
arranged in a different order, i.e. each term of the series (14) is to
be found somewhere in the series (15), and each term of the series
(15) occurs in the series (14).

Let S'_m be the sum of the first m terms of the series (15).   Since
all these terms occur in the series (14), it is evident that n may be
chosen so large that the first m terms of the series (15) are to be
found among the first n terms of the series (14).   Hence we shall have

$$S'_m < S_n < S,$$

which shows that the series (15) converges and that its sum S' does
not exceed S.   In a similar manner it is clear that $S \leqq S'$.   Hence
$S' = S$.   The same argument shows that if one of the above series
(14) and (15) diverges, the other does also.

*The terms of a convergent series of positive terms may also be
grouped together in any manner, that is, we may form a series each
of whose terms is equal to the sum of a certain number of terms of
the given series without altering the sum of the series.** Let us first
suppose that consecutive terms are grouped together, and let

(16) $A_0 + A_1 + A_2 + \cdots + A_m + \cdots$

be the new series obtained, where, for example,

$$A_0 = a_0 + a_1 + \cdots + a_p, \qquad A_1 = a_{p+1} + \cdots + a_q,$$
$$A_2 = a_{q+1} + \cdots + a_r, \qquad \cdots.$$

Then the sum S'_m of the first m terms of the series (16) is equal to
the sum S_N of the first N terms of the given series, where $N > m$.
As m becomes infinite, N also becomes infinite, and hence S'_m also
approaches the limit S.

Combining the two preceding operations, it becomes clear that *any
convergent series of positive terms may be replaced by another series
each of whose terms is the sum of a certain number of terms of the
given series taken in any order whatever, without altering the sum of*

---

* It is often said that *parentheses may be inserted in a convergent series of positive
terms in any manner whatever without altering the sum of the series.* — TRANS.

the series. It is only necessary that each term of the given series should occur in one and in only one of the groups which form the terms of the second series.

Any absolutely convergent series may be regarded as the difference of two convergent series of positive terms; hence the preceding operations are permissible in any such series. It is evident that an absolutely convergent series may be treated from the point of view of numerical calculation as if it were a sum of a finite number of terms.

165. Conditionally convergent series. A series whose terms do not all have the same sign may be convergent without being absolutely convergent. This fact is brought out clearly by the following theorem on alternating series, which we shall merely state, assuming that it is already familiar to the student.*

A series whose terms are alternately positive and negative converges if the absolute value of each term is less than that of the preceding, and if, in addition, the absolute value of the terms of the series diminishes indefinitely as the number of terms increases indefinitely.

For example, the series

$$1 - \frac{1}{2} + \frac{1}{3} - \frac{1}{4} + \cdots + (-1)^{n-1}\frac{1}{n} + \cdots$$

converges. We saw in § 49 that its sum is log 2. The series of the absolute values of the terms of this series is precisely the *harmonic* series, which diverges. A series which converges but which does not converge absolutely is called a *conditionally convergent series.* The investigations of Cauchy, Lejeune-Dirichlet, and Riemann have shown clearly the necessity of distinguishing between absolutely convergent series and conditionally convergent series. For instance, in a conditionally convergent series it is *not* always allowable to change the order of the terms nor to group the terms together in parentheses in an arbitrary manner. These operations may alter the sum of such a series, or may change a convergent series into a divergent series, or *vice versa.* For example, let us again consider the convergent series

$$1 - \frac{1}{2} + \frac{1}{3} - \frac{1}{4} + \cdots + \frac{1}{2n+1} - \frac{1}{2n+2} + \cdots,$$

---

* It is pointed out in § 166 that this theorem is a special case of the theorem proved there. — TRANS.

whose sum is evidently equal to the limit of the expression

$$\sum_{n=0}^{n=m} \left(\frac{1}{2n+1} - \frac{1}{2n+2} \right)$$

as m becomes infinite. Let us write the terms of this series in another order, putting two negative terms after each positive term, as follows:

$$1 - \frac{1}{2} - \frac{1}{4} + \frac{1}{3} - \frac{1}{6} - \frac{1}{8} + \cdots + \frac{1}{2n+1} - \frac{1}{4n+2} - \frac{1}{4n+4} + \cdots.$$

It is easy to show from a consideration of the sums S_{3n}, S_{3n+1}, and S_{3n+2} that the new series converges. Its sum is the limit of the expression

$$\sum_{n=0}^{n=m} \left(\frac{1}{2n+1} - \frac{1}{4n+2} - \frac{1}{4n+4} \right)$$

as m becomes infinite. From the identity

$$\frac{1}{2n+1} - \frac{1}{4n+2} - \frac{1}{4n+4} = \frac{1}{2} \left(\frac{1}{2n+1} - \frac{1}{2n+2} \right)$$

it is evident that the sum of the second series is half the sum of the given series.

In general, given a series which is convergent but not absolutely convergent, it is possible to arrange the terms in such a way that the new series converges toward any preassigned number A whatever. Let S_p denote the sum of the first p positive terms of the series, and S'_q the sum of the absolute values of the first q negative terms, taken in such a way that the p positive terms and the q negative terms constitute the first $p + q$ terms of the series. Then the sum of the first $p + q$ terms is evidently $S_p - S'_q$. As the two numbers p and q increase indefinitely, each of the sums S_p and S'_q must increase indefinitely, for otherwise the series would diverge, or else converge absolutely. On the other hand, since the series is supposed to converge, the general term must approach zero.

We may now form a new series whose sum is A in the following manner: Let us take positive terms from the given series in the order in which they occur in it until their sum exceeds A. Let us then add to these, in the order in which they occur in the given series, negative terms until the total sum is less than A. Again, beginning with the positive terms where we left off, let us add positive terms until the total sum is greater than A. We should then return to the negative terms, and so on. It is clear that the sum of the first n terms of the new series thus obtained is alternately greater than and then less than A, and that it differs from A by a quantity which approaches zero as its limit.

166. Abel's test. The following test, due to Abel, enables us to establish the convergence of certain series for which the preceding tests fail. The proof is based upon the lemma stated and proved in § 75.

Let

$$u_0 + u_1 + \cdots + u_n + \cdots$$

be a series which converges or which is *indeterminate* (that is, for which the sum of the first n terms is always less than a fixed number A in absolute value). Again, let

$$\epsilon_0, \quad \epsilon_1, \quad \cdots, \quad \epsilon_n, \quad \cdots$$

be a monotonically decreasing sequence of positive numbers which approach zero as n becomes infinite. *Then the series*

$$(17) \qquad \epsilon_0 u_0 + \epsilon_1 u_1 + \cdots + \epsilon_n u_n + \cdots$$

converges under the hypotheses made above.

For by the hypotheses made above it follows that

$$|u_{n+1} + \cdots + u_{n+p}| < 2A$$

for any value of n and p. Hence, by the lemma just referred to, we may write

$$|u_{n+1}\epsilon_{n+1} + \cdots + u_{n+p}\epsilon_{n+p}| < 2A\epsilon_{n+1}.$$

Since ϵ_{n+1} approaches zero as n becomes infinite, n may be chosen so large that the absolute value of the sum

$$\epsilon_{n+1}u_{n+1} + \cdots + \epsilon_{n+p}u_{n+p}$$

will be less than any preassigned positive number for all values of p. The series (17) therefore converges by the general theorem of § 157.

When the series $u_0 + u_1 + \cdots + u_n + \cdots$ reduces to the series

$$1 - 1 + 1 - 1 + 1 - 1 \cdots,$$

whose terms are alternately $+1$ and -1, the theorem of this article reduces to the theorem stated in § 165 with regard to alternating series.

As an example under the general theorem consider the series

$$\sin \theta + \sin 2\,\theta + \sin 3\,\theta + \cdots + \sin n\,\theta + \cdots,$$

which is convergent or indeterminate. For if $\sin \theta = 0$, every term of the series is zero, while if $\sin \theta \neq 0$, the sum of the first n terms, by a formula of Trigonometry, is equal to the expression

$$\frac{\sin \dfrac{n\theta}{2}}{\sin \dfrac{\theta}{2}} \sin \left(\frac{n+1}{2}\theta\right),$$

which is less than $|1/\sin(\theta/2)|$ in absolute value. It follows that the series

$$\frac{\sin \theta}{1} + \frac{\sin 2\,\theta}{2} + \cdots + \frac{\sin n\,\theta}{n} + \cdots$$

converges for all values of θ. It may be shown in a similar manner that the series

$$\frac{\cos \theta}{1} + \frac{\cos 2\,\theta}{2} + \cdots + \frac{\cos n\,\theta}{n} + \cdots$$

converges for all values of θ except $\theta = 2k\pi$.

Corollary. Restricting ourselves to convergent series, we may state a more general theorem. Let

$$u_0 + u_1 + \cdots + u_n + \cdots$$

be a convergent series, and let

$$\epsilon_0, \quad \epsilon_1, \quad \cdots, \quad \epsilon_n, \quad \cdots$$

be any monotonically increasing or decreasing sequence of positive numbers which approach a limit k different from zero as n increases indefinitely. *Then the series*

$$(18) \qquad \epsilon_0 u_0 + \epsilon_1 u_1 + \cdots + \epsilon_n u_n + \cdots$$

also converges.

For definiteness let us suppose that the ϵ's always increase. Then we may write

$$\epsilon_0 = k - \alpha_0, \quad \epsilon_1 = k - \alpha_1, \quad \cdots, \quad \epsilon_n = k - \alpha_n, \quad \cdots,$$

where the numbers $\alpha_0, \alpha_1, \cdots, \alpha_n, \cdots$ form a sequence of decreasing positive numbers which approach zero as n becomes infinite. It follows that the two series

$$ku_0 + ku_1 + \cdots + ku_n + \cdots,$$
$$\alpha_0 u_0 + \alpha_1 u_1 + \cdots + \alpha_n u_n + \cdots$$

both converge, and therefore the series (18) also converges.

II. SERIES OF COMPLEX TERMS   MULTIPLE SERIES

167. Definitions. In this section we shall deal with certain generalizations of the idea of an infinite series.

Let

$$(19) \qquad u_0 + u_1 + u_2 + \cdots + u_n + \cdots$$

be a series whose terms are imaginary quantities:

$$u_0 = a_0 + b_0 i, \quad u_1 = a_1 + b_1 i, \quad \cdots, \quad u_n = a_n + b_n i, \quad \cdots.$$

Such a series is said to be *convergent* if the two series formed of the real parts of the successive terms and of the coefficients of the imaginary parts, respectively, both converge:

$$(20) \qquad a_0 + a_1 + a_2 + \cdots + a_n + \cdots = S',$$
$$(21) \qquad b_0 + b_1 + b_2 + \cdots + b_n + \cdots = S''.$$

Let S' and S'' be the sums of the series (20) and (21), respectively. Then the quantity $S = S' + iS''$ is called *the sum of the series* (19). It is evident that S is, as before, the limit of the sum S_n of the first n terms of the given series as n becomes infinite. It is evident that a series of complex terms is essentially only a combination of two series of real terms.

When the series of absolute values of the terms of the series (19)

$$(22) \qquad \sqrt{a_0^2 + b_0^2} + \sqrt{a_1^2 + b_1^2} + \cdots + \sqrt{a_n^2 + b_n^2} + \cdots$$

converges, each of the series (20) *and* (21) *evidently converges absolutely, for* $|a_n| \leqq \sqrt{a_n^2 + b_n^2}$ *and* $|b_n| \leqq \sqrt{a_n^2 + b_n^2}$.

In this case the series (19) is said to be *absolutely convergent. The sum of such a series is not altered by a change in the order of the terms, nor by grouping the terms together in any way.*

Conversely, if each of the series (20) *and* (21) *converges absolutely, the series* (22) *converges absolutely, for* $\sqrt{a_n^2 + b_n^2} \leqq |a_n| + |b_n|$.

Corresponding to every test for the convergence of a series of positive terms there exists a test for the absolute convergence of any series whatever, real or imaginary. Thus, *if the absolute value of the ratio of two consecutive terms of a series* $|u_{n+1}/u_n|$, *after a certain term, is less than a fixed number less than unity, the series converges absolutely.* For, let $U_i = |u_i|$. Then, since $|u_{n+1}/u_n| < k < 1$ after a certain term, we shall have also

$$\frac{U_{n+1}}{U_n} < k < 1,$$

which shows that the series of absolute values

$$U_0 + U_1 + \cdots + U_n + \cdots$$

converges. *If* $|u_{n+1}/u_n|$ *approaches a limit* l *as* n *becomes infinite, the series converges if* $l < 1$, *and diverges if* $l > 1$. The first half is self-evident. In the second case the general term u_n does not approach zero, and consequently the series (20) and (21) cannot both be convergent. The case $l = 1$ remains in doubt.

More generally, if ω be the greatest limit of $\sqrt[n]{U_n}$ as n becomes infinite, *the series* (19) *converges if* $\omega < 1$, *and diverges if* $\omega > 1$. For in the latter case the modulus of the general term does not approach zero (see § 161). The case in which $\omega = 1$ remains in doubt — the series may be absolutely convergent, simply convergent, or divergent.

168. Multiplication of series. Let

$$(23) \qquad u_0 + u_1 + u_2 + \cdots + u_n + \cdots,$$

$$(24) \qquad v_0 + v_1 + v_2 + \cdots + v_n + \cdots$$

be any two series whatever. Let us multiply terms of the first series by terms of the second in all possible ways, and then group together all the products $u_i v_j$ for which the sum $i + j$ of the subscripts is the same; we obtain in this way a new series

$$(25) \quad \begin{cases} u_0 v_0 + (u_0 v_1 + u_1 v_0) + (u_0 v_2 + u_1 v_1 + u_2 v_0) + \cdots \\ \quad + (u_0 v_n + u_1 v_{n-1} + \cdots + u_n v_0) + \cdots. \end{cases}$$

If each of the series (23) and (24) is absolutely convergent, the series (25) converges, and its sum is the product of the sums of the two given series. This theorem, which is due to Cauchy, was generalized by Mertens,* who showed that it still holds if only one of the series (23) and (24) is absolutely convergent and the other is merely convergent.

Let us suppose for definiteness that the series (23) converges absolutely, and let w_n be the general term of the series (25):

$$w_n = u_0 v_n + u_1 v_{n-1} + \cdots + u_n v_0.$$

The proposition will be proved if we can show that each of the differences

$$w_0 + w_1 + \cdots + w_{2n} \quad - (u_0 + u_1 + \cdots + u_n) \quad (v_0 + v_1 + \cdots + v_n),$$

$$w_0 + w_1 + \cdots + w_{2n+1} - (u_0 + u_1 + \cdots + u_{n+1})(v_0 + v_1 + \cdots + v_{n+1})$$

approaches zero as n becomes infinite. Since the proof is the same in each case, we shall consider the first difference only. Arranging it according to the u's, it becomes

$$\delta = \quad u_0(v_{n+1} + \cdots + v_{2n}) + u_1(v_{n+1} + \cdots + v_{2n-1}) + \cdots + u_{n-1} v_{n+1}$$
$$+ u_{n+1}(v_0 + \cdots + v_{n-1}) + u_{n+2}(v_0 + \cdots + v_{n-2}) + \cdots + u_{2n} v_0.$$

Since the series (23) converges absolutely, the sum $U_0 + U_1 + \cdots + U_n$ is less than a fixed positive number A for all values of n. Likewise, since the series (24) converges, the absolute value of the sum $v_0 + v_1 + \cdots + v_n$ is less than a fixed positive number B. Moreover, corresponding to any preassigned positive number ϵ a number m exists such that

$$U_{n+1} + \cdots + U_{n+p} < \frac{\epsilon}{A + B},$$

$$|v_{n+1} + \cdots + v_{n+p}| < \frac{\epsilon}{A + B},$$

for any value of p whatever, provided that $n \geq m$. Having so chosen n that all these inequalities are satisfied, an upper limit of the quantity $|\delta|$ is given by replacing $u_0, u_1, u_2, \cdots, u_{2n}$ by $U_0, U_1, U_2, \cdots, U_{2n}$, respectively, $v_{n+1} + v_{n+2} + \cdots + v_{n+p}$ by $\epsilon/(A + B)$, and finally each of the expressions $v_0 + v_1 + \cdots + v_{n-1}$, $v_0 + \cdots + v_{n-2}$, $\cdots$, v_0 by B. This gives

$$|\delta| < U_0 \frac{\epsilon}{A + B} + U_1 \frac{\epsilon}{A + B} + \cdots + U_{n-1} \frac{\epsilon}{A + B}$$
$$+ U_{n+1}B + U_{n+2}B + \cdots + U_{2n}B,$$

or

$$|\delta| < \frac{\epsilon}{A + B}(U_0 + U_1 + \cdots + U_{n-1}) + B(U_{n+1} + \cdots + U_{2n})$$
$$< \frac{\epsilon A}{A + B} + \frac{\epsilon B}{A + B},$$

whence, finally, $|\delta| < \epsilon$. Hence the difference δ actually does approach zero as n becomes infinite.

169. Double series. Consider a rectangular network which is limited upward and to the left, but which extends indefinitely downward and to the right. The network will contain an infinite number of vertical columns, which we shall number from left to right from 0 to $+\infty$. It will also contain an infinite number of horizontal rows, which we shall number from the top downward from 0 to $+\infty$. Let us now suppose that to each of the rectangles of the network a certain quantity is assigned and written in the corresponding rectangle. Let a_{ik} be the quantity which lies in the ith row and in the kth column. Then we shall have an array of the form

(26)

$$\begin{vmatrix} a_{00} & a_{01} & a_{02} & \cdots & a_{0n} & \cdots \\ a_{10} & a_{11} & a_{12} & \cdots & a_{1n} & \cdots \\ a_{20} & a_{21} & a_{22} & \cdots & a_{2n} & \cdots \\ \cdots & \cdots & \cdots & \cdots & \cdots & \cdots \\ \cdots & \cdots & \cdots & \cdots & \cdots & \cdots \\ a_{m0} & a_{m1} & a_{m2} & \cdots & a_{mn} & \cdots \\ \cdots & \cdots & \cdots & \cdots & \cdots & \cdots \end{vmatrix}$$

We shall first suppose that each of the elements of this array is real and positive.

Now let an infinite sequence of curves $C_1, C_2, \cdots, C_n, \cdots$ be drawn across this array as follows : 1) Any one of them forms with the two straight lines which bound the array a closed curve which entirely surrounds the preceding one; 2) The distance from any fixed point to any point of the curve C_n, which is otherwise entirely arbitrary, becomes infinite with n. Let S_i be the sum of the elements of the array which lie entirely inside the closed curve composed of C_i and the two straight lines which bound the array. If S_n approaches a limit S as n becomes infinite, we shall say that the double series

$$(27) \qquad \sum_{i=0}^{+\infty} \sum_{k=0}^{+\infty} a_{ik}$$

converges, and that its *sum* is S. In order to justify this definition, it is necessary to show that the limit S is independent of the form of the curves C. Let C_1', C_2', $\cdots$, C_m', $\cdots$ be another set of curves which recede indefinitely, and let S_i' be the sum of the elements inside the closed curve formed by C_i' and the two boundaries. If m be assigned any fixed value, n can always be so chosen that the curve C_n lies entirely outside of C_m'. Hence $S_m' \leqq S_n$, and therefore $S_m' \leqq S$, for any value of m. Since S_m' increases steadily with m, it must approach a limit $S' \leqq S$ as m becomes infinite. In the same way it follows that $S \leqq S'$. Hence $S' = S$.

For example, the curve C_i may be chosen as the two lines which form with the boundaries of the array a square whose side increases indefinitely with i, or as a straight line equally inclined to the two boundaries. The corresponding sums are, respectively, the following:

$$a_{00} + (a_{10} + a_{11} + a_{01}) + \cdots + (a_{n0} + a_{n1} + \cdots + a_{nn} + a_{n-1,\,n} + \cdots + a_{0n}),$$

$$a_{00} + (a_{10} + a_{01}) + (a_{20} + a_{11} + a_{02}) + \cdots + (a_{n0} + a_{n-1,\,1} + \cdots + a_{0n}).$$

If either of these sums approaches a limit as n becomes infinite, the other will also, and the two limits are equal.

The array may also be added by rows or by columns. For, suppose that the double series (27) converges, and let its sum be S. It is evident that the sum of any finite number of elements of the series cannot exceed S. It follows that each of the series formed of the elements in a single row

$$(28) \qquad a_{i0} + a_{i1} + \cdots + a_{in} + \cdots, \qquad i = 0, 1, 2, \cdots,$$

converges, for the sum of the first $n + 1$ terms $a_{i0} + a_{i1} + \cdots + a_{in}$ cannot exceed S and increases steadily with n. Let σ_i be the sum of the series formed of the elements in the ith row. Then the new series

$$(29) \qquad \sigma_0 + \sigma_1 + \cdots + \sigma_i + \cdots$$

surely converges. For, let us consider the sum of the terms of the array Σa_{ik} for which $i \leqq p$, $k \leqq r$. This sum cannot exceed S, and increases steadily with r for any fixed value of p; hence it approaches a limit as r becomes infinite, and that limit is equal to

$$(30) \qquad \sigma_0 + \sigma_1 + \cdots + \sigma_p$$

for any fixed value of p.   It follows that $\sigma_0 + \sigma_1 + \cdots + \sigma_p$ cannot exceed S and increases steadily with p.   Consequently the series (29) converges, and its sum Σ is less than or equal to S.   Conversely, if each of the series (28) converges, and the series (29) converges to a sum Σ, it is evident that the sum of any finite number of elements of the array (26) cannot exceed Σ.   Hence $S \leq \Sigma$, and consequently $\Sigma = S$.

The argument just given for the series formed from the elements in individual rows evidently holds equally well for the series formed from the elements in individual columns.   *The sum of a convergent double series whose elements are all positive may be evaluated by rows, by columns, or by means of curves of any form which recede indefinitely.   In particular, if the series converges when added by rows, it will surely converge when added by columns, and the sum will be the same.*   A number of theorems proved for simple series of positive terms may be extended to double series of positive elements.   For example: *if each of the elements of a double series of positive elements is less, respectively, than the corresponding elements of a known convergent double series, the first series is also convergent;* and so forth.

A double series of positive terms which is *not convergent* is said to be *divergent*.   The sum of the elements of the corresponding array which lie inside any closed curve increases beyond all limit as the curve recedes indefinitely in every direction.

Let us now consider an array whose elements are not all positive. It is evident that it is unnecessary to consider the cases in which all the elements are negative, or in which only a finite number of elements are either positive or negative, since each of these cases reduces immediately to the preceding case.   We shall therefore suppose that there are an infinite number of positive elements and an infinite number of negative elements in the array.   Let a_{ik} be the general term of this array T.   If the array T_1 of positive elements, each of which is the absolute value $|a_{ik}|$ of the corresponding element in T, converges, the array T is said to be *absolutely convergent*.   Such an array has all of the essential properties of a convergent array of positive elements.

In order to prove this, let us consider two auxiliary arrays T' and T'', defined as follows.   The array T' is formed from the array T by replacing each negative element by a zero, retaining the positive elements as they stand.   Likewise, the array T'' is obtained from the array T by replacing each positive element by a zero and changing the sign of each negative element.   Each of the arrays T' and T'''

converges whenever the array T_1 converges, for each element of T', for example, is less than the corresponding element of T_1. The sum of the terms of the series T which lie inside any closed curve is equal to the difference between the sum of the terms of T' which lie inside the same curve and the sum of the terms of T'' which lie inside it. Since the two latter sums each approach limits as the curve recedes indefinitely in all directions, the first sum also approaches a limit, and that limit is independent of the form of the boundary curve. This limit is called *the sum of the array T*. The argument given above for arrays of positive elements shows that the same sum will be obtained by evaluating the array T by rows or by columns. It is now clear that an array whose elements are indiscriminately positive and negative, *if it converges absolutely,* may be treated as if it were a convergent array of positive terms. But it is essential that the series T_1 of positive terms be shown to be convergent.

If the array T_1 diverges, at least one of the arrays T' and T'' diverges. If only one of them, T' for example, diverges, the other T'' being convergent, the sum of the elements of the array T which lie inside a closed curve C becomes infinite as the curve recedes indefinitely in all directions, irrespective of the form of the curve. If both arrays T' and T'' diverge, the above reasoning shows only one thing, — that the sum of the elements of the array T inside a closed curve C is equal to the difference between two sums, each of which increases indefinitely as the curve C recedes indefinitely in all directions. It may happen that the sum of the elements of T inside C approach different limits according to the form of the curves C and the manner in which they recede, that is to say, according to the relative rate at which the number of positive terms and the number of negative terms in the sum are made to increase. The sum may even become infinite or approach no limit whatever for certain methods of recession. As a particular case, the sum obtained on evaluating by rows may be entirely different from that obtained on evaluating by columns if the array is not absolutely convergent.

The following example is due to Arndt.* Let us consider the array

$$(31) \quad \begin{array}{l} \dfrac{1}{2}\left(\dfrac{1}{2}\right) - \dfrac{1}{3}\left(\dfrac{2}{3}\right),\ \dfrac{1}{3}\left(\dfrac{2}{3}\right) - \dfrac{1}{4}\left(\dfrac{3}{4}\right),\ \cdots,\ \dfrac{1}{p}\left(\dfrac{p-1}{p}\right) - \dfrac{1}{p+1}\left(\dfrac{p}{p+1}\right),\ \cdots \\[2ex] \dfrac{1}{2}\left(\dfrac{1}{2}\right)^2 - \dfrac{1}{3}\left(\dfrac{2}{3}\right)^2,\ \dfrac{1}{3}\left(\dfrac{2}{3}\right)^2 - \dfrac{1}{4}\left(\dfrac{3}{4}\right)^2,\ \cdots,\ \dfrac{1}{p}\left(\dfrac{p-1}{p}\right)^2 - \dfrac{1}{p+1}\left(\dfrac{p}{p+1}\right)^2,\ \cdots \\[2ex] \cdots\cdots\cdots\cdots\cdots \\[2ex] \dfrac{1}{2}\left(\dfrac{1}{2}\right)^n - \dfrac{1}{3}\left(\dfrac{2}{3}\right)^n,\ \dfrac{1}{3}\left(\dfrac{2}{3}\right)^n - \dfrac{1}{4}\left(\dfrac{3}{4}\right)^n,\ \cdots,\ \dfrac{1}{p}\left(\dfrac{p-1}{p}\right)^n - \dfrac{1}{p+1}\left(\dfrac{p}{p+1}\right)^n,\ \cdots \\[2ex] \cdots\cdots\cdots\cdots\cdots \end{array}$$

* Grunert's *Archiv*, Vol. XI, p. 319.

which contains an infinite number of positive and an infinite number of negative elements.   Each of the series formed from the elements in a single row or from those in a single column converges.   The sum of the series formed from the terms in the nth row is evidently

$$\frac{1}{2}\left(\frac{1}{2}\right)^n = \frac{1}{2^{n+1}}.$$

Hence, evaluating the array (31) by rows, the result obtained is equal to the sum of the convergent series

$$\frac{1}{2^2} + \frac{1}{2^3} + \cdots + \frac{1}{2^{n+1}} + \cdots,$$

which is 1/2.   On the other hand, the series formed from the elements in the $(p-1)$th column, that is,

$$\frac{1}{p}\left[\left(\frac{p-1}{p}\right) + \left(\frac{p-1}{p}\right)^2 + \cdots + \left(\frac{p-1}{p}\right)^n + \cdots\right]$$
$$- \frac{1}{p+1}\left[\left(\frac{p}{p+1}\right) + \left(\frac{p}{p+1}\right)^2 + \cdots + \left(\frac{p}{p+1}\right)^n + \cdots\right]$$

converges, and its sum is

$$\frac{p-1}{p} - \frac{p}{p+1} = \frac{-1}{p(p+1)} = \frac{1}{p+1} - \frac{1}{p}.$$

Hence, evaluating the array (31) by columns, the result obtained is equal to the sum of the convergent series

$$\left(\frac{1}{3} - \frac{1}{2}\right) + \left(\frac{1}{4} - \frac{1}{3}\right) + \cdots + \left(\frac{1}{p+1} - \frac{1}{p}\right) + \cdots,$$

which is $-1/2$.

This example shows clearly that a double series should not be used in a calculation unless it is absolutely convergent.

We shall also meet with double series whose elements are complex quantities.   If the elements of the array (26) are complex, two other arrays T' and T'' may be formed where each element of T' is the real part of the corresponding element of T and each element of T'' is the coefficient of i in the corresponding element of T.   If the array T_1 of absolute values of the elements of T, each of whose elements is the absolute value of the corresponding element of T, converges, each of the arrays T' and T'' converges absolutely, and the given array T is said to be *absolutely convergent*.   The sum of the elements of the array which lie inside a variable closed curve approaches a limit as the curve recedes indefinitely in all directions. This limit is independent of the form of the variable curve, and it is called the *sum* of the given array.   The sum of any absolutely convergent array may also be evaluated by rows or by columns.

170. An absolutely convergent double series may be replaced by a simple series formed from the same elements. It will be sufficient to show that the rectangles of the network (26) can be numbered in such a way that each rectangle has a definite number, without exception, different from that of any other rectangle. In other words, we need merely show that the sequence of natural numbers

$$(32) \qquad\qquad 0, \quad 1, \quad 2, \quad \cdots, \quad n, \quad \cdots,$$

and the assemblage of all pairs of positive integers (i, k), where $i \geqq 0$, $k \geqq 0$, can be paired off in such a way that one and only one number of the sequence (32) will correspond to any given pair (i, k), and conversely, no number n corresponds to more than one of the pairs (i, k). Let us write the pairs (i, k) in order as follows :

$$(0, 0), \quad (1, 0), \quad (0, 1), \quad (2, 0), \quad (1, 1), \quad (0, 2), \quad \cdots,$$

where, in general, all those pairs for which $i + k = n$ are written down after those for which $i + k < n$ have all been written down, the order in which those of any one set are written being the same as that of the values of i for the various pairs beginning with $(n, 0)$ and going to $(0, n)$. It is evident that any pair (i, k) will be preceded by only a *finite* number of other pairs. Hence each pair will have a distinct number when the sequence just written down is counted off according to the natural numbers.

Suppose that the elements of the absolutely convergent double series $\Sigma\Sigma a_{ik}$ are written down in the order just determined. Then we shall have an ordinary series

$$(33) \quad a_{00} + a_{10} + a_{01} + a_{20} + a_{11} + a_{02} + \cdots + a_{n0} + a_{n-1, 1} + \cdots$$

whose terms coincide with the elements of the given double series. This simple series evidently converges absolutely, and its sum is equal to the sum of the given double series. It is clear that the method we have employed is not the only possible method of transforming the given double series into a simple series, since the order of the terms of the series (33) can be altered at pleasure. Conversely, any absolutely convergent simple series can be transformed into a double series in an infinite variety of ways, and that process constitutes a powerful instrument in the proof of certain identities.[*]

It is evident that the concept of double series is not essentially different from that of simple series. In studying absolutely convergent series we found that the order of the terms could be altered at will, and that any *finite* number of terms could be replaced by their sum without altering the sum of the series. An attempt to generalize this property leads very naturally to the introduction of double series.

171. Multiple series. The notion of double series may be generalized. In the first place we may consider a series of elements a_{mn} with two subscripts m and n, each of which may vary from $-\infty$ to $+\infty$. The elements of such a series may be arranged in the rectangles of a rectangular network which extends indefinitely in all directions;

---

[*] Tannery, *Introduction à la théorie des fonctions d'une variable*, p. 67.

it is evident that it may be divided into four double series of the type we have just studied.

A more important generalization is the following. Let us consider a series of elements of the type $a_{m_1, m_2, \cdots, m_p}$, where the subscripts $m_1, m_2, \cdots, m_p$ may take on any values from 0 to $+\infty$, or from $-\infty$ to $+\infty$, but may be restricted by certain inequalities. Although no such convenient geometrical form as that used above is available when the number of subscripts exceeds three, a slight consideration shows that the theorems proved for double series admit of immediate generalization to multiple series of any order p. Let us first suppose that all the elements $a_{m_1, m_2, \cdots, m_p}$ are real and positive. Let S_1 be the sum of a certain number of elements of the given series, S_2 the sum of S_1 and a certain number of terms previously neglected, S_3 the sum of S_2 and further terms, and so on, the successive sums $S_1, S_2, \cdots, S_n, \cdots$ being formed in such a way that any particular element of the given series occurs in all the sums past a certain one. If S_n approaches a limit S as n becomes infinite, the given series is said to be *convergent*, and S is called its *sum*. As in the case of double series, this limit is independent of the way in which the successive sums are formed.

If the elements of the given multiple series have different signs or are complex quantities, the series will still surely converge if the series of absolute values of the terms of the given series converges.

172. Generalization of Cauchy's theorem. The following theorem, which is a generalization of Cauchy's theorem (§ 161), enables us to determine in many cases whether a given multiple series is convergent or divergent. Let $f(x, y)$ be a function of the two variables x and y which is positive for all points (x, y) outside a certain closed curve Γ, and which steadily diminishes in value as the point (x, y) recedes from the origin.* Let us consider the value of the double integral $\int\int f(x, y)\, dx\, dy$ extended over the ring-shaped region between Γ and a variable curve C outside Γ, which we shall allow to recede indefinitely in all directions; and let us compare it with the double series $\Sigma f(m, n)$, where the subscripts m and n may assume any positive or negative integral values for which the point (m, n) lies outside the fixed curve Γ. Then *the double series converges if the double integral approaches a limit, and conversely.*

---

* All that is necessary for the present proof is that $f(x_1, y_1) \geqq f(x_2, y_2)$ whenever $x_1 \geqq x_2$ *and* $y_1 \geqq y_2$ outside Γ. It is easy to adapt the proof to still more general hypotheses. — TRANS.

The lines $x = 0, x = \pm 1, x = \pm 2, \cdots$ and $y = 0, y = \pm 1, y = \pm 2, \cdots$
divide the region between Γ and C into squares or portions of squares.
Selecting from the double series the term which corresponds to that
corner of each of these squares which is farthest from the origin, it
is evident that the sum $\Sigma f(m, n)$ of these terms will be less than the
value of the double integral $\int \int f(x, y)\, dx\, dy$ extended over the region
between Γ and C. If the double integral approaches a limit as C
recedes indefinitely in all directions, it follows that the sum of any
number of terms of the series whatever is always less than a fixed
number; hence the series converges. Similarly, if the double series
converges, the value of the double integral taken over any finite
region is always less than a fixed number; hence the integral
approaches a limit. The theorem may be extended to multiple
series of any order p, with suitable hypotheses; in that case the
integral of comparison is a multiple integral of order p.

As an example consider the double series whose general term is
$1/(m^2 + n^2)^\mu$, where the subscripts m and n may assume all integral
values from $-\infty$ to $+\infty$ except the values $m = n = 0$. This series
converges for $\mu > 1$, and diverges for $\mu \leq 1$. For the double integral

$$(34) \qquad \int \int \frac{dx\, dy}{(x^2 + y^2)^\mu}$$

extended over the region of the plane outside any circle whose
center is the origin has a definite value if $\mu > 1$ and becomes
infinite if $\mu \leq 1$ (§ 133).

More generally the multiple series whose general term is

$$\frac{1}{(m_1^2 + m_2^2 + \cdots + m_p^2)^\mu},$$

where the set of values $m_1 = m_2 = \cdots = m_p = 0$ is excluded, converges if $2\mu > p$.*

III. SERIES OF VARIABLE TERMS   UNIFORM CONVERGENCE

173. Definition of uniform convergence. A series of the form

$$(35) \qquad u_0(x) + u_1(x) + \cdots + u_n(x) + \cdots,$$

whose terms are continuous functions of a variable x in an interval (a, b), and which converges for every value of x belonging to
that interval, does not necessarily represent a continuous function,

* More general theorems are to be found in Jordan's *Cours d'Analyse*, Vol. I, p. 163.

as we might be tempted to believe. In order to prove the fact we
need only consider the series studied in § 4 :

$$x^2 + \frac{x^2}{1+x^2} + \frac{x^2}{(1+x^2)^2} + \cdots + \frac{x^2}{(1+x^2)^n} + \cdots,$$

which satisfies the above conditions, but whose sum is discontinuous
for $x = 0$. Since a large number of the functions which occur in
mathematics are defined by series, it has been found necessary to
study the properties of functions given in the form of a series. The
first question which arises is precisely that of determining whether
or not the sum of a given series is a continuous function of the
variable. Although no general solution of this problem is known,
its study has led to the development of the very important notion
of *uniform convergence.*

A series of the type (35), each of whose terms is a function of x
which is defined in an interval (a, b), is said to be *uniformly convergent* in that interval if it converges for every value of x between
a and b, and if, corresponding to any arbitrarily preassigned positive
number ϵ, a positive integer N, independent of x, can be found such
that the absolute value of the remainder R_n of the given series

$$R_n = u_{n+1}(x) + u_{n+2}(x) + \cdots + u_{n+p}(x) + \cdots$$

is less than ϵ for every value of $n \geq N$ and for every value of x
which lies in the interval (a, b).

The latter condition is essential in this definition. For any preassigned value of x for which the series converges it is apparent
from the very definition of convergence that, corresponding to any
positive number ϵ, a number N can be found which will satisfy
the condition in question. But, in order that the series should converge uniformly, it is necessary further that the same number N
should satisfy this condition, no matter what value of x be selected
in the interval (a, b). The following examples show that such is not
always the case. Thus in the series considered just above we have

$$R_n(x) = \frac{1}{(1+x^2)^n} \quad \text{when} \quad x \neq 0.$$

The series in question is not uniformly convergent in the interval $(0, 1)$. For, in order that it should be, it would be *necessary*
(though not sufficient) that a number N exist, such that

$$\frac{1}{(1+x^2)^N} < \epsilon$$

for all values of x in the interval $(0, 1)$, or, what amounts to the same thing, that

$$1 + x^2 > e^{\frac{1}{N} \log \frac{1}{\epsilon}}.$$

Whatever be the values of N and ϵ, there always exist, however, positive values of x which do not satisfy this inequality, since the right-hand side is greater than unity.

Again, consider the series defined by the equations

$$S_n(x) = nxe^{-nx^2}, \quad S_0(x) = 0, \quad u_n(x) = S_n - S_{n-1}, \quad n = 1, 2, \cdots.$$

The sum of the first n terms of this series is evidently $S_n(x)$, which approaches zero as n increases indefinitely. The series is therefore convergent, and the remainder $R_n(x)$ is equal to $-nxe^{-nx^2}$. In order that the series should be uniformly convergent in the interval $(0, 1)$, it would be necessary and sufficient that, corresponding to any arbitrarily preassigned positive number ϵ, a positive integer N exist such that for all values of $n \geq N$

$$nxe^{-nx^2} < \epsilon, \qquad 0 < x < 1.$$

But, if x be replaced by $1/n$, the left-hand side of this inequality is equal to $e^{-1/n}$, which is greater than $1/e$ whenever $n > 1$. Since ϵ may be chosen less than $1/e$, it follows that the given series is not uniformly convergent.

The importance of uniformly convergent series rests upon the following property:

The sum of a series whose terms are continuous functions of a variable x in an interval (a, b) and which converges uniformly in that interval, is itself a continuous function of x in the same interval.

Let x_0 be a value of x between a and b, and let $x_0 + h$ be a value in the neighborhood of x_0 which also lies between a and b. Let n be chosen so large that the remainder

$$R_n(x) = u_{n+1}(x) + u_{n+2}(x) + \cdots$$

is less than $\epsilon/3$ in absolute value for all values of x in the interval (a, b), where ϵ is an arbitrarily preassigned positive number. Let $f(x)$ be the sum of the given convergent series. Then we may write

$$f(x) = \phi(x) + R_n(x),$$

where $\phi(x)$ denotes the sum of the first $n + 1$ terms,

$$\phi(x) = u_0(x) + u_1(x) + \cdots + u_n(x).$$

Subtracting the two equalities

$$f(x_0) = \phi(x_0) + R_n(x_0),$$

$$f(x_0 + h) = \phi(x_0 + h) + R_n(x_0 + h),$$

we find

$$f(x_0 + h) - f(x_0) = [\phi(x_0 + h) - \phi(x_0)] + R_n(x_0 + h) - R_n(x_0).$$

The number n was so chosen that we have

$$|R_n(x_0)| < \frac{\epsilon}{3}, \qquad |R_n(x_0 + h)| < \frac{\epsilon}{3}.$$

On the other hand, since each of the terms of the series is a continuous function of x, $\phi(x)$ is itself a continuous function of x. Hence a positive number η may be found such that

$$|\phi(x_0 + h) - \phi(x_0)| < \frac{\epsilon}{3}$$

whenever $|h|$ is less than η. It follows that we shall have, *a fortiori*,

$$|f(x_0 + h) - f(x_0)| < 3\,\frac{\epsilon}{3}$$

whenever $|h|$ is less than η. This shows that $f(x)$ is continuous for $x = x_0$.

Note. It would seem at first very difficult to determine whether or not a given series is uniformly convergent in a given interval. The following theorem enables us to show in many cases that a given series converges uniformly.

Let

$$(36) \qquad u_0(x) + u_1(x) + \cdots + u_n(x) + \cdots$$

be a series each of whose terms is a continuous function of x in an interval (a, b), and let

$$(37) \qquad M_0 + M_1 + \cdots + M_n + \cdots$$

be a convergent series whose terms are positive constants. Then, if $|u_n| \leq M_n$ for all values of x in the interval (a, b) and for all values of n, the first series (36) converges uniformly in the interval considered.

For it is evident that we shall have

$$|u_{n+1} + u_{n+2} + \cdots| \leq M_{n+1} + M_{n+2} + \cdots$$

for all values of x between a and b. If N be chosen so large that the remainder R_n of the second series is less than ϵ for all values of n greater than N, we shall also have

$$|u_{n+1} + u_{n+2} + \cdots| < \epsilon,$$

whenever n is greater than N, for all values of x in the interval (a, b). For example, the series

$$M_0 + M_1 \sin x + M_2 \sin 2x + \cdots + M_n \sin nx + \cdots,$$

where M_0, M_1, M_2, $\cdots$ have the same meaning as above, converges uniformly in any interval whatever.

174. Integration and differentiation of series.

Any series of continuous functions which converges uniformly in an interval (a, b) may be integrated term by term, provided the limits of integration are finite and lie in the interval (a, b).

Let x_0 and x_1 be any two values of x which lie between a and b, and let N be a positive integer such that $|R_n(x)| < \epsilon$ for all values of x in the interval (a, b) whenever $n \geq N$. Let $f(x)$ be the sum of the series

$$f(x) = u_0(x) + u_1(x) + \cdots + u_n(x) + \cdots,$$

and let us set

$$D_n = \int_{x_0}^{x_1} f(x)\,dx - \int_{x_0}^{x_1} u_0\,dx - \int_{x_0}^{x_1} u_1\,dx - \cdots - \int_{x_0}^{x_1} u_n\,dx = \int_{x_0}^{x_1} R_n\,dx.$$

The absolute value of D_n is less than $\epsilon |x_1 - x_0|$ whenever $n \geq N$. Hence D_n approaches zero as n increases indefinitely, and we have the equation

$$\int_{x_0}^{x_1} f(x)\,dx = \int_{x_0}^{x_1} u_0(x)\,dx + \int_{x_0}^{x_1} u_1(x)\,dx + \cdots + \int_{x_0}^{x_1} u_n(x)\,dx + \cdots.$$

Considering x_0 as fixed and x_1 as variable, we obtain a series

$$\int_{x_0}^{x} u_0(x)\,dx + \cdots + \int_{x_0}^{x} u_n(x)\,dx + \cdots$$

which converges uniformly in the interval (a, b) and represents a continuous function whose derivative is $f(x)$.

*Conversely, any convergent series may be differentiated term by term if the resulting series converges uniformly.**

For, let

$$f(x) = u_0(x) + u_1(x) + \cdots + u_n(x) + \cdots$$

be a series which converges in the interval (a, b). Let us suppose that the series whose terms are the derivatives of the terms of the given series, respectively, converges uniformly in the same interval, and let $\phi(x)$ denote the sum of the new series

$$\phi(x) = \frac{d u_0}{dx} + \frac{d u_1}{dx} + \cdots + \frac{d u_n}{dx} + \cdots.$$

Integrating this series term by term between two limits x_0 and x, each of which lies between a and b, we find

$$\int_{x_0}^{x} \phi(x)\, dx = [u_0(x) - u_0(x_0)] + [u_1(x) - u_1(x_0)] + \cdots$$

or

$$\int_{x_0}^{x} \phi(x)\, dx = f(x) - f(x_0).$$

This shows that $\phi(x)$ is the derivative of $f(x)$.

Examples. 1) The integral

$$\int \frac{e^x}{x}\, dx$$

cannot be expressed by means of a finite number of elementary functions. Let us write it as follows:

$$\int \frac{e^x}{x}\, dx = \int \frac{dx}{x} + \int \frac{e^x - 1}{x}\, dx = \log x + \int \frac{e^x - 1}{x}\, dx.$$

The last integral may be developed in a series which holds for all values of x. For we have

$$\frac{e^x - 1}{x} = 1 + \frac{x}{1 \cdot 2} + \frac{x^2}{1 \cdot 2 \cdot 3} + \cdots + \frac{x^{n-1}}{1 \cdot 2 \cdots n} + \cdots,$$

and this series converges uniformly in the interval from $- R$ to $+ R$, no matter how large R be taken, since the absolute value of any

---

* It is assumed in the proof also that each term of the new series is a continuous function. The theorem is true, however, in general. — TRANS.

term of the series is less than the corresponding term of the convergent series

$$1 + \frac{R}{1.2} + \cdots + \frac{R^{n-1}}{1.2 \cdots n} + \cdots.$$

It follows that the series obtained by term-by-term integration

$$F(x) = 1 + \frac{x}{1} + \frac{1}{2}\frac{x^2}{1.2} + \cdots + \frac{1}{n}\frac{x^n}{1.2 \cdots n} + \cdots$$

converges for any value of x and represents a function whose derivative is $(e^x - 1)/x$.

2) The perimeter of an ellipse whose major axis is $2a$ and whose eccentricity is e is equal, by § 112, to the definite integral

$$S = 4a \int_0^{\frac{\pi}{2}} \sqrt{1 - e^2 \sin^2 \phi}\, d\phi.$$

The product $e^2 \sin^2 \phi$ lies between 0 and $e^2 (< 1)$. Hence the radical is equal to the sum of the series given by the binomial theorem

$$\sqrt{1 - e^2 \sin^2 \phi} = 1 - \frac{1}{2} e^2 \sin^2 \phi - \frac{1}{2.4} e^4 \sin^4 \phi - \cdots$$
$$- \frac{1.3.5 \cdots (2n-3)}{2.4.6 \cdots 2n} e^{2n} \sin^{2n} \phi - \cdots.$$

The series on the right converges uniformly, for the absolute value of each of its terms is less than the corresponding term of the convergent series obtained by setting $\sin \phi = 1$. Hence the series may be integrated term by term; and since, by § 116,

$$\int_0^{\frac{\pi}{2}} \sin^{2n} \phi\, d\phi = \frac{1.3.5 \cdots (2n-1)}{2.4.6 \cdots 2n}\, \frac{\pi}{2},$$

we shall have

$$\int_0^{\frac{\pi}{2}} \sqrt{1 - e^2 \sin^2 \phi}\, d\phi = \frac{\pi}{2}\left\{ 1 - \frac{1}{4} e^2 - \frac{3}{64} e^4 - \frac{5}{256} e^6 - \cdots \right.$$
$$\left. - \left[\frac{1.3.5 \cdots (2n-3)}{2.4.6 \cdots 2n} \right]^2 (2n-1) e^{2n} - \cdots \right\}.$$

If the eccentricity e is small, a very good approximation to the exact value of the integral is obtained by computing a few terms.

Similarly, we may develop the integral

$$\int_0^{\phi} \sqrt{1 - e^2 \sin^2 \phi}\, d\phi$$

in a series for any value of the upper limit ϕ.

Finally, the development of Legendre's complete integral of the first kind leads to the formula

$$\int_0^{\frac{\pi}{2}} \frac{d\phi}{\sqrt{1 - e^2 \sin^2 \phi}} = \frac{\pi}{2}\left\{ 1 + \frac{1}{4} e^2 + \frac{9}{64} e^4 + \cdots + \left[\frac{1.3.5 \cdots (2n-1)}{2.4.6 \cdots 2n} \right]^2 e^{2n} + \cdots \right\}.$$

The definition of uniform convergence may be extended to series whose terms are functions of several independent variables. For example, let

$$u_0(x, y) + u_1(x, y) + \cdots + u_n(x, y) + \cdots$$

be a series whose terms are functions of two independent variables x and y, and let us suppose that this series converges whenever the point (x, y) lies in a region R bounded by a closed contour C. The series is said to be *uniformly convergent* in the region R if, corresponding to every positive number ϵ, an integer N can be found such that the absolute value of the remainder R_n is less than ϵ whenever n is equal to or greater than N, for every point (x, y) inside the contour C. It can be shown as above that the sum of such a series is a continuous function of the two variables x and y in this region, provided the terms of the series are all continuous in R.

The theorem on term-by-term integration also may be generalized. If each of the terms of the series is continuous in R and if $f(x, y)$ denotes the sum of the series, we shall have

$$\iint f(x, y)\, dx\, dy = \iint u_0(x, y)\, dx\, dy + \iint u_1(x, y)\, dx\, dy + \cdots$$
$$+ \iint u_n(x, y)\, dx\, dy + \cdots,$$

where each of the double integrals is extended over the whole interior of any contour inside of the region R.

Again, let us consider a double series whose elements are functions of one or more variables and which converges absolutely for all sets of values of those variables inside of a certain domain D. Let the elements of the series be arranged in the ordinary rectangular array, and let R_c denote the sum of the double series outside any closed curve C drawn in the plane of the array. Then the given double series is said to *converge uniformly* in the domain D if corresponding to any preassigned number ϵ, a closed curve K, not dependent on the values of the variables, can be drawn such that $|R_c| < \epsilon$ for any curve C whatever lying outside of K and for any set of values of the variables inside the domain D.

It is evident that the preceding definitions and theorems may be extended without difficulty to a multiple series of any order whose elements are functions of any number of variables.

Note. If a series does not converge uniformly, it is not always allowable to integrate it term by term. For example, let us set

$$S_n(x) = nxe^{-nx^2}, \qquad S_0(x) = 0, \qquad u_n(x) = S_n - S_{n-1}. \qquad n = 1, 2, \cdots.$$

The series whose general term is $u_n(x)$ converges, and its sum is zero, since $S_n(x)$ approaches zero as n becomes infinite. Hence we may write

$$f(x) = 0 = u_1(x) + u_2(x) + \cdots + u_n(x) + \cdots,$$

whence $\int_0^1 f(x)\,dx = 0$. On the other hand, if we integrate the series term by term between the limits zero and unity, we obtain a new series for which the sum of the first n terms is

$$\int_0^1 S_n(x)\,dx = -\left[\frac{e^{-nx^2}}{2}\right]_0^1 = \frac{1}{2}(1 - e^{-n}),$$

which approaches $1/2$ as its limit as n becomes infinite.

175. Application to differentiation under the integral sign. The proof of the formula for differentiation under the integral sign given in § 97 is based essentially upon the supposition that the limits x_0 and X are finite. If X is infinite, the formula does not always hold. Let us consider, for example, the integral

$$F(\alpha) = \int_0^{+\infty} \frac{\sin \alpha x}{x}\,dx, \qquad \alpha > 0.$$

This integral does not depend on α, for if we make the substitution $y = \alpha x$ it becomes

$$F(\alpha) = \int_0^{+\infty} \frac{\sin y}{y}\,dy.$$

If we tried to apply the ordinary formula for differentiation to $F(\alpha)$, we should find

$$F'(\alpha) = \int_0^{+\infty} \cos \alpha x\,dx$$

This is surely incorrect, for the left-hand side is zero, while the right-hand side has no definite value.

Sufficient conditions may be found for the application of the ordinary formula for differentiation, even when one of the limits is infinite, by connecting the subject with the study of series. Let us first consider the integral

$$\int_{a_0}^{+\infty} f(x)\,dx,$$

which we shall suppose to have a determinate value (§ 90). Let $a_1, a_2, \cdots, a_n, \cdots$ be an infinite increasing sequence of numbers, all greater than a_0, where a_n becomes infinite with n. If we set

$$U_0 = \int_{a_0}^{a_1} f(x)\,dx, \quad U_1 = \int_{a_1}^{a_2} f(x)\,dx, \quad \cdots, \quad U_n = \int_{a_n}^{a_{n+1}} f(x)\,dx, \quad \cdots,$$

the series

$$U_0 + U_1 + U_2 + \cdots + U_n + \cdots$$

converges and its sum is $\int_{a_0}^{+\infty} f(x)\,dx$, for the sum S_n of the first n terms is equal to $\int_{a_0}^{a_n} f(x)\,dx$.

It should be noticed that the converse is not always true. If, for example, we set

$$f(x) = \cos x, \quad a_0 = 0, \quad a_1 = \pi, \quad \cdots, \quad a_n = n\pi, \quad \cdots,$$

we shall have

$$U_n = \int_{n\pi}^{(n+1)\pi} \cos x\,dx = 0.$$

Hence the series converges, whereas the integral $\int_0^l \cos x\,dx$ approaches no limit whatever as l becomes infinite.

Now let $f(x, \alpha)$ be a function of the two variables x and α which is continuous whenever x is equal to or greater than a_0 and α lies in an interval (α_0, α_1). If the integral $\int_{a_0}^l f(x, \alpha)\,dx$ approaches a limit as l becomes infinite, for any value of α, that limit is a function of α,

$$F(\alpha) = \int_{a_0}^{+\infty} f(x, \alpha)\,dx,$$

which may be replaced, as we have just shown, by the sum of a convergent series whose terms are continuous functions of α:

$$F(\alpha) = U_0(\alpha) + U_1(\alpha) + \cdots + U_n(\alpha) + \cdots,$$

$$U_0(\alpha) = \int_{a_0}^{a_1} f(x, \alpha)\,dx, \qquad U_1(\alpha) = \int_{a_1}^{a_2} f(x, \alpha)\,dx, \qquad \cdots.$$

This function $F(\alpha)$ is continuous whenever the series converges uniformly. By analogy we shall say that *the integral* $\int_{a_0}^{+\infty} f(x, \alpha)\,dx$ *converges uniformly* in the interval (α_0, α_1) if, corresponding to any preassigned positive quantity ϵ, a number N independent of α can be found such that $\left| \int_l^{+\infty} f(x, \alpha)\,dx \right| < \epsilon$ whenever $l \geqq N$, for any value of α which lies in the interval (α_0, α_1).[*]   If the integral converges

---

uniformly, the series will also.   For if a_n be taken greater than N, we shall have

$$|R_n| = \left| \int_{a_n}^{+\infty} f(x, \alpha) \, dx \right| < \epsilon;$$

hence the function $F(\alpha)$ is continuous in this case throughout the interval (α_0, α_1).

Let us now suppose that the derivative $\partial f / \partial \alpha$ is a continuous function of x and α when $x \geqq a_0$ and $\alpha_0 \leqq \alpha \leqq \alpha_1$, that the integral

$$\int_{a_0}^{+\infty} \frac{\partial f}{\partial \alpha} \, dx$$

has a finite value for every value of α in the interval (α_0, α_1), and that the integral converges uniformly in that interval.   The integral in question may be replaced by the sum of the series

$$\int_{a_0}^{+\infty} \frac{\partial f}{\partial \alpha} \, dx = V_0(\alpha) + V_1(\alpha) + \cdots + V_n(\alpha) + \cdots,$$

where

$$V_0 = \int_{a_0}^{a_1} \frac{\partial f}{\partial \alpha} \, dx, \quad \cdots, \quad V_n = \int_{a_n}^{a_{n+1}} \frac{\partial f}{\partial \alpha} \, dx, \quad \cdots.$$

The new series converges uniformly, and its terms are equal to the corresponding terms of the preceding series.   Hence, by the theorem proved above for the differentiation of series, we may write

$$F'(\alpha) = \int_{a_0}^{+\infty} \frac{\partial f}{\partial \alpha} \, dx.$$

In other words, *the formula for differentiation under the integral sign still holds, provided that the integral on the right converges uniformly.*

The formula for integration under the integral sign (§ 123) also may be extended to the case in which one of the limits becomes infinite.   Let $f(x, \alpha)$ be a continuous function of the two variables x and α, for $x \geqq a_0$, $\alpha_0 \leqq \alpha \leqq \alpha_1$.   If the integral $\int_{a_0}^{+\infty} f(x, \alpha) \, dx$ is uniformly convergent in the interval (α_0, α_1), we shall have

(A) $$\int_{a_0}^{+\infty} dx \int_{\alpha_0}^{\alpha_1} f(x, \alpha) \, d\alpha = \int_{\alpha_0}^{\alpha_1} d\alpha \int_{a_0}^{+\infty} f(x, \alpha) \, dx.$$

To prove this, let us first select a number $l > a_0$; then we shall have

(B) $$\int_{a_0}^{l} dx \int_{\alpha_0}^{\alpha_1} f(x, \alpha) \, d\alpha = \int_{\alpha_0}^{\alpha_1} d\alpha \int_{a_0}^{l} f(x, \alpha) \, dx.$$

As l increases indefinitely the right-hand side of this equation approaches the double integral

$$\int_{\alpha_0}^{\alpha_1} d\alpha \int_{a_0}^{+\infty} f(x, \alpha)\, dx,$$

for the difference between these two double integrals is equal to

$$\int_{\alpha_0}^{\alpha_1} d\alpha \int_{l}^{+\infty} f(x, \alpha)\, dx.$$

Suppose N chosen so large that the absolute value of the integral $\int_{l}^{+\infty} f(x, \alpha)\, dx$ is less than ϵ whenever l is greater than N, for any value of α in the interval (α_0, α_1). Then the absolute value of the difference in question will be less than $\epsilon |\alpha_1 - \alpha_0|$, and therefore it will approach zero as l increases indefinitely. Hence the left-hand side of the equation (B) also approaches a limit as l becomes infinite, and this limit is represented by the symbol

$$\int_{a_0}^{+\infty} dx \int_{\alpha_0}^{\alpha_1} f(x, \alpha)\, d\alpha.$$

This gives the formula (A) which was to be proved.*

176. Examples. 1) Let us return to the integral of § 91:

$$F(\alpha) = \int_0^{+\infty} e^{-\alpha x} \frac{\sin x}{x}\, dx,$$

where α is positive. The integral

$$-\int_0^{+\infty} e^{-\alpha x} \sin x\, dx,$$

---

* The formula for differentiation may be deduced easily from the formula (A). For, suppose that the two functions $f(x, \alpha)$ and $f_\alpha(x, \alpha)$ are continuous for $\alpha_0 \leqq \alpha \leqq \alpha_1$, $x \geqq a_0$; that the two integrals $F(\alpha) = \int_{a_0}^{+\infty} f(x, \alpha)\, dx$ and $\Phi(\alpha) = \int_{a_0}^{+\infty} f_\alpha(x, \alpha)\, dx$ have finite values; and that the latter converges uniformly in the interval (α_0, α_1). From the formula (A), if α lies in the interval (α_0, α_1), we have

$$\int_{\alpha_0}^{\alpha} du \int_{a_0}^{+\infty} f_u(x, u)\, dx = \int_{a_0}^{+\infty} dx \int_{\alpha_0}^{\alpha} f_u(x, u)\, du,$$

where for distinctness α has been replaced by u under the integral sign. But this formula may be written in the form

$$\int_{\alpha_0}^{\alpha} \Phi(u)\, du = \int_{a_0}^{+\infty} f(x, \alpha)\, dx - \int_{a_0}^{+\infty} f(x, \alpha_0)\, dx = F(\alpha) - F(\alpha_0),$$

whence, taking the derivative of each side with respect to α, we find

$$F'(\alpha) = \Phi(\alpha).$$

obtained by differentiating under the integral sign with respect to α, converges uniformly for all values of α greater than an arbitrary positive number k. For we have

$$\left| \int_l^{+\infty} e^{-\alpha x} \sin x \, dx \right| < \int_l^{+\infty} e^{-\alpha x} \, dx = \frac{1}{\alpha} e^{-\alpha l},$$

and hence the absolute value of the integral on the left will be less than ϵ for all values of α greater than k, if $l \geqq N$, where N is chosen so large that $ke^{kN} > 1/\epsilon$. It follows that

$$F'(\alpha) = - \int_0^{+\infty} e^{-\alpha x} \sin x \, dx.$$

The indefinite integral was calculated in § 119 and gives

$$F'(\alpha) = \left[\frac{e^{-\alpha x} (\cos x + \alpha \sin x)}{1 + \alpha^2} \right]_0^{+\infty} = \frac{-1}{1 + \alpha^2},$$

whence we find

$$F(\alpha) = C - \arctan \alpha,$$

and the constant C may be determined by noting that the definite integral $F(\alpha)$ approaches zero as α becomes infinite. Hence $C = \pi/2$, and we finally find the formula

$$(38) \qquad \int_0^{+\infty} e^{-\alpha x} \frac{\sin x}{x} \, dx = \arctan \frac{1}{\alpha}.$$

This formula is established only for positive values of α, but we saw in § 91 that the left-hand side is the sum of an alternating series whose remainder R_n is always less than $1/n$. Hence the series converges uniformly, and the integral is a continuous function of α, even for $\alpha = 0$. As α approaches zero we shall have in the limit

$$(39) \qquad \int_0^{+\infty} \frac{\sin x}{x} \, dx = \frac{\pi}{2}.$$

2) If in the formula

$$\int_0^{+\infty} e^{-x^2} \, dx = \frac{\sqrt{\pi}}{2}$$

of § 134 we set $x = y \sqrt{\alpha}$, where α is positive, we find

$$(40) \qquad \int_0^{+\infty} e^{-\alpha y^2} \, dy = \frac{\sqrt{\pi}}{2} \alpha^{-\frac{1}{2}},$$

and it is easy to show that all the integrals derived from this one by successive differentiations with respect to the parameter α converge uniformly, provided that α is always greater than a certain positive constant k. From the preceding formula we may deduce the values of a whole series of integrals:

$$(41) \qquad \begin{cases} \displaystyle\int_0^{+\infty} y^2 \, e^{-\alpha y^2} \, dy = \frac{\sqrt{\pi}}{2^2} \alpha^{-\frac{3}{2}}, \\[2mm] \displaystyle\int_0^{+\infty} y^4 \, e^{-\alpha y^2} \, dy = \frac{1 \cdot 3}{2^3} \sqrt{\pi} \alpha^{-\frac{5}{2}}, \\[1mm] \cdot \quad \cdot \quad \cdot \quad \cdot \quad \cdot \quad \cdot \quad \cdot \quad \cdot \quad \cdot \quad \cdot \quad \cdot \quad \cdot, \\[1mm] \displaystyle\int_0^{+\infty} y^{2n} e^{-\alpha y^2} \, dy = \frac{1 \cdot 3 \cdot 5 \cdots (2n-1)}{2^{n+1}} \sqrt{\pi} \alpha^{-\frac{2n+1}{2}}. \end{cases}$$

By combining these an infinite number of other integrals may be evaluated. We have, for example,

$$\int_0^{+\infty} e^{-\alpha y^2} \cos 2\beta y \, dy = \int_0^{+\infty} e^{-\alpha y^2} dy \left[1 - \frac{(2\beta y)^2}{1 \cdot 2} + \cdots + (-1)^n \frac{(2\beta y)^{2n}}{1 \cdot 2 \cdots 2n} + \cdots \right]$$

$$= \int_0^{+\infty} e^{-\alpha y^2} dy - \int_0^{+\infty} e^{-\alpha y^2} \frac{(2\beta y)^2}{1 \cdot 2} dy + \cdots$$

$$+ (-1)^n \int_0^{+\infty} e^{-\alpha y^2} \frac{(2\beta y)^{2n}}{1 \cdot 2 \cdots 2n} dy + \cdots.$$

All the integrals on the right have been evaluated above, and we find

$$\int_0^{+\infty} e^{-\alpha y^2} \cos 2\beta y \, dy = \frac{1}{2} \sqrt{\frac{\pi}{\alpha}} - \frac{(2\beta)^2}{1 \cdot 2} \frac{\sqrt{\pi}}{2} \frac{\alpha^{-\frac{3}{2}}}{2} + \cdots$$

$$+ (-1)^n \frac{(2\beta)^{2n}}{1 \cdot 2 \cdot 3 \cdots 2n} \frac{\sqrt{\pi}}{2} \frac{1 \cdot 3 \cdot 5 \cdots (2n-1)}{2^n} \alpha^{-\frac{2n+1}{2}} + \cdots,$$

or, simplifying,

$$(42) \qquad \int_0^{+\infty} e^{-\alpha y^2} \cos 2\beta y \, dy = \frac{1}{2} \sqrt{\frac{\pi}{\alpha}} \, e^{-\frac{\beta^2}{\alpha}}.$$

EXERCISES

1. Derive the formula

$$\frac{1}{1 \cdot 2 \cdots n} \frac{d^n}{dx^n} [x^n (\log x)^n] = 1 + S_1 \log x + \frac{S_2}{1 \cdot 2} (\log x)^2 + \cdots + \frac{S_n}{1 \cdot 2 \cdots n} (\log x)^n,$$

where S_p denotes the sum of the products of the first n natural numbers taken p at a time.

[Murphy.]

[Start with the formula

$$x^{n+\alpha} = x^n \left[1 + \alpha \log x + \frac{\alpha^2 (\log x)^2}{1 \cdot 2} + \cdots + \frac{\alpha^n (\log x)^n}{1 \cdot 2 \cdots n} + \cdots \right]$$

and differentiate n times with respect to x.]

2. Calculate the value of the definite integral

$$\int_0^{+\infty} \frac{1 - e^{-x^2}}{x^2} dx$$

by means of the formula for differentiation under the integral sign.

3. Derive the formula

$$I = \int_0^{+\infty} e^{-x^2 - \frac{a^2}{x^2}} dx = \frac{\sqrt{\pi}}{2} e^{-2a}.$$

[First show that $dI/da = -2I$.]

4. Derive the formula

$$\int_0^{+\infty} e^{-\alpha - \frac{k^2}{\alpha}} \frac{d\alpha}{\sqrt{\alpha}} = \sqrt{\pi}\, e^{-2k}$$

by making use of the preceding exercise.

5. From the relation

$$\frac{1}{a^3} = \frac{1}{2} \int_0^{+\infty} x^2 e^{-ax}\, dx$$

derive the formula

$$\sum_{n=1}^{+\infty} \frac{1}{n^3} = \frac{1}{2} \int_0^{+\infty} \frac{x^2\, dx}{e^x - 1}.$$

CHAPTER IX

POWER SERIES   TRIGONOMETRIC SERIES

In this chapter we shall study two particularly important classes of series—power series and trigonometric series. Although we shall speak of real variables only, the arguments used in the study of power series are applicable without change to the case where the variables are complex quantities, by simply substituting the expression *modulus* or *absolute value* (of a complex variable) for the expression *absolute value* (of a real variable).*

I. POWER SERIES OF A SINGLE VARIABLE

177. Interval of convergence. Let us first consider a series of the form

$$(1) \qquad A_0 + A_1 X + A_2 X^2 + \cdots + A_n X^n + \cdots,$$

where the coefficients A_0, A_1, A_2, $\cdots$ are all positive, and where the independent variable X is assigned only positive values. It is evident that each of the terms increases with X. Hence, if the series converges for any particular value of X, say X_1, it converges *a fortiori* for any value of X less than X_1. Conversely, if the series diverges for the value X_2, it surely diverges for any value of X greater than X_2. We shall distinguish the following cases.

1) The series (1) may converge for any value of X whatever. Such is the case, for example, for the series

$$1 + \frac{X}{1} + \frac{X^2}{1 \cdot 2} + \cdots + \frac{X^n}{1 \cdot 2 \cdots n} + \cdots.$$

2) The series (1) may diverge for any value of X except $X = 0$ The following series, for example, has this property:

$$1 + X + 1 \cdot 2 X^2 + \cdots + 1 \cdot 2 \cdot 3 \cdots n X^n + \cdots.$$

3) Finally, let us suppose that the series converges for certain values of X and diverges for other values. Let X_1 be a value of X for which it converges, and let X_2 be a value for which it diverges.

* See Vol. II, §§ 266–275. — TRANS.

From the remark made above, it follows that X_1 is less than X_2. The series converges if $X < X_1$, and it diverges if $X > X_2$. The only uncertainty is about the values of X between X_1 and X_2. But all the values of X for which the series converges are less than X_2, and hence they have an upper limit, which we shall call R. Since all the values of X for which the series diverges are greater than any value of X for which it converges, the number R is also the lower limit of the values of X for which the series diverges. *Hence the series* (1) *diverges for all values of X greater than R, and converges for all values of X less than R.* It may either converge or diverge when $X = R$.

For example, the series

$$1 + X + X^2 + \cdots + X^n + \cdots$$

converges if $X < 1$, and diverges if $X \geqq 1$. In this case $R = 1$.

This third case may be said to include the other two by supposing that R may be zero or may become infinite.

Let us now consider a *power series*, i.e. a series of the form

$$(2) \qquad a_0 + a_1 x + a_2 x^2 + \cdots + a_n x^n + \cdots,$$

where the coefficients a_i and the variable x may have any real values whatever. From now on we shall set $A_i = |a_i|$, $X = |x|$. Then the series (1) is the series of absolute values of the terms of the series (2). Let R be the number defined above for the series (1). Then the series (2) evidently converges absolutely for any value of x between $-R$ and $+R$, by the very definition of the number R. It remains to be shown that the series (2) diverges for any value of x whose absolute value exceeds R. This follows immediately from a fundamental theorem due to Abel: *

If the series (2) *converges for any particular value x_0, it converges absolutely for any values of x whose absolute value is less than $|x_0|$.*

In order to prove this theorem, let us suppose that the series (2) converges for $x = x_0$, and let M be a positive number greater than the absolute value of any term of the series for that value of x. Then we shall have, for any value of n,

$$A_n |x_0|^n < M,$$

and we may write

$$A_n X^n = A_n |x_0|^n \left(\frac{X}{|x_0|}\right)^n < M\left(\frac{X}{|x_0|}\right)^n.$$

---

* *Recherche sur la série* $1 + \dfrac{m}{1} x + \dfrac{m(m-1)}{1.2} x^2 + \cdots.$

It follows that the series (1) converges whenever $X < |x_0|$, which proves the theorem.

In other words, if the series (2) converges for $x = x_0$, the series (1) of absolute values converges whenever X is less than $|x_0|$. Hence $|x_0|$ cannot exceed R, for R was supposed to be the upper limit of the values of X for which the series (1) converges.

To sum up, given a power series (2) whose coefficients may have either sign, there exists a positive number R which has the following properties : *The series (2) converges absolutely for any value of x between $- R$ and $+ R$, and diverges for any value of x whose absolute value exceeds R.* The interval $(- R, + R)$ is called the *interval of convergence*. This interval extends from $- \infty$ to $+ \infty$ in the case in which R is conceived to have become infinite, and reduces to the origin if $R = 0$. The latter case will be neglected in what follows.

The preceding demonstration gives us no information about what happens when $x = R$ or $x = - R$. The series (2) may be absolutely convergent, simply convergent, or divergent. For example, $R = 1$ for each of the three series

$$1 + x + x^2 + \cdots + x^n + \cdots,$$

$$1 + \frac{x}{1} + \frac{x^2}{2} + \cdots + \frac{x^n}{n} + \cdots,$$

$$1 + \frac{x}{1^2} + \frac{x^2}{2^2} + \cdots + \frac{x^n}{n^2} + \cdots,$$

for the ratio of any term to the preceding approaches x as its limit in each case. The first series diverges for $x = \pm 1$. The second series diverges for $x = 1$, and converges for $x = - 1$. The third converges absolutely for $x = \pm 1$.

Note. The statement of Abel's theorem may be made more general, for it is sufficient for the argument that the absolute value of any term of the series

$$a_0 + a_1 x_0 + \cdots + a_n x_0^n + \cdots$$

be less than a fixed number. Whenever this condition is satisfied, the series (2) converges absolutely for any value of x whose absolute value is less than $|x_0|$.

The number R is connected in a very simple way with the number ω defined in § 160, which is the *greatest limit* of the sequence

$$A_1, \quad \sqrt{A_2}, \quad \sqrt[3]{A_3}, \quad \cdots, \quad \sqrt[n]{A_n}, \quad \cdots.$$

For if we consider the analogous sequence

$$A_1 X, \quad \sqrt{A_2 X^2}, \quad \sqrt[3]{A_3 X^3}, \quad \cdots, \quad \sqrt[n]{A_n X^n}, \quad \cdots,$$

it is evident that the greatest limit of the terms of the new sequence is ωX. The sequence (1) therefore converges if $X < 1/\omega$, and diverges if $X > 1/\omega$; hence $R = 1/\omega$.*

178. Continuity of a power series. Let $f(x)$ be the sum of a power series which converges in the interval from $-R$ to $+R$,

$$(3) \qquad f(x) = a_0 + a_1 x + \cdots + a_n x^n + \cdots,$$

and let R' be a positive number less than R. We shall first show that the series (3) converges uniformly in the interval from $-R'$ to $+R'$. For, if the absolute value of x is less than R', the remainder R_n

$$R_n = a_{n+1} x^{n+1} + \cdots + a_{n+p} x^{n+p} + \cdots$$

of the series (3) is less in absolute value than the remainder

$$A_{n+1} R'^{n+1} + A_{n+2} R'^{n+2} + \cdots$$

of the corresponding series (1). But the series (1) converges for $X = R'$, since $R' < R$. Consequently a number N may be found such that the latter remainder will be less than any preassigned positive number ϵ whenever $n \geqq N$. Hence $|R_n| < \epsilon$ whenever $n \geqq N$ provided that $|x| < R'$.

It follows that *the sum $f(x)$ of the given series is a continuous function of x for all values of x between $-R$ and $+R$*. For, let x_0 be any number whose absolute value is less than R. It is evident that a number R' may be found which is less than R and greater than $|x_0|$. Then the series converges uniformly in the interval $(-R', +R')$, as we have just seen, and hence the sum $f(x)$ of the series is continuous for the value x_0, since x_0 belongs to the interval in question.

This proof does not apply to the end points $+R$ and $-R$ of the interval of convergence. The function $f(x)$ remains continuous, however, provided that the series converges for those values. Indeed, Abel showed that *if the series (3) converges for $x = R$, its sum for $x = R$ is the limit which the sum $f(x)$ of the series approaches as x approaches R through values less than R.*†

Let S be the sum of the convergent series

$$S = a_0 + a_1 R + a_2 R^2 + \cdots + a_n R^n + \cdots,$$

---

* This theorem was proved by Cauchy in his *Cours d'Analyse*. It was rediscovered by Hadamard in his thesis.

† As stated above, these theorems can be immediately generalized to the case of series of imaginary terms. In this case, however, care is necessary in formulating the generalization. See Vol. II, § 266. — TRANS.

and let n be a positive integer such that any one of the sums

$$a_{n+1}R^{n+1}, \quad a_{n+1}R^{n+1} + a_{n+2}R^{n+2}, \quad \cdots,$$
$$a_{n+1}R^{n+1} + \cdots + a_{n+p}R^{n+p}, \quad \cdots$$

is less than a preassigned positive number ϵ. If we set $x = R\theta$, and then let θ increase from 0 to 1, x will increase from 0 to R, and we shall have

$$f(x) = f(\theta R) = a_0 + a_1\theta R + a_2\theta^2 R^2 + \cdots + a_n\theta^n R^n + \cdots.$$

If n be chosen as above, we may write

$$(4) \begin{cases} S - f(x) = a_1 R(1 - \theta) + a_2 R^2(1 - \theta^2) + \cdots + a_n R^n(1 - \theta^n) \\ \quad + a_{n+1}R^{n+1} + \cdots + a_{n+p}R^{n+p} + \cdots \\ \quad - a_{n+1}\theta^{n+1}R^{n+1} - \cdots - a_{n+p}\theta^{n+p}R^{n+p} - \cdots, \end{cases}$$

and the absolute value of the sum of the series in the second line cannot exceed ϵ. On the other hand, the numbers θ^{n+1}, θ^{n+2}, $\cdots$, θ^{n+p} form a decreasing sequence. Hence, by Abel's lemma proved in § 75, we shall have

$$|a_{n+1}\theta^{n+1}R^{n+1} + \cdots + a_{n+p}\theta^{n+p}R^{n+p}| < \theta^{n+1}\epsilon < \epsilon.$$

It follows that the absolute value of the sum of the series in the third line cannot exceed ϵ. Finally, the first line of the right-hand side of the equation (4) is a polynomial of degree n in θ which vanishes when $\theta = 1$. Therefore another positive number η may be found such that the absolute value of this polynomial is less than ϵ whenever θ lies between $1 - \eta$ and unity. Hence for all such values of θ we shall have

$$|S - f(x)| < 3\epsilon.$$

But ϵ is an arbitrarily preassigned positive number. Hence $f(x)$ approaches S as its limit as x approaches R.

In a similar manner it may be shown that if the series (3) converges for $x = -R$, the sum of the series for $x = -R$ is equal to the limit which $f(x)$ approaches as x approaches $-R$ through values greater than $-R$. Indeed, if we replace x by $-x$, this case reduces to the preceding.

An application. This theorem enables us to complete the results of § 168 regarding the multiplication of series. Let

$$(5) \qquad S = u_0 + u_1 + u_2 + \cdots + u_n + \cdots,$$
$$(6) \qquad S' = v_0 + v_1 + v_2 + \cdots + v_n + \cdots$$

be two convergent series, neither of which converges absolutely. The series

$$(7) \qquad u_0 v_0 + (u_0 v_1 + u_1 v_0) + \cdots + (u_0 v_n + \cdots + u_n v_0) + \cdots$$

may converge or diverge. If it converges, its sum Σ is equal to the product of the sums of the two given series, i.e. $\Sigma = SS'$. For, let us consider the three power series

$$f(x) = u_0 + u_1 x + \cdots + u_n x^n + \cdots,$$
$$\phi(x) = v_0 + v_1 x + \cdots + v_n x^n + \cdots,$$
$$\psi(x) = u_0 v_0 + (u_0 v_1 + u_1 v_0) x + \cdots + (u_0 v_n + \cdots + u_n v_0) x^n + \cdots.$$

Each of these series converges, by hypothesis, when $x = 1$. Hence each of them converges absolutely for any value of x between -1 and $+1$. For any such value of x Cauchy's theorem regarding the multiplication of series applies and gives us the equation

$$(8) \qquad f(x)\,\phi(x) = \psi(x).$$

By Abel's theorem, as x approaches unity the three functions $f(x)$, $\phi(x)$, $\psi(x)$ approach S, S', and Σ, respectively. Since the two sides of the equation (8) meanwhile remain equal, we shall have, in the limit, $\Sigma = SS'$.

The theorem remains true for series whose terms are imaginary, and the proof follows precisely the same lines.

179. Successive derivatives of a power series. If a power series

$$f(x) = a_0 + a_1 x + a_2 x^2 + \cdots + a_n x^n + \cdots$$

which converges in the interval $(-R, +R)$ be differentiated term by term, the resulting power series

$$(9) \qquad a_1 + 2a_2 x + \cdots + na_n x^{n-1} + \cdots$$

converges in the same interval. In order to prove this, it will be sufficient to show that the series of absolute values of the terms of the new series,

$$A_1 + 2A_2 X + \cdots + nA_n X^{n-1} + \cdots,$$

where $A_i = |a_i|$ and $X = |x|$, converges for $X < R$ and diverges for $X > R$.

For the first part let us suppose that $X < R$, and let R' be a number between X and R, $X < R' < R$. Then the auxiliary series

$$\frac{1}{R'} + \frac{2}{R'}\frac{X}{R'} + \frac{3}{R'}\left(\frac{X}{R'}\right)^2 + \cdots + \frac{n}{R'}\left(\frac{X}{R'}\right)^{n-1} + \cdots$$

converges, for the ratio of any term to the preceding approaches X/R', which is less than unity. Multiplying the successive terms of this series, respectively, by the factors

$$A_1 R', \quad A_2 R'^2, \quad \cdots, \quad A_n R'^n, \quad \cdots,$$

each of which is less than a certain fixed number, since $R' < R$, we obtain a new series

$$A_1 + 2A_2X + \cdots + nA_nX^{n-1} + \cdots$$

which also evidently converges.

The proof of the second part is similar to the above. If the series

$$A_1 + 2A_2X_1 + \cdots + nA_nX_1^{n-1} + \cdots,$$

where X_1 is greater than R, were convergent, the series

$$A_1X_1 + 2A_2X_1^2 + \cdots + nA_nX_1^n + \cdots$$

would converge also, and consequently the series $\overset{+\infty}{\underset{1}{\Sigma}}A_nX_1^n$ would converge, since each of its terms is less than the corresponding term of the preceding series. Then R would not be the upper limit of the values of X for which the series (1) converges.

The sum $f_1(x)$ of the series (9) is therefore a continuous function of the variable x inside the same interval. Since this series converges uniformly in any interval $(-R', +R')$, where $R' < R$, $f_1(x)$ is the derivative of $f(x)$ throughout such an interval, by § 174. Since R' may be chosen as near R as we please, we may assert that the function $f(x)$ possesses a derivative for any value of x between $-R$ and $+R$, and that that derivative is represented by the series obtained by differentiating the given series term by term : *

$$(10) \qquad f'(x) = a_1 + 2a_2x + \cdots + na_nx^{n-1} + \cdots.$$

Repeating the above reasoning for the series (10), we see that $f(x)$ has a second derivative,

$$f''(x) = 2a_2 + 6a_3x + \cdots + n(n-1)a_nx^{n-2} + \cdots,$$

and so forth. The function $f(x)$ possesses an unlimited sequence of derivatives for any value of x inside the interval $(-R, +R)$, and these derivatives are represented by the series obtained by differentiating the given series successively term by term :

$$(11) \quad f^{(n)}(x) = 1 . 2 \cdots na_n + 2 . 3 \cdots n(n+1)a_{n+1}x + \cdots.$$

If we set $x = 0$ in these formulæ, we find

$$a_0 = f(0), \qquad a_1 = f'(0), \qquad a_2 = \frac{f''(0)}{2}, \qquad \cdots,$$

or, in general,

$$a_n = \frac{f^{(n)}(0)}{1 . 2 \cdots n}.$$

---

* Although the corresponding theorem is true for series of imaginary terms, the proof follows somewhat different lines. See Vol. II, § 266. — TRANS.

The development of $f(x)$ thus obtained is identical with the development given by Maclaurin's formula:

$$f(x) = f(0) + \frac{x}{1} f'(0) + \frac{x^2}{1.2} f''(0) + \cdots + \frac{x^n}{1.2\cdots n} f^{(n)}(0) + \cdots.$$

The coefficients a_0, a_1, $\cdots$, a_n, $\cdots$ are equal, except for certain numerical factors, to the values of the function $f(x)$ and its successive derivatives for $x = 0$. *It follows that no function can have two distinct developments in power series.*

Similarly, if a power series be integrated term by term, a new power series is obtained which has an arbitrary constant term and which converges in the same interval as the given series, the given series being the derivative of the new series. If we integrate again, we obtain a third series whose first two terms are arbitrary; and so forth.

Examples. 1) The geometrical progression

$$1 - x + x^2 - x^3 + \cdots + (-1)^n x^n + \cdots,$$

whose ratio is $-x$, converges for every value of x between -1 and $+1$, and its sum is $1/(1+x)$. Integrating it term by term between the limits 0 and x, where $|x| < 1$, we obtain again the development of $\log(1+x)$ found in § 49:

$$\log(1+x) = \frac{x}{1} - \frac{x^2}{2} + \frac{x^3}{3} - \cdots + (-1)^n \frac{x^{n+1}}{n+1} + \cdots.$$

This formula holds also for $x = 1$, for the series on the right converges when $x = 1$.

2) For any value of x between -1 and $+1$ we may write

$$\frac{1}{1+x^2} = 1 - x^2 + x^4 - x^6 + \cdots + (-1)^n x^{2n} + \cdots.$$

Integrating this series term by term between the limits 0 and x, where $|x| < 1$, we find

$$\arctan x = \frac{x}{1} - \frac{x^3}{3} + \frac{x^5}{5} - \cdots + (-1)^n \frac{x^{2n+1}}{2n+1} + \cdots.$$

Since the new series converges for $x = 1$, it follows that

$$\frac{\pi}{4} = 1 - \frac{1}{3} + \frac{1}{5} - \frac{1}{7} + \cdots + (-1)^n \frac{1}{2n+1} + \cdots.$$

3) Let $F(x)$ be the sum of the convergent series

$$F(x) = 1 + \frac{m}{1} x + \frac{m(m-1)}{1 \cdot 2} x^2 + \cdots + \frac{m(m-1)\cdots(m-p+1)}{1 \cdot 2 \cdots p} x^p + \cdots,$$

where m is any number whatever and $|x| < 1$. Then we shall have

$$F'(x) = m \left[1 + \frac{m-1}{1} x + \cdots + \frac{(m-1)\cdots(m-p+1)}{1 \cdot 2 \cdots (p-1)} x^{p-1} + \cdots \right].$$

Let us multiply each side by $(1 + x)$ and then collect the terms in like powers of x. Using the identity

$$\frac{(m-1)\cdots(m-p+1)}{1 \cdot 2 \cdots (p-1)} + \frac{(m-1)\cdots(m-p)}{1 \cdot 2 \cdots p} = \frac{m(m-1)\cdots(m-p+1)}{1 \cdot 2 \cdots p},$$

which is easily verified, we find the formula

$$(1+x)F'(x) = m \left[1 + \frac{m}{1} x + \frac{m(m-1)}{1 \cdot 2} x^2 + \cdots \right. $$
$$\left. + \frac{m(m-1)\cdots(m-p+1)}{1 \cdot 2 \cdots p} x^p + \cdots \right]$$

or

$$(1+x)F'(x) = mF(x).$$

From this result we find, successively,

$$\frac{F'(x)}{F(x)} = \frac{m}{1+x},$$

$$\log[F(x)] = m \log(1+x) + \log C,$$

or

$$F(x) = C(1+x)^m.$$

To determine the constant C we need merely notice that $F(0) = 1$. Hence $C = 1$. This gives the development of $(1 + x)^m$ found in § 50:

$$(1+x)^m = 1 + \frac{m}{1} x + \cdots + \frac{m(m-1)\cdots(m-p+1)}{1 \cdot 2 \cdots p} x^p + \cdots.$$

4) Replacing x by $-x^2$ and m by $-1/2$ in the last formula above, we find

$$\frac{1}{\sqrt{1-x^2}} = 1 + \frac{1}{2} x^2 + \frac{1 \cdot 3}{2 \cdot 4} x^4 + \cdots + \frac{1 \cdot 3 \cdot 5 \cdots (2n-1)}{2 \cdot 4 \cdot 6 \cdots 2n} x^{2n} + \cdots.$$

This formula holds for any value of x between -1 and $+1$. Integrating both sides between the limits 0 and x, where $|x| < 1$, we obtain the following development for the arcsine:

$$\arcsin x = \frac{x}{1} + \frac{1}{2} \frac{x^3}{3} + \frac{1 \cdot 3}{2 \cdot 4} \frac{x^5}{5} + \cdots + \frac{1 \cdot 3 \cdot 5 \cdots (2n-1)}{2 \cdot 4 \cdot 6 \cdots 2n} \frac{x^{2n+1}}{2n+1} + \cdots.$$

180. Extension of Taylor's series. Let $f(x)$ be the sum of a power series which converges in the interval $(-R, +R)$, x_0 a point inside that interval, and $x_0 + h$ another point of the same interval such that $|x_0| + |h| < R$. The series whose sum is $f(x_0 + h)$,

$$a_0 + a_1(x_0 + h) + a_2(x_0 + h)^2 + \cdots + a_n(x_0 + h)^n + \cdots,$$

may be replaced by the double series obtained by developing each of the powers of $(x_0 + h)$ and writing the terms in the same power of h upon the same line:

$$(12) \quad \begin{cases} a_0 + a_1 x_0 + a_2 x_0^2 + \cdots + \quad\quad a_n x_0^n \quad + \cdots \\ \quad + a_1 h + 2a_2 x_0 h + \cdots + \quad n \quad a_n x_0^{n-1} h + \cdots \\ \quad\quad + a_2 h^2 + \cdots + \dfrac{n(n-1)}{1 \cdot 2} a_n x_0^{n-2} h^2 + \cdots \\ \quad\quad\quad + \cdots\cdots\cdots\cdots\cdots\cdots\cdots\cdots. \end{cases}$$

This double series converges absolutely. For if each of its terms be replaced by its absolute value, a new double series of positive terms is obtained:

$$(13) \quad \begin{cases} A_0 + A_1|x_0| + A_2|x_0|^2 + \cdots + \quad\quad A_n|x_0|^n \quad + \cdots \\ \quad + A_1|h| + 2A_2|x_0||h| + \cdots + \quad n \quad A_n|x_0|^{n-1}|h| + \cdots \\ \quad\quad + A_2|h|^2 + \cdots + \dfrac{n(n-1)}{1 \cdot 2} A_n|x_0|^{n-2}|h|^2 + \cdots \\ \quad\quad\quad + \cdots\cdots\cdots\cdots\cdots\cdots\cdots\cdots. \end{cases}$$

If we add the elements in any one column, we obtain a series

$$A_0 + A_1\big[|x_0| + |h|\big] + \cdots + A_n\big[|x_0| + |h|\big]^n + \cdots$$

which converges, since we have supposed that $|x_0| + |h| < R$. Hence the array (12) may be summed by rows or by columns. Taking the sums of the columns, we obtain $f(x_0 + h)$. Taking the sums of the rows, the resulting series is arranged according to powers of h, and the coefficients of h, h^2, $\cdots$ are $f'(x_0)$, $f''(x_0)/2!$, $\cdots$, respectively. Hence we may write

$$(14) \quad f(x_0 + h) = f(x_0) + \frac{h}{1}f'(x_0) + \cdots + \frac{h^n}{1 \cdot 2 \cdots n}f^{(n)}(x_0) + \cdots,$$

if we assume that $|h| < R - |x_0|$.

This formula surely holds inside the interval from $x_0 - R + |x_0|$ to $x_0 + R - |x_0|$, but it may happen that the series on the right converges in a larger interval. As an example consider the function

$(1+x)^m$, where m is not a positive integer. The development according to powers of x holds for all values of x between -1 and $+1$. Let x_0 be a value of x which lies in that interval. Then we may write

$$(1+x)^m = (1+x_0+x-x_0)^m = (1+x_0)^m (1+z)^m,$$

where

$$z = \frac{x-x_0}{1+x_0}.$$

We may now develop $(1+z)^m$ according to powers of z, and this new development will hold whenever $|z| < 1$, i.e. for all values of x between -1 and $1+2x_0$. If x_0 is positive, the new interval will be larger than the former interval $(-1, +1)$. Hence the new formula enables us to calculate the values of the function for values of the variable which lie outside the original interval. Further investigation of this remark leads to an extremely important notion, — that of *analytic extension*. We shall consider this subject in the second volume.

Note. It is evident that the theorems proved for series arranged according to positive powers of a variable x may be extended immediately to series arranged according to positive powers of $x-a$, or, more generally still, to series arranged according to positive powers of any continuous function $\phi(x)$ whatever. We need only consider them as composite functions, $\phi(x)$ being the auxiliary function. Thus a series arranged according to positive powers of $1/x$ converges for all values of x which exceed a certain positive constant in absolute value, and it represents a continuous function of x for all such values of the variable. The function $\sqrt{x^2-a}$, for example, may be written in the form $\pm x(1-a/x^2)^{\frac{1}{2}}$. The expression $(1-a/x^2)^{\frac{1}{2}}$ may be developed according to powers of $1/x^2$ for all values of x which exceed $\sqrt{a}$ in absolute value. This gives the formula

$$\sqrt{x^2-a} = x - \frac{1}{2}\frac{a}{x} - \frac{1}{2\cdot4}\frac{a^2}{x^3} - \cdots - \frac{1\cdot2\cdot3\cdots(2p-3)}{2\cdot4\cdot6\cdots2p}\frac{a^p}{x^{2p-1}}\cdots,$$

which constitutes a valid development of $\sqrt{x^2-a}$ whenever $x > \sqrt{a}$. When $x < -\sqrt{a}$, the same series converges and represents the function $-\sqrt{x^2-a}$. This formula may be used advantageously to obtain a development for the square root of an integer whenever the first perfect square which exceeds that integer is known.

181. Dominant functions. The theorems proved above establish a close analogy between polynomials and power series. Let $(-r, +r)$ be the least of the intervals of convergence of several given power series $f_1(x)$, $f_2(x)$, $\cdots$, $f_n(x)$. When $|x| < r$, each of these series converges absolutely, and they may be added or multiplied together by the ordinary rules for polynomials. In general, any integral polynomial in $f_1(x)$, $f_2(x)$, $\cdots$, $f_n(x)$ may be developed in a convergent power series in the same interval.

For purposes of generalization we shall now define certain expressions which will be useful in what follows. Let $f(x)$ be a power series

$$f(x) = a_0 + a_1 x + a_2 x^2 + \cdots + a_n x^n + \cdots,$$

and let $\phi(x)$ be another power series with positive coefficients

$$\phi(x) = \alpha_0 + \alpha_1 x + \alpha_2 x^2 + \cdots + \alpha_n x^n + \cdots$$

which converges in a suitable interval. Then the function $\phi(x)$ is said to *dominate*[*] the function $f(x)$ if each of the coefficients α_n is greater than the absolute value of the corresponding coefficient of $f(x)$:

$$|a_0| < \alpha_0, \quad |a_1| < \alpha_1, \quad \cdots, \quad |a_n| < \alpha_n, \quad \cdots.$$

Poincaré has proposed the notation

$$f(x) \ll \phi(x)$$

to express the relation which exists between the two functions $f(x)$ and $\phi(x)$.

The utility of these dominant functions is based upon the following fact, which is an immediate consequence of the definition. Let $P(a_0, a_1, \cdots, a_n)$ be a polynomial in the first $n + 1$ coefficients of $f(x)$ whose coefficients are all real and positive. If the quantities $a_0, a_1, \cdots, a_n$ be replaced by the corresponding coefficients of $\phi(x)$, it is clear that we shall have

$$|P(a_0, a_1, \cdots, a_n)| \leq P(\alpha_0, \alpha_1, \cdots, \alpha_n).$$

For instance, if the function $\phi(x)$ dominates the function $f(x)$, the series which represents $[\phi(x)]^2$ will dominate $[f(x)]^2$, and so on. In general, $[\phi(x)]^n$ will dominate $[f(x)]^n$. Similarly, if ϕ and ϕ_1 are dominant functions for f and f_1, respectively, the product $\phi\phi_1$ will dominate the product ff_1; and so forth.

---

[*] This expression will be used as a translation of the phrase " $\phi(x)$ est majorante pour la fonction $f(x)$." Likewise, "dominant functions" will be used for " fonctions majorantes." — TRANS.

Given a power series $f(x)$ which converges in an interval $(-R, +R)$, the problem of determining a dominant function is of course indeterminate. But it is convenient in what follows to make the dominant function as simple as possible. Let r be any number less than R and arbitrarily near R. Since the given series converges for $x = r$, the absolute value of its terms will have an upper limit, which we shall call M. Then we may write, for any value of n,

$$A_n r^n \leqq M \qquad \text{or} \qquad |a_n| = A_n \leqq \frac{M}{r^n}.$$

Hence the series

$$M + M \cdot \frac{x}{r} + \cdots + \frac{Mx^n}{r^n} + \cdots = \frac{M}{1 - \dfrac{x}{r}},$$

whose general term is $M(x^n/r^n)$, dominates the given function $f(x)$. This is the dominant function most frequently used. If the series $f(x)$ contains no constant term, the function

$$\frac{M}{1 - \dfrac{x}{r}} - M$$

may be taken as a dominant function.

It is evident that r may be assigned any value less than R, and that M decreases, in general, with r. But M can never be less than A_0. If A_0 is not zero, a number ρ less than R can always be found such that the function $A_0/(1 - x/\rho)$ dominates the function $f(x)$. For, let the series

$$M + M \frac{x}{r} + M \frac{x^2}{r^2} + \cdots + M \frac{x^n}{r^n} + \cdots,$$

where $M > A_0$, be a first dominant function. If ρ be a number less than rA_0/M and $n \geqq 1$, we shall have

$$|a_n \rho^n| = |a_n r^n| \times \left(\frac{\rho}{r}\right)^n < M \frac{\rho}{r} \left(\frac{\rho}{r}\right)^{n-1},$$

whence $|a_n \rho^n| < A_0$. On the other hand, $|a_0| = A_0$. Hence the series

$$A_0 + A_0 \frac{x}{\rho} + A_0 \frac{x^2}{\rho^2} + \cdots + A_0 \frac{x^n}{\rho^n} + \cdots$$

dominates the function $f(x)$. We shall make use of this fact presently. More generally still, any number whatever which is greater than or equal to A_0 may be used in place of M.

It may be shown in a similar manner that if $a_0 = 0$, the function

$$\frac{\mu}{1 - \dfrac{x}{\rho}} - \mu$$

is a dominant function, where μ is any positive number whatever.

Note. The knowledge of a geometrical progression which dominates the function $f(x)$ also enables us to estimate the error made in replacing the function $f(x)$ by the sum of the first $n + 1$ terms of the series. If the series $M/(1 - x/r)$ dominates $f(x)$, it is evident that the remainder

$$a_{n+1} x^{n+1} + a_{n+2} x^{n+2} + \cdots$$

of the given series is less in absolute value than the corresponding remainder

$$M\left(\frac{x^{n+1}}{r^{n+1}} + \frac{x^{n+2}}{r^{n+2}} + \cdots\right)$$

of the dominant series. It follows that the error in question will be less than

$$M \frac{\left(\dfrac{x}{r}\right)^{n+1}}{1 - \dfrac{x}{r}}.$$

182. Substitution of one series in another. Let

$$(15) \qquad z = f(y) = a_0 + a_1 y + \cdots + a_n y^n + \cdots$$

be a series arranged according to powers of a variable y which converges whenever $|y| < R$. Again let

$$(16) \qquad y = \phi(x) = b_0 + b_1 x + \cdots + b_n x^n + \cdots$$

be another series, which converges in the interval $(-r, +r)$. If $y, y^2, y^3, \cdots$ in the series (15) be replaced by their developments in series arranged according to powers of x from (16), a double series

$$(17) \quad \begin{cases} a_0 + a_1 b_0 \quad + \ a_2 \ b_0^2 \qquad\quad + \cdots + \ a_n b_0^n \qquad + \cdots \\ \quad + a_1 b_1 x \ + 2 a_2 \ b_0 b_1 x \qquad\quad + \cdots + n a_n b_0^{n-1} b_1 x + \cdots \\ \quad + a_1 b_2 x^2 + \ a_2 (b_1^2 + 2 b_0 b_2) x^2 + \cdots\cdots\cdots\cdots\cdots \\ \quad + \cdots\cdots\cdots\cdots\cdots\cdots\cdots\cdots\cdots\cdots\cdots\cdots \end{cases}$$

is obtained. We shall now investigate the conditions under which this double series converges absolutely. In the first place, it is necessary that the series written in the first row,

$$a_0 + a_1 b_0 + a_2 b_0^2 + \cdots,$$

should converge absolutely, i.e. that $|b_0|$ should be less than R.* *This condition is also sufficient.* For if it is satisfied, the function $\phi(x)$ will be dominated by an expression of the form $m/(1 - x/\rho)$, where m is any positive number greater than $|b_0|$ and where $\rho < r$. We may therefore suppose that m is less than R. Let R' be another positive number which lies between m and R. Then the function $f(y)$ is dominated by an expression of the form

$$\frac{M}{1 - \dfrac{y}{R'}} = M + M\frac{y}{R'} + M\frac{y^2}{R'^2} + \cdots.$$

If y be replaced by $m/(1 - x/\rho)$ in this last series, and the powers of y be developed according to increasing powers of x by the binomial theorem, a new double series

$$(18) \quad \begin{cases} M + M\left(\dfrac{m}{R'}\right) + \cdots + M\left(\dfrac{m}{R'}\right)^n + \cdots \\ \quad + M\,\dfrac{m}{R'}\dfrac{x}{\rho} + \cdots + nM\left(\dfrac{m}{R'}\right)^n \dfrac{x}{\rho} + \cdots \\ \quad + \cdots\cdots\cdots\cdots\cdots\cdots\cdots\cdots\cdots\cdots \end{cases}$$

is obtained, each of whose coefficients is positive and greater than the absolute value of the corresponding coefficients in the array (17), since each of the coefficients in (17) is formed from the coefficients $a_0, a_1, a_2, \cdots, b_0, b_1, b_2, \cdots$ by means of additions and multiplications only. The double series (17) therefore converges absolutely provided the double series (18) converges absolutely. If x be replaced by its absolute value in the series (18), a necessary condition for absolute convergence is that each of the series formed of the terms in any one column should converge, i.e. that $|x| < \rho$. If this condition be satisfied, the sum of the terms in the $(n + 1)$th column is equal to

$$M\left[\frac{m}{R'\left(1 - \frac{|x|}{\rho}\right)}\right]^n.$$

Then a further necessary condition is that we should have

$$m < R'\left(1 - \frac{|x|}{\rho}\right),$$

or

$$(19) \qquad |x| < \rho\left(1 - \frac{m}{R'}\right).$$

---

* The case in which the series (15) converges for $y = R$ (see § 177) will be neglected in what follows. — TRANS.

Since this latter condition includes the former, $|x| < \rho$, it follows that it is a necessary and sufficient condition for the absolute convergence of the double series (18). The double series (17) will therefore converge absolutely for values of x which satisfy the inequality (19). It is to be noticed that the series $\phi(x)$ converges for all these values of x, and that the corresponding value of y is less than R' in absolute value. For the inequalities

$$|\phi(x)| < \frac{m}{1 - \frac{|x|}{\rho}}, \qquad \frac{|x|}{\rho} < 1 - \frac{m}{R'}$$

necessitate the inequality $|\phi(x)| < R'$. Taking the sum of the series (17) by columns, we find

$$a_0 + a_1\phi(x) + a_2[\phi(x)]^2 + \cdots + a_n[\phi(x)]^n + \cdots,$$

that is, $f[\phi(x)]$. On the other hand, adding by rows, we obtain a series arranged according to powers of x. Hence we may write

$$(20) \qquad f[\phi(x)] = c_0 + c_1 x + c_2 x^2 + \cdots + c_n x^n + \cdots,$$

where the coefficients $c_0, c_1, c_2, \cdots$ are given by the formulæ

$$(21) \quad \begin{cases} c_0 = a_0 + a_1 b_0 + a_2 b_0^2 + \cdots + a_n b_0^n + \cdots, \\ c_1 = a_1 b_1 + 2a_2 b_1 b_0 + \cdots + n a_n b_0^{n-1} b_1 + \cdots, \\ c_2 = a_1 b_2 + a_2 (b_1^2 + 2b_0 b_2) + \cdots, \\ \cdot \quad \cdot \quad \cdot \quad \cdot \quad \cdot \quad \cdot \quad \cdot \quad \cdot \quad \cdot \quad \cdot \quad \cdot \quad \cdot \quad \cdot \quad \cdot, \end{cases}$$

which are easily verified.

The formula (20) has been established only for values of x which satisfy the inequality (19), but the latter merely gives an under limit of the size of the interval in which the formula holds. It may be valid in a much larger interval. This raises a question whose solution requires a knowledge of functions of a complex variable. We shall return to it later.

Special cases. 1) Since the number R' which occurs in (19) may be taken as near R as we please, the formula (20) holds whenever x satisfies the inequality $|x| < \rho(1 - m/R)$. Hence, if the series (15) converges for any value of y whatever, R may be thought of as infinite, ρ may be taken as near r as we please, and the formula (20) applies whenever $|x| < r$, that is, in the same interval in which the series (16) converges. In particular, if the series (16) converges for all values of x, and (15) converges for all values of y, the formula (20) is valid for all values of x.

2) When the constant term b_0 of the series (16) is zero, the function $\phi(x)$ is dominated by an expression of the form

$$\frac{m}{1 - \dfrac{x}{\rho}} - m,$$

where $\rho < r$ and where m is any positive number whatever. An argument similar to that used in the general case shows that the formula (20) holds in this case whenever x satisfies the inequality

$$(22) \qquad\qquad |x| < \rho \, \frac{R'}{R' + m},$$

where R' is as near to R as we please. The corresponding interval of validity is larger than that given by the inequality (19).

This special case often arises in practice. The inequality $|b_0| < R$ is evidently satisfied, and the coefficients c_n depend upon $a_0, a_1, \cdots, a_n, b_1, \cdots, b_n$ only:

$$c_0 = a_0, \quad c_1 = a_1 b_1, \quad c_2 = a_1 b_2 + a_2 b_1^2, \quad \cdots, \quad c_n = a_1 b_n + \cdots + a_n b_1^n.$$

Examples. 1) Cauchy gave a method for obtaining the binomial theorem from the development of $\log(1 + x)$. Setting

$$y = \mu \log(1 + x) = \mu \left(\frac{x}{1} - \frac{x^2}{2} + \frac{x^3}{3} - \frac{x^4}{4} \cdots \right),$$

we may write

$$(1 + x)^\mu = e^{\mu \log(1 + x)} = e^y = 1 + \frac{y}{1} + \frac{y^2}{1 \cdot 2} + \cdots,$$

whence, substituting the first expansion in the second,

$$(1 + x)^\mu = 1 + \mu \left(\frac{x}{1} - \frac{x^2}{2} + \frac{x^3}{3} \cdots \right) + \frac{\mu^2}{1 \cdot 2} \left(\frac{x}{1} - \frac{x^2}{2} + \frac{x^3}{3} \cdots \right)^2 + \cdots.$$

If the right-hand side be arranged according to powers of x, it is evident that the coefficient of x^n will be a polynomial of degree n in μ, which we shall call $P_n(\mu)$. This polynomial must vanish when $\mu = 0, 1, 2, \cdots, n-1$, and must reduce to unity when $\mu = n$. These facts completely determine P_n in the form

$$(23) \qquad\qquad P_n = \frac{\mu(\mu - 1) \cdots (\mu - n + 1)}{1 \cdot 2 \cdots n}.$$

2) Setting $z = (1 + x)^{1/x}$, where x lies between -1 and $+1$, we may write

$$z = e^y = 1 + \frac{y}{1} + \frac{y^2}{1 \cdot 2} + \cdots,$$

where

$$y = \frac{1}{x} \log(1 + x) = 1 - \frac{x}{2} + \frac{x^2}{3} - \cdots + (-1)^n \frac{x^n}{n + 1} + \cdots.$$

The first expansion is valid for all values of y, and the second is valid whenever $|x| < 1$. Hence the formula obtained by substituting the second expansion in the first holds for any value of x between -1 and $+1$. The first two terms of this formula are

$$(24) \quad (1+x)^{\frac{1}{x}} = e - \frac{x}{2}\left(1 + 1 + \frac{1}{1.2} + \cdots + \frac{1}{1.2\cdots n} + \cdots\right) + \cdots = e - \frac{e}{2}x + \cdots.$$

It follows that $(1 + x)^{1/x}$ approaches e through values less than e as x approaches zero through positive values.

183. Division of power series. Let us first consider the reciprocal

$$f(x) = \frac{1}{1 + b_1 x + b_2 x^2 + \cdots}$$

of a power series which begins with unity and which converges in the interval $(-r, +r)$. Setting

$$y = b_1 x + b_2 x^2 + \cdots,$$

we may write

$$f(x) = \frac{1}{1 + y} = 1 - y + y^2 - y^3 + \cdots,$$

whence, substituting the first development in the second, we obtain an expansion for $f(x)$ in power series,

$$(25) \qquad f(x) = 1 - b_1 x + (b_1^2 - b_2) x^2 + \cdots,$$

which holds inside a certain interval. In a similar manner a development may be obtained for the reciprocal of any power series whose constant term is different from zero.

Let us now try to develop the quotient of two convergent power series

$$\frac{\phi(x)}{\psi(x)} = \frac{a_0 + a_1 x + a_2 x^2 + \cdots}{b_0 + b_1 x + b_2 x^2 + \cdots}.$$

If b_0 is not zero, this quotient may be written in the form

$$\frac{\phi(x)}{\psi(x)} = (a_0 + a_1 x + a_2 x^2 + \cdots) \times \frac{1}{b_0 + b_1 x + b_2 x^2 + \cdots}.$$

Then by the case just treated the left-hand side of this equation is the product of two convergent power series. Hence it may be written in the form of a power series which converges near the origin:

$$(26) \qquad \frac{a_0 + a_1 x + a_2 x^2 + \cdots}{b_0 + b_1 x + b_2 x^2 + \cdots} = c_0 + c_1 x + c_2 x^2 + \cdots.$$

Clearing of fractions and equating the coefficients of like powers of x, we find the formulæ

(27) $a_n = b_0 c_n + b_1 c_{n-1} + \cdots + b_n c_0,$ $n = 0, 1, 2, \cdots,$

from which the coefficients $c_0, c_1, \cdots, c_n$ may be calculated successively. It will be noticed that these coefficients are the same as those we should obtain by performing the division indicated by the ordinary rule for the division of polynomials arranged according to increasing powers of x.

If $b_0 = 0$, the result is different. Let us suppose for generality that $\psi(x) = x^k \psi_1(x)$, where k is a positive integer and $\psi_1(x)$ is a power series whose constant term is not zero. Then we may write

$$\frac{\phi(x)}{\psi(x)} = \frac{1}{x^k} \frac{(x\phi)}{\psi_1(x)},$$

and by the above we shall have also

$$\frac{\phi(x)}{\psi_1(x)} = c_0 + c_1 x + \cdots + c_{k-1} x^{k-1} + c_k x^k + c_{k+1} x^{k+1} + \cdots.$$

It follows that the given quotient is expressible in the form

(28) $$\frac{\phi(x)}{\psi(x)} = \frac{c_0}{x^k} + \frac{c_1}{x^{k-1}} + \cdots + \frac{c_{k-1}}{x} + c_k + c_{k+1} x + \cdots,$$

where the right-hand side is the sum of a rational fraction which becomes infinite for $x = 0$ and a power series which converges near the origin.

Note. In order to calculate the successive powers of a power series, it is convenient to proceed as follows. Assuming the identity

$$(a_0 + a_1 x + \cdots + a_n x^n + \cdots)^m = c_0 + c_1 x + \cdots + c_n x^n + \cdots,$$

let us take the logarithmic derivative of each side and then clear of fractions. This leads to the new identity

(29) $$\begin{cases} m(a_1 + 2a_2 x + \cdots + na_n x^{n-1} + \cdots)(c_0 + c_1 x + \cdots + c_n x^n + \cdots) \\ = (a_0 + a_1 x + \cdots + a_n x^n + \cdots)(c_1 + 2c_2 x + \cdots + nc_n x^{n-1} + \cdots). \end{cases}$$

The coefficients of the various powers of x are easily calculated. Equating coefficients of like powers, we find a sequence of formulæ from which $c_0, c_1, \cdots, c_n, \cdots$ may be found successively if c_0 be known. It is evident that $c_0 = a_0^m$.

184. Development of $1/\sqrt{1 - 2xz + z^2}$. Let us develop $1/\sqrt{1 - 2xz + z^2}$ according to powers of z. Setting $y = 2xz - z^2$, we shall have, when $|y| < 1$,

$$\frac{1}{\sqrt{1 - y}} = (1 - y)^{-\frac{1}{2}} = 1 + \frac{1}{2} y + \frac{1 \cdot 3}{2 \cdot 4} y^2 + \cdots,$$

or

(30) $$\frac{1}{\sqrt{1 - 2xz + z^2}} = 1 + \frac{2xz - z^2}{2} + \frac{3}{8}(2xz - z^2)^2 + \cdots.$$

Collecting the terms which are divisible by the same power of z, we obtain an expansion of the form

$$(31) \qquad \frac{1}{\sqrt{1 - 2xz + z^2}} = P_0 + P_1 z + P_2 z^2 + \cdots + P_n z^n + \cdots,$$

where

$$P_0 = 1, \qquad P_1 = x, \qquad P_2 = \frac{3x^2 - 1}{2}, \qquad \cdots,$$

and where, in general, P_n is a polynomial of the nth degree in x. These polynomials may be determined successively by means of a recurrent formula. Differentiating the equation (31) with respect to z, we find

$$\frac{x - z}{(1 - 2xz + z^2)^{\frac{3}{2}}} = P_1 + 2P_2 z + \cdots + nP_n z^{n-1} + \cdots,$$

or, by the equation (31),

$$(x - z)(P_0 + P_1 z + \cdots + P_n z^n + \cdots) = (1 - 2xz + z^2)(P_1 + 2P_2 z + \cdots).$$

Equating the coefficients of z^n, we obtain the desired recurrent formula

$$(n + 1) P_{n+1} = (2n + 1) x P_n - n P_{n-1}.$$

This equation is identical with the relation between three consecutive Legendre polynomials (§ 88), and moreover $P_0 = X_0$, $P_1 = X_1$, $P_2 = X_2$. Hence $P_n = X_n$ for all values of n, and the formula (31) may be written

$$(32) \qquad \frac{1}{\sqrt{1 - 2xz + z^2}} = 1 + X_1 z + X_2 z^2 + \cdots + X_n z^n + \cdots,$$

where X_n is the Legendre polynomial of the nth order

$$X_n = \frac{1}{2 \cdot 4 \cdot 6 \cdots 2n} \frac{d^n}{dx^n} [(x^2 - 1)^n].$$

We shall find later the interval in which this formula holds.

II. POWER SERIES IN SEVERAL VARIABLES

185. General principles. The properties of power series of a single variable may be extended easily to power series in several independent variables. Let us first consider a double series $\Sigma a_{mn} x^m y^n$, where the integers m and n vary from zero to $+\infty$ and where the coefficients a_{mn} may have either sign. *If no element of this series exceeds a certain positive constant in absolute value for a set of values $x = x_0$, $y = y_0$, the series converges absolutely for all values of x and y which satisfy the inequalities $|x| < |x_0|$, $|y| < |y_0|$.*

For, suppose that the inequality

$$|a_{mn} x_0^m y_0^n| < M \quad \text{or} \quad |a_{mn}| < \frac{M}{|x_0|^m |y_0|^n}$$

is satisfied for all sets of values of m and n. Then the absolute value of the general element of the double series $\Sigma a_{mn} x^m y^n$ is less than the corresponding element of the double series $\Sigma M |x/x_0|^m |y/y_0|^n$. But the latter series converges whenever $|x| < |x_0|$, $|y| < |y_0|$, and its sum is

$$\frac{M}{\left(1 - \left|\dfrac{x}{x_0}\right|\right)\left(1 - \left|\dfrac{y}{y_0}\right|\right)},$$

as we see by taking the sums of the elements by columns and then adding these sums.

Let r and ρ be two positive numbers for which the double series $\Sigma |a_{mn}| r^m \rho^n$ converges, and let R denote the rectangle formed by the four straight lines $x = r$, $x = -r$, $y = \rho$, $y = -\rho$. For every point inside this rectangle or upon one of its sides no element of the double series

$$(33) \qquad\qquad F(x,\, y) = \Sigma a_{mn} x^m y^n$$

exceeds the corresponding element of the series $\Sigma |a_{mn}| r^m \rho^n$ in absolute value. Hence the series (33) converges absolutely and uniformly inside of R, and it therefore defines a continuous function of the two variables x and y inside that region.

It may be shown, as for series in a single variable, that the double series obtained by any number of term-by-term differentiations converges absolutely and uniformly inside the rectangle bounded by the lines $x = r - \epsilon$, $x = -r + \epsilon$, $y = \rho - \epsilon'$, $y = -\rho + \epsilon'$, where ϵ and ϵ' are any positive numbers less than r and ρ, respectively. These series represent the various partial derivatives of $F(x, y)$. For example, the sum of the series $\Sigma m a_{mn} x^{m-1} y^n$ is equal to $\partial F/\partial x$. For if the elements of the two series be arranged according to increasing powers of x, each element of the second series is equal to the derivative of the corresponding element of the first. Likewise, the partial derivative $\partial^{m+n} F/\partial x^m \partial y^n$ is equal to the sum of a double series whose constant factor is $a_{mn} 1 . 2 \cdots m . 1 . 2 \cdots n$. Hence the coefficients a_{mn} are equal to the values of the corresponding derivatives of the function $F(x, y)$ at the point $x = y = 0$, except for certain numerical factors, and the formula (33) may be written in the form

$$(34) \qquad F(x,\, y) = \sum \frac{\left(\dfrac{\partial^{m+n} F}{\partial x^m \partial y^n}\right)_0}{1 . 2 \cdots m . 1 . 2 \cdots n} x^m y^n.$$

It follows, incidentally, that *no function of two variables can have two distinct developments in power series.*

If the elements of the double series be collected according to their degrees in x and y, a simple series is obtained:

$$(35) \qquad F(x, y) = \phi_0 + \phi_1 + \phi_2 + \cdots + \phi_n + \cdots,$$

where ϕ_n is a homogeneous polynomial of the nth degree in x and y which may be written, symbolically,

$$\phi_n = \frac{1}{1 . 2 \cdots n} \left(x \frac{\partial F}{\partial x} + y \frac{\partial F}{\partial y} \right)^{(n)}.$$

The preceding development therefore coincides with that given by Taylor's series (§ 51).

Let (x_0, y_0) be a point inside the rectangle R, and $(x_0 + h, y_0 + k)$ be a neighboring point such that $|x_0| + |h| < r$, $|y_0| + |k| < \rho$. Then for any point inside the rectangle formed by the lines

$$x = x_0 \pm [r - |x_0|], \qquad y = y_0 \pm [\rho - |y_0|],$$

the function $F(x, y)$ may be developed in a power series arranged according to positive powers of $x - x_0$ and $y - y_0$:

$$(36) \qquad F(x_0 + h, y_0 + k) = \sum \frac{\left(\dfrac{\partial^{m+n} F}{\partial x^m \partial y^n} \right)_{\substack{x = x_0 \\ y = y_0}}}{1 . 2 \cdots m . 1 . 2 \cdots n} h^m k^n.$$

For if each element of the double series

$$\Sigma a_{mn} (x_0 + h)^m (y_0 + k)^n$$

be replaced by its development in powers of h and k, the new multiple series will converge absolutely under the hypotheses. Arranging the elements of this new series according to powers of h and k, we obtain the formula (36).

The reader will be able to show without difficulty that all the preceding arguments and theorems hold without essential alteration for power series in any number of variables whatever.

186. Dominant functions. Given a power series $f(x, y, z, \cdots)$ in n variables, we shall say that another series in n variables $\phi(x, y, z, \cdots)$ *dominates* the first series if each coefficient of $\phi(x, y, z, \cdots)$ is positive and greater than the absolute value of the corresponding coefficient of $f(x, y, z, \cdots)$. The argument in § 185 depends essentially upon the use of a dominant function. For if the series $\Sigma|a_{mn}x^m y^n|$ converges for $x = r$, $y = \rho$, the function

$$\phi(x, y) = \frac{M}{\left(1 - \dfrac{x}{r}\right)\left(1 - \dfrac{y}{\rho}\right)} = M\Sigma \left(\frac{x}{r}\right)^m \left(\frac{y}{\rho}\right)^n,$$

where M is greater than any coefficient in the series $\Sigma|a_{mn}r^m\rho^n|$, dominates the series $\Sigma a_{mn}x^m y^n$. The function

$$\psi(x, y) = \frac{M}{1 - \left(\dfrac{x}{r} + \dfrac{y}{\rho}\right)}$$

is another dominant function. For the coefficient of $x^m y^n$ in $\psi(x, y)$ is equal to the coefficient of the corresponding term in the expansion of $M(x/r + y/\rho)^{m+n}$, and therefore it is at least equal to the coefficient of $x^m y^n$ in $\phi(x, y)$.

Similarly, a triple series

$$f(x, y, z) = \Sigma a_{mnp} x^m y^n z^p,$$

which converges absolutely for $x = r$, $y = r'$, $z = r''$, where r, r', r'' are three positive numbers, is dominated by an expression of the form

$$\phi(x, y, z) = \frac{M}{\left(1 - \dfrac{x}{r}\right)\left(1 - \dfrac{y}{r'}\right)\left(1 - \dfrac{z}{r''}\right)},$$

and also by any one of the expressions

$$\frac{M}{1 - \left(\dfrac{x}{r} + \dfrac{y}{r'} + \dfrac{z}{r''}\right)}, \qquad \frac{M}{\left(1 - \dfrac{x}{r}\right)\left[1 - \left(\dfrac{y}{r'} + \dfrac{z}{r''}\right)\right]}, \qquad \cdots .$$

If $f(x, y, z)$ contains no constant term, any one of the preceding expressions diminished by M may be selected as a dominant function.

The theorem regarding the substitution of one power series in another (§ 182) may be extended to power series in several variables.

If each of the variables in a convergent power series in p variables $y_1, y_2, \cdots, y_p$ be replaced by a convergent power series in q variables $x_1, x_2, \cdots, x_q$ which has no constant term, the result of the substitution may be written in the form of a power series arranged according to powers of $x_1, x_2, \cdots, x_q$, provided that the absolute value of each of these variables is less than a certain constant.

Since the proof of the theorem is essentially the same for any number of variables, we shall restrict ourselves for definiteness to the following particular case. Let

$$(37) \qquad F(y, z) = \Sigma a_{mn} y^m z^n$$

be a power series which converges whenever $|y| \leqq r$ and $|z| \leqq r'$, and let

$$(38) \qquad \begin{cases} y = b_1 x + b_2 x^2 + \cdots + b_n x^n + \cdots, \\ z = c_1 x + c_2 x^2 + \cdots + c_n x^n + \cdots \end{cases}$$

be two series without constant terms both of which converge if the absolute value of x does not exceed ρ. If y and z in the series (37) be replaced by their developments from (38), the term in $y^m z^n$ becomes a new power series in x, and the double series (37) becomes a triple series, each of whose coefficients may be calculated from the coefficients a_{mn}, b_n, and c_n by means of additions and multiplications only. It remains to be shown that this triple series converges absolutely when the absolute value of x does not exceed a certain constant, from which it would then follow that the series could be arranged according to increasing powers of x. In the first place, the function $f(y, z)$ is dominated by the function

$$(39) \qquad \phi(y, z) = \cfrac{M}{\left(1 - \cfrac{y}{r}\right)\left(1 - \cfrac{z}{r'}\right)} = \Sigma M \left(\frac{y}{r}\right)^m \left(\frac{z}{r'}\right)^n,$$

and both of the series (38) are dominated by an expression of the form

$$(40) \qquad \cfrac{N}{1 - \cfrac{x}{\rho}} - N = \sum_{n=1}^{+\infty} N \left(\frac{x}{\rho}\right)^n,$$

where M and N are two positive numbers. If y and z in the double series (39) be replaced by the function (40) and each of the products $y^m z^n$ be developed in powers of x, each of the coefficients of the resulting triple series will be positive and greater than the absolute value of the corresponding coefficient in the triple series found above. It will therefore be sufficient to show that this new triple series converges for sufficiently small positive values of x. Now the sum of the terms which arise from the expansion of any term $y^m z^n$ of the series (39) is

$$M \frac{N^{m+n}}{r^m r'^n} \frac{\left(\dfrac{x}{\rho}\right)^{m+n}}{\left(1 - \dfrac{x}{\rho}\right)^{m+n}},$$

which is the general term of the series obtained by multiplying the two series

$$\sum \left(\frac{N}{r}\right)^m \left(\frac{\frac{x}{\rho}}{1 - \frac{x}{\rho}}\right)^m, \qquad \sum \left(\frac{N}{r'}\right)^n \left(\frac{\frac{x}{\rho}}{1 - \frac{x}{\rho}}\right)^n$$

term by term, except for the constant factor M. Both of the latter series converge if x satisfies both of the inequalities

$$x < \rho \frac{r}{r + N}, \qquad x < \rho \frac{r'}{r' + N}.$$

It follows that all the series considered will converge absolutely, and therefore that the original triple series may be arranged according to positive powers of x, whenever the absolute value of x is less than the smaller of the two numbers $\rho r/(r + N)$ and $\rho r'/(r' + N)$.

Note. The theorem remains valid when the series (38) contain constant terms b_0 and c_0, provided that $|b_0| < r$ and $|c_0| < r'$. For the expansion (37) may be replaced by a series arranged according to powers of $y - b_0$ and $z - c_0$, by § 185, which reduces the discussion to the case just treated.

III. IMPLICIT FUNCTIONS
ANALYTIC CURVES AND SURFACES

187. Implicit functions of a single variable. The existence of implicit functions has already been established (Chapter II, § 20 et ff.) under certain conditions regarding continuity. When the left-hand sides of the given equations are power series, more thorough investigation is possible, as we shall proceed to show.

Let $F(x, y) = 0$ be an equation whose left-hand side can be developed in a convergent power series arranged according to increasing powers of $x - x_0$ and $y - y_0$, where the constant term is zero and the coefficient of $y - y_0$ is different from zero. Then the equation has one and only one root which approaches y_0 as x approaches x_0, and that root can be developed in a power series arranged according to powers of $x - x_0$.

For simplicity let us suppose that $x_0 = y_0 = 0$, which amounts to moving the origin of coördinates. Transposing the term of the first degree in y, we may write the given equation in the form

$$(41) \qquad y = f(x, y) = a_{10}x + a_{20}x^2 + a_{11}xy + a_{02}y^2 + \cdots,$$

where the terms not written down are of degrees greater than the
second. We shall first show that this equation can be *formally* satisfied by replacing y by a series of the form

$$(42) \qquad y = c_1 x + c_2 x^2 + \cdots + c_n x^n + \cdots$$

if the rules for operation on convergent series be applied to the series
on the right. For, making the substitution and comparing the coefficients of x, we find the equations

$$c_1 = a_{10}, \qquad c_2 = a_{20} + a_{11} c_1 + a_{02} c_1^2, \qquad \cdots;$$

and, in general, c_n can be expressed in terms of the preceding c's
and the coefficients a_{ik}, where $i + k \leqq n$, by means of additions and
multiplications only. Thus we may write

$$(43) \qquad c_n = P_n(a_{10}, a_{20}, a_{11}, \cdots, a_{0n}),$$

where P_n is a polynomial each of whose coefficients is a positive
integer. The validity of the operations performed will be established if we can show that the series (42) determined in this way
converges for all sufficiently small values of x. We shall do this by
means of a device which is frequently used. Its conception is due
to Cauchy, and it is based essentially upon the idea of dominant
functions. Let

$$\phi(x, Y) = \Sigma b_{mn} x^m Y^n$$

be a function which dominates the function $f(x, y)$, where $b_{00} = b_{01} = 0$
and where b_{mn} is positive and at least equal to $|a_{mn}|$. Let us then
consider the auxiliary equation

$$(41') \qquad Y = \phi(x, Y) = \Sigma b_{mn} x^m Y^n$$

and try to find a solution of this equation of the form

$$(42') \qquad Y = C_1 x + C_2 x^2 + \cdots + C_n x^n + \cdots.$$

The values of the coefficients $C_1, C_2, \cdots$ can be determined as above,
and are

$$C_1 = b_{10}, \qquad C_2 = b_{20} + b_{11} C_1 + b_{02} C_1^2, \qquad \cdots,$$

and in general

$$(43') \qquad C_n = P_n(b_{10}, b_{20}, \cdots, b_{0n}).$$

It is evident from a comparison of the formulæ (43) and (43')
that $|c_n| < C_n$, since each of the coefficients of the polynomial P_n is
positive and $|a_{mn}| \leqq b_{mn}$. Hence the series (42) surely converges

whenever the series (42') converges. Now we may select for the dominant function $\phi(x, Y)$ the function

$$\phi(x, Y) = \frac{M}{\left(1 - \dfrac{x}{r}\right)\left(1 - \dfrac{Y}{\rho}\right)} - M - M\frac{Y}{\rho},$$

where M, r, and ρ are three positive numbers. Then the auxiliary equation (41') becomes, after clearing of fractions,

$$Y^2 - \frac{\rho^2 Y}{\rho + M} + \frac{M\rho^2}{\rho + M}\frac{\dfrac{x}{r}}{1 - \dfrac{x}{r}} = 0.$$

This equation has a root which vanishes for $x = 0$, namely:

$$Y = \frac{\rho^2}{2(\rho + M)} - \frac{\rho^2}{2(\rho + M)}\sqrt{1 - \frac{4M(\rho + M)}{\rho^2}\frac{\dfrac{x}{r}}{1 - \dfrac{x}{r}}}.$$

The quantity under the radical may be written in the form

$$\left(1 - \frac{x}{\alpha}\right)\left(1 - \frac{x}{r}\right)^{-1},$$

where

$$\alpha = r\left(\frac{\rho}{\rho + 2M}\right)^2.$$

Hence the root Y may be written

$$Y = \frac{\rho^2}{2(\rho + M)}\left[1 - \left(1 - \frac{x}{\alpha}\right)^{\frac{1}{2}}\left(1 - \frac{x}{r}\right)^{-\frac{1}{2}}\right].$$

It follows that this root Y may be developed in a series which converges in the interval $(-\alpha, +\alpha)$, and this development must coincide with that which we should obtain by direct substitution, that is, with (42'). Accordingly the series (42) converges, *a fortiori*, in the interval $(-\alpha, +\alpha)$. This is, however, merely a lower limit of the true interval of convergence of the series (42), which may be very much larger.

It is evident from the manner in which the coefficients c_n were determined that the sum of the series (42) satisfies the equation (41). Let us write the equation $F(x, y)$ in the form $y - f(x, y) = 0$, and let $y = P(x)$ be the root just found. Then if $P(x) + z$ be substituted for y in $F(x, y)$, and the result be arranged according to powers of x and z, each term must be divisible by z, since the whole expression vanishes when $z = 0$ for any value of x. We shall have then $F[x, P(x) + z] = zQ(x, z)$, where $Q(x, z)$ is a power series in x

and z. Finally, if z be replaced by $y - P(x)$ in $Q(x, z)$, we obtain the identity

$$F(x, y) = [y - P(x)] Q_1(x, y),$$

where the constant term of Q_1 must be unity, since the coefficient of y on the left-hand side is unity. Hence we may write

$$(44) \qquad F(x, y) = [y - P(x)](1 + \alpha x + \beta y + \cdots).$$

This decomposition of $F(x, y)$ into a product of two factors is due to Weierstrass. It exhibits the root $y = P(x)$, and also shows that there is no other root of the equation $F(x, y) = 0$ which vanishes with x, since the second factor does not approach zero with x and y.

Note. The preceding method for determining the coefficients c_n is essentially the same as that given in § 46. But it is now evident that the series obtained by carrying on the process indefinitely is convergent.

188. The general theorem. Let us now consider a system of p equations in $p + q$ variables.

$$(45) \quad \begin{cases} F_1(x_1, x_2, \cdots, x_q; y_1, y_2, \cdots, y_p) = 0, \\ F_2(x_1, x_2, \cdots, x_q; y_1, y_2, \cdots, y_p) = 0, \\ \cdots \cdots \cdots \cdots \cdots \cdots \cdots \cdots \cdots, \\ F_p(x_1, x_2, \cdots, x_q; y_1, y_2, \cdots, y_p) = 0, \end{cases}$$

where each of the functions $F_1, F_2, \cdots, F_p$ vanishes when $x_i = y_k = 0$, and is developable in power series near that point. We shall further suppose that the Jacobian $D(F_1, F_2, \cdots, F_p)/D(y_1, y_2, \cdots, y_p)$ *does not vanish* for the set of values considered. Under these conditions *there exists one and only one system of solutions of the equations* (45) *of the form*

$$y_1 = \phi_1(x_1, x_2, \cdots, x_q), \qquad \cdots, \qquad y_p = \phi_p(x_1, x_2, \cdots, x_q),$$

where $\phi_1, \phi_2, \cdots, \phi_p$ *are power series in* $x_1, x_2, \cdots, x_q$ *which vanish when* $x_1 = x_2 = \cdots = x_q = 0$.

In order to simplify the notation, we shall restrict ourselves to the case of two equations between two dependent variables u and v and three independent variables x, y, and z:

$$(46) \quad \begin{cases} F_1 = au + bv + cx + dy + ez + \cdots = 0, \\ F_2 = a'u + b'v + c'x + d'y + e'z + \cdots = 0. \end{cases}$$

Since the determinant $ab' - ba'$ is not zero, by hypothesis, the two equations (46) may be replaced by two equations of the form

(47)
$$\begin{cases} u = \Sigma a_{mnpqr} x^m y^n z^p u^q v^r, \\ v = \Sigma b_{mnpqr} x^m y^n z^p u^q v^r, \end{cases}$$

where the left-hand sides contain no constant terms and no terms of the first degree in u and v. It is easy to show, as above, that these equations may be satisfied *formally* by replacing u and v by power series in x, y, and z:

(48) $$u = \Sigma c_{ikl} x^i y^k z^l, \qquad v = \Sigma c'_{ikl} x^i y^k z^l,$$

where the coefficients c_{ikl} and c'_{ikl} may be calculated from a_{mnpqr} and b_{mnpqr} by means of additions and multiplications only. In order to show that these series converge, we need merely compare them with the analogous expansions obtained by solving the two auxiliary equations

$$U = V = \cfrac{M}{\left(1 - \dfrac{x+y+z}{r}\right)\left(1 - \dfrac{U+V}{\rho}\right)} - M\left(1 + \frac{U+V}{\rho}\right),$$

where M, r, and ρ are positive numbers whose meaning has been explained above. These two auxiliary equations reduce to a single equation of the second degree

$$U^2 - \frac{\rho^2 U}{2\rho + 4M} + \frac{M\rho^2}{2\rho + 4M} \cfrac{\dfrac{x+y+z}{r}}{1 - \dfrac{x+y+z}{r}} = 0,$$

which has a single root which vanishes for $x = y = z = 0$, namely:

$$U = \frac{\rho^2}{4(\rho + 2M)} - \frac{\rho^2}{4(\rho + 2M)} \sqrt{\cfrac{1 - \dfrac{x+y+z}{\alpha}}{1 - \dfrac{x+y+z}{r}}},$$

where $\alpha = r\left[\rho/(\rho + 4M)\right]^2$.

This root may be developed in a convergent power series whenever the absolute values of x, y, and z are all less than or equal to $\alpha/3$. Hence the series (48) converges under the same conditions.

Let u_1 and v_1 be the solutions of (47) which are developable in series. If we set $u = u_1 + u'$, $v = v_1 + v'$ in (47) and arrange the result according to powers of x, y, z, u', v', each of the terms must be divisible by u' or by v'. Hence, returning to the original variables x, y, z, u, v, the given equations may be written in the form

(47′)
$$\begin{cases} (u - u_1)f \;+ (v - v_1)\phi \;= 0, \\ (u - u_1)f_1 + (v - v_1)\phi_1 = 0, \end{cases}$$

where f, ϕ, f_1, ϕ_1 are power series in x, y, z, u, and v. In this form the solutions $u = u_1$, $v = v_1$ are exhibited. It is evident also that no other solutions of (47') exist which vanish for $x = y = z = 0$. For any other set of solutions must cause $f\phi_1 - \phi f_1$ to vanish, and a comparison of (47) with (47') shows that the constant term is unity in both f and ϕ_1, whereas the constant term is zero in both f_1 and ϕ; hence the condition $f\phi_1 - \phi f_1 = 0$ cannot be met by replacing u and v by functions which vanish when $x = y = z = 0$.

189. Lagrange's formula. Let us consider the equation

$$(49) \qquad y = a + x\phi(y),$$

where $\phi(y)$ is a function which is developable in a power series in $y - a$,

$$\phi(y) = \phi(a) + (y - a)\,\phi'(a) + \frac{(y - a)^2}{1 \cdot 2}\,\phi''(a) + \cdots,$$

which converges whenever $y - a$ does not exceed a certain number. By the general theorem of § 187, this equation has one and only one root which approaches a as x approaches zero, and this root is represented for sufficiently small values of x by a convergent power series

$$y = a + a_1 x + a_2 x^2 + \cdots.$$

In general, if $f(y)$ is a function which is developable according to positive powers of $y - a$, an expansion of $f(y)$ according to powers of x may be obtained by replacing y by the development just found,

$$(50) \qquad f(y) = f(a) + A_1 x + A_2 x^2 + \cdots + A_n x^n + \cdots,$$

and this expansion holds for all values of x between certain limits.

The purpose of Lagrange's formula is to determine the coefficients

$$A_1,\, A_2,\, \cdots,\, A_n,\, \cdots$$

in terms of a. It will be noticed that this problem does not differ essentially from the general problem. The coefficient A_n is equal to the nth derivative of $f(y)$ for $y = 0$, except for a constant factor $n!$, where y is defined by (49); and this derivative can be calculated by the usual rules. The calculation appears to be very complicated, but it may be substantially shortened by applying the following remarks of Laplace (cf. Ex. 8, Chapter II). The partial derivatives of the function y defined by (49), with respect to the variables x and a, are given by the formulæ

$$[1 - x\phi'(y)]\,\frac{\partial y}{\partial x} = \phi(y), \qquad [1 - x\phi'(y)]\,\frac{\partial y}{\partial a} = 1,$$

whence we find immediately

$$(51) \qquad \frac{\partial u}{\partial x} = \phi(y)\,\frac{\partial u}{\partial a},$$

where $u = f(y)$. On the other hand, it is easy to show that the formula

$$(51') \qquad \frac{\partial}{\partial a}\left[F(y)\,\frac{\partial u}{\partial x}\right] = \frac{\partial}{\partial x}\left[F(y)\,\frac{\partial u}{\partial a}\right]$$

is identically satisfied, where $F(y)$ is an arbitrary function of y. For either side becomes

$$F'(y)f'(y)\frac{\partial y}{\partial a}\frac{\partial y}{\partial x} + F(y)\frac{\partial^2 u}{\partial a\,\partial x}$$

on performing the indicated differentiations. We shall now prove the formula

$$\frac{\partial^n u}{\partial x^n} = \frac{\partial^{n-1}}{\partial a^{n-1}}\left[\phi(y)^n\frac{\partial u}{\partial a}\right]$$

for any value of n. It holds, by (51), for $n = 1$. In order to prove it in general, let us assume that it holds for a certain number n. Then we shall have

$$\frac{\partial^{n+1} u}{\partial x^{n+1}} = \frac{\partial^n}{\partial a^{n-1}\partial x}\left[\phi(y)^n\frac{\partial u}{\partial a}\right].$$

But we also have, from (51) and (51′),

$$\frac{\partial}{\partial x}\left[\phi(y)^n\frac{\partial u}{\partial a}\right] = \frac{\partial}{\partial a}\left[\phi(y)^n\frac{\partial u}{\partial x}\right] = \frac{\partial}{\partial a}\left[\phi(y)^{n+1}\frac{\partial u}{\partial a}\right],$$

whence the preceding formula reduces to the form

$$\frac{\partial^{n+1} u}{\partial x^{n+1}} = \frac{\partial^n}{\partial a^n}\left[\phi(y)^{n+1}\frac{\partial u}{\partial a}\right],$$

which shows that the formula in question holds for all values of n.

Now if we set $x = 0$, y reduces to a, u to $f(a)$, and the nth derivative of u with respect to x is given by the formula

$$\left(\frac{\partial^n u}{\partial x^n}\right)_0 = \frac{d^{n-1}}{da^{n-1}}[\phi(a)^n f'(a)].$$

Hence the development of $f(y)$ by Taylor's series becomes

(52)
$$\begin{cases} f(y) = f(a) + x\phi(a)f'(a) + \dfrac{x^2}{1\,.\,2}\dfrac{d}{da}[\phi(a)^2 f'(a)] + \cdots \\ \qquad\qquad + \dfrac{x^n}{n!}\dfrac{d^{n-1}}{da^{n-1}}[\phi(a)^n f'(a)] + \cdots. \end{cases}$$

This is the noted formula due to Lagrange. It gives an expression for the root y which approaches zero as x approaches zero. We shall find later the limits between which this formula is applicable.

Note. It follows from the general theorem that the root y, considered as a function of x and a, may be represented as a double series arranged according to powers of x and a. This series can be obtained by replacing each of the coefficients A_n by its development in powers of a. Hence the series (52) may be differentiated term by term with respect to a.

Examples. 1) The equation

(53)
$$y = a + \frac{x}{2}(y^2 - 1)$$

has one root which is equal to a when $x = 0$. Lagrange's formula gives the following development for that root:

$$(54) \quad \begin{cases} y = a + \dfrac{x}{2}(a^2 - 1) + \dfrac{1}{1 \cdot 2}\left(\dfrac{x}{2}\right)^2 \dfrac{d(a^2 - 1)^2}{da} + \cdots \\[2ex] \qquad\qquad + \dfrac{1}{1 \cdot 2 \cdots n}\left(\dfrac{x}{2}\right)^n \dfrac{d^{n-1}(a^2 - 1)^n}{da^{n-1}} + \cdots. \end{cases}$$

On the other hand, the equation (53) may be solved directly, and its roots are

$$y = \frac{1}{x} \pm \frac{1}{x}\sqrt{1 - 2ax + x^2}.$$

The root which is equal to a when $x = 0$ is that given by taking the sign $-$. Differentiating both sides of (54) with respect to a, we obtain a formula which differs from the formula (32) of § 184 only in notation.

2) Kepler's equation for the eccentric anomaly u,[*]

$$(55) \qquad\qquad\qquad u = a + e \sin u,$$

which occurs in Astronomy, has a root u which is equal to a for $e = 0$. Lagrange's formula gives the development of this root near $e = 0$ in the form

$$(56) \quad u = a + e \sin a + \frac{e^2}{1 \cdot 2}\frac{d}{da}(\sin^2 a) + \cdots + \frac{e^n}{1 \cdot 2 \cdots n}\frac{d^{n-1}(\sin^n a)}{da^{n-1}} + \cdots.$$

Laplace was the first to show, by a profound process of reasoning, that this series converges whenever e is less than the limit $0.662743 \cdots$

190. Inversion. Let us consider a series of the form

$$(57) \qquad\qquad y = a_1 x + a_2 x^2 + \cdots + a_n x^n + \cdots,$$

where a_1 is different from zero and where the interval of convergence is $(-r, +r)$. If y be taken as the independent variable and x be thought of as a function of y, by the general theorem of § 187 the equation (57) has one and only one root which approaches zero with y, and this root can be developed in a power series in y:

$$(58) \qquad\qquad x = b_1 y + b_2 y^2 + b_3 y^3 + \cdots + b_n y^n + \cdots.$$

The coefficients b_1, b_2, b_3, $\cdots$ may be determined successively by replacing x in (57) by this expansion and then equating the coefficients of like powers of y. The values thus found are

$$b_1 = \frac{1}{a_1}, \qquad b_2 = -\frac{a_2}{a_1^3}, \qquad b_3 = \frac{2a_2 - a_1 a_3}{a_1^5}, \qquad \cdots$$

The value of the coefficient b of the general term may be obtained from Lagrange's formula. For, setting

$$\psi(x) = a_1 + a_2 x + \cdots + a_n x^{n-1} + \cdots,$$

the equation (57) may be written in the form

$$x = y \frac{1}{\psi(x)},$$

---

* See p. 248, Ex. 19; and ZIWET, *Elements of Theoretical Mechanics*, 2d ed., p. 356. — TRANS.

and the development of the root of this equation which approaches zero with y is given by Lagrange's formula in the form

$$x = y\,\frac{1}{\psi(0)} + \cdots + \frac{y^n}{1 . 2 \cdots n}\,\frac{d^{n-1}}{dx^{n-1}}\left(\frac{1}{\psi(x)}\right)_0^n + \cdots,$$

where the subscript 0 indicates that we are to set $x = 0$ after performing the indicated differentiations.

The problem just treated has sometimes been called the *reversion of series*.

191. Analytic functions. In the future we shall say that a function of any number of variables x, y, z, $\cdots$ is *analytic* if it can be developed, for values of the variables near the point x_0, y_0, z_0, $\cdots$, in a power series arranged according to increasing powers of $x - x_0$, $y - y_0$, $z - z_0$, $\cdots$ which converges for sufficiently small values of the differences $x - x_0$, $\cdots$. The values which x_0, y_0, z_0, $\cdots$ may take on may be restricted by certain conditions, but we shall not go into the matter further here. The developments of the present chapter make clear that such functions are, so to speak, interrelated. Given one or more analytic functions, the operations of integration and differentiation, the algebraic operations of multiplication, division, substitution, etc., lead to new *analytic* functions. Likewise, the solution of equations whose left-hand member is analytic leads to analytic functions. Since the very simplest functions, such as polynomials, the exponential function, the trigonometric functions, etc., are analytic, it is easy to see why the first functions studied by mathematicians were analytic. These functions are still predominant in the theory of functions of a complex variable and in the study of differential equations. Nevertheless, despite the fundamental importance of analytic functions, it must not be forgotten that they actually constitute merely a very particular group among the whole assemblage of continuous functions.*

192. Plane curves. Let us consider an arc AB of a plane curve. We shall say that *the curve is analytic along the arc AB* if the coördinates of any point M which lies in the neighborhood of any fixed point M_0 of that arc can be developed in power series arranged according to powers of a parameter $t - t_0$,

$$(59) \quad \begin{cases} x = \phi(t) = x_0 + a_1(t - t_0) + a_2(t - t_0)^2 + \cdots + a_n(t - t_0)^n + \cdots, \\ y = \psi(t) = y_0 + b_1(t - t_0) + b_2(t - t_0)^2 + \cdots + b_n(t - t_0)^n + \cdots, \end{cases}$$

which converge for sufficiently small values of $t - t_0$.

---

* In the second volume an example of a non-analytic function will be given, all of whose derivatives exist throughout an interval (a, b).

A point M_0 will be called an *ordinary point* if in the neighborhood of that point one of the differences $y - y_0$, $x - x_0$ can be represented as a convergent power series in powers of the other. If, for example, $y - y_0$ can be developed in a power series in $x - x_0$,

$$(60) \quad y - y_0 = c_1(x - x_0) + c_2(x - x_0)^2 + \cdots + c_n(x - x_0)^n + \cdots,$$

for all values of x between $x_0 - h$ and $x_0 + h$, the point (x_0, y_0) is an ordinary point. It is easy to replace the equation (60) by two equations of the form (59), for we need only set

$$(61) \quad \begin{cases} x = x_0 + t - t_0, \\ y = y_0 + c_1(t - t_0) + \cdots + c_n(t - t_0)^n + \cdots. \end{cases}$$

If c_1 is different from zero, which is the case in general, the equation (60) may be solved for $x - x_0$ in a power series in $y - y_0$ which is valid whenever $y - y_0$ is sufficiently small. In this case each of the differences $x - x_0$, $y - y_0$ can be represented as a convergent power series in powers of the other. This ceases to be true if c_1 is zero, that is to say, if the tangent to the curve is parallel to the x axis. In that case, as we shall see presently, $x - x_0$ may be developed in a series arranged according to *fractional* powers of $y - y_0$. It is evident also that at a point where the tangent is parallel to the y axis $x - x_0$ can be developed in power series in $y - y_0$, but $y - y_0$ cannot be developed in power series in $x - x_0$.

If the coördinates (x, y) of a point on the curve are given by the equations (59) near a point M_0, that point is an ordinary point if at least one of the coefficients a_1, b_1 is different from zero.* If a_1 is not zero, for example, the first equation can be solved for $t - t_0$ in powers of $x - x_0$, and the second equation becomes an expansion of $y - y_0$ in powers of $x - x_0$ when this solution is substituted for $t - t_0$.

The appearance of a curve at an ordinary point is either the customary appearance or else that of a point of inflection. Any point which is not an ordinary point is called a *singular* point. If all the points of an arc of an analytic curve are ordinary points, the arc is said to be *regular*.

---

* This condition is sufficient, but not necessary. However, the equations of any curve, near an ordinary point M_0, *may* always be written in such a way that a_1 and b_1 do not both vanish, *by a suitable choice of the parameter.* For this is actually accomplished in equations (61). See also second footnote, p. 409. — TRANS.

If each of the coefficients a_1 and b_1 is zero, but a_2, for example, is different from zero, the first of equations (59) may be written in the form $(x - x_0)^{\frac{1}{2}} = (t - t_0)[a_2 + a_3(t - t_0) + \cdots]^{\frac{1}{2}}$, where the right-hand member is developable according to powers of $t - t_0$. Hence $t - t_0$ is developable in powers of $(x - x_0)^{\frac{1}{2}}$, and if $t - t_0$ in the second equation of (59) be replaced by that development, we obtain a development for $y - y_0$ in powers of $(x - x_0)^{\frac{1}{2}}$:

$$y - y_0 = c_1(x - x_0) + c_2(x - x_0)^{\frac{3}{2}} + c_3(x - x_0)^2 + \cdots.$$

In this case the point (x_0, y_0) is usually a cusp of the first kind.*

The argument just given is general. If the development of $x - x_0$ in powers of $t - t_0$ begins with a term of degree n, $y - y_0$ can be developed according to powers of $(x - x_0)$. The appearance of a curve given by the equation (59) near a point (x_0, y_0) is of one of four types: a point with none of these peculiarities, a point of inflection, a cusp of the first kind, or a cusp of the second kind.*

193. Skew curves. A skew curve is said to be *analytic along an arc* AB if the coördinates x, y, z of a variable point M can be developed in power series arranged according to powers of a parameter $t - t_0$

$$(62) \quad \begin{cases} x = x_0 + a_1(t - t_0) + \cdots + a_n(t - t_0)^n + \cdots, \\ y = y_0 + b_1(t - t_0) + \cdots + b_n(t - t_0)^n + \cdots, \\ z = z_0 + c_1(t - t_0) + \cdots + c_n(t - t_0)^n + \cdots, \end{cases}$$

in the neighborhood of any fixed point M_0 of the arc. A point M_0 is said to be an ordinary point if two of the three differences $x - x_0$, $y - y_0$, $z - z_0$ can be developed in power series arranged according to powers of the third.

It can be shown, as in the preceding paragraph, that the point M_0 will surely be an ordinary point if not all three of the coefficients a_1, b_1, c_1 vanish. Hence the value of the parameter t for a singular point must satisfy the equations †

$$\frac{dx}{dt} = 0, \qquad \frac{dy}{dt} = 0, \qquad \frac{dz}{dt} = 0.$$

---

* For a cusp of the first kind the tangent lies between the two branches. For a cusp of the second kind both branches lie on the same side of the tangent. The point is an ordinary point, of course, if the coefficients of the fractional powers happen to be all zeros. — TRANS.

† These conditions are not sufficient to make the point M_0, which corresponds to a value t_0 of the parameter, a singular point when a point M of the curve near M_0 corresponds to several values of t which approach t_0 as M approaches M_0. Such is the case, for example, at the origin on the curve defined by the equations $x = t^2$, $y = t^4$, $z = t^6$.

Let x_0, y_0, z_0 be the coördinates of a point M_0 on a skew curve Γ whose equations are given in the form

$$(63) \qquad F(x, y, z) = 0, \qquad F_1(x, y, z) = 0,$$

where the functions F and F_1 are power series in $x - x_0$, $y - y_0$, $z - z_0$. The point M_0 will surely be an ordinary point if not all three of the functional determinants

$$\frac{D(F, F_1)}{D(x, y)}, \qquad \frac{D(F, F_1)}{D(y, z)}, \qquad \frac{D(F, F_1)}{D(z, x)}$$

vanish simultaneously at the point $x = x_0$, $y = y_0$, $z = z_0$. For if the determinant $D(F, F_1)/D(x, y)$, for example, does not vanish at M_0, the equations (63) can be solved, by § 188, for $x - x_0$ and $y - y_0$ as power series in $z - z_0$.

194. Surfaces. A surface S will be said to be *analytic* throughout a certain region if the coördinates x, y, z of any variable point M can be expressed as double power series in terms of two variable parameters $t - t_0$ and $u - u_0$

$$(64) \qquad \begin{cases} x - x_0 = a_{10}(t - t_0) + a_{01}(u - u_0) + \cdots, \\ y - y_0 = b_{10}(t - t_0) + b_{01}(u - u_0) + \cdots, \\ z - z_0 = c_{10}(t - t_0) + c_{01}(u - u_0) + \cdots, \end{cases}$$

in the neighborhood of any fixed point M_0 of that region, where the three series converge for sufficiently small values of $t - t_0$ and $u - u_0$. A point M_0 of the surface will be said to be an ordinary point if one of the three differences $x - x_0$, $y - y_0$, $z - z_0$ can be expressed as a power series in terms of the other two. Every point M_0 for which not all three of the determinants

$$\frac{D(y, z)}{D(t, u)}, \qquad \frac{D(z, x)}{D(t, u)}, \qquad \frac{D(x, y)}{D(t, u)}$$

vanish simultaneously is surely an ordinary point. If, for example, the first of these determinants does not vanish, the last two of the equations (64) can be solved for $t - t_0$ and $u - u_0$, and the first equation becomes an expansion of $x - x_0$ in terms of $y - y_0$ and $z - z_0$ upon replacing $t - t_0$ and $u - u_0$ by these values.

Let the surface S be given by means of an unsolved equation $F(x, y, z) = 0$, and let x_0, y_0, z_0 be the coördinates of a point M_0 of the surface. If the function $F(x, y, z)$ is a power series in $x - x_0$, $y - y_0$, $z - z_0$, and if not all three of the partial derivatives $\partial F/\partial x_0$, $\partial F/\partial y_0$, $\partial F/\partial z_0$ vanish simultaneously, the point M_0 is surely an ordinary point, by § 188.

Note. The definition of an ordinary point on a curve or on a surface is independent of the choice of axes. For, let $M_0 (x_0, y_0, z_0)$ be an ordinary point on a surface S. Then the coördinates of any neighboring point *can* * be written in the form (64), where not all three of the determinants $D(y, z)/D(t, u)$, $D(z, x)/D(t, u)$, $D(x, y)/D(t, u)$ vanish simultaneously for $t = t_0$, $u = u_0$. Let us now select any new axes whatever and let

$$X = \alpha_1 x + \beta_1 y + \gamma_1 z + \delta_1,$$
$$Y = \alpha_2 x + \beta_2 y + \gamma_2 z + \delta_2,$$
$$Z = \alpha_3 x + \beta_3 y + \gamma_3 z + \delta_3$$

be the transformation which carries x, y, z into the new coördinates X, Y, Z, where the determinant $\Delta = D(X, Y, Z)/D(x, y, z)$ is different from zero. Replacing x, y, z by their developments in series (64), we obtain three analogous developments for X, Y, Z; and we cannot have

$$\frac{D(X, Y)}{D(t, u)} = \frac{D(Y, Z)}{D(t, u)} = \frac{D(Z, X)}{D(t, u)} = 0$$

for $t = t_0$, $u = u_0$, since the transformation can be written in the form

$$x = A_1 X + B_1 Y + C_1 Z + D_1,$$
$$y = A_2 X + B_2 Y + C_2 Z + D_2,$$
$$z = A_3 X + B_3 Y + C_3 Z + D_3,$$

and the three functional determinants involving X, Y, Z cannot vanish simultaneously unless the three involving x, y, z also vanish simultaneously.

IV. TRIGONOMETRIC SERIES   MISCELLANEOUS SERIES

195. Calculation of the coefficients. The series which we shall study in this section are entirely different from those studied above. Trigonometric series appear to have been first studied by D. Bernoulli, in connection with the problem of the stretched string. The process for determining the coefficients, which we are about to give, is due to Euler.

Let $f(x)$ be a function defined in the interval (a, b). We shall first suppose that a and b have the values $-\pi$ and $+\pi$, respectively, which is always allowable, since the substitution

$$x' = \frac{2\pi x - (a + b)\pi}{b - a}$$

---

* See footnote, p. 408. — TRANS.

reduces any case to the preceding. Then if the equation

$$(65) \quad f(x) = \frac{a_0}{2} + (a_1 \cos x + b_1 \sin x) + \cdots + (a_m \cos mx + b_m \sin mx) + \cdots$$

holds for all values of x between $-\pi$ and $+\pi$, where the coefficients $a_0, a_1, b_1, \cdots, a_m, b_m, \cdots$ are unknown constants, the following device enables us to determine those constants. We shall first write down for reference the following formulæ, which were established above, for positive integral values of m and n:

$$(66) \begin{cases} \displaystyle\int_{-\pi}^{+\pi} \sin mx \, dx = 0; \\[2ex] \displaystyle\int_{-\pi}^{+\pi} \cos mx \, dx = 0, & \text{if } m \neq 0; \\[2ex] \displaystyle\int_{-\pi}^{+\pi} \cos mx \cos nx \, dx \\[2ex] \quad = \displaystyle\int_{-\pi}^{+\pi} \frac{\cos (m-n)x + \cos (m+n)x}{2} \, dx = 0, \text{ if } m \neq n; \\[2ex] \displaystyle\int_{-\pi}^{+\pi} \cos^2 mx \, dx = \displaystyle\int_{-\pi}^{+\pi} \frac{1 + \cos 2mx}{2} \, dx = \pi, \text{ if } m \neq 0; \\[2ex] \displaystyle\int_{-\pi}^{+\pi} \sin mx \sin nx \, dx \\[2ex] \quad = \displaystyle\int_{-\pi}^{+\pi} \frac{\cos (m-n)x - \cos (m+n)x}{2} \, dx = 0, \text{ if } m \neq n; \\[2ex] \displaystyle\int_{-\pi}^{+\pi} \sin^2 mx \, dx = \displaystyle\int_{-\pi}^{+\pi} \frac{1 - \cos 2mx}{2} \, dx = \pi, \text{ if } m \neq 0; \\[2ex] \displaystyle\int_{-\pi}^{+\pi} \sin mx \cos nx \, dx \\[2ex] \quad = \displaystyle\int_{-\pi}^{+\pi} \frac{\sin (m+n)x + \sin (m-n)x}{2} \, dx = 0. \end{cases}$$

Integrating both sides of (65) between the limits $-\pi$ and $+\pi$, the right-hand side being integrated term by term, we find

$$\int_{-\pi}^{+\pi} f(x) \, dx = \frac{a_0}{2} \int_{-\pi}^{+\pi} dx = \pi a_0,$$

which gives the value of a_0. Performing the same operations upon the equation (65) after having multiplied both sides either by $\cos mx$

or by $\sin mx$, the only term on the right whose integral between $-\pi$ and $+\pi$ is different from zero is the one in $\cos^2 mx$ or in $\sin^2 mx$. Hence we find the formulæ

$$\int_{-\pi}^{+\pi} f(x) \cos mx\, dx = \pi a_m, \qquad \int_{-\pi}^{+\pi} f(x) \sin mx\, dx = \pi b_m,$$

respectively. The values of the coefficients may be assembled as follows :

$$(67) \quad \begin{cases} a_0 = \dfrac{1}{\pi} \displaystyle\int_{-\pi}^{+\pi} f(\alpha)\, d\alpha, \qquad a_m = \dfrac{1}{\pi} \displaystyle\int_{-\pi}^{+\pi} f(\alpha) \cos m\alpha\, d\alpha, \\[2ex] \qquad\qquad b_m = \dfrac{1}{\pi} \displaystyle\int_{-\pi}^{+\pi} f(\alpha) \sin m\alpha\, d\alpha. \end{cases}$$

The preceding calculation is merely formal, and therefore tentative. For we have assumed that the function $f(x)$ can be developed in the form (65), and that that development converges uniformly between the limits $-\pi$ and $+\pi$. Since there is nothing to prove, *a priori*, that these assumptions are justifiable, it is essential that we investigate whether the series thus obtained converges or not. Replacing the coefficients a_i and b_i by their values from (67) and simplifying, the sum of the first $(m+1)$ terms is seen to be

$$S_{m+1} = \frac{1}{\pi} \int_{-\pi}^{+\pi} f(\alpha) \left[\frac{1}{2} + \cos(\alpha - x) + \cos 2(\alpha - x) + \cdots + \cos m(\alpha - x) \right] d\alpha.$$

But by a well-known trigonometric formula we have

$$\frac{1}{2} + \cos a + \cos 2a + \cdots + \cos ma = \frac{\sin \dfrac{2m+1}{2} a}{2 \sin \dfrac{a}{2}},$$

whence

$$S_{m+1} = \frac{1}{\pi} \int_{-\pi}^{+\pi} f(\alpha)\, \frac{\sin \dfrac{2m+1}{2}(\alpha - x)}{2 \sin \dfrac{\alpha - x}{2}}\, d\alpha,$$

or, setting $\alpha = x + 2y$,

$$(68) \qquad S_{m+1} = \frac{1}{\pi} \int_{-\frac{\pi+x}{2}}^{\frac{\pi-x}{2}} f(x+2y)\, \frac{\sin(2m+1)y}{\sin y}\, dy.$$

The whole question is reduced to that of finding the limit of this sum as the integer m increases indefinitely. In order to study this question, we shall assume that the function $f(x)$ satisfies the following conditions :

1) The function $f(x)$ shall be in general continuous between $-\pi$ and $+\pi$, except for a *finite* number of values of x, for which its value may change suddenly in the following manner. Let c be a number between $-\pi$ and $+\pi$. For any value of c a number h can be found such that $f(x)$ is continuous between $c-h$ and c and also between c and $c+h$. As ϵ approaches zero, $f(c+\epsilon)$ approaches a limit which we shall call $f(c+0)$. Likewise, $f(c-\epsilon)$ approaches a limit which we shall call $f(c-0)$ as ϵ approaches zero. If the function $f(x)$ is continuous for $x=c$, we shall have $f(c)=f(c+0)=f(c-0)$. If $f(c+0) \neq f(c-0)$, $f(x)$ is discontinuous for $x=c$, and we shall agree to take the arithmetic mean of these values $[f(c+0)+f(c-0)]/2$ for $f(c)$. It is evident that this definition of $f(c)$ holds also at points where $f(x)$ is continuous. We shall further suppose that $f(-\pi+\epsilon)$ and $f(\pi-\epsilon)$ approach limits, which we shall call $f(-\pi+0)$ and $f(\pi-0)$, respectively, as ϵ approaches zero through positive values. The curve whose equation is $y=f(x)$ must be similar to that of Fig. 11 on page 160, if there are any discontinuities. We have already seen that the function $f(x)$ is integrable in the interval from $-\pi$ to $+\pi$, and it is evident that the same is true for the product of $f(x)$ by any function which is continuous in the same interval.

2) It shall be possible to divide the interval $(-\pi, +\pi)$ into a finite number of subintervals in such a way that $f(x)$ is a monotonically increasing or a monotonically decreasing function in each of the subintervals.

For brevity we shall say that the function $f(x)$ satisfies *Dirichlet's conditions* in the interval $(-\pi, +\pi)$. It is clear that a function which is continuous in the interval $(-\pi, +\pi)$ and which has a finite number of maxima and minima in that interval, satisfies Dirichlet's conditions.

196. The integral $\int_0^h f(x)[\sin nx/\sin x]dx$. The expression obtained for S_{m+1} leads us to seek the limit of the definite integral

$$\int_0^h f(x) \frac{\sin nx}{\sin x} dx$$

as n becomes infinite. The first rigorous discussion of this question was given by Lejeune-Dirichlet.[*] The method which we shall employ is essentially the same as that given by Bonnet.[†]

---

[*] *Crelle's Journal*, Vol. IV, 1829.

[†] *Mémoires des savants étrangers* publiés par l'Académie de Belgique, Vol. XXIII.

Let us first consider the integral

(69)
$$J = \int_0^h \phi(x) \frac{\sin nx}{x} \, dx,$$

where h is a positive number less than π, and $\phi(x)$ is a function which satisfies Dirichlet's conditions in the interval $(0, h)$. If $\phi(x)$ is a constant C, it is easy to find the limit of J. For, setting $y = nx$, we may write

$$J = C \int_0^{nh} \frac{\sin y}{y} \, dy,$$

and the limit of J as n becomes infinite is $C\pi/2$, by (39), § 176.

Next suppose that $\phi(x)$ is a positive monotonically decreasing function in the interval $(0, h)$. The integrand changes sign for all values of x of the form $k\pi/n$. Hence J may be written

$$J = u_0 - u_1 + u_2 - u_3 + \cdots + (-1)^k u_k + \cdots + (-1)^m \theta u_m, \quad 0 < \theta < 1,$$

where

$$u_k = \left| \int_{\frac{k\pi}{n}}^{\frac{(k+1)\pi}{n}} \phi(x) \frac{\sin nx}{x} \, dx \right|$$

and where the upper limit h is supposed to lie between $m\pi/n$ and $(m+1)\pi/n$. Each of the integrals u_k is less than the preceding. For, if we set $nx = k\pi + y$ in u_k, we find

$$u_k = \int_0^\pi \phi\left(\frac{y + k\pi}{n}\right) \frac{\sin y}{y + k\pi} \, dy,$$

and it is evident, by the hypotheses regarding $\phi(x)$, that this integral decreases as the subscript k increases. Hence we shall have the equations

$$J = u_0 - (u_1 - u_2) - (u_3 - u_4) - \cdots,$$
$$J = u_0 - u_1 + (u_2 - u_3) + (u_4 - u_5) + \cdots,$$

which show that J lies between u_0 and $u_0 - u_1$. It follows that J is a positive number less than u_0, that is to say, less than the integral

$$\int_0^{\frac{\pi}{n}} \phi(x) \frac{\sin nx}{x} \, dx.$$

But this integral is itself less than the integral

$$\phi(+0) \int_0^{\frac{\pi}{n}} \frac{\sin nx}{x} \, dx = \phi(+0) \int_0^\pi \frac{\sin y}{y} \, dy = A\phi(+0),$$

where A denotes the value of the definite integral $\int_0^\pi [(\sin y)/y] \, dy$.

The same argument shows that the definite integral

$$J' = \int_c^h \phi(x)\, \frac{\sin nx}{x}\, dx,$$

where c is any positive number less than h, approaches zero as n becomes infinite. If c lies between $(i-1)\pi/n$ and $i\pi/n$, it can be shown as above that the absolute value of J' is less than

$$\left| \int_c^{\frac{i\pi}{n}} \phi(x)\, \frac{\sin nx}{x}\, dx \right| + \left| \int_{\frac{i\pi}{n}}^{\frac{(i+1)\pi}{n}} \phi(x)\, \frac{\sin nx}{x}\, dx \right|$$

and hence, *a fortiori*, less than

$$\frac{\phi(c)}{c}\left(\frac{i\pi}{n} - c\right) + \frac{\phi\left(\dfrac{i\pi}{n}\right)}{\dfrac{i\pi}{n}}\,\frac{\pi}{n} < \frac{2\pi}{n}\,\frac{\phi(c)}{c}.$$

Hence the integral approaches zero as n becomes infinite.*

This method gives us no information if $c = 0$. In order to discover the limit of the integral J, let c be a number between 0 and h, such that $\phi(x)$ is continuous from 0 to c, and let us set $\phi(x) = \phi(c) + \psi(x)$. Then $\psi(x)$ is positive and decreases in the interval $(0, c)$ from the value $\phi(+0) - \phi(c)$ when $x = 0$ to the value zero when $x = c$. If we write J in the form

$$J = \phi(c) \int_0^c \frac{\sin nx}{x}\, dx + \int_0^c \psi(x)\, \frac{\sin nx}{x}\, dx + \int_c^h \phi(x)\, \frac{\sin nx}{x}\, dx$$

and then subtract $(\pi/2)\,\phi(+0)$, we find

$$(70) \quad \begin{cases} J - \dfrac{\pi}{2}\,\phi(+0) = \phi(c)\left[\displaystyle\int_0^c \frac{\sin nx}{x}\, dx - \frac{\pi}{2} \right] + \frac{\pi}{2}\left[\phi(c) - \phi(+0)\right] \\[2mm] \qquad\qquad + \displaystyle\int_0^c \psi(x)\, \frac{\sin nx}{x}\, dx + \int_c^h \phi(x)\, \frac{\sin nx}{x}\, dx. \end{cases}$$

In order to prove that J approaches the limit $(\pi/2)\,\phi(+0)$, it will be sufficient to show that a number m exists such that the absolute

---

* This result may be obtained even more simply by the use of the second theorem of the mean for integrals (§ 75). Since the function $\phi(x)$ is a decreasing function, that formula gives

$$\int_c^h \phi(x)\, \frac{\sin nx}{x}\, dx = \frac{\phi(c)}{c} \int_c^\xi \sin nx\, dx = \frac{1}{n}\,\frac{\phi(c)}{c}\,(\cos nc - \cos n\xi),$$

and the right-hand member evidently approaches zero.

value of each of the terms on the right is less than a preassigned positive number $\epsilon/4$ when n is greater than m. By the remark made above, the absolute value of the integral

$$\int_0^c \psi(x)\, \frac{\sin nx}{x}\, dx$$

is less than $A\psi(+0) = A[\phi(+0) - \phi(c)]$. Since $\phi(x)$ approaches $\phi(+0)$ as x approaches zero, c may be taken so near to zero that $A[\phi(+0) - \phi(c)]$ and $(\pi/2)[\phi(+0) - \phi(c)]$ are both less than $\epsilon/4$. The number c having been chosen in this way, the other two terms on the right-hand side of equation (70) both approach zero as n becomes infinite. Hence n may be chosen so large that the absolute value of either of them is less than $\epsilon/4$. It follows that

$$(71) \qquad\qquad \lim_{n=\infty} J = \frac{\pi}{2}\, \phi(+0).$$

We shall now proceed to remove the various restrictions which have been placed upon $\phi(x)$ in the preceding argument. If $\phi(x)$ is a monotonically decreasing function, but is not always positive, the function $\psi(x) = \phi(x) + C$ is a positive monotonically decreasing function from 0 to h if the constant C be suitably chosen. Then the formula (71) applies to $\psi(x)$. Moreover we may write

$$\int_0^h \phi(x)\, \frac{\sin nx}{x}\, dx = \int_0^h \psi(x)\, \frac{\sin nx}{x}\, dx - C \int_0^h \frac{\sin nx}{x}\, dx,$$

and the right-hand side approaches the limit $(\pi/2)\psi(+0) - (\pi/2)C$, that is, $(\pi/2)\phi(+0)$.

If $\phi(x)$ is a monotonically increasing function from 0 to h, $-\phi(x)$ is a monotonically decreasing function, and we shall have

$$\int_0^h \phi(x)\, \frac{\sin nx}{x}\, dx = -\int_0^h -\phi(x)\, \frac{\sin nx}{x}\, dx.$$

Hence the integral approaches $(\pi/2)\phi(+0)$ in this case also.

Finally, suppose that $\phi(x)$ is any function which satisfies Dirichlet's conditions in the interval $(0, h)$. Then the interval $(0, h)$ may be divided into a finite number of subintervals $(0, a)$, (a, b), (b, c), $\cdots$, (l, h), in each of which $\phi(x)$ is a monotonically increasing or decreasing function. The integral from 0 to a approaches the limit $(\pi/2)\phi(+0)$. Each of the other integrals, which are of the type

$$H = \int_a^b \phi(x)\, \frac{\sin nx}{x}\, dx,$$

approaches zero. For if $\phi(x)$ is a monotonically increasing function, for instance, from a to b, an auxiliary function $\psi(x)$ can be formed in an infinite variety of ways, which increases monotonically from 0 to b, is continuous from 0 to a, and coincides with $\phi(x)$ from a to b. Then each of the integrals

$$\int_0^a \psi(x)\,\frac{\sin nx}{x}\,dx, \qquad \int_0^b \psi(x)\,\frac{\sin nx}{x}\,dx$$

approaches $\psi(+0)$ as n becomes infinite. Hence their difference, which is precisely H, approaches zero. It follows that the formula (71) holds for any function $\phi(x)$ which satisfies Dirichlet's conditions in the interval $(0, h)$.

Let us now consider the integral

$$(72) \qquad I = \int_0^h f(x)\,\frac{\sin nx}{\sin x}\,dx, \qquad 0 < h < \pi,$$

where $f(x)$ is a positive monotonically increasing function from 0 to h. This integral may be written

$$I = \int_0^h \left[f(x)\,\frac{x}{\sin x} \right]\frac{\sin nx}{x}\,dx,$$

and the function $\phi(x) = f(x)\,x/\sin x$ is a positive monotonically increasing function from 0 to h. Since $f(+0) = \phi(+0)$, it follows that

$$(73) \qquad \lim_{n=\infty} I = \frac{\pi}{2}f(+0).$$

This formula therefore holds if $f(x)$ is a positive monotonically increasing function from 0 to h. It can be shown by successive steps, as above, that the restrictions upon $f(x)$ can all be removed, and that the formula holds for any function $f(x)$ which satisfies Dirichlet's conditions in the interval $(0, h)$.

197. Fourier series. A trigonometric series whose coefficients are given by the formulæ (67) is usually called a *Fourier series*. Indeed it was Fourier who first stated the theorem that any function *arbitrarily defined* in an interval of length 2π may be represented by a series of that type. By an *arbitrary function* Fourier understood a function which could be represented graphically by several curvilinear arcs of curves which are usually regarded as distinct curves. We shall render this rather vague notion precise by restricting our discussion to functions which satisfy Dirichlet's conditions.

In order to show that a function of this kind can be represented by a Fourier series in the interval $(-\pi, +\pi)$, we must find the limit of the integral (68) as m becomes infinite. Let us divide this integral into two integrals whose limits of integration are 0 and $(\pi - x)/2$, and $-(\pi + x)/2$ and 0, respectively, and let us make the substitution $y = -z$ in the second of these integrals. Then the formula (68) becomes

$$S_{m+1} = \frac{1}{\pi} \int_0^{\frac{\pi-x}{2}} f(x + 2y) \frac{\sin(2m+1)y}{\sin y} \, dy$$

$$+ \frac{1}{\pi} \int_0^{\frac{\pi+x}{2}} f(x - 2z) \frac{\sin(2m+1)z}{\sin z} \, dz.$$

When x lies between $-\pi$ and $+\pi$, $(\pi - x)/2$ and $(\pi + x)/2$ both lie between 0 and π. Hence by the last article the right-hand side of the preceding formula approaches

$$\frac{1}{\pi} \left[\frac{\pi}{2} f(x + 0) + \frac{\pi}{2} f(x - 0) \right] = \frac{f(x+0) + f(x-0)}{2}$$

as m becomes infinite. It follows that the series (65) converges and that its sum is $f(x)$ for every value of x between $-\pi$ and $+\pi$.

Let us now suppose that x is equal to one of the limits of the interval, $-\pi$ for example. Then S_{m+1} may be written in the form

$$S_{m+1} = \frac{1}{\pi} \int_0^{\pi} f(-\pi + 2y) \frac{\sin(2m+1)y}{\sin y} \, dy$$

$$= \frac{1}{\pi} \int_0^{\frac{\pi}{2}} f(-\pi + 2y) \frac{\sin(2m+1)y}{\sin y} \, dy$$

$$+ \frac{1}{\pi} \int_{\frac{\pi}{2}}^{\pi} f(-\pi + 2y) \frac{\sin(2m+1)y}{\sin y} \, dy.$$

The first integral on the right approaches the limit $f(-\pi + 0)/2$. Setting $y = \pi - z$ in the second integral, it takes the form

$$\frac{1}{\pi} \int_0^{\frac{\pi}{2}} f(\pi - 2z) \frac{\sin(2m+1)z}{\sin z} \, dz,$$

which approaches $f(\pi - 0)/2$. Hence the sum of the trigonometric series is $[f(\pi - 0) + f(-\pi + 0)]/2$ when $x = -\pi$. It is evident that the sum of the series is the same when $x = +\pi$.

If, instead of laying off x as a length along a straight line, we lay it off as the length of an arc of a unit circle, counting in the positive direction from the point of intersection of the circle with the positive direction of some initial diameter, the sum of the series at any point whatever will be the arithmetic mean of the two limits approached by the sum of the series as each of the variable points m' and m'', taken on the circumference on opposite sides of m, approaches m. If the two limits $f(-\pi+0)$ and $f(\pi-0)$ are different, the point of the circumference on the negative direction of the initial line will be a point of discontinuity.

In conclusion, *every function which is defined in the interval $(-\pi, +\pi)$ and which satisfies Dirichlet's conditions in that interval may be represented by a Fourier series in the same interval.*

More generally, let $f(x)$ be a function which is defined in an interval $(\alpha, \alpha+2\pi)$ of length 2π, and which satisfies Dirichlet's conditions in that interval. It is evident that there exists one and only one function $F(x)$ which has the period 2π and coincides with $f(x)$ in the interval $(\alpha, \alpha+2\pi)$. This function is represented, for all values of x, by the sum of a trigonometric series whose coefficients a_m and b_m are given by the formulæ (67):

$$a_m = \frac{1}{\pi}\int_{-\pi}^{+\pi} F(x)\cos mx\,dx, \qquad b_m = \frac{1}{\pi}\int_{-\pi}^{+\pi} F(x)\sin mx\,dx.$$

The coefficient a_m, for example, may be written in the form

$$a_m = \frac{1}{\pi}\int_{\alpha-2h\pi}^{\pi} F(x)\cos mx\,dx + \frac{1}{\pi}\int_{-\pi}^{\alpha-2h\pi} F(x)\cos mx\,dx,$$

where α is supposed to lie between $2h\pi-\pi$ and $2h\pi+\pi$. Since $F(x)$ has the period 2π and coincides with $f(x)$ in the interval $(\alpha, \alpha+2\pi)$, this value may be rewritten in the form

$$(74)\quad \begin{cases} a_m = \dfrac{1}{\pi}\displaystyle\int_{\alpha}^{2h\pi+\pi} f(x)\cos mx\,dx + \int_{2h\pi+\pi}^{\alpha+2\pi} f(x)\cos mx\,dx \\ = \dfrac{1}{\pi}\displaystyle\int_{\alpha}^{\alpha+2\pi} f(x)\cos mx\,dx. \end{cases}$$

Similarly, we should find

$$(75)\qquad b_m = \frac{1}{\pi}\int_{\alpha}^{\alpha+2\pi} f(x)\sin mx\,dx.$$

Whenever a function $f(x)$ is defined in any interval of length 2π, the preceding formulæ enable us to calculate the coefficients of its development in a Fourier series without reducing the given interval to the interval $(-\pi, +\pi)$.

198. Examples. 1) Let us find a Fourier series whose sum is -1 for $-\pi < x < 0$, and $+1$ for $0 < x < +\pi$. The formulæ (67) give the values

$$a_0 = \frac{1}{\pi} \int_{-\pi}^{0} - dx + \frac{1}{\pi} \int_{0}^{\pi} dx = 0,$$

$$a_m = \frac{1}{\pi} \int_{-\pi}^{0} - \cos mx \, dx + \frac{1}{\pi} \int_{0}^{\pi} \cos mx \, dx = 0,$$

$$b_m = \frac{1}{\pi} \int_{-\pi}^{0} - \sin mx \, dx + \frac{1}{\pi} \int_{0}^{\pi} \sin mx \, dx = \frac{2 - \cos m\pi - \cos(-m\pi)}{m\pi}.$$

If m is even, b_m is zero. If m is odd, b_m is $4/m\pi$. Multiplying all the coefficients by $\pi/4$, we see that the sum of the series

$$(76) \qquad y = \frac{\sin x}{1} + \frac{\sin 3x}{3} + \cdots + \frac{\sin(2m+1)x}{2m+1} + \cdots$$

is $-\pi/4$ for $-\pi < x < 0$, and $+\pi/4$ for $0 < x < \pi$. The point $x = 0$ is a point of discontinuity, and the sum of the series is zero when $x = 0$, as it should be. More generally the sum of the series (76) is $\pi/4$ when $\sin x$ is positive, $-\pi/4$ when $\sin x$ is negative, and zero when $\sin x = 0$.

The curve represented by the equation (76) is composed of an infinite number of segments of length π of the straight lines $y = \pm \pi/4$ and an infinite number of isolated points ($y = 0$, $x = k\pi$) on the x axis.

2) The coefficients of the Fourier development of x in the interval from 0 to 2π are

$$a_0 = \frac{1}{\pi} \int_{0}^{2\pi} x \, dx = 2\pi,$$

$$a_m = \frac{1}{\pi} \int_{0}^{2\pi} x \cos mx \, dx = \left[\frac{x \sin mx}{m\pi} \right]_{0}^{2\pi} + \frac{1}{m\pi} \int_{0}^{2\pi} \sin mx \, dx = 0,$$

$$b_m = \frac{1}{\pi} \int_{0}^{2\pi} x \sin mx \, dx = - \left[\frac{x \cos mx}{m\pi} \right]_{0}^{2\pi} + \frac{1}{m\pi} \int_{0}^{2\pi} \cos mx \, dx = -\frac{2}{m}.$$

Hence the formula

$$(77) \qquad \frac{x}{2} = \frac{\pi}{2} - \frac{\sin x}{1} - \frac{\sin 2x}{2} - \frac{\sin 3x}{3} - \cdots$$

is valid for all values of x between 0 and 2π. If we set y equal to the series on the right, the resulting equation represents a curve composed of an infinite number of segments of straight lines parallel to $y = x/2$ and an infinite number of isolated points.

Note. If the function $f(x)$ defined in the interval $(-\pi, +\pi)$ is *even*, that is to say, if $f(-x) = f(x)$, each of the coefficients b_m is zero, since it is evident that

$$\int_{-\pi}^{0} f(x) \sin mx \, dx = - \int_{0}^{\pi} f(x) \sin mx \, dx.$$

Similarly, if $f(x)$ is an *odd* function, that is, if $f(-x) = -f(x)$, each of the coefficients a_m is zero, including a_0. A function $f(x)$ which is defined only in

the interval from 0 to π may be defined in the interval from $-\pi$ to 0 by either
of the equations

$$f(-x) = f(x) \quad \text{or} \quad f(-x) = -f(x)$$

if we choose to do so. Hence the given function $f(x)$ may be represented either
by a series of cosines or by a series of sines, in the interval from 0 to π.

199. Expansion of a continuous function. Weierstrass' theorem. Let $f(x)$ be a
function which is defined and continuous in the interval (a, b). The following
remarkable theorem was discovered by Weierstrass: *Given any preassigned positive number* ϵ, *a polynomial* $P(x)$ *can always be found such that the difference*
$f(x) - P(x)$ *is less than* ϵ *in absolute value for all values of x in the interval* (a, b).

Among the many proofs of this theorem, that due to Lebesgue is one of the
simplest.* Let us first consider a special function $\psi(x)$ which is continuous in
the interval $(-1, +1)$ and which is defined as follows: $\psi(x) = 0$ for $-1 \leq x \leq 0$,
$\psi(x) = 2kx$ for $0 \leq x \leq 1$, where k is a given constant. Then $\psi(x) = (x + |x|) k$.
Moreover for $-1 \leq x \leq +1$ we shall have

$$|x| = \sqrt{1 - (1 - x^2)},$$

and for the same values of x the radical can be developed in a *uniformly con-
vergent* series arranged according to powers of $(1 - x^2)$. It follows that $|x|$, and
hence also $\psi(x)$, may be represented to any desired degree of approximation in
the interval $(-1, +1)$ by a polynomial.

Let us now consider any function whatever, $f(x)$, which is continuous in
the interval (a, b), and let us divide that interval into a suite of subintervals
$(a_0, a_1), (a_1, a_2), \cdots, (a_{n-1}, a_n)$, where $a = a_0 < a_1 < a_2 < \cdots < a_{n-1} < a_n = b$,
in such a way that the oscillation of $f(x)$ in any one of the subintervals is less
than $\epsilon/2$. Let L be the broken line formed by connecting the points of the
curve $y = f(x)$ whose abscissæ are $a_0, a_1, a_2, \cdots, b$. The ordinate of any point
on L is evidently a continuous function $\phi(x)$, and the difference $f(x) - \phi(x)$ is
less than $\epsilon/2$ in absolute value. For in the interval $(a_{\mu-1}, a_\mu)$, for example,
we shall have

$$f(x) - \phi(x) = [f(x) - f(a_{\mu-1})](1 - \theta) + [f(x) - f(a_\mu)]\theta,$$

where $x - a_{\mu-1} = \theta(a_\mu - a_{\mu-1})$. Since the factor θ is positive and less than
unity, the absolute value of the difference $f - \phi$ is less than $\epsilon(1 - \theta + \theta)/2 = \epsilon/2$.
The function $\phi(x)$ can be split up into a sum of n functions of the same type as
$\psi(x)$. For, let $A_0, A_1, A_2, \cdots, A_n$ be the successive vertices of L. Then $\phi(x)$
is equal to the continuous function $\psi_1(x)$ which is represented throughout the
interval (a, b) by the straight line $A_0 A_1$ extended, plus a function $\phi_1(x)$ which
is represented by a broken line $A_0' A_1' \cdots A_n'$ whose first side $A_0' A_1'$ lies on the
x axis and whose other sides are readily constructed from the sides of L. Again,
the function $\phi_1(x)$ is equal to the sum of two functions ψ_2 and ϕ_2, where ψ_2 is
zero between a_0 and a_1, and is represented by the straight line $A_1' A_2'$ extended
between a_1 and b, while ϕ_2 is represented by a broken line $A_0'' A_1'' A_2'' \cdots A_n''$ whose
first three vertices lie on the x axis. Finally, we shall obtain the equation
$\phi = \psi_1 + \psi_2 + \cdots + \psi_n$, where ψ_i is a continuous function which vanishes
between a_0 and a_{i-1} and which is represented by a segment of a straight line

---

* *Bulletin des sciences mathématiques*, p. 278, 1898.

between a_{i-1} and b. If we then make the substitution $X = mx + n$, where m and n are suitably chosen numbers, the function $\psi_i(x)$ may be defined in the interval $(-1, +1)$ by the equation

$$\psi_i(x) = k(X + |X|),$$

and hence it can be represented by a polynomial with any desired degree of approximation. Since each of the functions $\psi_i(x)$ can be represented in the interval (a, b) by a polynomial with an error less than $\epsilon/2n$, it is evident that the sum of these polynomials will differ from $f(x)$ by less than ϵ.

It follows from the preceding theorem that *any function $f(x)$ which is continuous in an interval (a, b) may be represented by an infinite series of polynomials which converges uniformly in that interval.* For, let $\epsilon_1, \epsilon_2, \cdots, \epsilon_n, \cdots$ be a sequence of positive numbers, each of which is less than the preceding, where ϵ_n approaches zero as n becomes infinite. By the preceding theorem, corresponding to each of the ϵ's a polynomial $P_i(x)$ can be found such that the difference $f(x) - P_i(x)$ is less than ϵ_i in absolute value throughout the interval (a, b). Then the series

$$P_1(x) + [P_2(x) - P_1(x)] + \cdots + [P_n(x) - P_{n-1}(x)] + \cdots$$

converges, and its sum is $f(x)$ for any value of x inside the interval (a, b). For the sum of the first n terms is equal to $P_n(x)$, and the difference $f(x) - S_n$, which is less than ϵ_n, approaches zero as n becomes infinite. Moreover the series converges uniformly, since the absolute value of the difference $f(x) - S_n$ will be less than any preassigned positive number for all values of n which exceed a certain fixed integer N, when x has any value whatever between a and b.

200. A continuous function without a derivative. We shall conclude this chapter by giving an example due to Weierstrass of a continuous function which does not possess a derivative for any value of the variable whatever. Let b be a positive constant less than unity and let a be an odd integer. Then the function $F(x)$ defined by the convergent infinite series

$$(78) \qquad F(x) = \sum_{n=0}^{+\infty} b^n \cos(a^n \pi x)$$

is continuous for all values of x, since the series converges uniformly in any interval whatever. If the product ab is less than unity, the same statements hold for the series obtained by term-by-term differentiation. Hence the function $F(x)$ possesses a derivative which is itself a continuous function. We shall now show that the state of affairs is essentially different if the product ab exceeds a certain limit.

In the first place, setting

$$S_m = \frac{1}{h} \sum_{n=0}^{m-1} b^n \{\cos[a^n \pi(x+h)] - \cos(a^n \pi x)\},$$

$$R_m = \frac{1}{h} \sum_{n=m}^{+\infty} b^n \{\cos[a^n \pi(x+h)] - \cos(a^n \pi x)\},$$

we may write

$$(79) \qquad \frac{F(x+h) - F(x)}{h} = S_m + R_m.$$

On the other hand, it is easy to show, by applying the law of the mean to the function $\cos(a^n \pi x)$, that the difference $\cos[a^n \pi(x+h)] - \cos(a^n \pi x)$ is less than $\pi a^n |h|$ in absolute value. Hence the absolute value of S_m is less than

$$\pi \sum_{n=0}^{m-1} a^n b^n = \pi \frac{a^m b^m - 1}{ab - 1},$$

and consequently also less than $\pi(ab)^m/(ab-1)$, if $ab > 1$. Let us try to find a lower limit of the absolute value of R_m when h is assigned a particular value. We shall always have

$$a^m x = \alpha_m + \xi_m,$$

where α_m is an integer and ξ_m lies between $-1/2$ and $+1/2$. If we set

$$h = \frac{e_m - \xi_m}{a^m},$$

where e_m is equal to ± 1, it is evident that the sign of h is the same as that of e_m, and that the absolute value of h is less than $3/2a^m$. Having chosen h in this way, we shall have

$$a^n \pi(x+h) = a^{n-m} a^m \pi(x+h) = a^{n-m} \pi(\alpha_m + e_m).$$

Since a is odd and $e_m = \pm 1$, the product $a^{n-m}(\alpha_m + e_m)$ is even or odd with $\alpha_m + 1$, and hence

$$\cos[a^n \pi(x+h)] = (-1)^{\alpha_m + 1}.$$

Moreover we shall have

$$\cos(a^n \pi x) = \cos(a^{n-m} a^m \pi x) = \cos[a^{n-m} \pi(\alpha_m + \xi_m)]$$
$$= \cos(a^{n-m} \alpha_m \pi) \cos(a^{n-m} \xi_m \pi),$$

or, since $a^{n-m} \alpha_m$ is even or odd with α_m,

$$\cos(a^n \pi x) = (-1)^{\alpha_m} \cos(a^{n-m} \xi_m \pi).$$

It follows that we may write

$$R_m = \frac{(-1)^{\alpha_m + 1}}{h} \sum_{n=m}^{+\infty} b^n [1 + \cos(a^{n-m} \xi_m \pi)].$$

Since every term of the series is positive, its sum is greater than the first term, and consequently it is greater than b^m since ξ_m lies between $-1/2$ and $+1/2$. Hence

$$|R_m| > \frac{b^m}{|h|},$$

or, since $|h| < 3/2a^m$,

$$|R_m| > \frac{2}{3}(ab)^m.$$

If a and b satisfy the inequality

(80) $$ab > 1 + \frac{3\pi}{2},$$

we shall have

$$\frac{2}{3}(ab)^m > \frac{\pi(ab)^m}{ab-1},$$

whence, by (79),

$$\left| \frac{F(x+h) - F(x)}{h} \right| > |R_m| - |S_m| > \frac{2}{3}(ab)^m \frac{ab - 1 - \frac{3\pi}{2}}{ab-1}.$$

As m becomes infinite the expression on the extreme right increases indefinitely, while the absolute value of h approaches zero. Consequently, no matter how small ϵ be chosen, an increment h can be found which is less than ϵ in absolute value, and for which the absolute value of $[F(x+h) - F(x)]/h$ exceeds any preassigned number whatever. It follows that if a and b satisfy the relation (80), the function $F(x)$ possesses no derivative for any value of x whatever.

EXERCISES

1. Apply Lagrange's formula to derive a development in powers of x of that root of the equation $y^2 = ay + x$ which is equal to a when $x = 0$.

2. Solve the similar problem for the equation $y - a + xy^{m+1} = 0$. Apply the result to the quadratic equation $a - bx + cx^2 = 0$. Develop in powers of c that root of the quadratic which approaches a/b as c approaches zero.

3. Derive the formula

$$\frac{\log(1+x)}{1+x} = x - \left(1 + \frac{1}{2}\right)x^2 + \left(1 + \frac{1}{2} + \frac{1}{3}\right)x^3 - \left(1 + \frac{1}{2} + \frac{1}{3} + \frac{1}{4}\right)x^4 + \cdots.$$

4. Show that the formula

$$\frac{x}{\sqrt{1+x}} = \frac{x}{1+x} + \frac{1}{2}\left(\frac{x}{1+x}\right)^2 + \frac{1.3}{2.4}\left(\frac{x}{1+x}\right)^3 + \cdots$$

holds whenever x is greater than $-1/2$.

5. Show that the equation

$$x = \frac{1}{2}\frac{2x}{1+x^2} + \frac{1}{2.4}\left(\frac{2x}{1+x^2}\right)^3 + \frac{1.3}{2.4.6}\left(\frac{2x}{1+x^2}\right)^5 + \cdots$$

holds for values of x less than 1 in absolute value. What is the sum of the series when $|x| > 1$?

6. Derive the formula

$$(a+x)^{-n} = \frac{1}{a^n}\left[1 - \frac{nx}{a+x} + \frac{n(n-1)}{1.2}\left(\frac{x}{a+x}\right)^2 - \frac{n(n-1)(n-2)}{1.2.3}\left(\frac{x}{a+x}\right)^3 + \cdots\right].$$

7. Show that the branches of the function $\sin mx$ and $\cos mx$ which reduce to 0 and 1, respectively, when $\sin x = 0$ are developable in series according to powers of $\sin x$:

$$\sin mx = m\left[\sin x - \frac{m^2-1}{1.2.3}\sin^3 x + \frac{(m^2-1)(m^2-9)}{1.2.3.4.5}\sin^5 x - \cdots\right],$$

$$\cos mx = 1 - \frac{m^2}{1.2}\sin^2 x + \frac{m^2(m^2-4)}{1.2.3.4}\sin^4 x - \cdots.$$

[Make use of the differential equation

$$(1-y^2)\frac{d^2u}{dy^2} - y\frac{du}{dy} + m^2 u = 0,$$

which is satisfied by $u = \cos mx$ and by $u = \sin mx$, where $y = \sin x$.]

8. From the preceding formulæ deduce developments for the functions

$$\cos(n \arccos x), \qquad \sin(n \arccos x).$$

CHAPTER X

PLANE CURVES

The curves and surfaces treated in Analytic Geometry, properly speaking, are *analytic* curves and surfaces. However, the geometrical concepts which we are about to consider involve only the existence of a certain number of successive derivatives. Thus the curve whose equation is $y = f(x)$ possesses a tangent if the function $f(x)$ has a derivative $f'(x)$; it has a radius of curvature if $f'(x)$ has a derivative $f''(x)$; and so forth.

I. ENVELOPES

201. Determination of envelopes. Given a plane curve C whose equation

$$(1) \qquad f(x, y, a) = 0$$

involves an arbitrary parameter a, the form and the position of the curve will vary with a. If each of the positions of the curve C is tangent to a fixed curve E, the curve E is called the *envelope* of the curves C, and the curves C are said to be *enveloped* by E. The problem before us is to establish the existence (or non-existence) of an envelope for a given family of curves C, and to determine that envelope when it does exist.

Assuming that an envelope E exists, let (x, y) be the point of tangency of E with that one of the curves C which corresponds to a certain value a of the parameter. The quantities x and y are unknown functions of the parameter a which satisfy the equation (1). In order to determine these functions, let us express the fact that the tangents to the two curves E and C coincide for all values of a. Let δx and δy be two quantities proportional to the direction cosines of the tangent to the curve C, and let dx/da and dy/da be the derivatives of the unknown functions $x = \phi(a)$, $y = \psi(a)$. Then a necessary condition for tangency is

$$(2) \qquad \frac{\dfrac{dx}{da}}{\delta x} = \frac{\dfrac{dy}{da}}{\delta y}.$$

On the other hand, since a in equation (1) has a constant value for the particular curve C considered, we shall have

$$(3) \qquad \frac{\partial f}{\partial x}\delta x + \frac{\partial f}{\partial y}\delta y = 0,$$

which determines the tangent to C. Again, the two unknown functions $x = \phi(a)$, $y = \psi(a)$ satisfy the equation

$$f(x, y, a) = 0,$$

also, where a is now the independent variable. Hence

$$(4) \qquad \frac{\partial f}{\partial x}\frac{dx}{da} + \frac{\partial f}{\partial y}\frac{dy}{da} + \frac{\partial f}{\partial a} = 0,$$

or, combining the equations (2), (3), and (4),

$$(5) \qquad \frac{\partial f}{\partial a} = 0.$$

The unknown functions $x = \phi(a)$, $y = \psi(a)$ are solutions of this equation and the equation (1). *Hence the equation of the envelope, in case an envelope exists, is to be found by eliminating the parameter a between the equations $f = 0$, $\partial f/\partial a = 0$.*

Let $R(x, y) = 0$ be the equation obtained by eliminating a between (1) and (5), and let us try to determine whether or not this equation represents an envelope of the given curves. Let C_0 be the particular curve which corresponds to a value a_0 of the parameter, and let (x_0, y_0) be the coördinates of the point M_0 of intersection of the two curves

$$(6) \qquad f(x, y, a_0) = 0, \qquad \frac{\partial f}{\partial a_0} = 0.$$

The equations (1) and (5) have, in general, solutions of the form $x = \phi(a)$, $y = \psi(a)$, which reduce to x_0 and y_0, respectively, for $a = a_0$. Hence for $a = a_0$ we shall have

$$\frac{\partial f}{\partial x_0}\left(\frac{dx}{da}\right)_0 + \frac{\partial f}{\partial y_0}\left(\frac{dy}{da}\right)_0 = 0.$$

This equation taken in connection with the equation (3) shows that the tangent to the curve C_0 coincides with the tangent to the curve described by the point (x, y), at least unless $\partial f/\partial x$ and $\partial f/\partial y$ are both zero, that is, unless the point M_0 is a singular point for the curve C_0. *It follows that the equation $R(x, y) = 0$ represents either the envelope of the curves C or else the locus of singular points on these curves.*

This result may be supplemented. If each of the curves C has one or more singular points, the locus of such points is surely a part of the curve $R(x, y) = 0$. Suppose, for example, that the point (x, y) is such a singular point. Then x and y are functions of a which satisfy the three equations

$$f(x, y, a) = 0, \qquad \frac{\partial f}{\partial x} = 0, \qquad \frac{\partial f}{\partial y} = 0,$$

and hence also the equation $\partial f/\partial a = 0$. It follows that x and y satisfy the equation $R(x, y) = 0$ obtained by eliminating a between the two equations $f = 0$ and $\partial f/\partial a = 0$. In the general case the curve $R(x, y) = 0$ is composed of two analytically distinct parts, one of which is the true envelope, while the other is the locus of the singular points.

Example. Let us consider the family of curves

$$f(x, y, a) = y^4 - y^2 + (x - a)^2 = 0.$$

The elimination of a between this equation and the derived equation

$$\frac{\partial f}{\partial a} = -2(x - a) = 0$$

gives $y^4 - y^2 = 0$, which represents the three straight lines $y = 0$, $y = +1$, $y = -1$. The given family of curves may be generated by a translation of the curve $y^4 - y^2 + x^2 = 0$ along the x axis. This curve has a double point at the origin, and it is tangent to each of the straight lines $y = \pm 1$ at the points where it cuts the y axis. Hence the straight line $y = 0$ is the locus of double points, whereas the two straight lines $y = \pm 1$ constitute the real envelope.

202. If the curves C have an envelope E, *any point of the envelope is the limiting position of the point of intersection of two curves of the family for which the values of the parameter differ by an infinitesimal.* For, let

(7) $$f(x, y, a) = 0, \qquad f(x, y, a + h) = 0$$

be the equations of two neighboring curves of the family. The equations (7), which determine the points of intersection of the two curves, may evidently be replaced by the equivalent system

$$f(x, y, a) = 0, \qquad \frac{f(x, y, a + h) - f(x, y, a)}{h} = 0,$$

the second of which reduces to $\partial f/\partial a = 0$ as h approaches zero, that is, as the second of the two curves approaches the first. This property is fairly evident geometrically. In Fig. 37, a, for instance, the point of intersection N of the two neighboring curves C and C' approaches the point of tangency M as C' approaches the curve C

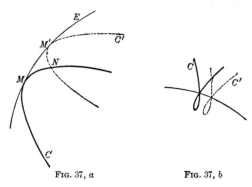

FIG. 37, a FIG. 37, b

as its limiting position. Likewise, in Fig. 37, b, where the given curves (1) are supposed to have double points, the point of intersection of two neighboring curves C and C' approaches the point where C cuts the envelope as C' approaches C.

The remark just made explains why the locus of singular points is found along with the envelope. For, suppose that $f(x, y, a)$ is a polynomial of degree m in a. For any point $M_0(x_0, y_0)$ chosen at random in the plane the equation

(8) $f(x_0, y_0, a) = 0$

will have, in general, m distinct roots. Through such a point there pass, in general, m different curves of the given family. But if the point M_0 lies on the curve $R(x, y) = 0$, the equations

$$f(x_0, y_0, a) = 0, \qquad \frac{\partial f}{\partial a} = 0$$

are satisfied simultaneously, and the equation (8) has a double root. The equation $R(x, y) = 0$ may therefore be said to represent the locus of those points in the plane for which two of the curves of the given family which pass through it have merged into a single one. The figures 37, a, and 37, b, show clearly the manner in which two of the curves through a given point merge into a single one as that point approaches a point of the curve $R(x, y) = 0$, whether on the true envelope or on a locus of double points.

Note. It often becomes necessary to find the envelope of a family of curves

(9) $F(x, y, a, b) = 0$

whose equation involves two variable parameters a and b, which themselves satisfy a relation of the form $\phi(a, b) = 0$. This case does not differ essentially from the preceding general case, however, for b may be thought of as a function of a defined by the equation $\phi = 0$. By the rule obtained above, we should join with the given equation the equation obtained by equating to zero the derivative of its left-hand member with respect to a:

$$\frac{\partial F}{\partial a} + \frac{\partial F}{\partial b} \frac{db}{da} = 0.$$

But from the relation $\phi(a, b) = 0$ we have also

$$\frac{\partial \phi}{\partial a} + \frac{\partial \phi}{\partial b} \frac{db}{da} = 0,$$

whence, eliminating db/da, we obtain the equation

(10) $\dfrac{\partial F}{\partial a} \dfrac{\partial \phi}{\partial b} - \dfrac{\partial F}{\partial b} \dfrac{\partial \phi}{\partial a} = 0,$

which, together with the equations $F = 0$ and $\phi = 0$, determine the required envelope. The parameters a and b may be eliminated between these three equations if desired.

203. Envelope of a straight line. As an example let us consider the equation of a straight line D in normal form

(11) $x \cos \alpha + y \sin \alpha - f(\alpha) = 0,$

where the variable parameter is the angle α. Differentiating the left-hand side with respect to this parameter, we find as the second equation

(12) $- x \sin \alpha + y \cos \alpha - f'(\alpha) = 0.$

These two equations (11) and (12) determine the point of intersection of any one of the family (11) with the envelope E in the form

(13) $\begin{cases} x = f(\alpha) \cos \alpha - f'(\alpha) \sin \alpha, \\ y = f(\alpha) \sin \alpha + f'(\alpha) \cos \alpha. \end{cases}$

It is easy to show that the tangent to the envelope E which is described by this point (x, y) is precisely the line D. For from the equations (13) we find

(14) $\begin{cases} dx = - [f(\alpha) + f''(\alpha)] \sin \alpha \, d\alpha, \\ dy = \quad [f(\alpha) + f''(\alpha)] \cos \alpha \, d\alpha, \end{cases}$

whence $dy/dx = - \cot \alpha$, which is precisely the slope of the line D.

Moreover, if s denote the length of the arc of the envelope from any fixed point upon it, we have, from (14),

$$ds = \sqrt{dx^2 + dy^2} = \pm\,[\,f(\alpha) + f''(\alpha)\,]\,d\alpha\,,$$

whence

$$s = \pm\left[\,\int f(\alpha)\,d\alpha + f'(\alpha)\,\right].$$

Hence the envelope will be a curve which is easily rectifiable if we merely choose for $f(\alpha)$ the derivative of a known function.*

As an example let us set $f(\alpha) = l\sin\alpha\cos\alpha$. Taking $y = 0$ and $x = 0$ successively in the equation (11), we find (Fig. 38) $OA = l\sin\alpha$, $OB = l\cos\alpha$, respectively; hence $AB = l$. The required curve is therefore the envelope of a straight line of constant length l, whose extremities always lie on the two axes. The formulæ (13) give in this case

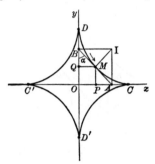

$$x = l\sin^3\alpha,\qquad y = l\cos^3\alpha,$$

and the equation of the envelope is

$$\left(\frac{x}{l}\right)^{\frac{2}{3}} + \left(\frac{y}{l}\right)^{\frac{2}{3}} = 1,$$

which represents a hypocycloid with four cusps, of the form indicated in the figure. As α varies from 0 to $\pi/2$, the point of con-

Fig. 38

tact describes the arc DC. Hence the length of the arc, counted from D, is

$$s = \int_0^\alpha 3l\sin\alpha\cos\alpha\,d\alpha = \frac{3l}{2}\sin^2\alpha\,.$$

Let I be the fourth vertex of the rectangle determined by OA and OB, and M the foot of the perpendicular let fall from I upon AB. Then, from the triangles AMI and APM, we find, successively,

$$AM = AI\cos\alpha = l\cos^2\alpha,\qquad AP = AM\sin\alpha = l\cos^2\alpha\sin\alpha.$$

Hence $OP = OA - AP = l\sin^3\alpha$, and the point M is the point of tangency of the line AB with the envelope. Moreover

$$BM = l - AM = l\sin^2\alpha\,;$$

hence the length of the arc $DM = 3\,BM/2$.

---

* Each of the quantities which occur in the formula for s, $s = f'(\alpha) + \int f(\alpha)\,d\alpha$, has a geometrical meaning: α is the angle between the x axis and the perpendicular ON let fall upon the variable line from the origin; $f(\alpha)$ is the distance ON from the origin to the variable line; and $f'(\alpha)$ is, except for sign, the distance MN from the point M where the variable line touches its envelope to the foot N of the perpendicular let fall upon the line from the origin. The formula for s is often called *Legendre's formula*.

204. Envelope of a circle. Let us consider the family of circles

(15) $(x - a)^2 + (y - b)^2 - \rho^2 = 0,$

where a, b, and ρ are functions of a variable parameter t. The points where a circle of this family touches the envelope are the points of intersection of the circle and the straight line

(16) $(x - a)\, a' + (y - b)\, b' + \rho\rho' = 0.$

This straight line is perpendicular to the tangent MT to the curve C described by the center (a, b) of the variable circle (15), and its distance from the center is

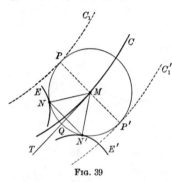

$\rho\, d\rho/ds$, where s denotes the length of the arc of the curve C measured from some fixed point. Consequently, if the line (16) meets the circle in the two points N and N', the chord NN' is bisected by the tangent MT at right angles. It follows that the envelope consists of two parts, which are, in general, branches of the same analytic curve. Let us now consider several special cases.

1) If ρ is constant, the chord of contact NN' reduces to the normal PP' to the curve C, and the envelope is composed of the two parallel curves C_1 and

Fig. 39

C_1' which are obtained by laying off the constant distance ρ along the normal, on either side of the curve C.

2) If $\rho = s + K$, we have $\rho\, d\rho/ds = \rho$, and the chord NN' reduces to the tangent to the circle at the point Q. The two portions of the envelope are merged into a single curve Γ, whose normals are tangents to the curve C. The curve C is called the *evolute* of Γ, and, conversely, Γ is called an *involute* of C (see § 206).

If $d\rho > ds$, the straight line (16) no longer cuts the circle, and the envelope is imaginary.

Secondary caustics. Let us suppose that the radius of the variable circle is proportional to the distance from the center to a fixed point O. Taking the fixed point O as the origin of coördinates, the equation of the circle becomes

$$(x - a)^2 + (y - b)^2 = k^2(a^2 + b^2),$$

where k is a constant factor, and the equation of the chord of contact is

$$(x - a)\, a' + (y - b)\, b' + k^2(aa' + bb') = 0.$$

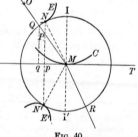

Fig. 40

If δ and δ' denote the distances from the center of the circle to the chord of contact and to the parallel to it through the origin, respectively, the preceding equation shows that $\delta = k^2\delta'$. Let P be a point on the radius MO (Fig. 40), such that $MP = k^2 MO$, and let C be the locus of the center. Then the equation just found shows that the chord of contact is the perpendicular let fall from P upon the tangent to C at the center M. Let us suppose that k is less than unity, and let E denote that branch of the envelope which lies on the same side of the tangent MT as does the point O. Let i and r, respectively, denote the two angles which the two lines MO and MN make with the normal MI to the curve C. Then we shall have

$$\sin i = \frac{Mq}{MQ}, \qquad \sin r = \frac{Mp}{MN}, \qquad \frac{\sin i}{\sin r} = \frac{Mq}{Mp} = \frac{MQ}{MP} = \frac{1}{k}.$$

Now let us imagine that the point O is a source of light, and that the curve C separates a certain homogeneous medium in which O lies from another medium whose index of refraction with respect to the first is $1/k$. After refraction the incident ray OM will be turned into a refracted ray MR, which, by the law of refraction, is the extension of the line NM. Hence all the refracted rays MR are normal to the envelope, which is called the *secondary caustic* of refraction. The true caustic, that is, the envelope of the refracted rays, is the evolute of the secondary caustic.

The second branch E' of the envelope evidently has no physical meaning; it would correspond to a negative index of refraction. If we set $k = 1$, the envelope E reduces to the single point O, while the portion E' becomes the locus of the points situated symmetrically with O with respect to the tangents to C. This portion of the envelope is also the secondary caustic *of reflection* for incident rays reflected from C which issue from the fixed point O. It may be shown in a manner similar to the above that if a circle be described about each point of C with a radius proportional to the distance from its center to a fixed straight line, the envelope of the family will be a secondary caustic with respect to a system of parallel rays.

II. CURVATURE

205. Radius of curvature. The first idea of curvature is that the curvature of one curve is greater than that of another if it recedes more rapidly from its tangent. In order to render this somewhat vague idea precise, let us first consider the case of a circle. Its curvature increases as its radius diminishes; it is therefore quite natural to select as the measure of its curvature the simplest function of the radius which increases as the radius diminishes, that is, the reciprocal $1/R$ of the radius. Let AB be an arc of a circle of radius R which subtends an angle ω at the center. The angle between the tangents at the extremities of the arc AB is also ω, and the length of the arc is $s = R\omega$. Hence the measure of the curvature of the circle is ω/s. This last definition may be extended to an arc of any curve. Let AB be an arc of a plane curve without a point of inflection, and ω the angle between the tangents at the extremities of the arc, the directions of the tangents being taken in the same sense according to some rule, — the direction from A

toward B, for instance. Then the quotient $\omega/\text{arc } AB$ is called the *average curvature* of the arc AB. As the point B approaches the point A this quotient in general approaches a limit, which is called

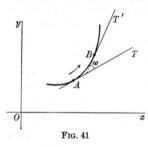

FIG. 41

the *curvature at the point A*. The *radius of curvature* at the point A is defined to be the radius of the circle which would have the same curvature which the given curve has at the point A; it is therefore equal to the reciprocal of the curvature. Let s be the length of the arc of the given curve measured from some fixed point, and α the angle between the tangent and

some fixed direction, — the x axis, for example. Then it is clear that the average curvature of the arc AB is equal to the absolute value of the quotient $\Delta\alpha/\Delta s$; hence the radius of curvature is given by the formula

$$R = \pm \lim \frac{\Delta s}{\Delta \alpha} = \pm \frac{ds}{d\alpha}.$$

Let us suppose the equation of the given curve to be solved for y in the form $y = f(x)$. Then we shall have

$$\alpha = \arctan y', \qquad d\alpha = \frac{y'' dx}{1 + y'^2}, \qquad ds = \sqrt{1 + y'^2}\, dx,$$

and hence

$$(17) \qquad\qquad R = \pm \frac{(1 + y'^2)^{\frac{3}{2}}}{y''}.$$

Since the radius of curvature is essentially positive, the sign $\pm$ indicates that we are to take the absolute value of the expression on the right. If a length equal to the radius of curvature be laid off from A upon the normal to the given curve on the side toward which the curve is concave, the extremity I is called the *center of curvature*. The circle described about I as center with R as radius is called the *circle of curvature*. The coördinates (x_0, y_0) of the center of curvature satisfy the two equations

$$(x_1 - x) + (y_1 - y)y' = 0, \qquad (x_1 - x)^2 + (y_1 - y)^2 = \frac{(1 + y'^2)^3}{y''^2},$$

which express the fact that the point lies on the normal at a distance R from A. From these equations we find, on eliminating x_1,

$$y_1 - y = \pm \frac{1 + y'^2}{y''}.$$

In order to tell which sign should be taken, let us note that if y'' is positive, as in Fig. 41, $y_1 - y$ must be positive; hence the positive sign should be taken in this case. If y'' is negative, $y_1 - y$ is negative, and the positive sign should be taken in this case also. The coördinates of the center of curvature are therefore given by the formulæ

$$(18) \qquad y_1 - y = \frac{1 + y'^2}{y''}, \qquad x_1 - x = - y' \frac{1 + y'^2}{y''}.$$

When the coördinates of a point (x, y) of the variable curve are given as functions of a variable parameter t, we have, by § 33,

$$y' = \frac{dy}{dx}, \qquad y'' = \frac{dx\, d^2y - dy\, d^2x}{dx^3},$$

and the formulæ (17) and (18) become

$$(19) \begin{cases} R = \pm \dfrac{(dx^2 + dy^2)^{\frac{3}{2}}}{dx\, d^2y - dy\, d^2x}, \\[2mm] x_1 - x = - \dfrac{dy(dx^2 + dy^2)}{dx\, d^2y - dy\, d^2x}, \qquad y_1 - y = \dfrac{dx(dx^2 + dy^2)}{dx\, d^2y - dy\, d^2x}. \end{cases}$$

At a point of inflection $y'' = 0$, and the radius of curvature is infinite. At a cusp of the first kind y can be developed according to powers of $x^{1/2}$ in a series which begins with a term in x; hence y' has a finite value, but y'' is infinite, and therefore the radius of curvature is zero.

Note. When the coördinates are expressed as functions of the arc s of the curve,

$$x = \phi(s), \qquad y = \psi(s),$$

the functions ϕ and ψ satisfy the relation

$$\phi'^2(s) + \psi'^2(s) = 1,$$

since $dx^2 + dy^2 = ds^2$, and hence they also satisfy the relation

$$\phi'\phi'' + \psi'\psi'' = 0.$$

Solving these equations for ϕ' and ψ', we find

$$\phi' = \epsilon \frac{\psi''}{\sqrt{\phi''^2 + \psi''^2}}, \qquad \psi' = - \epsilon \frac{\phi''}{\sqrt{\phi''^2 + \psi''^2}},$$

where $\epsilon = \pm 1$, and the formula for the radius of curvature takes on the especially elegant form

$$(20) \qquad \frac{1}{R^2} = [\phi''(s)]^2 + [\psi''(s)]^2.$$

206. Evolutes. The center of curvature at any point is the limiting position of the point of intersection of the normal at that point with a second normal which approaches the first one as its limiting position.   For the equation of the normal is

$$X - x + (Y - y)y' = 0,$$

where X and Y are the running coördinates.   In order to find the limiting position of the point of intersection of this normal with another which approaches it, we must solve this equation simultaneously with the equation obtained by equating the derivative of the left-hand side with respect to the variable parameter x, i.e.

$$-1 - y'^2 + (Y - y)y'' = 0.$$

The value of Y found from this equation is precisely the ordinate of the center of curvature, which proves the proposition.   It follows that the locus of the center of curvature is the envelope of the normals of the given curve, i.e. its *evolute*.

Before entering upon a more precise discussion of the relations between a given curve and its evolute, we shall explain certain conventions.   Counting the length of the arc of the given curve in a definite sense from a fixed point as origin, and denoting by α the angle between the positive direction of the x axis and the direction of the tangent which corresponds to increasing values of the arc, we shall have $\tan \alpha = \pm y'$, and therefore

$$\cos \alpha = \pm \frac{1}{\sqrt{1 + y'^2}} = \pm \frac{dx}{ds}.$$

On the right the sign $+$ should be taken, for if x and s increase simultaneously, the angle α is acute, whereas if one of the variables x and s increases as the other decreases, the angle α is obtuse (§ 81).   Likewise, if β denote the angle between the y axis and the tangent, $\cos \beta = dy/ds$.   The two formulæ may then be written

$$\cos \alpha = \frac{dx}{ds}, \qquad \sin \alpha = \frac{dy}{ds},$$

where the angle α is counted as in Trigonometry.

On the other hand, if there be no point of inflection upon the given arc, the positive sense on the curve may be chosen in such a way that s and α increase simultaneously, in which case $R = ds/d\alpha$ all along the arc.   Then it is easily seen by examining the two possible cases in an actual figure that the direction of the segment starting at the point of the curve and going to the center of curvature makes an angle $\alpha_1 = \alpha + \pi/2$ with the x axis. The coördinates (x_1, y_1) of the center of curvature are therefore given by the formulæ

$$x_1 = x + R \cos\left(\alpha + \frac{\pi}{2}\right) = x - R \sin \alpha,$$

$$y_1 = y + R \sin\left(\alpha + \frac{\pi}{2}\right) = y + R \cos \alpha,$$

whence we find

$$dx_1 = \cos \alpha \, ds - R \cos \alpha \, d\alpha - \sin \alpha \, dR = -\sin \alpha \, dR,$$
$$dy_1 = \sin \alpha \, ds - R \sin \alpha \, d\alpha + \cos \alpha \, dR = \cos \alpha \, dR.$$

In the first place, these formulæ show that $dy_1/dx_1 = -\cot \alpha$, which proves that the tangent to the evolute is the normal to the given curve, as we have already seen. Moreover

$$ds_1^2 = dx_1^2 + dy_1^2 = dR^2,$$

or $ds_1 = \pm \, dR$. Let us suppose for definiteness that the radius of curvature constantly increases as we proceed along the curve C (Fig. 42) from M_1 to M_2, and let us choose the positive sense of motion upon the evolute (D) in such a way that the arc s_1 of (D) increases simultaneously with R. Then the preceding formula becomes $ds_1 = dR$, whence $s_1 = R + C$. It follows that the arc $I_1 I_2 = R_2 - R_1$, and we see that *the length of any arc of the evolute is equal to the difference between the two radii of curvature of the curve C which correspond to the extremities of that arc.*

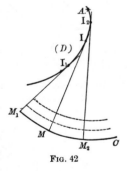

FIG. 42

This property enables us to construct the *involute C* mechanically if the evolute (D) be given. If a string be attached to (D) at an arbitrary point A and rolled around (D) to I_2, thence following the tangent to M_2, the point M_2 will describe the involute C as the string, now held taut, is wound further on round (D). This construction may be stated as follows: On each of the tangents IM of the evolute lay off a distance $IM = l$, where $l + s = \text{const.}$, s being the length of the arc AI of the evolute. Assigning various values to the constant in question, an infinite number of involutes may be drawn, all of which are obtainable from any one of them by laying off constant lengths along the normals.

All of these properties may be deduced from the general formula for the differential of the length of a straight line segment (§ 82)

$$dl = - d\sigma_1 \cos \omega_1 - d\sigma_2 \cos \omega_2.$$

If the segment is tangent to the curve described by one of its extremities and normal to that described by the other, we may set $\omega_1 = \pi$, $\omega_2 = \pi/2$, and the formula becomes $dl - d\sigma_1 = 0$. If the straight line is normal to one of the two curves and l is constant, $dl = 0$, $\cos \omega_1 = 0$, and therefore $\cos \omega_2 = 0$.

The theorem stated above regarding the arc of the evolute depends essentially upon the assumption that the radius of curvature constantly increases (or decreases) along the whole arc considered. If this condition is not satisfied, the statement of the theorem must be altered. In the first place, if the radius of curvature is a maximum or a minimum at any point, $dR = 0$ at that point, and hence

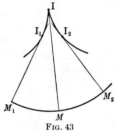

$dx_1 = dy_1 = 0$. Such a point is a cusp on the evolute. If, for example, the radius of curvature is a maximum at the point M (Fig. 43), we shall have

$$\text{arc } II_1 = IM - I_1 M_1,$$
$$\text{arc } II_2 = IM - I_2 M_2,$$

whence

$$\text{arc } I_1 II_2 = 2IM - I_1 M_1 - I_2 M_2.$$

Fig. 43

Hence the difference $I_1 M_1 - I_2 M_2$ is equal to the *difference* between the two arcs II_1 and II_2 and *not* their sum.

207. Cycloid. The cycloid is the path of a point upon the circumference of a circle which rolls without slipping on a fixed straight line. Let us take the

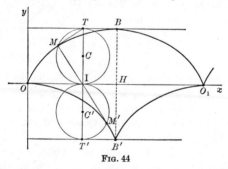

Fig. 44

fixed line as the x axis and locate the origin at a point where the point chosen on the circle lies in the x axis. When the circle has rolled to the point I (Fig. 44) the point on the circumference which was at O has come into the position M, where the circular arc IM is equal to the segment OI. Let us take the angle ϕ between the radii CM and CI as the variable parameter. Then the coördinates of the point M are

$$x = OI - IP = R\phi - R\sin\phi, \qquad y = MP = IC + CQ = R - R\cos\phi,$$

where P and Q are the projections of M on the two lines OI and IT, respectively. It is easy to show that these formulæ hold for any value of the angle ϕ. In one complete revolution the point whose path is sought describes the arc OBO_1. If the motion be continued indefinitely, we obtain an infinite number of arcs congruent to this one. From the preceding formulæ we find

$$x = R(\phi - \sin\phi), \qquad dx = R(1 - \cos\phi)\,d\phi, \qquad d^2x = R\sin\phi\,d\phi^2,$$
$$y = R(1 - \cos\phi), \qquad dy = R\sin\phi\,d\phi, \qquad d^2y = R\cos\phi\,d\phi^2,$$

and the slope of the tangent is seen to be

$$\frac{dy}{dx} = \frac{\sin\phi}{1 - \cos\phi} = \cot\frac{\phi}{2},$$

which shows that the tangent at M is the straight line MT, since the angle $MTC = \phi/2$, the triangle MTC being isosceles. Hence the normal at M is the straight line MI through the point of tangency I of the fixed straight line with the moving circle. For the length of the arc of the cycloid we find

$$ds^2 = R^2\,d\phi^2\left[\sin^2\phi + (1 - \cos\phi)^2\right] = 4R^2\sin^2\frac{\phi}{2}\,d\phi^2 \qquad \text{or} \qquad ds = 2R\sin\frac{\phi}{2}\,d\phi,$$

if the arc be counted in the sense in which it increases with ϕ. Hence, counting the arc from the point O as origin, we shall have

$$s = 4R\left(1 - \cos\frac{\phi}{2}\right).$$

Setting $\phi = 2\pi$, we find that the length of one whole section OBO_1 is $8R$. The length of the arc OMB from the origin to the maximum B is therefore $4R$, and the length of the arc BM (Fig. 44) is $4R\cos\phi/2$. From the triangle MTC the length of the segment MT is $2R\cos\phi/2$; hence arc $BM = 2MT$.

Again, the area up to the ordinate through M is

$$A = \int_0^\phi y\,dx = \int_0^\phi R^2(1 - 2\cos\phi + \cos^2\phi)\,d\phi$$
$$= R^2\int_0^\phi\left(\frac{3}{2} - 2\cos\phi + \frac{\cos 2\phi}{2}\right)d\phi,$$

or

$$A = \left(\frac{3}{2}\phi - 2\sin\phi + \frac{\sin 2\phi}{4}\right)R^2.$$

Hence the area bounded by the whole arc OBO_1 and the base OO_1 is $3\pi R^2$, that is, *three times the area of the generating circle.* (GALILEO.)

The formula for the radius of curvature of a plane curve gives for the cycloid

$$\rho = \frac{8R^3\sin^3\dfrac{\phi}{2}\,d\phi^3}{2R^2\sin^2\dfrac{\phi}{2}\,d\phi^3} = 4R\sin\frac{\phi}{2}.$$

On the other hand, from the triangle MCI, $MI = 2R \sin \phi/2$. Hence $\rho = 2MI$, and the center of curvature may be found by extending the straight line MI past I by its own length. This fact enables us to determine the evolute easily. For, consider the circle which is symmetrical to the generating circle with respect to the point I. Then the point M' where the line MI cuts this second circle is evidently the center of curvature, since $M'I = MI$. But we have

$$\text{arc } T'M' = \pi R - \text{arc } IM' = \pi R - \text{arc } IM = \pi R - OI,$$

or

$$\text{arc } T'M' = OH - OI = IH = T'B'.$$

Hence the point M' describes a cycloid which is congruent to the first one, the cusp being at B' and the maximum at O. As the point M describes the arc BO_1, the point M' describes a second arc $B'O_1$ which is symmetrical to the arc OB' already described, with respect to BB'.

208. Catenary. The catenary is the plane curve whose equation with respect to a suitably chosen set of rectangular axes is

$$(21) \qquad\qquad y = \frac{a}{2}\left(e^{\frac{x}{a}} + e^{-\frac{x}{a}}\right).$$

Its appearance is indicated by the arc MAM' in the figure (Fig. 45).

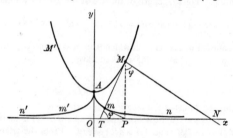

FIG. 45

From (21) we find

$$y' = \frac{1}{2}\left(e^{\frac{x}{a}} - e^{-\frac{x}{a}}\right), \quad y'' = \frac{1}{2a}\left(e^{\frac{x}{a}} + e^{-\frac{x}{a}}\right) = \frac{y}{a^2}, \quad 1 + y'^2 = \frac{\left(e^{\frac{x}{a}} + e^{-\frac{x}{a}}\right)^2}{4} = \frac{y^2}{a^2}.$$

If ϕ denote the angle which the tangent TM makes with the x axis, the formula for y' gives

$$\sin \phi = \frac{e^{\frac{x}{a}} - e^{-\frac{x}{a}}}{e^{\frac{x}{a}} + e^{-\frac{x}{a}}}, \quad \cos \phi = \frac{2}{e^{\frac{x}{a}} + e^{-\frac{x}{a}}} = \frac{a}{y}.$$

The radius of curvature is given by the formula

$$R = \frac{(1 + y'^2)^{\frac{3}{2}}}{y''} = \frac{y^2}{a}.$$

But, in the triangle MPN, $MP = MN \cos \phi$; hence

$$MN = \frac{MP}{\cos \phi} = \frac{y^2}{a} = R.$$

It follows that the radius of curvature of the catenary is equal to the length of the normal MN. The evolute may be found without difficulty from this fact.

The length of the arc AM of the catenary is given by the formula

$$s = \int_0^x \frac{e^{\frac{x}{a}} + e^{-\frac{x}{a}}}{2}\, dx = \frac{a}{2}\left(e^{\frac{x}{a}} - e^{-\frac{x}{a}}\right),$$

or $s = y \sin \phi$. If a perpendicular Pm be dropped from P (Fig. 45) upon the tangent MT, we find, from the triangle PMm,

$$Mm = MP \sin \phi = s.$$

Hence the arc AM is equal to the distance Mm.

209. Tractrix. The curve described by the point m (Fig. 45) is called the *tractrix*. It is an involute of the catenary and has a cusp at the point A. The length of the tangent to the tractrix is the distance mP. But, in the triangle MPm, $mP = y \cos \phi = a$; hence the length mP measured along the tangent to the tractrix from the point of tangency to the x axis is constant and equal to a. The tractrix is the only curve which has this property.

Moreover, in the triangle MTP, $Mm \times mT = a^2$. Hence the product of the radius of curvature and the normal is a constant for the tractrix. This property is shared, however, by an infinite number of other plane curves.

The coördinates (x_1, y_1) of the point m are given by the formulæ

$$x_1 = x - s \cos \phi = x - a\, \frac{e^{\frac{x}{a}} - e^{-\frac{x}{a}}}{e^{\frac{x}{a}} + e^{-\frac{x}{a}}},$$

$$y_1 = y - s \sin \phi = \frac{2a}{e^{\frac{x}{a}} + e^{-\frac{x}{a}}},$$

or, setting $e^{x/a} = \tan \theta/2$, the equations of the tractrix are

$$(22) \qquad x_1 = a \cos \theta + a \log\left(\tan \frac{\theta}{2}\right), \qquad y_1 = a \sin \theta.$$

As the parameter θ varies from $\pi/2$ to π, the point (x_1, y_1) describes the arc Amn, approaching the x axis as asymptote. As θ varies from $\pi/2$ to 0, the point (x_1, y_1) describes the arc $Am'n'$, symmetrical to the first with respect to the y axis. The arcs Amn and $Am'n'$ correspond, respectively, to the arcs AM and AM' of the catenary.

210. Intrinsic equation. Let us try to determine the equation of a plane curve when the radius of curvature R is given as a function of the arc s, $R = \phi(s)$. Let α be the angle between the tangent and the x axis; then $R = \pm\, ds/d\alpha$, and therefore

$$d\alpha = \pm \frac{ds}{R} = \pm \frac{ds}{\phi(s)}.$$

A first integration gives

$$\alpha = \alpha_0 \pm \int_{s_0}^s \frac{ds}{\phi(s)},$$

and two further integrations give x and y in the form

$$x = x_0 + \int_{s_0}^{s} \cos\alpha\, ds, \qquad y = y_0 + \int_{s_0}^{s} \sin\alpha\, ds.$$

The curves defined by these equations depend upon the three arbitrary constants x_0, y_0, and α_0. But if we disregard the position of the curve and think only of its form, we have in reality merely a single curve. For, if we first consider the curve C defined by the equations

$$X = \int_{s_0}^{s} \cos\left[\int_{s_0}^{s} \frac{ds}{\phi(s)}\right] ds, \qquad Y = \int_{s_0}^{s} \sin\left[\int_{s_0}^{s} \frac{ds}{\phi(s)}\right] ds,$$

the general formulæ may be written in the form

$$x = x_0 + X \cos\alpha_0 - Y \sin\alpha_0,$$
$$y = y_0 + X \sin\alpha_0 + Y \cos\alpha_0,$$

if the positive sign be taken. These last formulæ define simply a transformation to a new set of axes. If the negative sign be selected, the curve obtained is symmetrical to the curve C with respect to the X axis. A plane curve is therefore completely determined, in so far as its form is concerned, if its radius of curvature be known as a function of the arc. The equation $R = \phi(s)$ is called the *intrinsic equation* of the curve. More generally, if a relation between any two of the quantities R, s, and α be given, the curve is completely determined in form, and the expressions for the coördinates of any point upon it may be obtained by simple quadratures.

For example, if R be known as a function of α, $R = f(\alpha)$, we first find $ds = f(\alpha)\, d\alpha$, and then

$$dx = \cos\alpha f(\alpha)\, d\alpha,$$
$$dy = \sin\alpha f(\alpha)\, d\alpha,$$

whence x and y may be found by quadratures. If R is a constant, for instance, these formulæ give

$$x = x_0 + R \sin\alpha, \qquad y = y_0 - R \cos\alpha,$$

and the required curve is a circle of radius R. This result is otherwise evident from the consideration of the evolute of the required curve, which must reduce to a single point, since the length of its arc is identically zero.

As another example let us try to find a plane curve whose radius of curvature is proportional to the reciprocal of the arc, $R = a^2/s$. The formulæ give

$$\alpha = \int_{0}^{s} \frac{s\, ds}{a^2} = \frac{s^2}{2a^2},$$

and then

$$x = \int_{0}^{s} \cos\frac{s^2}{2a^2}\, ds, \qquad y = \int_{0}^{s} \sin\frac{s^2}{2a^2}\, ds.$$

Although these integrals cannot be evaluated in explicit form, it is easy to gain an idea of the appearance of the curve. As s increases from 0 to $+\infty$, x and y each pass through an infinite number of maxima and minima, and they approach the same finite limit. Hence the curve has a spiral form and approaches asymptotically a certain point on the line $y = x$.

III. CONTACT OF PLANE CURVES

211. Order of contact. Let C and C' be two plane curves which are tangent at some point A. To every point m on C let us assign, according to any arbitrary law whatever, a point m' on C', the only requirement being that the point m' should approach A with m. Taking the arc Am — or, what amounts to the same thing, the chord Am — as the principal infinitesimal, let us first investigate what law of correspondence will make the order of the infinitesimal mm' with respect to Am as large as possible. Let the two curves be referred to a system of rectangular

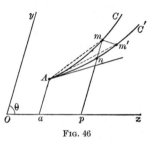

Fig. 46

or oblique cartesian coördinates, *the axis of y not being parallel to the common tangent AT.* Let

$$(C) \qquad\qquad y = f(x),$$
$$(C') \qquad\qquad Y = F(x)$$

be the equations of the two curves, respectively, and let (x_0, y_0) be the coördinates of the point A. Then the coördinates of m will be $[x_0 + h, f(x_0 + h)]$, and those of m' will be $[x_0 + k, F(x_0 + k)]$, where k is a function of h which defines the correspondence between the two curves and which approaches zero with h.

The principal infinitesimal Am may be replaced by $h = ap$, for the ratio ap/Am approaches a finite limit different from zero as the point m approaches the point A. Let us now suppose that mm' is an infinitesimal of order $r + 1$ with respect to h, for a certain method of correspondence. Then $\overline{mm'}^2$ is of order $2r + 2$. If θ denote the angle between the axes, we shall have

$$\overline{mm'}^2 = [F(x_0 + k) - f(x_0 + h) + (k - h)\cos\theta]^2 + (k - h)^2 \sin^2\theta;$$

hence each of the differences $k - h$ and $F(x_0 + k) - f(x_0 + h)$ must be an infinitesimal of order not less than $r + 1$, that is,

$$k = h + \alpha h^{r+1}, \qquad F(x_0 + k) - f(x_0 + h) = \beta h^{r+1},$$

where α and β are functions of h which approach finite limits as h approaches zero. The second of these formulæ may be written in the form

$$F(x_0 + h + \alpha h^{r+1}) - f(x_0 + h) = \beta h^{r+1}.$$

If the expression $F(x_0 + h + \alpha h^{r+1})$ be developed in powers of α, the terms which contain α form an infinitesimal of order not less than $r + 1$. Hence the difference

$$\Delta = F(x_0 + h) - f(x_0 + h)$$

is an infinitesimal whose order is not less than $r + 1$ and may exceed $r + 1$. But this difference Δ is equal to the distance mn between the two points in which the curves C and C' are cut by a parallel to the y axis through m. Since the order of the infinitesimal mm' is *increased* or else unaltered by replacing m' by n, it follows that *the distance between two corresponding points on the two curves is an infinitesimal of the greatest possible order if the two corresponding points always lie on a parallel to the y axis.* If this greatest possible order is $r + 1$, the two curves are said to have *contact of order r* at the point A.

Notes. This definition gives rise to several remarks. The y axis was any line whatever not parallel to the tangent AT. Hence, in order to find the order of contact, corresponding points on the two curves may be defined to be those in which the curves are cut by lines parallel to any fixed line D which is not parallel to the tangent at their common point. The preceding argument shows that the order of the infinitesimal obtained is independent of the direction of D, — a conclusion which is easily verified. Let mn and mm' be any two lines through a point m of the curve C which are not parallel to the common tangent (Fig. 46). Then, from the triangle $mm'n$,

$$\frac{mm'}{mn} = \frac{\sin mnm'}{\sin mm'n}.$$

As the point m approaches the point A, the angles mnm' and $mm'n$ approach limits neither of which is zero or π, since the chord $m'n$ approaches the tangent AT. Hence mm'/mn approaches a finite limit different from zero, and mm' is an infinitesimal of the same order as mn. The same reasoning shows that mm' cannot be of higher order than mn, no matter what construction of this kind is used to determine m' from m, for the numerator $\sin mnm'$ always approaches a finite limit different from zero.

The principal infinitesimal used above was the arc Am or the chord Am. We should obtain the same results by taking the arc An of the curve C' for the principal infinitesimal, since Am and An are infinitesimals of the same order.

If two curves C and C' have a contact of order r, the points m' on C' may be assigned to the points m on C in an infinite number of ways which will make mm' an infinitesimal of order $r + 1$, — for that purpose it is sufficient to set $k = h + \alpha h^{s+1}$, where $s \leqq r$ and where α is a function of h which remains finite for $h = 0$. On the other hand, if $s < r$, the order of mm' cannot exceed $s + 1$.

212. Analytic method. It follows from the preceding section that the order of contact of two curves C and C' is given by evaluating the order of the infinitesimal

$$Y - y = F(x_0 + h) - f(x_0 + h)$$

with respect to h. Since the two curves are tangent at A, $F(x_0) = f(x_0)$ and $F'(x_0) = f'(x_0)$. It may happen that others of the derivatives are equal at the same point, and we shall suppose for the sake of generality that this is true of the first n derivatives:

$$(23) \quad \begin{cases} F(x_0) = f(x_0), & F'(x_0) = f'(x_0), \\ F''(x_0) = f''(x_0), & \cdots, & F^{(n)}(x_0) = f^{(n)}(x_0), \end{cases}$$

but that the next derivatives $F^{(n+1)}(x_0)$ and $f^{(n+1)}(x_0)$ are unequal. Applying Taylor's series to each of the functions $F(x)$ and $f(x)$, we find

$$Y = F(x_0) + \frac{h}{1} F'(x_0) + \cdots$$
$$+ \frac{h^n}{1.2\cdots n} F^{(n)}(x_0) + \frac{h^{n+1}}{1.2\cdots(n+1)} \left[F^{(n+1)}(x_0) + \epsilon \right],$$

$$y = f(x_0) + \frac{h}{1} f'(x_0) + \cdots$$
$$+ \frac{h^n}{1.2\cdots n} f^{(n)}(x_0) + \frac{h^{n+1}}{1.2\cdots(n+1)} \left[f^{(n+1)}(x_0) + \epsilon' \right],$$

or, subtracting,

$$(24) \quad Y - y = \frac{h^{n+1}}{1.2\cdots(n+1)} \left[F^{(n+1)}(x_0) - f^{(n+1)}(x_0) + \epsilon - \epsilon' \right],$$

where ϵ and ϵ' are infinitesimals. *It follows that the order of contact of two curves is equal to the order n of the highest derivatives of $F(x)$ and $f(x)$ which are equal for $x = x_0$.*

The conditions (23), which are due to Lagrange, are the necessary and sufficient conditions that $x = x_0$ should be a multiple root of order $n + 1$ of the equation $F(x) = f(x)$. But the roots of this equation are the abscissæ of the points of intersection of the two curves C and C'; hence it may be said that two curves which have contact of order n have $n + 1$ *coincident* points of intersection.

The equation (24) shows that $Y - y$ changes sign with h if n is even, and that it does not if n is odd. *Hence curves which have contact of odd order do not cross, but curves which have contact of even order do cross at their point of tangency.* It is easy to see why this should be true. Let us consider for definiteness a curve C' which cuts another curve C in three points near the point A. If the curve C' be deformed continuously in such a way that each of the three points of intersection approaches A, the limiting position of C' has contact of the second order with C, and a figure shows that the two curves cross at the point A. This argument is evidently general.

If the equations of the two curves are not solved with respect to Y and y, which is the case in general, the ordinary rules for the calculation of the derivatives in question enable us to write down the necessary conditions that the curves should have contact of order n. The problem is therefore free from any particular difficulties. We shall examine only a few special cases which arise frequently. First let us suppose that the equations of each of the curves are given in terms of an auxiliary variable

$$(C) \quad \begin{cases} x = f(t), \\ y = \phi(t), \end{cases} \qquad\qquad (C') \quad \begin{cases} X = f(u), \\ Y = \psi(u), \end{cases}$$

and that $\psi(t_0) = \phi(t_0)$ and $\psi'(t_0) = \phi'(t_0)$, i.e. that the curves are tangent at a point A whose coördinates are $f(t_0)$, $\phi(t_0)$. *If $f'(t_0)$ is not zero,* as we shall suppose, *the common tangent is not parallel to the y axis,* and we may obtain the points of the two curves which have the same abscissæ by setting $u = t$. On the other hand, $x - x_0$ is of the first order with respect to $t - t_0$, and we are led to evaluate the order of $\psi(t) - \phi(t)$ with respect to $t - t_0$. In order that the two curves have at least contact of order n, it is necessary and sufficient that we should have

$$(25) \quad \psi(t_0) = \phi(t_0), \quad \psi'(t_0) = \phi'(t_0), \quad \cdots, \quad \psi^{(n)}(t_0) = \phi^{(n)}(t_0),$$

and the order of contact will not exceed n if the next derivatives $\psi^{(n+1)}(t_0)$ and $\phi^{(n+1)}(t_0)$ are unequal.

Again, consider the case where the curve C is represented by the two equations

$$(26) \qquad\qquad x = f(t), \qquad y = \phi(t),$$

and the curve C' by the single equation $F(x, y) = 0$. This case may be reduced to the preceding by replacing x in $F(x, y)$ by $f(t)$ and considering the implicit function $y = \psi(t)$ defined by the equation

$$(27) \qquad\qquad F[f(t), \psi(t)] = 0.$$

Then the curve C' is also represented by two equations of the form

$$(28) \qquad\qquad x = f(t), \qquad y = \psi(t).$$

In order that the curves C and C' should have contact of order n at a point A which corresponds to a value t_0 of the parameter, it is necessary that the conditions (25) should be satisfied. But the successive derivatives of the implicit function $\psi(t)$ are given by the equations

$$(29) \quad \begin{cases} \dfrac{\partial F}{\partial x} f'(t) + \dfrac{\partial F}{\partial y} \psi'(t) = 0, \\[2mm] \dfrac{\partial^2 F}{\partial x^2} [f'(t)]^2 + 2 \dfrac{\partial^2 F}{\partial x \, \partial y} f'(t)\psi'(t) \\[2mm] \qquad\qquad + \dfrac{\partial^2 F}{\partial y^2} [\psi'(t)]^2 + \dfrac{\partial F}{\partial x} f''(t) + \dfrac{\partial F}{\partial y} \psi''(t) = 0, \\[2mm] \cdot\;\cdot\;\cdot\;\cdot\;\cdot\;\cdot\;\cdot\;\cdot\;\cdot\;\cdot\;\cdot\;\cdot\;\cdot\;\cdot\;\cdot\;\cdot, \\[2mm] \dfrac{\partial^n F}{\partial x^n} [f'(t)]^n + \cdots + \dfrac{\partial F}{\partial y} \psi^{(n)}(t) = 0. \end{cases}$$

Hence necessary conditions for contact of order n will be obtained by inserting in these equations the relations

$$t = t_0, \; x = f(t_0), \; \psi(t_0) = \phi(t_0), \; \psi'(t_0) = \phi'(t_0), \; \cdots, \; \psi^{(n)}(t_0) = \phi^{(n)}(t_0).$$

The resulting conditions may be expressed as follows:

Let

$$\mathsf{F}(t) = F[f(t), \phi(t)];$$

then the two given curves will have at least contact of order n if and only if

$$(30) \qquad \mathsf{F}(t_0) = 0, \qquad \mathsf{F}'(t_0) = 0, \qquad \cdots, \qquad \mathsf{F}^{(n)}(t_0) = 0.$$

The roots of the equation $\mathsf{F}(t) = 0$ are the values of t which correspond to points of intersection of the two given curves. Hence the preceding conditions amount to saying that $t = t_0$ is a multiple root of order n, i.e. that the two curves have $n + 1$ coincident points of intersection.

213. Osculating curves. Given a fixed curve C and another curve C' which depends upon $n + 1$ parameters $a, b, c, \cdots, l$,

(31) $$F(x, y, a, b, c, \cdots, l) = 0,$$

it is possible in general to choose these $n + 1$ parameters in such a way that C' and C shall have contact of order n at any preassigned point of C. For, let C be given by the equations $x = f(t), y = \phi(t)$. Then the conditions that the curves C and C' should have contact of order n at the point where $t = t_0$ are given by the equations (30), where

$$\mathsf{F}(t) = F[f(t), \phi(t), a, b, c, \cdots, l].$$

If t_0 be given, these $n + 1$ equations determine in general the $n + 1$ parameters $a, b, c, \cdots, l$. The curve C' obtained in this way is called an *osculating curve* to the curve C.

Let us apply this theory to the simpler classes of curves. The equation of a straight line $y = ax + b$ depends upon the two parameters a and b; the corresponding osculating straight lines will have contact of the first order. If $y = f(x)$ is the equation of the curve C, the parameters a and b must satisfy the two equations

$$f(x_0) = ax_0 + b, \qquad f'(x_0) = a;$$

hence the osculating line is the ordinary tangent, as we should expect.

The equation of a circle

(32) $$(x - a)^2 + (y - b)^2 - R^2 = 0$$

depends upon the three parameters a, b, and R; hence the corresponding osculating circles will have contact of the second order. Let $y = f(x)$ be the equation of the given curve C; we shall obtain the correct values of a, b, and R by requiring that the circle should meet this curve in three coincident points. This gives, besides the equation (32), the two equations

(33) $$x - a + (y - b)y' = 0, \qquad 1 + y'^2 + (y - b)y'' = 0.$$

The values of a and b found from the equations (33) are precisely the coördinates of the center of curvature (§ 205); hence *the osculating circle coincides with the circle of curvature*. Since the contact is in general of order two, we may conclude that in general *the circle of curvature of a plane curve crosses the curve at their point of tangency*.

All the above results might have been foreseen *a priori*. For, since the coördinates of the center of curvature depend only on x, y, y', and y'', any two curves which have contact of the second order have the same center of curvature. But the center of curvature of the osculating circle is evidently the center of that circle itself; hence the circle of curvature must coincide with the osculating circle. On the other hand, let us consider two circles of curvature near each other. The difference between their radii, which is equal to the arc of the evolute between the two centers, is greater than the distance between the centers; hence one of the two circles must lie wholly inside the other, which could not happen if both of them lay wholly on one side of the curve C in the neighborhood of the point of contact. It follows that they cross the curve C.

There are, however, on any plane curve, in general, certain points at which the osculating circle does not cross the curve; this exception to the rule is, in fact, typical. Given a curve C' which depends upon $n+1$ parameters, we may add to the $n+1$ equations (30) the new equation

$$F^{(n+1)}(t_0) = 0$$

provided that we regard t_0 as one of the unknown quantities and determine it at the same time that we determine the parameters a, b, c, $\cdots$, l. It follows that there are, in general, on any plane curve C, a certain number of points at which the order of contact with the osculating curve C' is $n+1$. For example, there are usually points at which the tangent has contact of the second order; these are the points of inflection, for which $y'' = 0$. In order to find the points at which the osculating circle has contact of the third order, the last of equations (33) must be differentiated again, which gives

$$3y'y'' + (y-b)y''' = 0,$$

or finally, eliminating $y - b$,

$$(34) \qquad (1 + y'^2)y''' - 3y'y''^2 = 0.$$

The points which satisfy this last condition are those for which $dR/dx = 0$, i.e. those at which the radius of curvature is a maximum or a minimum. On the ellipse, for example, these points are the vertices; on the cycloid they are the points at which the tangent is parallel to the base.

214. Osculating curves as limiting curves. It is evident that an osculating curve may be thought of as the limiting position of a curve C' which meets the fixed curve C in $n + 1$ points near a fixed point A of C, which is the limiting position of each of the points of intersection. Let us consider for definiteness a family of curves which depends upon three parameters a, b, and c, and let $t_0 + h_1$, $t_0 + h_2$, and $t_0 + h_3$ be three values of t near t_0. The curve C' which meets the curve C in the three corresponding points is given by the three equations

$$(35) \quad F(t_0 + h_1) = 0, \qquad F(t_0 + h_2) = 0, \qquad F(t_0 + h_3) = 0.$$

Subtracting the first of these equations from each of the others and applying the law of the mean to each of the differences obtained, we find the equivalent system

$$(36) \quad F(t_0 + h_1) = 0, \qquad F'(t_0 + k_1) = 0, \qquad F'(t_0 + k_2) = 0,$$

where k_1 lies between h_1 and h_2, and k_2 between h_1 and h_3. Again, subtracting the second of these equations from the third and applying the law of the mean, we find a third system equivalent to either of the preceding,

$$(37) \quad F(t_0 + h_1) = 0, \qquad F'(t_0 + k_1) = 0, \qquad F''(t_0 + l_1) = 0,$$

where l_1 lies between k_1 and k_2. As h_1, h_2, and h_3 all approach zero, k_1, k_2, and l_1 also all approach zero, and the preceding equations become, in the limit,

$$F(t_0) = 0, \qquad F'(t_0) = 0, \qquad F''(t_0) = 0,$$

which are the very equations which determine the osculating curve. The same argument applies for any number of parameters whatever. Indeed, we might define the osculating curve to be the limiting position of a curve C' which is tangent to C at p points and cuts C at q other points, where $2p + q = n + 1$, as all these $p + q$ points approach coincidence.

For instance, the osculating circle is the limiting position of a circle which cuts the given curve C in three neighboring points. It is also the limiting position of a circle which is tangent to C and which cuts C at another point whose distance from the point of tangency is infinitesimal. Let us consider for a moment the latter property, which is easily verified.

Let us take the given point on C as the origin, the tangent at that point as the x axis, and the direction of the normal toward the center of curvature as the positive direction of the y axis. At the origin, $y' = 0$. Hence $R = 1/y''$, and therefore, by Taylor's series,

$$y = x^2\left(\frac{1}{2R} + \epsilon\right),$$

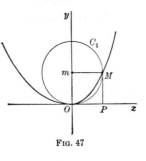

where ϵ approaches zero with x. It follows that R is the limit of the expression $x^2/(2y) = \overline{OP}^2/(2MP)$ as the point M approaches the origin. On the other hand, let R_1 be the radius of the circle C_1 which is tangent to the x axis at the origin and which passes through M. Then we shall have

Fig. 47

$$\overline{OP}^2 = \overline{Mm}^2 = MP(2R_1 - MP),$$

or

$$\frac{\overline{OP}^2}{2MP} = R_1 - \frac{MP}{2};$$

hence the limit of the radius R_1 is really equal to the radius of curvature R.

EXERCISES

1. Apply the general formulæ to find the evolute of an ellipse; of an hyperbola; of a parabola.

2. Show that the radius of curvature of a conic is proportional to the cube of the segment of the normal between its points of intersection with the curve and with an axis of symmetry.

3. Show that the radius of curvature of the parabola is equal to twice the segment of the normal between the curve and the directrix.

4. Let F and F' be the foci of an ellipse, M a point on the ellipse, MN the normal at that point, and N the point of intersection of that normal and the major axis of the ellipse. Erect a perpendicular NK to MN at N, meeting MF at K. At K erect a perpendicular KO to MF, meeting MN at O. Show that O is the center of curvature of the ellipse at the point M.

5. For the extremities of the major axis the preceding construction becomes illusory. Let AOA' be the major axis and $BO'B$ the minor axis of the ellipse. On the segments OA and OB construct the rectangle $OAEB$. From E let fall a perpendicular on AB, meeting the major and minor axes at C and D, respectively. Show that C and D are the centers of curvature of the ellipse for the points A and B, respectively.

6. Show that the evolute of the spiral $\rho = ae^{m\omega}$ is a spiral congruent to the given spiral.

7. The path of any point on the circumference of a circle which rolls without slipping along another (fixed) circle is called an *epicycloid* or an *hypocycloid*. Show that the evolute of any such curve is another curve of the same kind.

8. Let AB be an arc of a curve upon which there are no singular points and no points of inflection. At each point m of this arc lay off from the point m along the normal at m a given constant length l in each direction. Let m_1 and m_2 be the extremities of these segments. As the point m describes the arc AB, the points m_1 and m_2 will describe two corresponding arcs A_1B_1 and A_2B_2. Derive the formulæ $S_1 = S - l\theta$, $S_2 = S + l\theta$, where S, S_1, and S_2 are the lengths of the arcs AB, A_1B_1, and A_2B_2, respectively, and where θ is the angle between the normals at the points A and B. It is supposed that the arc A_1B_1 lies on the same side of AB as the evolute, and that it does not meet the evolute.

[*Licence*, Paris, July, 1879.]

9. Determine a curve such that the radius of curvatures ρ at any point M and the length of the arc $s = AM$ measured from any fixed point A on the curve satisfy the equation $as = \rho^2 + a^2$, where a is a given constant length.

[*Licence*, Paris, July, 1883.]

10. Let C be a given curve of the third degree which has a double point at O. A right angle MON revolves about the point O, meeting the curve C in two variable points M and N. Determine the envelope of the straight line MN. In particular, solve the problem for each of the curves $\lambda y^2 = x^3$ and $x^3 + y^3 = \mu xy$.

[*Licence*, Bordeaux, July, 1885.]

11. Find the points at which the curve represented by the equations

$$x = a(n\omega - \sin\omega), \qquad y = a(n - \cos\omega)$$

has contact of higher order than the second with the osculating circle.

[*Licence*, Grenoble, July, 1885.]

12. Let m, m_1, and m_2 be three neighboring points on a plane curve. Find the limit approached by the radius of the circle circumscribed about the triangle formed by the tangents at these three points as the points approach coincidence.

13. If the evolute of a plane curve without points of inflection is a closed curve, the total length of the evolute is equal to twice the difference between the sum of the maximum radii of curvature and the sum of the minimum radii of curvature of the given curve.

14. At each point of a curve lay off a constant segment at a constant angle with the normal. Show that the locus of the extremity of this segment is a curve whose normal passes through the center of curvature of the given curve.

15. Let r be the length of the radius vector from a fixed pole to any point of a plane curve, and p the perpendicular distance from the pole to the tangent. Derive the formula $R = \pm\, r\, dr/dp$, where R is the radius of curvature.

16. Show that the locus of the foci of the parabolas which have contact of the second order with a given curve at a fixed point is a circle.

17. Find the locus of the centers of the ellipses whose axes have a fixed direction, and which have contact of the second order at a fixed point with a given curve.

CHAPTER XI

SKEW CURVES

I. OSCULATING PLANE

215. Definition and equation. Let MT be the tangent at a point M of a given skew curve Γ. A plane through MT and a point M' of Γ near M in general approaches a limiting position as the point M' approaches the point M. If it does, the limiting position of the plane is called the *osculating plane* to the curve Γ at the point M. We shall proceed to find its equation.

Let

$$(1) \qquad x = f(t), \qquad y = \phi(t), \qquad z = \psi(t)$$

be the equations of the curve Γ in terms of a parameter t, and let t and $t + h$ be the values of t which correspond to the points M and M', respectively. Then the equation of the plane MTM' is

$$A(X - x) + B(Y - y) + C(Z - z) = 0,$$

where the coefficients $A, B,$ and C must satisfy the two relations

$$(2) \qquad Af'(t) + B\phi'(t) + C\psi'(t) = 0,$$

$$(3) \quad A[f(t+h) - f(t)] + B[\phi(t+h) - \phi(t)] + C[\psi(t+h) - \psi(t)] = 0.$$

Expanding $f(t + h)$, $\phi(t + h)$ and $\psi(t + h)$ by Taylor's series, the equation (3) becomes

$$A\left\{ hf'(t) + \frac{h^2}{1.2}[f''(t) + \epsilon_1] \right\} + B\left\{ h\phi'(t) + \frac{h^2}{1.2}[\phi''(t) + \epsilon_2] \right\} + \cdots = 0.$$

After multiplying by h, let us subtract from this equation the equation (2), and then divide both sides of the resulting equation by $h^2/2$. Doing so, we find a system equivalent to (2) and (3):

$$Af'(t) + B\phi'(t) + C\psi'(t) = 0,$$
$$A[f''(t) + \epsilon_1] + B[\phi''(t) + \epsilon_2] + C[\psi''(t) + \epsilon_3] = 0,$$

where ϵ_1, ϵ_2, and ϵ_3 approach zero with h. In the limit as h approaches zero the second of these equations becomes

$$(4) \qquad Af''(t) + B\phi''(t) + C\psi''(t) = 0.$$

Hence the equation of the osculating plane is

(5) $$A(X - x) + B(Y - y) + C(Z - z) = \mathbf{0},$$

where A, B, and C satisfy the relations

(6) $$\begin{cases} A\,dx + B\,dy + C\,dz = 0, \\ A\,d^2x + B\,d^2y + C\,d^2z = 0. \end{cases}$$

The coefficients A, B, and C may be eliminated from (5) and (6), and the equation of the osculating plane may be written in the form

$$\begin{vmatrix} X - x & Y - y & Z - z \\ dx & dy & dz \\ d^2x & d^2y & d^2z \end{vmatrix} = 0.$$

Among the planes which pass through the tangent, *the osculating plane is the one which the curve lies nearest* near the point of tangency. To show this, let us consider any other plane through the tangent, and let $F(t)$ be the function obtained by substituting $f(t + h)$, $\phi(t + h)$, $\psi(t + h)$ for X, Y, Z, respectively, in the left-hand side of the equation (5), which we shall now assume to be the equation of the new tangent plane. Then we shall have

$$F(t) = \frac{h^2}{1 \cdot 2} \left[Af''(t) + B\phi''(t) + C\psi''(t) + \eta \right],$$

where η approaches zero with h. The distance from any second point M' of Γ near M to this plane is therefore an infinitesimal *of the second order;* and, since $F(t)$ has the same sign for all sufficiently small values of h, it is clear that the given curve lies wholly on one side of the tangent plane considered, near the point of tangency.

These results do not hold for the osculating plane, however. For that plane, $Af'' + B\phi'' + C\psi'' = 0$; hence the expansions for the coördinates of a point of Γ must be carried to terms of the third order. Doing so, we find

$$F(t) = \frac{h^3}{1 \cdot 2 \cdot 3} \left(\frac{A\,d^3x + B\,d^3y + C\,d^3z}{dt^3} + \eta \right).$$

It follows that the distance from a point of Γ to the osculating plane is an infinitesimal *of the third order;* and, since $F(t)$ changes sign with h, it is clear that *a skew curve crosses its osculating plane at their common point.* These characteristics distinguish the osculating plane sharply from the other tangent planes.

216. Stationary osculating plane. The results just obtained are not valid if the coefficients A, B, C of the osculating plane satisfy the relation

(7) $$A\,d^3x + B\,d^3y + C\,d^3z = 0.$$

If this relation is satisfied, the expansions for the coördinates must be carried to terms of the fourth order, and we should obtain a relation of the form

$$F(t) = \frac{h^4}{1.2.3.4}\left(\frac{A\,d^4x + B\,d^4y + C\,d^4z}{dt^4} + \eta\right).$$

The osculating plane is said to be *stationary* at any point of Γ for which (7) is satisfied; if $A\,d^4x + B\,d^4y + C\,d^4z$ does not vanish also, — and it does not in general, — $F(t)$ changes sign with h and *the curve does not cross its osculating plane.* Moreover the distance from a point on the curve to the osculating plane at such a point is an infinitesimal of the fourth order. On the other hand, if the relation $A\,d^4x + B\,d^4y + C\,d^4z = 0$ is satisfied at the same point, the expansions would have to be carried to terms of the fifth order; and so on.

Eliminating A, B, and C between the equations (6) and (7), we obtain the equation

(8) $$\Delta = \begin{vmatrix} dx & dy & dz \\ d^2x & d^2y & d^2z \\ d^3x & d^3y & d^3z \end{vmatrix} = 0,$$

whose roots are the values of t which correspond to the points of Γ where the osculating plane is stationary. There are then, usually, on any skew curve, points of this kind.

This leads us to inquire whether there are curves all of whose osculating planes are stationary. To be precise, let us try to find all the possible sets of three functions x, y, z of a single variable t, which, together with all their derivatives up to and including those of the third order, are continuous, and which satisfy the equation (8) for all values of t between two limits a and b $(a < b)$.

Let us suppose first that at least one of the minors of Δ which correspond to the elements of the third row, say $dx\,d^2y - dy\,d^2x$, does not vanish in the interval (a, b). The two equations

(9) $$\begin{cases} dz = C_1\,dx + C_2\,dy, \\ d^2z = C_1\,d^2x + C_2\,d^2y, \end{cases}$$

which are equivalent to (6), determine C_1 and C_2 as continuous functions of t in the interval (a, b). Since $\Delta = 0$, these functions also satisfy the relation

(10) $d^3z = C_1 d^3x + C_2 d^3y.$

Differentiating each of the equations (9) and making use of (10), we find

$$dC_1 dx + dC_2 dy = 0, \qquad dC_1 d^2x + dC_2 d^2y = 0,$$

whence $dC_1 = dC_2 = 0$. It follows that each of the coefficients C_1 and C_2 is a constant; hence a single integration of the first of equations (9) gives

$$z = C_1 x + C_2 y + C_3,$$

where C_3 is another constant. This shows that the curve Γ is a plane curve.

If the determinant $dx\,d^2y - dy\,d^2x$ vanishes for some value c of the variable t between a and b, the preceding proof fails, for the coefficients C_1 and C_2 might be infinite or indeterminate at such a point. Let us suppose for definiteness that the preceding determinant vanishes for no other value of t in the interval (a, b), and that the analogous determinant $dx\,d^2z - dz\,d^2x$ does not vanish for $t = c$. The argument given above shows that all the points of the curve Γ which correspond to values of t between a and c lie in a plane P, and that all the points of Γ which correspond to values of t between c and b also lie in some plane Q. But $dx\,d^2z - dz\,d^2x$ does not vanish for $t = c$; hence a number h can be found such that that minor does not vanish anywhere in the interval $(c - h, c + h)$. Hence all the points on Γ which correspond to values of t between $c - h$ and $c + h$ must lie in some plane R. Since R must have an infinite number of points in common with P and also with Q, it follows that these three planes must coincide.

Similar reasoning shows that all the points of Γ lie in the same plane unless all three of the determinants

$$dx\,d^2y - dy\,d^2x, \qquad dx\,d^2z - dz\,d^2x, \qquad dy\,d^2z - dz\,d^2y$$

vanish at the same point in the interval (a, b). If these three determinants do vanish simultaneously, it may happen that the curve Γ is composed of several portions which lie in different planes, the points of junction being points at which the osculating plane is indeterminate.*

If all three of the preceding determinants vanish identically in a certain interval, the curve Γ is a straight line, or is composed of several portions of straight lines. If dx/dt does not vanish in the interval (a, b), for example, we may write

$$\frac{d^2y\,dx - dy\,d^2x}{(dx)^2} = 0, \qquad \frac{d^2z\,dx - dz\,d^2x}{(dx)^2} = 0,$$

whence

$$dy = C_1 dx, \qquad dz = C_2 dx,$$

---

* This singular case seems to have been noticed first by Peano. It is evidently of interest only from a purely analytical standpoint.

where C_1 and C_2 are constants. Finally, another integration gives

$$y = C_1 x + C_1', \qquad z = C_2 x + C_2',$$

which shows that Γ is a straight line.

217. Stationary tangents. The preceding paragraph suggests the study of certain points on a skew curve which we had not previously defined, namely the points at which we have

(11) $$\frac{d^2 x}{dx} = \frac{d^2 y}{dy} = \frac{d^2 z}{dz}.$$

The tangent at such a point is said to be *stationary*. It is easy to show by the formula for the distance between a point and a straight line that the distance from a point of Γ to the tangent at a neighboring point, which is in general an infinitesimal of the second order, is of the third order for a stationary tangent. If the given curve Γ is a plane curve, the stationary tangents are the tangents at the points of inflection. The preceding paragraph shows that the only curve whose tangents are all stationary is the straight line.

At a point where the tangent is stationary, $\Delta = 0$, and the equation of the osculating plane becomes indeterminate. But in general this indetermination can be removed. For, returning to the calculation at the beginning of § 215 and carrying the expansions of the coördinates of M' to terms of the third order, it is easy to show, by means of (11), that the equation of the plane through M' and the tangent at M is of the form

$$\begin{vmatrix} X - x & Y - y & Z - z \\ f'(t) & \phi'(t) & \psi'(t) \\ f'''(t) + \epsilon_1 & \phi'''(t) + \epsilon_2 & \psi'''(t) + \epsilon_3 \end{vmatrix} = 0,$$

where $\epsilon_1, \epsilon_2, \epsilon_3$ approach zero with h. Hence that plane approaches a perfectly definite limiting position, and the equation of the osculating plane is given by replacing the second of equations (6) by the equation

$$A \, d^3 x + B \, d^3 y + C \, d^3 z = 0.$$

If the coördinates of the point M also satisfy the equation

$$\frac{d^3 x}{dx} = \frac{d^3 y}{dy} = \frac{d^3 z}{dz},$$

the second of the equations (6) should be replaced by the equation

$$A \, d^q x = B \, d^q y + C \, d^q z = 0,$$

where q is the least integer for which this latter equation is distinct from the equation $A \, dx = B \, dy + C \, dz = 0$. The proof of this statement and the examination of the behavior of the curve with respect to its osculating plane are left to the reader.

Usually the preceding equation involving the third differentials is sufficient, and the coefficients A, B, C do not satisfy the equation

$$A \, d^4 x + B \, d^4 y + C \, d^4 z = 0.$$

In this case the curve crosses every tangent plane except the osculating plane.

218. Special curves. Let us consider the skew curves Γ which satisfy a relation of the form

$$(12) \qquad x\,dy - y\,dx = K\,dz,$$

where K is a given constant. From (12) we find immediately

$$(13) \qquad \begin{cases} x\,d^2y - y\,d^2x = K\,d^2z, \\ x\,d^3y - y\,d^3x + dx\,d^2y - dy\,d^2x = K\,d^3z. \end{cases}$$

Let us try to find the osculating plane of Γ which passes through a given point (a, b, c) of space. The coördinates (x, y, z) of the point of tangency must satisfy the equation

$$\begin{vmatrix} a - x & b - y & c - z \\ dx & dy & dz \\ d^2x & d^2y & d^2z \end{vmatrix} = 0,$$

which, by means of (12) and (13), may be written in the form

$$(14) \qquad ay - bx + K(c - z) = 0.$$

Hence the possible points of tangency are the points of intersection of the curve Γ with the plane (14), which passes through (a, b, c).

Again, replacing dz, d^2z and d^3z by their values from (12) and (13), the equation $\Delta = 0$, which gives the points at which the osculating plane is stationary, becomes

$$\Delta = \frac{1}{K}(dx\,d^2y - dy\,d^2x)^2 = 0;$$

hence we shall have at the same points

$$\frac{d^2x}{dx} = \frac{d^2y}{dy} = \frac{y\,d^2x - x\,d^2y}{y\,dx - x\,dy} = \frac{d^2z}{dz},$$

which shows that the tangent is stationary at any point at which the osculating plane is stationary.

It is easy to write down the equations of skew curves which satisfy (12); for example, the curves

$$x = At^m, \qquad y = Bt^n, \qquad z = Ct^{m+n},$$

where A, B, C, m, and n are any constants, are of that kind. Of these the simplest are the skew cubic $x = t$, $y = t^2$, $z = t^3$, and the skew quartic $x = t$, $y = t^3$, $z = t^4$. The circular helix

$$x = a\cos t, \qquad y = a\sin t, \qquad z = Kt$$

is another example of the same kind.

In order to find all the curves which satisfy (12), let us write that equation in the form

$$d(xy - Kz) = 2y\,dx.$$

If we set

$$x = f(t), \qquad xy - Kz = \phi(t),$$

the preceding equation becomes

$$2yf'(t) = \phi'(t).$$

Solving these three equations for x, y, and z, we find the general equations of Γ in the form

$$(15) \qquad x = f(t), \qquad y = \frac{\phi'(t)}{2f'(t)}, \qquad Kz = \frac{f(t)\,\phi'(t)}{2f'(t)} - \phi(t),$$

where $f(t)$ and $\phi(t)$ are arbitrary functions of the parameter t. It is clear, however, that one of these functions may be assigned at random without loss of generality. In fact we may set $f(t) = t$, since this amounts to choosing $f(t)$ as a new parameter.

II. ENVELOPES OF SURFACES

Before taking up the study of the curvature of skew curves, we shall discuss the theory of envelopes of surfaces.

219. One-parameter families. Let S be a surface of the family

$$(16) \qquad f(x, y, z, a) = 0,$$

where a is the variable parameter. If there exists a surface E which is tangent to each of the surfaces S along a curve C, the surface E is called the *envelope* of the family (16), and the curve of tangency C of the two surfaces S and E is called the *characteristic curve.*

In order to see whether an envelope exists it is evidently necessary to discover whether it is possible to find a curve C on each of the surfaces S such that the locus of all these curves is tangent to each surface S along the corresponding curve C. Let (x, y, z) be the coördinates of a point M on a characteristic. If M is not a singular point of S, the equation of the tangent plane to S at M is

$$\frac{\partial f}{dx}(X - x) + \frac{\partial f}{dy}(Y - y) + \frac{\partial f}{dz}(Z - z) = 0.$$

As we pass from point to point of the surface E, x, y, z, and a are evidently functions of the two independent variables which express the position of the point upon E, and these functions satisfy the equation (16). Hence their differentials satisfy the relation

$$(17) \qquad \frac{\partial f}{\partial x}\,dx + \frac{\partial f}{\partial y}\,dy + \frac{\partial f}{\partial z}\,dz + \frac{\partial f}{\partial a}\,da = 0.$$

Moreover the necessary and sufficient condition that the tangent plane to E should coincide with the tangent plane to S is

$$\frac{\partial f}{\partial x}\,dx + \frac{\partial f}{\partial y}\,dy + \frac{\partial f}{\partial z}\,dz = 0,$$

or, by (17),

$$(18) \qquad \frac{\partial f}{\partial a} = 0.$$

Conversely, it is easy to show, as we did for plane curves (§ 201), that the equation $R(x, y, z) = 0$, found by eliminating the parameter a between the two equations (16) and (18), represents one or more analytically distinct surfaces, each of which is an envelope of the surfaces S or else the locus of singular points of S, or a combination of the two. Finally, as in § 201, the characteristic curve represented by the equations (16) and (18) for any given value of a is the limiting position of the curve of intersection of S with a neighboring surface of the same family.

220. Two-parameter families. Let S be any surface of the two-parameter family

(19) $$f(x, y, z, a, b) = 0,$$

where a and b are the variable parameters. There does not exist, in general, any one surface which is tangent to each member of this family all along a curve. Indeed, let $b = \phi(a)$ be any arbitrarily assigned relation between a and b which reduces the family (19) to a one-parameter family. Then the equation (19), the equation $b = \phi(a)$, and the equation

(20) $$\frac{\partial f}{\partial a} + \frac{\partial f}{\partial b} \phi'(a) = 0$$

represent the envelope of this one-parameter family, or, for any fixed value of a, they represent the characteristic on the corresponding surface S. This characteristic depends, in general, on $\phi'(a)$, and there are an infinite number of characteristics on each of the surfaces S corresponding to various assignments of $\phi(a)$. Therefore the totality of all the characteristics, as a and b both vary arbitrarily, does not, in general, form a surface. We shall now try to discover whether there is a surface E which touches each of the family (19) in one or more points, — not along a curve. If such a surface exists, the coördinates (x, y, z) of the point of tangency of any surface S with this *envelope* E are functions of the two variable parameters a and b which satisfy the equation (19); hence their differentials dx, dy, dz with respect to the independent variables a and b satisfy the relation

(21) $$\frac{\partial f}{\partial x} dx + \frac{\partial f}{\partial y} dy + \frac{\partial f}{\partial z} dz + \frac{\partial f}{\partial a} da + \frac{\partial f}{\partial b} db = 0.$$

Moreover, in order that the surface which is the locus of the point of tangency (x, y, z) should be tangent to S, it is also necessary that we should have

$$\frac{\partial f}{\partial x}\, dx + \frac{\partial f}{\partial y}\, dy + \frac{\partial f}{\partial z}\, dz = 0,$$

or, by (21),

$$\frac{\partial f}{\partial a}\, da + \frac{\partial f}{\partial b}\, db = 0.$$

Since a and b are independent variables, it follows that the equations

$$(22) \qquad \frac{\partial f}{\partial a} = 0, \qquad \frac{\partial f}{\partial b} = 0$$

must be satisfied simultaneously by the coördinates (x, y, z) of the point of tangency. Hence we shall obtain the equation of the envelope, if one exists, by eliminating a and b between the three equations (19) and (22). The surface obtained will surely be tangent to S at (x, y, z) unless the equations

$$\frac{\partial f}{\partial x} = \frac{\partial f}{\partial y} = \frac{\partial f}{\partial z} = 0$$

are satisfied simultaneously by the values (x, y, z) which satisfy (19) and (22); hence this surface is either the envelope or else the locus of singular points of S.

We have seen that there are two kinds of envelopes, depending on the number of parameters in the given family. For example, the tangent planes to a sphere form a two-parameter family, and each plane of the family touches the surface at only one point. On the other hand, the tangent planes to a cone or to a cylinder form a one-parameter family, and each member of the family is tangent to the surface along the whole length of a generator.

221. Developable surfaces. The envelope of any one-parameter family of planes is called a *developable surface.* Let

$$(23) \qquad z = \alpha x + y f(\alpha) + \phi(\alpha)$$

be the equation of a variable plane P, where α is a parameter and where $f(\alpha)$ and $\phi(\alpha)$ are any two functions of α. Then the equation (23) and the equation

$$(24) \qquad x + y f'(\alpha) + \phi'(\alpha) = 0$$

represent the envelope of the family, or, for a given value of α, they represent the characteristic on the corresponding plane. But these two equations represent a straight line; hence each characteristic is a straight line G, and the developable surface is a ruled surface. We proceed to show that all the straight lines G are tangent to the same skew curve. In order to do so let us differentiate (24) again with regard to α. The equation obtained

$$(25) \qquad\qquad y f''(\alpha) + \phi''(\alpha) = 0$$

determines a particular point M on G. We proceed to show that G is tangent at M to the skew curve Γ which M describes as α varies. The equations of Γ are precisely (23), (24), (25), from which, if we desired, we might find x, y, and z as functions of the variable parameter α. Differentiating the first two of these and using the third of them, we find the relations

$$(26) \qquad dz = \alpha\,dx + f(\alpha)\,dy, \qquad dx + f'(\alpha)\,dy = 0,$$

which show that the tangent to Γ is parallel to G. But these two straight lines also have a common point; hence they coincide.

The osculating plane to the curve Γ is the plane P itself. To prove this it is only necessary to show that the first and second differentials of x, y, and z with respect to α satisfy the relations

$$dz = \alpha\,dx\ + f(\alpha)\,dy,$$
$$d^2z = \alpha\,d^2x + f(\alpha)\,d^2y.$$

The first of these is the first of equations (26), which is known to hold. Differentiating it again with respect to α, we find

$$d^2z = \alpha\,d^2x + f(\alpha)\,d^2y + [dx + f'(\alpha)\,dy]\,d\alpha,$$

which, by the second of equations (26), reduces to the second of the equations to be proved.

It follows that *any developable surface may be defined as the locus of the tangents to a certain skew curve* Γ. In exceptional cases the curve Γ may reduce to a point at a finite or at an infinite distance; then the surface is either a cone or a cylinder. This will happen whenever $f''(\alpha) = 0$.

Conversely, the locus of the tangents to any skew curve Γ is a developable surface. For, let

$$x = f(t), \qquad y = \phi(t), \qquad z = \psi(t)$$

be the equations of any skew curve Γ. The osculating planes

$$A(X - x) + B(Y - y) + C(Z - z) = 0$$

form a one-parameter family, whose envelope is given by the preceding equation and the equation

$$dA(X - x) + dB(Y - y) + dC(Z - z) = 0.$$

For any fixed value of t the same equations represent the characteristic in the corresponding osculating plane. We shall show that this characteristic is precisely the tangent at the corresponding point of Γ. It will be sufficient to establish the equations

$$A\, dx + B\, dy + C\, dz = 0, \qquad dA\, dx + dB\, dy + dC\, dz = 0.$$

The first of these is the first of (6), while the second is easily obtained by differentiating the first and then making use of the second of (6). It follows that the characteristic is parallel to the tangent, and it is evident that each of them passes through the point (x, y, z); hence they coincide.

This method of forming the developable gives a clear idea of the appearance of the surface. Let AB be an arc of a skew curve. At each point M of AB draw the tangent, and consider only that half of the tangent which extends in a certain direction, — from A toward B, for example. These half rays form one nappe S_1 of the developable, bounded on three sides by the arc AB and the tangents A and B and extending to infinity. The other ends of the tangents form another nappe S_2 similar to S_1 and joined to S_1 along the arc AB. To an observer placed above them these two nappes appear to cover each other partially. It is evident that any plane not tangent to Γ through any point O of AB cuts the two nappes S_1 and S_2 of the developable in two branches of a curve which has a cusp at O. The skew curve Γ is often called the *edge of regression* of the developable surface.*

It is easy to verify directly the statement just made. Let us take O as origin, the secant plane as the xy plane, the tangent to Γ as the axis of z, and the osculating plane as the xz plane. Assuming that the coördinates x and y of a point of Γ can be expanded in powers of the independent variable z, the equations of Γ are of the form

$$x = a_2 z^2 + a_3 z^3 + \cdots, \qquad y = b_3 z^3 + \cdots,$$

for the equations

$$\frac{dx}{dz} = \frac{dy}{dz} = \frac{d^2 y}{dz^2} = 0$$

---

* The English term "edge of regression" does not suggest that the curve is a locus of cusps. The French terms "arête de rebroussement" and "point de rebroussement" are more suggestive. — TRANS.

must be satisfied at the origin. Hence the equations of a tangent at a point near the origin are

$$\frac{X - a_2 z^2 - a_3 z^3 - \cdots}{2a_2 z + \cdots} = \frac{Y - b_3 z^3 - \cdots}{3b_3 z^2 + \cdots} = Z - z.$$

Setting $Z = 0$, the coördinates X and Y of the point where the tangent meets the secant plane are found to have developments which begin with terms in z^2 and in z^3, respectively; hence there is surely a cusp at the origin.

Example. Let us select as the edge of regression the skew cubic $x = t$, $y = t^2$, $z = t^3$. The equation of the osculating plane to the curve is

$$(27) \qquad t^3 - 3t^2 X + 3tY - Z = 0;$$

hence we shall obtain the equation of the corresponding developable by writing down the condition that (27) should have a double root in t, which amounts to eliminating t between the equations

$$(28) \qquad \begin{cases} t^2 - 2tX + Y = 0, \\ Xt^2 - 2tY + Z = 0. \end{cases}$$

The result of this elimination is the equation

$$(XY - Z)^2 - 4(X^2 - Y)(Y^2 - XZ) = 0,$$

which shows that the developable is of the fourth order.

It should be noticed that the equations (28) represent the tangent to the given cubic.

222. Differential equation of developable surfaces. If $z = F(x, y)$ be the equation of a developable surface, *the function $F(x, y)$ satisfies the equation $s^2 - rt = 0$*, where r, s, and t represent, as usual, the three second partial derivatives of the function $F(x, y)$.

For the tangent planes to the given surface,

$$Z = pX + qY + z - px - qy,$$

must form a one-parameter family; hence only one of the three coefficients p, q, and $z - px - qy$ can vary arbitrarily. In particular there must be a relation between p and q of the form $f(p, q) = 0$. It follows that the Jacobian $D(p, q)/D(x, y) = rt - s^2$ must vanish identically.

Conversely, if $F(x, y)$ satisfies the equation $rt - s^2 = 0$, p and q are connected by at least one relation. If there were two distinct relations, p and q would be constants, $F(x, y)$ would be of the form $ax + by + c$, and the surface $z = F(x, y)$ would be a plane. If there is a single relation between p and q, it may be written in the form $q = f(p)$, *where p does not reduce to a constant.* But we also have

$$y (rt - s^2) = \frac{D(z - px - qy, p)}{D(x, y)};$$

hence $z - px - qy$ is also a function of p, say $\psi(p)$, whenever $rt - s^2 = 0$. Then the unknown function $F(x, y)$ and its partial derivatives p and q satisfy the two equations

$$q = \phi(p), \qquad z - px - \phi(p)y = \psi(p).$$

Differentiating the second of these equations with respect to x and with respect to y, we find

$$[x + y \phi'(p) + \psi'(p)]\frac{\partial p}{\partial x} = 0, \qquad [x + y \phi'(p) + \psi'(p)]\frac{\partial p}{\partial y} = 0.$$

Since p does not reduce to a constant, we must have

$$x + y \phi'(p) + \psi'(p) = 0;$$

hence the equation of the surface is to be found by eliminating p between this equation and the equation

$$z = px + y \phi(p) + \psi(p),$$

which is exactly the process for finding the envelope of the family of planes represented by the latter equation, p being thought of as the variable parameter.

223. Envelope of a family of skew curves. A one-parameter family of skew curves has, in general, no envelope. Let us consider first a family of straight lines

$$(29) \qquad x = az + p, \qquad y = bz + q,$$

where a, b, p, and q are given functions of a variable parameter α. We shall proceed to find the conditions under which every member of this family is tangent to the same skew curve Γ. Let $z = \phi(\alpha)$ be the z coördinate of the point M at which the variable straight line D touches its envelope Γ. Then the required curve Γ will be represented by the equations (29) together with the equation $z = \phi(\alpha)$, and the direction cosines of the tangent to Γ will be proportional to $dx/d\alpha$, $dy/d\alpha$, $dz/d\alpha$, i.e. to the three quantities

$$a \phi'(\alpha) + a'\phi(\alpha) + p', \qquad b \phi'(\alpha) + b'\phi(\alpha) + q', \qquad \phi'(\alpha),$$

where a', b', p', and q' are the derivatives of a, b, p, and q, respectively. The necessary and sufficient condition that this tangent be the straight line D itself is that we should have

$$\frac{dx}{d\alpha} = a\,\frac{dz}{d\alpha}, \qquad \frac{dy}{d\alpha} = b\,\frac{dz}{d\alpha},$$

that is,

$$a'\phi(\alpha) + p' = 0, \qquad b'\phi(\alpha) + q' = 0.$$

The unknown function $\phi(\alpha)$ must satisfy these two equations; hence the family of straight lines has no envelope unless the two are compatible, that is, unless

$$a'q' - b'p' = 0.$$

If this condition is satisfied, we shall obtain the envelope by setting $\phi(\alpha) = -p'/a' = -q'/b'$.

It is easy to generalize the preceding argument. Let us consider a one-parameter family of skew curves (C) represented by the equations

$$(30) \qquad F(x, y, z, \alpha) = 0, \qquad \Phi(x, y, z, \alpha) = 0,$$

where α is the variable parameter. If each of these curves C is tangent to the same curve Γ, the coördinates (x, y, z) of the point M at which the envelope touches the curve C which corresponds to the parameter value α are functions of α which satisfy (30) and which also satisfy another relation distinct from those two. Let dx, dy, dz be the differentials with respect to a displacement of M along C; since α is constant along C, these differentials must satisfy the two equations

$$(31) \qquad \begin{cases} \dfrac{\partial F}{\partial x}\,dx + \dfrac{\partial F}{\partial y}\,dy + \dfrac{\partial F}{\partial z}\,dz = 0, \\[2mm] \dfrac{\partial \Phi}{\partial x}\,dx + \dfrac{\partial \Phi}{\partial y}\,dy + \dfrac{\partial \Phi}{\partial z}\,dz = 0. \end{cases}$$

On the other hand, let δx, δy, δz, $\delta\alpha$ be the differentials of x, y, z, and α with respect to a displacement of M along Γ. These differentials satisfy the equations

$$(32) \qquad \begin{cases} \dfrac{\partial F}{\partial x}\,\delta x + \dfrac{\partial F}{\partial y}\,\delta y + \dfrac{\partial F}{\partial z}\,\delta z + \dfrac{\partial F}{\partial \alpha}\,\delta\alpha = 0, \\[2mm] \dfrac{\partial \Phi}{\partial x}\,\delta x + \dfrac{\partial \Phi}{\partial y}\,\delta y + \dfrac{\partial \Phi}{\partial z}\,\delta z + \dfrac{\partial \Phi}{\partial \alpha}\,\delta\alpha = 0. \end{cases}$$

The necessary and sufficient conditions that the curves C and Γ be tangent are

$$\frac{dx}{\delta x} = \frac{dy}{\delta y} = \frac{dz}{\delta z},$$

or, making use of (31) and (32),

$$\frac{\partial F}{\partial \alpha} \delta \alpha = 0, \qquad \frac{\partial \Phi}{\partial \alpha} \delta \alpha = 0.$$

It follows that *the coördinates (x, y, z) of the point of tangency must satisfy the equations*

$$(33) \qquad F = 0, \qquad \Phi = 0, \qquad \frac{\partial F}{\partial \alpha} = 0, \qquad \frac{\partial \Phi}{\partial \alpha} = 0.$$

Hence, if the family (30) is to have an envelope, the four equations (33) must be compatible for all values of α. Conversely, if these four equations have a common solution in x, y, and z for all values of α, the argument shows that the curve Γ described by the point (x, y, z) is tangent at each point (x, y, z) upon it to the corresponding curve C. This is all under the supposition that the ratios between dx, dy, and dz are determined by the equations (31), that is, that the point (x, y, z) is not a singular point of the curve C.

Note. If the curves C are the characteristics of a one-parameter family of surfaces $F(x, y, z, \alpha) = 0$, the equations (33) reduce to the three distinct equations

$$(34) \qquad F = 0, \qquad \frac{\partial F}{\partial \alpha} = 0, \qquad \frac{\partial^2 F}{\partial \alpha^2} = 0;$$

hence the curve represented by these equations is the envelope of the characteristics. This is the generalization of the theorem proved above for the generators of a developable surface.

The equations of a one-parameter family of straight lines are cften written in the form

$$(35) \qquad \frac{x - x_0}{a} = \frac{y - y_0}{b} = \frac{z - z_0}{c},$$

where x_0, y_0, z_0, a, b, c are functions of a variable parameter α. It is easy to find directly the condition that this family should have an envelope. Let l denote the common value of each of the preceding ratios; then the coördinates of any point of the straight line are given by the equations

$$x = x_0 + la, \qquad y = y_0 + lb, \qquad z = z_0 + lc,$$

and the question is to determine whether it is possible to substitute for l such a function of α that the variable straight line should always remain tangent to the curve described by the point (x, y, z). The necessary condition for this is that we should have

(36)
$$\frac{x_0' + a'l}{a} = \frac{y_0' + b'l}{b} = \frac{z_0' + c'l}{c}.$$

Denoting by m the common value of these ratios and eliminating l and m from the three linear equations obtained, we find the equation of condition

(37)
$$\begin{vmatrix} x_0' & y_0' & z_0' \\ a & b & c \\ a' & b' & c' \end{vmatrix} = 0.$$

If this condition is satisfied, the equations (36) determine l, and hence also the equation of the envelope.

III. CURVATURE AND TORSION OF SKEW CURVES

224. Spherical indicatrix. Let us adopt upon a given skew curve Γ a definite sense of motion, and let s be the length of the arc AM measured from some fixed point A as origin to any point M, affixing the sign $+$ or the sign $-$ according as the direction from A toward M is the direction adopted or the opposite direction. Let MT be the *positive* direction of the tangent at M, that is, that which corresponds to increasing values of the arc. If through any point O in space lines be drawn parallel to these half rays, a cone S is formed which is called the *directing cone* of the developable surface formed by the tangents to Γ. Let us draw a sphere of unit radius about O as center, and let Σ be the line of intersection of this sphere with the directing cone. The curve Σ is called the *spherical indicatrix*

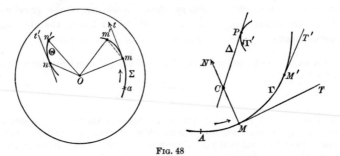

Fig. 48

of the curve Γ. The correspondence between the points of these two curves is one-to-one : to a point M of Γ corresponds the point m where the parallel to MT pierces the sphere. As the point M describes the curve Γ in the positive sense, the point m describes the curve Σ in a certain sense, which we shall adopt as positive. Then the corresponding arcs s and σ increase simultaneously (Fig. 48).

It is evident that if the point O be displaced, the whole curve Σ undergoes the same translation; hence we may suppose that O lies at the origin of coördinates. Likewise, if the positive sense on the curve Γ be reversed, the curve Σ is replaced by a curve symmetrical to it with respect to the point O; but it should be noticed that the positive sense of the tangent mt to Σ is independent of the sense of motion on Γ.

The tangent plane to the directing cone along the generator Om is *parallel to the osculating plane* at M. For, let $AX + BY + CZ = 0$ be the equation of the plane Omm', the center O of the sphere being at the origin. This plane is parallel to the two tangents at M and at M'; hence, if t and $t + h$ are the parameter values which correspond to M and M', respectively, we must have

$$(38) \qquad Af'(t) + B\phi'(t) + C\psi'(t) = 0.$$

$$(39) \qquad Af'(t + h) + B\phi'(t + h) + C\psi'(t + h) = 0.$$

The second of these equations may be replaced by the equation

$$A\,\frac{f'(t + h) - f'(t)}{h} + B\,\frac{\phi'(t + h) - \phi'(t)}{h} + C\,\frac{\psi'(t + h) - \psi'(t)}{h} = 0,$$

which becomes, in the limit as h approaches zero,

$$(40) \qquad Af''(t) + B\phi''(t) + C\psi''(t) = 0.$$

The equations (38) and (40), which determine A, B, and C for the tangent plane at m, are exactly the same as the equations (6) which determine A, B, and C for the osculating plane.

225. Radius of curvature. Let ω be the angle between the positive directions of the tangents MT and $M'T'$ at two neighboring points M and M' of Γ. Then the limit of the ratio $\omega/\text{arc } MM'$, as M approaches M', is called the *curvature* of Γ at the point M, just as for a plane curve. The reciprocal of the curvature is called the *radius of curvature*: it is the limit of arc MM'/ω.

Again, the radius of curvature R may be defined to be the limit of the ratio of the two infinitesimal arcs MM' and mm', for we have

$$\frac{\text{arc } MM'}{\omega} = \frac{\text{arc } MM'}{\text{arc } mm'} \times \frac{\text{arc } mm'}{\text{chord } mm'} \times \frac{\text{chord } mm'}{\omega},$$

and each of the fractions (arc mm')/(chord) mm' and (chord mm')/ω approaches the limit unity as m approaches m'. The arcs $s (= MM')$ and $\sigma (= mm')$ increase or decrease simultaneously; hence

$$(41) \qquad R = \frac{ds}{d\sigma}.$$

Let the equations of Γ be given in the form

$$(42) \qquad x = f(t), \qquad y = \phi(t), \qquad z = \psi(t),$$

where O is the origin of coördinates. Then the coördinates of the point m are nothing else than the direction cosines of MT, namely

$$\alpha = \frac{dx}{ds}, \qquad \beta = \frac{dy}{ds}, \qquad \gamma = \frac{dz}{ds}.$$

Differentiating these equations, we find

$$d\alpha = \frac{ds\, d^2x - dx\, d^2s}{ds^2}, \quad d\beta = \frac{ds\, d^2y - dy\, d^2s}{ds^2}, \quad d\gamma = \frac{ds\, d^2z - dz\, d^2s}{ds^2},$$

$$d\sigma^2 = d\alpha^2 + d\beta^2 + d\gamma^2 = \frac{S(ds\, d^2x - dx\, d^2s)^2}{ds^4},$$

where S indicates as usual the sum of the three similar terms obtained by replacing x by x, y, z successively. Finally, expanding and making use of the expressions for ds^2 and $ds\, d^2s$, we find

$$d\sigma^2 = \frac{S\, dx^2 \; S(d^2x)^2 - \left[S\, dx\, d^2x \right]^2}{ds^4}.$$

By Lagrange's identity (§ 131) this equation may be written in the form

$$d\sigma^2 = \frac{A^2 + B^2 + C^2}{ds^4},$$

where

$$(43) \quad \begin{cases} A = dy\, d^2z - dz\, d^2y, \qquad B = dz\, d^2x - dx\, d^2z, \\ \qquad\qquad C = dx\, d^2y - dy\, d^2x, \end{cases}$$

a notation which we shall use consistently in what follows. Then the formula (41) for the radius of curvature becomes

$$(44) \qquad R^2 = \frac{ds^6}{A^2 + B^2 + C^2},$$

and it is evident that R^2 is a rational function of x, y, z, x', y', z', x'', y'', z''. The expression for the radius of curvature itself is irrational, but it is essentially a positive quantity.

Note. If the independent variable selected is the arc s of the curve Γ, the functions $f(s)$, $\phi(s)$, and $\psi(s)$ satisfy the equation

$$f'^2(s) + \phi'^2(s) + \psi'^2(s) = 1.$$

Then we shall have

$$(45) \quad \begin{cases} \alpha = f'(s), & \beta = \phi'(s), & \gamma = \psi'(s), \\ d\alpha = f''(s)\,ds, & d\beta = \phi''(s)\,ds, & d\gamma = \psi''(s)\,ds, \\ d\sigma^2 = \{[f''(s)]^2 + [\phi''(s)]^2 + [\psi''(s)]^2\}\,ds^2, \end{cases}$$

and the expression for the radius of curvature assumes the particularly elegant form

$$(44') \qquad \frac{1}{R^2} = [f''(s)]^2 + [\phi''(s)]^2 + [\psi''(s)]^2.$$

226. Principal normal. Center of curvature. Let us draw a line through M (on Γ) parallel to mt, the tangent to Σ at m. Let MN be the direction on this line which corresponds to the positive direction mt. The new line MN is called the *principal normal* to Γ at M: it is that normal which lies in the osculating plane, since mt is perpendicular to Om and Omt is parallel to the osculating plane (§ 224). The direction MN is called *the positive direction of the principal normal*. This direction is uniquely defined, since the positive direction of mt does not depend upon the choice of the positive direction upon Γ. We shall see in a moment how the direction in question might be defined without using the indicatrix.

If a length MC equal to the radius of curvature at M be laid off on MN from the point M, the extremity C is called the *center of curvature* of Γ at M, and the circle drawn around C in the osculating plane with a radius MC is called the *circle of curvature*. Let α', β', γ' be the direction cosines of the principal normal. Then the coördinates (x_1, y_1, z_1) of the center of curvature are

$$x_1 = x + R\alpha', \qquad y_1 = y + R\beta', \qquad z_1 = z + R\gamma'.$$

But we also have

$$\alpha' = \frac{d\alpha}{d\sigma} = \frac{d\alpha}{ds}\frac{ds}{d\sigma} = R\frac{d\alpha}{ds} = R\frac{ds\,d^2x - dx\,d^2s}{ds^3}$$

and similar formulæ for β' and γ'. Replacing α' by its value in the expression for x, we find

$$x_1 = x + R^2\frac{ds\,d^2x - dx\,d^2s}{ds^3}.$$

But the coefficient of R^2 may be written in the form

$$\frac{ds^2\,d^2x - dx\,ds\,d^2s}{ds^4} = \frac{d^2x\ \text{\textcursive{S}}\,dx^2 - dx\ \text{\textcursive{S}}(dx\,d^2x)}{ds^4},$$

or, in terms of the quantities A, B, and C,

$$\frac{B\,dz - C\,dy}{ds^4}.$$

The values of y_1 and z_1 may be written down by cyclic permutation from this value of x_1, and the coördinates of the center of curvature may be written in the form

$$(46)\qquad \begin{cases} x_1 = x + R^2\,\dfrac{B\,dz - C\,dy}{ds^4}, \\[2mm] y_1 = y + R^2\,\dfrac{C\,dx - A\,dz}{ds^4}, \\[2mm] z_1 = z + R^2\,\dfrac{A\,dy - B\,dx}{ds^4}. \end{cases}$$

These expressions for x_1, y_1, and z_1 are rational in x, y, z, x', y', z', x'', y'', z''.

A plane Q through M perpendicular to MN passes through the tangent MT and does not cross the curve Γ at M. We shall proceed to show that the center of curvature and the points of Γ near M lie on the same side of Q. To show this, let us take as the independent variable the arc s of the curve Γ counted from M as origin. Then the coördinates X, Y, Z of a point M' of Γ near M are of the form

$$X = x + \frac{s}{1}\frac{dx}{ds} + \frac{s^2}{1.2}\left(\frac{d^2x}{ds^2} + \epsilon\right),$$

the expansions for Y and Z being similar to the expansion for X. But since s is the independent variable, we shall have

$$\frac{dx}{ds} = \alpha, \qquad \frac{d^2x}{ds^2} = \frac{d\alpha}{ds} = \frac{d\alpha}{d\sigma}\frac{d\sigma}{ds} = \frac{1}{R}\,\alpha'$$

and the formula for X becomes

$$X = x + \alpha s + \left(\frac{\alpha'}{R} + \epsilon\right)\frac{s^2}{1.2}.$$

If in the equation of the plane Q,

$$\alpha'(X - x) + \beta'(Y - y) + \gamma'(Z - z) = 0,$$

X, Y, and Z be replaced by these expansions in the left-hand member, the value of that member is found to be

$$\frac{s}{1}\left(\alpha\alpha' + \beta\beta' + \gamma\gamma'\right) + \frac{s^2}{1 \cdot 2}\left(\frac{1}{R} + \eta\right) = \frac{s^2}{2}\left(\frac{1}{R} + \eta\right),$$

where η approaches zero with s. This quantity is positive for all values of s near zero. Likewise, replacing (X, Y, Z) by the coördinates $(x + R\alpha', y + R\beta', z + R\gamma')$ of the center of curvature, the result of the substitution is R, which is essentially positive. Hence the theorem is proved.

227. Polar line. Polar surface. The perpendicular Δ to the osculating plane at the center of curvature is called the *polar line*. This straight line is the characteristic of the normal plane to Γ. For, in the first place, it is evident that the line of intersection D of the normal planes at two neighboring points M and M' is perpendicular to each of the lines MT and $M'T'$; hence it is also perpendicular to the plane mOm'. As M' approaches M, the plane mOm' approaches parallelism to the osculating plane; hence the line D approaches a line perpendicular to the osculating plane. On the other hand, to show that it passes through the center of curvature, let s be the independent variable; then the equation of the normal plane is

$$(47) \qquad \alpha(X - x) + \beta(Y - y) + \gamma(Z - z) = 0,$$

and the characteristic is defined by (47) together with the equation

$$(48) \qquad \frac{\alpha'}{R}(X - x) + \frac{\beta'}{R}(Y - y) + \frac{\gamma'}{R}(Z - z) - 1 = 0.$$

This new equation represents a plane perpendicular to the principal normal through the center of curvature; hence the intersection of the two planes is the polar line.

The polar lines form a ruled surface, which is called the *polar surface*. It is evident that this surface is a developable, since we have just seen that it is the envelope of the normal plane to Γ. If Γ is a plane curve, the polar surface is a cylinder whose right section is the evolute of Γ; in this special case the preceding statements are self-evident.

228. Torsion. If the words "tangent line" in the definition of curvature (§ 225) be replaced by the words "osculating plane," a new geometrical concept is introduced which measures, in a manner, the rate at which the osculating plane turns. Let ω' be the angle between the osculating planes at two neighboring points M and M';

then the limit of the ratio ω'/arc MM', as M approaches M', is called the *torsion* of the curve Γ at the point M. The reciprocal of the torsion is called the *radius of torsion*.

The perpendicular to the osculating plane at M is called the *binormal*. Let us choose a certain direction on it as positive, — we shall determine later which we shall take, — and let α'', β'', γ'' be the corresponding direction cosines. The parallel line through the origin pierces the unit sphere at a point n, which we shall now put into correspondence with the point M of Γ. The locus of n is a spherical curve Θ, and it is easy to show, as above, that the radius of torsion T may be defined as the limit of the ratio of the two corresponding arcs MM' and nn' of the two curves Γ and Θ. Hence we shall have

$$T^2 = \frac{ds^2}{d\tau^2},$$

where τ denotes the arc of the curve Θ.

The coördinates of n are α'', β'', γ'', which are given by the formulæ (§ 215)

$$\alpha'' = \frac{A}{\pm\sqrt{A^2+B^2+C^2}}, \quad \beta'' = \frac{B}{\pm\sqrt{A^2+B^2+C^2}}, \quad \gamma'' = \frac{C}{\pm\sqrt{A^2+B^2+C^2}},$$

where the radical is to be taken with the same sign in all three formulæ. From these formulæ it is easy to deduce the values of $d\alpha''$, $d\beta''$, $d\gamma''$; for example,

$$d\alpha'' = \pm \frac{(A^2 + B^2 + C^2)\,dA - A(A\,dA + B\,dB + C\,dC)}{(A^2 + B^2 + C^2)^{\frac{3}{2}}},$$

whence, since $d\tau^2 = d\alpha''^2 + d\beta''^2 + d\gamma''^2$,

$$d\tau^2 = \frac{S\,A^2\,S\,dA^2 - \left[S(A\,dA)\right]^2}{(A^2 + B^2 + C^2)^2},$$

or, by Lagrange's identity,

$$d\tau^2 = \frac{S(B\,dC - C\,dB)^2}{(A^2 + B^2 + C^2)^2},$$

where S denotes the sum of the three terms obtained by cyclic permutation of the three letters A, B, C. The numerator of this expression may be simplified by means of the relations

$$A\,dx + B\,dy + C\,dz = 0,$$
$$dA\,dx + dB\,dy + dC\,dz = 0,$$

whence

$$(49) \quad \frac{dx}{B\,dC - C\,dB} = \frac{dy}{C\,dA - A\,dC} = \frac{dz}{A\,dB - B\,dA} = \frac{1}{K},$$

where K is a quantity defined by the equation (49) itself. This gives

$$d\tau^2 = \frac{K^2 ds^2}{(A^2 + B^2 + C^2)^2},$$

where K is defined by (49); or, expanding,

$$K = \frac{1}{dx}\left\{\begin{vmatrix} dz & dx \\ d^2z & d^2x \end{vmatrix} \cdot \begin{vmatrix} dx & dy \\ d^3x & d^3y \end{vmatrix} - \begin{vmatrix} dx & dy \\ d^2x & d^2y \end{vmatrix} \cdot \begin{vmatrix} dz & dx \\ d^3z & d^3x \end{vmatrix}\right\}$$

$$= S\left(dz\, d^2x\, d^3y - dx\, d^2z\, d^3y\right),$$

where S denotes the sum of the three terms obtained by cyclic permutation of the three letters x, y, z. But this value of K is exactly the development of the determinant Δ [(8), § 216]; hence

$$d\tau = \pm \frac{\Delta\, ds}{A^2 + B^2 + C^2},$$

and therefore the radius of torsion is given by the formula

(50) $$T = \pm \frac{A^2 + B^2 + C^2}{\Delta}.$$

If we agree to consider T essentially positive, as we did the radius of curvature, its value will be the absolute value of the second member. But it should be noticed that the expression for T is rational in $x, y, z, x', y', z', x'', y'', z''$; hence it is natural to represent the radius of torsion by a length affected by a sign. The two signs which T may have correspond to entirely different aspects of the curve Γ at the point M.

Since the sign of T depends only on that of Δ, we shall investigate the difference in the appearance of Γ near M when Δ has different signs. Let us suppose that the trihedron $Oxyz$ is placed so that an observer standing on the xy plane with his feet at O and his head in the positive z axis would see the x axis turn through 90° *to his left* if the x axis turned round into the y axis (see footnote, p. 477). Suppose that the positive direction of the binormal MN_b has been so chosen that the trihedron formed from the lines MT, MN, MN_b has the same aspect as the trihedron formed from the lines Ox, Oy, Oz; that is, if the curve Γ be moved into such a position that M coincides with O, MT with Ox, and MN with Oy, the direction MN_b will coincide with the positive z axis. During this motion the absolute value of T remains unchanged; hence Δ cannot vanish, and hence it cannot

even change sign.*   In this position of the curve Γ with respect to
the axes now in the figure the coördinates of a point near the origin
will be given by the formulæ

$$(51) \qquad \begin{cases} x = a_1 t + t^2(a_2 + \epsilon), \\ y = b_2 t^2 + t^3(b_3 + \epsilon'), \\ z = t^3(c_3 + \epsilon''), \end{cases}$$

where ϵ, ϵ', ϵ'' approach zero with t, provided that the parameter t is
so chosen that $t = 0$ at the origin.   For with the system of axes
employed we must have $dy = dz = d^2z = 0$ when $t = 0$.   Moreover
we may suppose that $a_1 > 0$, for a change in the parameter from t to
$-t$ will change a_1 to $-a_1$.   The coefficient b_2 is positive since y must
be positive near the origin, but c_3 may be either positive or negative.
On the other hand, for $t = 0$, $\Delta = 12 a_1 b_2 c_3 \, dt^6$.   Hence the sign of Δ
is the sign of c_3.   There are then two cases to be distinguished.   If
$c_3 > 0$, x and z are both negative for $-h < t < 0$, and both positive
for $0 < t < .h$, where h is a sufficiently small positive number; i.e.
an observer standing on the xy plane with his feet at a point P on

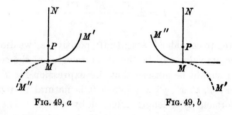

FIG. 49, a FIG. 49, b

the positive half of the principal normal would see the arc MM' at
his left and above the osculating plane, and the arc MM'' at his right
below that plane (Fig. 49, a).   In this case the curve is said to be
sinistrorsal.   On the other hand, if $c_3 < 0$, the aspect of the curve
would be exactly reversed (Fig. 49, b), and the curve would be said
to be *dextrorsal*.   These two aspects are essentially distinct.   For
example, if two spirals (helices) of the same pitch be drawn on the
same right circular cylinder, or on two congruent cylinders, they
will be superposable if they are both sinistrorsal or both dextrorsal;
but if one of them is sinistrorsal and the other dextrorsal, one of
them will be superposable upon the helix symmetrical to the other
one with respect to a plane of symmetry.

---

* It would be easy to show directly that Δ does not change sign when we pass from
one set of rectangular axes to another set which have the same aspect.

In consequence of these results we shall write

$$(52) \qquad T = -\frac{A^2 + B^2 + C^2}{\Delta};$$

i.e. at a point where the curve is dextrorsal T shall be positive, while T shall be negative at a point where the curve is sinistrorsal. A different arrangement of the original coördinate trihedron $Oxyz$ would lead to exactly opposite results.*

229. Frenet's formulæ. Each point M of Γ is the vertex of a trirectangular trihedron whose aspect is the same as that of the trihedron $Oxyz$, and whose edges are the tangent, the principal normal, and the binormal. The positive direction of the principal normal is already fixed. That of the tangent may be chosen at pleasure, but this choice then fixes the positive direction on the binormal. The differentials of the nine direction cosines (α, β, γ), $(\alpha', \beta', \gamma')$, $(\alpha'', \beta'', \gamma'')$ of these edges may be expressed very simply in terms of R, T, and the direction cosines themselves, by means of certain formulæ due to Frenet.† We have already found the formulæ for $d\alpha$, $d\beta$, and $d\gamma$:

$$(53) \qquad \frac{d\alpha}{ds} = \frac{\alpha'}{R}, \qquad \frac{d\beta}{ds} = \frac{\beta'}{R}, \qquad \frac{d\gamma}{ds} = \frac{\gamma'}{R}.$$

The direction cosines of the positive binormal (§ 228) are

$$\alpha'' = \epsilon\,\frac{A}{\sqrt{A^2+B^2+C^2}}, \quad \beta'' = \epsilon\,\frac{B}{\sqrt{A^2+B^2+C^2}}, \quad \gamma'' = \epsilon\,\frac{C}{\sqrt{A^2+B^2+C^2}},$$

where $\epsilon = \pm 1$. Since the trihedron (MT, MN, MN_b) has the same aspect as the trihedron $Oxyz$, we must have

$$\alpha' = \beta''\gamma - \beta\gamma'', \quad \text{or} \quad \alpha' = \epsilon\,\frac{B\gamma - C\beta}{\sqrt{A^2+B^2+C^2}}.$$

On the other hand, the formula for $d\alpha''$ may be written

$$d\alpha'' = \epsilon\,\frac{B(B\,dA - A\,dB) + C(C\,dA - A\,dC)}{(A^2+B^2+C^2)^{\frac{3}{2}}},$$

or, by (49) and the relation $K = \Delta$,

$$\frac{d\alpha''}{ds} = \epsilon\Delta\,\frac{C\beta - B\gamma}{(A^2+B^2+C^2)^{\frac{3}{2}}} = -\frac{\alpha'\Delta}{A^2+B^2+C^2}.$$

---

* It is usual in America to adopt an arrangement of axes precisely opposite to that described above. Hence we should write $T = + (A^2+B^2+C^2)/\Delta$, etc. See also the footnote to formula (54), § 229. — TRANS.

† *Nouvelles Annales de Mathématiques*, 1864, p. 281.

The coefficient of α' is precisely $1/T$, by (52). The formulæ for $d\beta''$ and $d\gamma''$ may be calculated in like manner, and we should find

$$(54) \qquad \frac{d\alpha''}{ds} = \frac{\alpha'}{T}, \qquad \frac{d\beta''}{ds} = \frac{\beta'}{T}, \qquad \frac{d\gamma''}{ds} = \frac{\gamma'}{T},$$

which are exactly analogous to (53).*

In order to find $d\alpha'$, $d\beta'$, $d\gamma'$, let us differentiate the well-known formulæ

$$\alpha'^2 + \beta'^2 + \gamma'^2 = 1,$$
$$\alpha\alpha' + \beta\beta' + \gamma\gamma' = 0,$$
$$\alpha'\alpha'' + \beta'\beta'' + \gamma'\gamma'' = 0,$$

replacing $d\alpha$, $d\beta$, $d\gamma$, $d\alpha''$, $d\beta''$, $d\gamma''$ by their values from (53) and (54). This gives

$$\alpha' \, d\alpha' + \beta' \, d\beta' + \gamma' \, d\gamma \qquad = 0,$$
$$\alpha \ d\alpha' + \beta \ d\beta' + \gamma \ d\gamma' + \frac{ds}{R} = 0,$$
$$\alpha'' d\alpha' + \beta'' d\beta' + \gamma'' d\gamma' + \frac{ds}{T} = 0;$$

whence, solving for $d\alpha'$, $d\beta'$, $d\gamma'$,

$$(55) \qquad \frac{d\alpha'}{ds} = -\frac{\alpha}{R} - \frac{\alpha''}{T}, \qquad \frac{d\beta'}{ds} = -\frac{\beta}{R} - \frac{\beta''}{T}, \qquad \frac{d\gamma'}{ds} = -\frac{\gamma}{R} - \frac{\gamma''}{T}.$$

The formulae (53), (54), and (55) constitute Frenet's formulæ.

Note. The formulæ (54) show that the tangent to the spherical curve Θ described by the point n whose coördinates are α'', β'', γ'' is parallel to the principal normal. This can be verified geometrically. Let S' be the cone whose vertex is at O and whose directrix is the curve Θ. The generator On is perpendicular to the plane which is tangent to the cone S along Om (§ 228). Hence S' is the polar cone to S. But this property is a reciprocal one, i.e. the generator Om of S is surely perpendicular to the plane which is tangent to S' along On. Hence the tangent mt to the curve Σ, since it is perpendicular to each of the lines On and Om, is perpendicular to the plane mOn. For the same reason the tangent nt' to the curve Θ is perpendicular to the plane mOn. It follows that mt and nt' are parallel.

---

* If we had written the formula for the torsion in the form $1/T = \Delta/(A^2 + B^2 + C^2)$, Frenet's formulæ would have to be written in the form $d\alpha''/ds = -\alpha'/T$, etc. [Hence this would be the form if the axes are taken as usual in America. — TRANS.]

230. Expansion of x, y, and z in powers of s. Given two functions $R = \phi(s)$, $T = \psi(s)$ of an independent variable s, the first of which is positive, there exists a skew curve Γ which is completely defined except for its position in space, and whose radius of curvature and radius of torsion are expressed by the given equations in terms of the arc s of the curve counted from some fixed point upon it. A rigorous proof of this theorem cannot be given until we have discussed the theory of differential equations. Just now we shall merely show how to find the expansions for the coördinates of a point on the required curve in powers of s, assuming that such expansions exist.

Let us take as axes the tangent, the principal normal, and the binormal at O, the origin of arcs on Γ. Then we shall have

$$(56) \quad \begin{cases} x = \dfrac{s}{1}\left(\dfrac{dx}{ds}\right)_0 + \dfrac{s^2}{1.2}\left(\dfrac{d^2x}{ds^2}\right)_0 + \dfrac{s^3}{1.2.3}\left(\dfrac{d^3x}{ds^3}\right)_0 + \cdots, \\[2ex] y = \dfrac{s}{1}\left(\dfrac{dy}{ds}\right)_0 + \dfrac{s^2}{1.2}\left(\dfrac{d^2y}{ds^2}\right)_0 + \dfrac{s^3}{1.2.3}\left(\dfrac{d^3y}{ds^3}\right)_0 + \cdots, \\[2ex] z = \dfrac{s}{1}\left(\dfrac{dz}{ds}\right)_0 + \dfrac{s^2}{1.2}\left(\dfrac{d^2z}{ds^2}\right)_0 + \dfrac{s^3}{1.2.3}\left(\dfrac{d^3z}{ds^3}\right)_0 + \cdots, \end{cases}$$

where x, y, and z are the coördinates of a point on Γ. But

$$\frac{dx}{ds} = \alpha, \qquad \frac{d^2x}{ds^2} = \frac{d\alpha}{ds} = \frac{\alpha'}{R},$$

whence, differentiating,

$$\frac{d^3x}{ds^3} = -\frac{\alpha'}{R^2}\frac{dR}{ds} - \frac{1}{R}\left(\frac{\alpha}{R} + \frac{\alpha''}{T}\right).$$

In general, the repeated application of Frenet's formulæ gives

$$\frac{d^nx}{ds^n} = L_n\alpha + M_n\alpha' + P_n\alpha'',$$

where L_n, M_n, P_n are known functions of R, T, and their successive derivatives with respect to s. In a similar manner the successive derivatives of y and z are to be found by replacing $(\alpha, \alpha', \alpha'')$ by (β, β', β'') and $(\gamma, \gamma', \gamma'')$, respectively. But we have, at the origin, $\alpha_0 = 1$, $\beta_0 = 0$, $\gamma_0 = 0$, $\alpha_0' = 0$, $\beta_0' = 1$, $\gamma_0' = 0$, $\alpha_0'' = 0$, $\beta_0'' = 0$, $\gamma_0'' = 1$; hence the formulæ (56) become

$$(56') \quad \begin{cases} x = \dfrac{s}{1} - \dfrac{s^3}{6R^2} + \cdots, \\[2ex] y = \dfrac{s^2}{2R} - \dfrac{s^3}{6R^2}\dfrac{dR}{ds} + \cdots, \\[2ex] z = -\dfrac{s^3}{6RT} + \cdots, \end{cases}$$

where the terms not written down are of degree higher than three. It is understood, of course, that R, T, dR/ds, $\cdots$ are to be replaced by their values for $s = 0$.

These formulæ enable us to calculate the principal parts of certain infinitesimals. For instance, the distance from a point of the curve to the osculating plane is an infinitesimal of the third order, and its principal part is $- s^3/6RT$. The distance from a point on the curve to the x axis, i.e. to the tangent, is of the second order, and its principal part is $s^2/2R$ (compare § 214). Again, let us calculate the length of an infinitesimal chord c. We find

$$c^2 = x^2 + y^2 + z^2 = s^2 - \frac{s^4}{12R^2} + \cdots,$$

where the terms not written down are of degree higher than four. This equation may be written in the form

$$c = s\left(1 - \frac{s^2}{12R^2} + \cdots\right)^{\frac{1}{2}} = s\left(1 - \frac{s^2}{24R^2} + \cdots\right),$$

which shows that the difference $s - c$ is an infinitesimal of the *third order* and that its principal part is $s^3/24R^2$.

In an exactly similar manner it may be shown that the shortest distance between the tangent at the origin and the tangent at a neighboring point is an infinitesimal of the third order whose principal part is $s^3/12RT$. This theorem is due to Bouquet.

231. Involutes and evolutes. A curve Γ_1 is called an *involute* of a second curve Γ if all the tangents to Γ are among the normals to Γ_1, and conversely, the curve Γ is called an *evolute* of Γ_1. It is evident that all the involutes of a given curve Γ lie on the developable surface of which Γ is the edge of regression, and cut the generators of the developable orthogonally.

Let (x, y, z) be the coördinates of a point M of Γ, (α, β, γ) the direction cosines of the tangent MT, and l the segment MM_1 between M and the point M_1 where a certain involute cuts MT. Then the coördinates of M_1 are

$$x_1 = x + l\alpha, \qquad y_1 = y + l\beta, \qquad z_1 = z + l\gamma,$$

whence

$$dx_1 = dx + l\,d\alpha + \alpha\,dl,$$
$$dy_1 = dy + l\,d\beta + \beta\,dl,$$
$$dz_1 = dz + l\,d\gamma + \gamma\,dl.$$

In order that the curve described by M_1 should be normal to MM_1 it is necessary and sufficient that $\alpha\,dx_1 + \beta\,dy_1 + \gamma\,dz_1$ should vanish, i.e. that we should have

$$\alpha\,dx + \beta\,dy + \gamma\,dz + dl + l(\alpha\,d\alpha + \beta\,d\beta + \gamma\,d\gamma) = 0,$$

which reduces to $ds + dl = 0$. It follows that the involutes to a given skew curve Γ may be drawn by the same construction which was used for plane curves (§ 206).

Let us try to find all the evolutes of a given curve Γ, that is, let us try to pick out a one-parameter family of normals to the given curve according to some continuous law which will group these normals into a developable surface (Fig. 50). Let D be an evolute, ϕ the angle between the normal MM_1 and the principal normal MN, and l the segment MP between M and the projection P of the point M_1 on the principal normal. Then the coördinates (x_1, y_1, z_1) of M_1 are

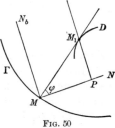

FIG. 50

$$(57) \quad \begin{cases} x_1 = x + l\alpha' + l\alpha'' \tan\phi, \\ y_1 = y + l\beta' + l\beta'' \tan\phi, \\ z_1 = z + l\gamma' + l\gamma'' \tan\phi, \end{cases}$$

as we see by projecting the broken line MPM_1 upon the three axes successively. The tangent to the curve described by the point M_1 must be the line MM_1 itself, that is, we must have

$$\frac{dx_1}{x_1 - x} = \frac{dy_1}{y_1 - y} = \frac{dz_1}{z_1 - z}.$$

Let k denote the common value of these ratios; then the condition $dx_1 = k(x_1 - x)$ may be transformed, by inserting the values of x_1 and dx_1 and applying Frenet's formulæ, into the form

$$\alpha\,ds\left(1 - \frac{l}{R}\right) + \alpha'\left(dl + l\tan\phi\,\frac{ds}{T} - kl\right)$$
$$+ \alpha''\left[d(l\tan\phi) - \frac{l\,ds}{T} - kl\tan\phi\right] = 0.$$

The conditions $dy_1 = k(y_1 - y)$ and $dz_1 = k(z_1 - z)$ lead to exactly similar forms, which may be deduced from the preceding by replacing $(\alpha, \alpha', \alpha'')$ by (β, β', β'') and $(\gamma, \gamma', \gamma'')$, respectively. Since the

determinant of the nine direction cosines is equal to unity, these
three equations are equivalent to the set

$$(58) \quad \begin{cases} \left(1 - \dfrac{l}{R}\right) ds = 0, \\[2ex] dl + l \tan \phi \, \dfrac{ds}{T} = kl, \\[2ex] d(l \tan \phi) - \dfrac{l \, ds}{T} = kl \tan \phi. \end{cases}$$

From the first of these $l = R$, which shows that the point P is the
center of curvature and that the line PM is the polar line. It follows that *all the evolutes of a given skew curve* Γ *lie on the polar surface.* In order to determine these evolutes completely it only remains
to eliminate k between the last two of equations (58). Doing so
and replacing l by R throughout, we find $ds = T \, d\phi$. Hence ϕ may
be found by a single quadrature:

$$(59) \qquad\qquad \phi = \phi_0 + \int_0^s \frac{ds}{T}.$$

If we consider two different determinations of the angle ϕ which
correspond to two different values of the constant ϕ_0, the difference
between these two determinations of ϕ remains constant all along Γ.
It follows that *two normals to the curve* Γ *which are tangent to two
different evolutes intersect at a constant angle.* Hence, if we know
a single family of normals to Γ which form a developable surface,
all other families of normals which form developable surfaces may
be found by turning each member of the given family of normals
through the same angle, which is otherwise arbitrary, around its
point of intersection with Γ.

Note I. If Γ is a plane curve, T is infinite, and the preceding
formula gives $\phi = \phi_0$. The evolute which corresponds to $\phi_0 = 0$ is
the plane evolute studied in § 206, which is the locus of the centers
of curvature of Γ. There are an infinite number of other evolutes,
which lie on the cylinder whose right section is the ordinary evolute. We shall study these curves, which are called *helices*, in the
next section. This is the only case in which the locus of the centers of curvature is an evolute. In order that (59) should be satisfied by taking $\phi = 0$, it is necessary that T should be infinite or
that Δ should vanish identically; hence the curve is in any case a
plane curve (§ 216).

Note II. If the curve D is an evolute of Γ, it follows that Γ is an involute of D. Hence

$$ds_1 = d(MM_1),$$

where s_1 denotes the length of the arc of the evolute counted from some fixed point. This shows that all the evolutes of any given curve are rectifiable.

232. Helices. Let C be any plane curve and let us lay off on the perpendicular to the plane of C erected at any point m on C a length mM proportional to the length of the arc σ of C counted from some fixed point A. Then the skew curve Γ described by the point M is called a *helix*. Let us take the plane of C as the xy plane and let

$$x = f(\sigma), \qquad y = \phi(\sigma)$$

be the coördinates of a point m of C in terms of the arc σ. Then the coördinates of the corresponding point M of the curve Γ will be

(60) $$x = f(\sigma), \qquad y = \phi(\sigma), \qquad z = K\sigma,$$

where K is the given factor of proportionality. The functions f and ϕ satisfy the relation $f'^2 + \phi'^2 = 1$; hence, from (60),

$$ds^2 = (f'^2 + \phi'^2 + K^2) d\sigma^2 = (1 + K^2) d\sigma^2,$$

where s denotes the length of the arc of Γ. It follows that $s = \sigma\sqrt{1 + K^2} + H$, or, if s and σ be counted from the same point A on C, $s = \sigma\sqrt{1 + K^2}$, since $H = 0$. The direction cosines of the tangent to Γ are

(61) $$\alpha = \frac{f'(\sigma)}{\sqrt{1 + K^2}}, \qquad \beta = \frac{\phi'(\sigma)}{\sqrt{1 + K^2}}, \qquad \gamma = \frac{K}{\sqrt{1 + K^2}}.$$

Since γ is independent of σ, it is evident that the tangent to Γ makes a constant angle with the z axis; this property is characteristic: *Any curve whose tangent makes a constant angle with a fixed straight line is a helix.* In order to prove this, let us take the z axis parallel to the given straight line, and let C be the projection of the given curve Γ on the xy plane. The equations of Γ may always be written in the form

(62) $$x = f(\sigma), \qquad y = \phi(\sigma), \qquad z = \psi(\sigma),$$

where the functions f and ϕ satisfy the relation $f'^2 + \phi'^2 = 1$, for this merely amounts to taking the arc σ of C as the independent variable. It follows that

$$\gamma = \frac{dz}{ds} = \frac{\psi'(\sigma)}{\sqrt{f'^2 + \phi'^2 + \psi'^2}} = \frac{\psi'}{\sqrt{1 + \psi'^2}};$$

hence the necessary and sufficient condition that γ be constant is that ψ' should be constant, that is, that $\psi(\sigma)$ should be of the form $K\sigma + z_0$. It follows that the equations of the curve Γ will be of the form (60) if the origin be moved to the point $x = 0$, $y = 0$, $z = z_0$.

Since γ is constant, the formula $d\gamma/ds = \gamma'/R$ shows that $\gamma' = 0$. Hence the principal normal is perpendicular to the generators of the cylinder. Since it is also perpendicular to the tangent to the helix, it is normal to the cylinder, and therefore the osculating plane is normal to the cylinder. It follows that the binormal lies in the tangent plane at right angles to the tangent to the helix; hence it also makes a constant angle with the z axis, i.e. γ'' is constant.

Since $\gamma' = 0$, the formula $d\gamma/ds = -\gamma/R - \gamma''/T$ shows that $\gamma/R + \gamma''/T = 0$; hence the ratio T/R is constant for the helix.

Each of the properties mentioned above is characteristic for the helix. Let us show, for example, that *every curve for which the ratio T/R is constant is a helix.* (J. BERTRAND.)

From Frenet's formulæ we have

$$\frac{d\alpha}{d\alpha''} = \frac{d\beta}{d\beta''} = \frac{d\gamma}{d\gamma''} = \frac{T}{R} = \frac{1}{H} ;$$

hence, if H is a constant, a single integration gives

$$\alpha'' = H\alpha - A, \qquad \beta'' = H\beta - B, \qquad \gamma'' = H\gamma - C,$$

where A, B, C are three new constants. Adding these three equations after multiplying them by α, β, γ, respectively, we find

$$A\alpha + B\beta + C\gamma = H,$$

or

$$\frac{A\alpha + B\beta + C\gamma}{\sqrt{A^2 + B^2 + C^2}} = \frac{H}{\sqrt{A^2 + B^2 + C^2}}.$$

But the three quantities

$$\frac{A}{\sqrt{A^2 + B^2 + C^2}}, \qquad \frac{B}{\sqrt{A^2 + B^2 + C^2}}, \qquad \frac{C}{\sqrt{A^2 + B^2 + C^2}}$$

are the direction cosines of a certain straight line Δ, and the preceding equation shows that the tangent makes a constant angle with this line. Hence the given curve is a helix.

Again, let us find the radius of curvature. By (53) and (61) we have

$$\frac{\alpha'}{R} = \frac{d\alpha}{ds} = \frac{1}{1 + K^2} f''(\sigma), \qquad \frac{\beta'}{R} = \frac{1}{1 + K^2} \phi''(\sigma),$$

whence, since $\gamma' = 0$,

$$(63) \qquad \frac{1}{R^2} = \frac{1}{(1 + K^2)^2} [f''^2(\sigma) + \phi''^2(\sigma)].$$

This shows that the ratio $(1 + K^2)/R$ is independent of K. But when $K = 0$ this ratio reduces to the reciprocal $1/r$ of the radius of curvature of the right section C, which is easily verified (§ 205). Hence the preceding formula may be written in the form $R = r(1 + K^2)$, which shows that the ratio of the radius of curvature of a helix to the radius of curvature of the corresponding curve C is a constant.

It is now easy to find all the curves for which R and T are both constant. For, since the ratio T/R is constant, all the curves must be helices, by Bertrand's theorem. Moreover, since R is a constant, the radius of curvature r of the curve C also is a constant. Hence C is a circle, and *the required curve is a helix which lies on a circular cylinder.* This proposition is due to Puiseux.[*]

---

[*] It is assumed in this proof that we are dealing only with real curves, for we assumed that $A^2 + B^2 + C^2$ does not vanish. (See the thesis by Lyon: *Sur les courbes à torsion constante,* 1890.)

233. Bertrand's curves. The principal normals to a plane curve are also the principal normals to an infinite number of other curves, — the parallels to the given curve. J. Bertrand attempted to find in a similar manner all the *skew* curves whose principal normals are the principal normals to a given skew curve Γ. Let the coördinates x, y, z of a point of Γ be given as functions of the arc s. Let us lay off on each principal normal a segment of length l, and let the coördinates of the extremity of this segment be X, Y, Z; then we shall have

$$(64) \qquad X = x + l\alpha', \qquad Y = y + l\beta', \qquad Z = z + l\gamma'.$$

The necessary and sufficient condition that the principal normal to the curve Γ′ described by the point (X, Y, Z) should coincide with the principal normal to Γ is that the two equations

$$\alpha' \, dX + \beta' \, dY + \gamma' \, dZ = 0,$$

$$\alpha'(dY \, d^2 Z - dZ \, d^2 Y) + \beta'(dZ \, d^2 X - dX \, d^2 Z) + \gamma'(dX \, d^2 Y - dY \, d^2 X) = 0$$

should be satisfied simultaneously. The meaning of each of these equations is evident. From the first, $dl = 0$; hence the length of the segment l should be a constant. Replacing dX, $d^2 X$, dY, $\cdots$ in the second equation by their values from Frenet's formulæ and from the formulæ obtained by differentiating Frenet's, and then simplifying, we finally find

$$\frac{1}{T} d\left(1 - \frac{l}{R}\right) = \left(1 - \frac{l}{R}\right) d\left(\frac{1}{T}\right),$$

whence, integrating,

$$(65) \qquad\qquad \frac{l}{R} + \frac{l'}{T} = 1,$$

where l' is the constant of integration. It follows that *the required curves are those for which there exists a linear relation between the curvature and the torsion.* On the other hand, it is easy to show that this condition is sufficient and that the length l is given by the relation (65).

A remarkable particular case had already been solved by Monge, namely that in which the radius of curvature is a constant. In that case (65) becomes $l = R$, and the curve Γ′ defined by the equations (64) is the locus of the centers of curvature of Γ. From (64), assuming $l = R =$ constant, we find the equations

$$dX = -\frac{R}{T}\alpha'' \, ds, \qquad dY = -\frac{R}{T}\beta'' \, ds, \qquad dZ = -\frac{R}{T}\gamma'' \, ds,$$

which show that the tangent to Γ′ is the polar line of Γ. The radius of curvature R' of Γ′ is given by the formula

$$R'^2 = \frac{dX^2 + dY^2 + dZ^2}{d\alpha''^2 + d\beta''^2 + d\gamma''^2} = R^2;$$

hence R' also is constant and equal to R. The relation between the two curves Γ and Γ′ is therefore a reciprocal one: each of them is the edge of regression of the polar surface of the other. It is easy to verify each of these statements for the particular case of the circular helix.

Note. It is easy to find the general formulæ for all skew curves whose radius of curvature is constant. Let R be the given constant radius and let α, β, γ be any three functions of a variable parameter which satisfy the relation $\alpha^2 + \beta^2 + \gamma^2 = 1$. Then the equations

$$(66) \qquad X = R \int \alpha \, d\sigma, \qquad Y = R \int \beta \, d\sigma, \qquad Z = R \int \gamma \, d\sigma,$$

where $d\sigma = \sqrt{d\alpha^2 + d\beta^2 + d\gamma^2}$, represent a curve which has the required property, and it is easy to show that all curves which have that property may be obtained in this manner. For α, β, γ are exactly the direction cosines of the curve defined by (66), and σ is the arc of its spherical indicatrix (§ 225).

IV. CONTACT BETWEEN SKEW CURVES
CONTACT BETWEEN CURVES AND SURFACES

234. Contact between two curves. The order of contact of two skew curves is defined in the same way as for plane curves. Let Γ and Γ' be two curves which are tangent at a point A. To each point M of Γ near A let us assign a point M' of Γ' according to such a law that M and M' approach A simultaneously. We proceed to find the maximum order of the infinitesimal MM' with respect to the principal infinitesimal AM, the arc of Γ. If this maximum order is $n + 1$, we shall say that the two curves have *contact of order n.*

Let us assume a system of trirectangular * axes in space, such that the yz plane is not parallel to the common tangent at A, and let the equations of the two curves be

$$(\Gamma) \quad \begin{cases} y = f(x), \\ z = \phi(x), \end{cases} \qquad (\Gamma') \quad \begin{cases} Y = F(x), \\ Z = \Phi(x). \end{cases}$$

If x_0, y_0, z_0 are the coördinates of A, the coördinates of M and M' are, respectively,

$$[x_0 + h, f(x_0 + h), \phi(x_0 + h)], \qquad [x_0 + k, F(x_0 + k), \Phi(x_0 + k)],$$

where k is a function of h which is defined by the law of correspondence assumed between M and M' and which approaches zero with h. We may select h as the principal infinitesimal instead of the arc AM (§ 211); and a necessary condition that MM' should be an infinitesimal of order $n + 1$ is that each of the differences

$$k - h, \qquad F(x_0 + k) - f(x_0 + h), \qquad \Phi(x_0 + k) - \phi(x_0 + h)$$

---

* It is easy to show, by passing to the formula for the distance between two points in oblique coördinates, that this assumption is not essential.

should be an infinitesimal of order $n + 1$ or more. It follows that we must have

$$k - h = \alpha h^{n+1}, \qquad F(x_0 + k) - f(x_0 + h) = \beta h^{n+1},$$
$$\Phi(x_0 + k) - \phi(x_0 + h) = \gamma h^{n+1},$$

where α, β, γ remain finite as h approaches zero. Replacing k by its value $h + \alpha h^{n+1}$ from the first of these equations, the latter two become

$$F(x_0 + h + \alpha h^{n+1}) - f(x_0 + h) = \beta h^{n+1},$$
$$\Phi(x_0 + h + \alpha h^{n+1}) - \phi(x_0 + h) = \gamma h^{n+1}.$$

Expanding $F(x_0 + h + \alpha h^{n+1})$ and $\Phi(x_0 + h + \alpha h^{n+1})$ by Taylor's series, all the terms which contain α will have a factor h^{n+1}; hence, in order that the preceding condition be satisfied, each of the differences

$$F(x_0 + h) - f(x_0 + h), \qquad \Phi(x_0 + h) - \phi(x_0 + h)$$

should be of order $n + 1$ or more. It follows that if MM' is of order $n + 1$, the distance MN between the points M and N of the two curves which have the same abscissa $x_0 + h$ will be at least of order $n + 1$. Hence the maximum order of the infinitesimal in question will be obtained *by putting into correspondence the points of the two curves which have the same abscissa.*

This maximum order is easily evaluated. Since the two curves are tangent we shall have

$$f(x_0) = F(x_0), \quad f'(x_0) = F'(x_0), \quad \phi(x_0) = \Phi(x_0), \quad \phi'(x_0) = \Phi'(x_0).$$

Let us suppose for generality that we also have

$$f''(x_0) = F''(x_0), \qquad \cdots, \qquad f^{(n)}(x_0) = F^{(n)}(x_0),$$
$$\phi''(x_0) = \Phi''(x_0), \qquad \cdots, \qquad \phi^{(n)}(x_0) = \Phi^{(n)}(x_0),$$

but that at least one of the differences

$$F^{(n+1)}(x_0) - f^{(n+1)}(x_0), \qquad \Phi^{(n+1)}(x_0) - \phi^{(n+1)}(x_0)$$

does not vanish. Then the distance MM' will be of order $n + 1$ and the contact will be of order n. This result may also be stated as follows: *To find the order of contact of two curves Γ and Γ', consider the two sets of projections (C, C') and (C_1, C_1') of the given curves on the xy plane and the xz plane, respectively, and find the order of contact of each set; then the order of contact of the given curves Γ and Γ' will be the smaller of these two.*

If the two curves Γ and Γ' are given in the form

(Γ) $\qquad x = f(t), \qquad y = \phi(t), \qquad z = \psi(t),$

(Γ') $\qquad X = f(u), \qquad Y = \Phi(u), \qquad Z = \Psi(u),$

they will be tangent at a point $u = t = t_0$ if

$$\Phi(t_0) = \phi(t_0), \quad \Phi'(t_0) = \phi'(t_0), \quad \Psi(t_0) = \psi(t_0), \quad \Psi'(t_0) = \psi'(t_0).$$

If we suppose that $f'(t_0)$ is not zero, the tangent at the point of contact is not parallel to the yz plane, and the points on the two curves which have the same abscissa correspond to the same value of t. In order that the contact should be of order n it is necessary and sufficient that each of the infinitesimals $\Phi(t) - \phi(t)$ and $\Psi(t) - \psi(t)$ should be of order $n + 1$ with respect to $t - t_0$, i.e. that we should have

$$\Phi'(t_0) = \phi'(t_0), \qquad \cdots, \qquad \Phi^{(n)}(t_0) = \phi^{(n)}(t_0),$$
$$\Psi'(t_0) = \psi'(t_0), \qquad \cdots, \qquad \Psi^{(n)}(t_0) = \psi^{(n)}(t_0),$$

and that at least one of the differences

$$\Phi^{(n+1)}(t_0) - \phi^{(n+1)}(t_0), \qquad \Psi^{(n+1)}(t_0) - \psi^{(n+1)}(t_0)$$

should not vanish.

It is easy to reduce to the preceding the case in which one of the curves Γ is given by equations of the form

(67) $\qquad x = f(t), \qquad y = \phi(t), \qquad z = \psi(t),$

and the other curve Γ' by two implicit equations

$$F(x, y, z) = 0, \qquad F_1(x, y, z) = 0.$$

Resuming the reasoning of § 212, we could show that a necessary condition that the contact should be of order n at a point of Γ where $t = t_0$ is that we should have

(68) $\qquad \begin{cases} \mathsf{F}\,(t_0) = 0, & \mathsf{F}'(t_0) = 0, & \cdots, & \mathsf{F}^{(n)}(t_0) = 0, \\ \mathsf{F}_1(t_0) = 0, & \mathsf{F}_1'(t_0) = 0, & \cdots, & \mathsf{F}_1^{(n)}(t_0) = 0, \end{cases}$

where

$$\mathsf{F}(t) = F[f(t), \phi(t), \psi(t)], \qquad \mathsf{F}_1(t) = F_1[f(t), \phi(t), \psi(t)].$$

235. Osculating curves. Let Γ be a curve whose equations are given in the form (67), and let Γ' be one of a family of curves in $2n + 2$ parameters $a, b, c, \cdots, l$, which is defined by the equations

(69) $\quad F(x, y, z, a, b, \cdots, l) = 0, \qquad F_1(x, y, z, a, b, c, \cdots, l) = 0.$

In general it is possible to determine the $2n + 2$ parameters in such a way that the corresponding curve Γ' has contact of order n with the given curve Γ at a given point. The curve thus determined is called the *osculating* curve of the family (69) to the curve Γ. The equations which determine the values of the parameters $a, b, c, \cdots, l$ are precisely the $2n + 2$ equations (68). It should be noted that these equations cannot be solved unless each of the functions F and F_1 contain at least $n + 1$ parameters. For example, if the curves Γ' are plane curves, one of the equations (69) contains only three parameters; hence a plane curve cannot have contact of order higher than two with a skew curve at a point taken at random on the curve.

Let us apply this theory to the simpler classes of curves, — the straight line and the circle. A straight line depends on four parameters; hence the osculating straight line will have contact of the first order. It is easy to show that it coincides with the tangent, for if we write the equations of the straight line in the form

$$x = az + p, \qquad y = bz + q,$$

the equations (68) become

$$x_0 = az_0 + p, \qquad x_0' = az_0', \qquad y_0 = bz_0 + q, \qquad y_0' = bz_0',$$

where (x_0, y_0, z_0) is the supposed point of contact on Γ. Solving these equations, we find

$$a = \frac{x_0'}{z_0'}, \qquad b = \frac{y_0'}{z_0'}, \qquad p = x_0 - \frac{x_0'}{z_0'} z_0, \qquad q = y_0 - \frac{y_0'}{z_0'} z_0,$$

which are precisely the values which give the tangent. A necessary condition that the tangent should have contact of the second order is that $x_0'' = az_0''$, $y_0'' = bz_0''$, that is,

$$\frac{x_0''}{x_0'} = \frac{y_0''}{y_0'} = \frac{z_0''}{z_0'}.$$

The points where this happens are those discussed in § 217.

The family of all circles in space depends on six parameters; hence the *osculating circle* will have contact of the second order. Let the equations of the circle be written in the form

$$F(x, y, z) = A(x - a) + B(y - b) + C(z - c) \qquad = 0,$$
$$F_1(x, y, z) = (x - a)^2 + (y - b)^2 + (z - c)^2 - R^2 = 0,$$

where the parameters are a, b, c, R, and the two ratios of the three coefficients A, B, C. The equations which determine the osculating circle are

$$A(x-a) + B(y-b) + C(z-c) = 0,$$

$$A\frac{dx}{dt} + B\frac{dy}{dt} + C\frac{dz}{dt} = 0,$$

$$A\frac{d^2x}{dt^2} + B\frac{d^2y}{dt^2} + C\frac{d^2z}{dt^2} = 0,$$

$$(x-a)^2 + (y-b)^2 + (z-c)^2 = R^2,$$

$$(x-a)\frac{dx}{dt} + (y-b)\frac{dy}{dt} + (z-c)\frac{dz}{dt} = 0,$$

$$(x-a)\frac{d^2x}{dt^2} + (y-b)\frac{d^2y}{dt^2} + (z-c)\frac{d^2z}{dt^2} + \frac{dx^2 + dy^2 + dz^2}{dt^2} = 0,$$

where x, y, and z are to be replaced by $f(t)$, $\phi(t)$, and $\psi(t)$, respectively. The second and the third of these equations show that the plane of the osculating circle is the osculating plane of the curve Γ. If a, b, and c be thought of as the running coördinates, the last two equations represent, respectively, the normal plane at the point (x, y, z) and the normal plane at a point whose distance from (x, y, z) is infinitesimal. Hence the center of the osculating circle is the point of intersection of the osculating plane and the polar line. It follows that the osculating circle coincides with the circle of curvature, as we might have foreseen by noticing that two curves which have contact of the second order have the same circle of curvature, since the values of y', z', y'', z'' are the same for the two curves.

236. Contact between a curve and a surface. Let S be a surface and Γ a curve tangent to S at a point A. To any point M of Γ near A let us assign a point M' of S according to such a law that M and M' approach A simultaneously. First let us try to find what law of correspondence between M and M' will render the order of the infinitesimal MM' with respect to the arc AM a maximum. Let us choose a system of rectangular coördinates in such a way that the tangent to Γ shall not be parallel to the yz plane, and that the tangent plane to S shall not be parallel to the z axis. Let (x_0, y_0, z_0) be the coördinates of A; $Z = F(x, y)$ the equation of S; $y = f(x)$, $z = \phi(x)$ the equations of Γ; and $n + 1$ the order of the infinitesimal MM' for the given law of correspondence. The coördinates of M are $[x_0 + h, f(x_0 + h), \phi(x_0 + h)]$. Let X, Y, and $Z = F(X, Y)$ be the coördinates of M'. In order that MM' should be of order $n + 1$ with respect to the arc AM, or, what amounts to the same thing, with respect to h, it is necessary that each of the differences $X - x$, $Y - y$, and $Z - z$ should be an infinitesimal at least of order $n + 1$, that is, that we should have

$$X - x = \alpha h^{n+1}, \quad Y - y = \beta h^{n+1}, \quad Z - z = F(X, Y) - z = \gamma h^{n+1},$$

where α, β, γ remain finite as h approaches zero. Hence we shall have

$$F(x + \alpha h^{n+1}, y + \beta h^{n+1}) - z = \gamma h^{n+1},$$

and the difference $F(x, y) - z$ will be itself at least of order $n + 1$. This shows that the order of the infinitesimal MN, where N is the point where a parallel to the z axis pierces the surface, will be at least as great as that of MM'. The maximum order of contact — which we shall call *the order of contact of the curve and the surface* — is therefore that of the distance MN with respect to the arc AM or with respect to h. Or, again, we may say that the order of contact of the curve and the surface is *the order of contact between Γ and the curve Γ' in which the surface S is cut by the cylinder which projects Γ upon the xy plane*. (It is evident that the z axis may be any line not parallel to the tangent plane.) For the equations of the curve Γ' are

$$y = f(x), \qquad Z = F[x, f(x)] = \Phi(x),$$

and, by hypothesis,

$$\Phi(x_0) = \phi(x_0), \qquad \Phi'(x_0) = \phi'(x_0).$$

If we also have

$$\Phi''(x_0) = \phi''(x_0), \quad \cdots, \quad \Phi^{(n)}(x_0) = \phi^{(n)}(x_0), \quad \Phi^{(n+1)}(x_0) \neq \phi^{(n+1)}(x_0),$$

the curve and the surface have contact of order n. Since the equation $\Phi(x) = \phi(x)$ gives the abscissæ of the points of intersection of the curve and the surface, these conditions for contact of order n at a point A may be expressed by saying that the curve meets the surface in $n + 1$ coincident points at A.

Finally, if the curve Γ is given by equations of the form $x = f(t)$, $y = \phi(t)$, $z = \psi(t)$, and the surface S is given by a single equation of the form $F(x, y, z) = 0$, the curve Γ' just defined will have equations of the form $x = f(t)$. $y = \phi(t)$, $z = \pi(t)$, where $\pi(t)$ is a function defined by the equation

$$F[f(t), \phi(t), \pi(t)] = 0.$$

In order that Γ and Γ' should have contact of order n, the infinitesimal $\pi(t) - \psi(t)$ must be of order $n+1$ with respect to $t - t_0$; that is, we must have

$$\pi(t_0) = \psi(t_0), \qquad \pi'(t_0) = \psi'(t_0), \qquad \cdots, \qquad \pi^{(n)}(t_0) = \psi^{(n)}(t_0).$$

Using $\mathsf{F}(t)$ to denote the function considered in § 234, these equations may be written in the form

$$\mathsf{F}(t_0) = 0, \qquad \mathsf{F}'(t_0) = 0, \qquad \cdots, \qquad \mathsf{F}^{(n)}(t_0) = 0.$$

These conditions may be expressed by saying that the curve and the surface have $n+1$ coincident points of intersection at their point of contact.

If S be one of a family of surfaces which depends on $n+1$ parameters $a, b, c, \cdots, l$, the parameters may be so chosen that S has contact of order n with a given curve at a given point; this surface is called the *osculating* surface.

In the case of a plane there are three parameters. The equations which determine these parameters for the osculating plane are

$$Af\ (t) + B\phi\ (t) + C\psi\ (t) + D = 0,$$
$$Af'\ (t) + B\phi'\ (t) + C\psi'\ (t) \qquad = 0,$$
$$Af''(t) + B\phi''(t) + C\psi''(t) \qquad = 0.$$

It is clear that these are the same equations we found before for the osculating plane, and that the contact is in general of the second order. If the order of contact is higher, we must have

$$Af'''(t) + B\phi'''(t) + C\psi'''(t) = 0,$$

i.e. the osculating plane must be stationary.

237. Osculating sphere. The equation of a sphere depends on four parameters; hence the osculating sphere will have contact of the third order. For simplicity let us suppose that the coördinates x, y, z of a point of the given curve Γ are expressed in terms of the arc s of that curve. In order that a sphere whose center is (a, b, c) and whose radius is ρ should have contact of the third order with Γ at a given point (x, y, z) on Γ, we must have

$$\mathsf{F}(s) = 0, \qquad \mathsf{F}'(s) = 0, \qquad \mathsf{F}''(s) = 0, \qquad \mathsf{F}'''(s) = 0,$$

where

$$\mathsf{F}(s) = (x-a)^2 + (y-b)^2 + (z-c)^2 - \rho^2$$

and where x, y, z are expressed as functions of s. Expanding the last three of the equations of condition and applying Frenet's formulæ, we find

$$F'(s) = (x-a)\alpha + (y-b)\beta + (z-c)\gamma = 0,$$

$$F''(s) = (x-a)\frac{\alpha'}{R} + (y-b)\frac{\beta'}{R} + (z-c)\frac{\gamma'}{R} + 1 = 0,$$

$$F'''(s) = -\frac{x-a}{R}\left(\frac{\alpha}{R}+\frac{\alpha''}{T}\right) - \frac{y-b}{R}\left(\frac{\beta}{R}+\frac{\beta''}{T}\right) - \frac{z-c}{R}\left(\frac{\gamma}{R}+\frac{\gamma''}{T}\right)$$
$$- \frac{1}{R^2}\frac{dR}{ds}\left[(x-a)\alpha' + (y-b)\beta' + (z-c)\gamma'\right] = 0.$$

These three equations determine a, b, and c. But the first of them represents the normal plane to the curve Γ at the point (x, y, z) in the running coördinates (a, b, c), and the other two may be derived from this one by differentiating twice with respect to s. Hence the center of the osculating sphere is the point where the polar line touches its envelope. In order to solve the three equations we may reduce the last one by means of the others to the form

$$(x-a)\alpha'' + (y-b)\beta'' + (z-c)\gamma'' = T\frac{dR}{ds},$$

from which it is easy to derive the formulæ

$$a = x + R\alpha' - T\frac{dR}{ds}\alpha'', \qquad b = y + R\beta' - T\frac{dR}{ds}\beta'',$$

$$c = z + R\gamma' - T\frac{dR}{ds}\gamma''.$$

Hence the radius of the osculating sphere is given by the formula

$$\rho^2 = R^2 + T^2\left(\frac{dR}{ds}\right)^2.$$

If R is constant, the center of the osculating sphere coincides with the center of curvature, which agrees with the result obtained in § 233.

238. Osculating straight lines. If the equations of a family of curves depend on $n+2$ parameters, the parameters may be chosen in such a way that the resulting curve C has contact of order n with a given surface S at a point M. For the equation which expresses that C meets S at M and the $n+1$ equations which express that there are $n+1$ coincident points of intersection at M constitute $n+2$ equations for the determination of the parameters.

For example, the equations of a straight line depend on four
parameters. Hence, through each point M of a given surface S,
there exist one or more straight lines which have contact of the
second order with the surface. In order to determine these lines,
let us take the origin at the point M, and let us suppose that the
z axis is not parallel to the tangent plane at M. Let $z = F(x, y)$
be the equation of the surface with respect to these axes. The
required line evidently passes through the origin, and its equations
are of the form

$$\frac{x}{a} = \frac{y}{b} = \frac{z}{c} = \rho.$$

Hence the equation $c\rho = F(a\rho, b\rho)$ should have a triple root $\rho = 0$;
that is, we should have

$$c = \ ap + bq,$$
$$0 = a^2 r + 2abs + b^2 t,$$

where p, q, r, s, t denote the values of the first and second derivatives of $F(x, y)$ at the origin. The first of these equations expresses
that the required line lies in the tangent plane, which is evident
a priori. The second equation is a quadratic equation in the ratio
b/a, and its roots are real if $s^2 - rt$ is positive. Hence there are in
general *two and only two* straight lines through any point of a given
surface which have contact of the second order with that surface.
These lines will be real or imaginary according as $s^2 - rt$ is positive
or negative. We shall meet these lines again in the following
chapter, in the study of the curvature of surfaces.

EXERCISES

1. Find, in finite form, the equations of the evolutes of the curve which
cuts the straight line generators of a right circular cone at a constant angle.
Discuss the problem.

[*Licence*, Marseilles, July, 1884.]

2. Do there exist skew curves Γ for which the three points of intersection
of a fixed plane P with the tangent, the principal normal, and the binormal are
the vertices of an equilateral triangle?

3. Let Γ be the edge of regression of a surface which is the envelope of
a one-parameter family of spheres, i.e. the envelope of the characteristic circles.
Show that the curve which is the locus of the centers of the spheres lies on
the polar surface of Γ. Also state and prove the converse.

4. Let Γ be a given skew curve, M a point on Γ, and O a fixed point in
space. Through O draw a line parallel to the polar line to Γ at M, and lay off
on this parallel a segment ON equal to the radius of curvature of Γ at M. Show

that the curve Γ' described by the point N and the curve Γ'' described by the center of curvature of Γ have their tangents perpendicular, their elements of length equal, and their radii of curvature equal, at corresponding points.

[ROUQUET.]

5. If the osculating sphere to a given skew curve Γ has a constant radius a, show that Γ lies on a sphere of radius a, at least unless the radius of curvature of Γ is constant and equal to a.

6. Show that the necessary and sufficient condition that the locus of the center of curvature of a helix drawn on a cylinder should be another helix on a cylinder parallel to the first one is that the right section of the second cylinder should be a circle or a logarithmic spiral. In the latter case show that all the helices lie on circular cones which have the same axis and the same vertex.

[TISSOT, *Nouvelles Annales*, Vol. XI, 1852.]

7*. If two skew curves have the same principal normals, the osculating planes of the two curves at the points where they meet make a constant angle with each other. The two points just mentioned and the centers of curvature of the two curves form a system of four points whose anharmonic ratio is constant. The product of the radii of torsion of the two curves at corresponding points is a constant.

[PAUL SERRET; MANNHEIM; SCHELL.]

8*. Let x, y, z be the rectangular coördinates of a point on a skew curve Γ, and s the arc of that curve. Then the curve Γ_0 defined by the equations

$$x_0 = \int \alpha'' \, ds, \qquad y_0 = \int \beta'' \, ds, \qquad z_0 = \int \gamma'' \, ds,$$

where x_0, y_0, z_0 are the running coördinates, is called the *conjugate curve* to Γ; and the curve defined by the equations

$$X = x \cos\theta + x_0 \sin\theta, \qquad Y = y \cos\theta + y_0 \sin\theta, \qquad Z = z \cos\theta + z_0 \sin\theta,$$

where X, Y, Z are the running coördinates and θ is a constant angle, is called a *related curve*. Find the orientation of the fundamental trihedron for each of these curves, and find their radii of curvature and of torsion.

If the curvature of Γ is constant, the torsion of the curve Γ_0 is constant, and the related curves are curves of the Bertrand type (§ 233). Hence find the general equations of the latter curves.

9. Let Γ and Γ' be two skew curves which are tangent at a point A. From A lay off infinitesimal arcs AM and AM' from A along the two curves in the same direction. Find the limiting position of the line MM'.

[CAUCHY.]

10. In order that a straight line rigidly connected to the fundamental trihedron of a skew curve and passing through the vertex of the trihedron should describe a developable surface, that straight line must coincide with the tangent, at least unless the given skew curve is a helix. In the latter case there are an infinite number of straight lines which have the required property.

For a curve of the Bertrand type there exist two hyperbolic paraboloids rigidly connected to the fundamental trihedron, each of whose generators describes a developable surface.

[CESÀRO, *Rivista di Mathematica*, Vol. II, 1892, p. 155.]

11*. In order that the principal normals of a given skew curve should be the binormals of another curve, the radii of curvature and the radii of torsion of the first curve must satisfy a relation of the form

$$A\left(\frac{1}{R^2} + \frac{1}{T^2}\right) = \frac{B}{R},$$

where A and B are constants.

[MANNHEIM, *Comptes rendus*, 1877.]

[The case in which a straight line through a point on a skew curve rigidly connected with the fundamental trihedron is also the principal normal (or the binormal) of another skew curve has been discussed by Pellet (*Comptes rendus*, May, 1887), by Cesàro (*Nouvelles Annales*, 1888, p. 147), and by Balitrand (*Mathesis*, 1894, p. 159).]

12. If the osculating plane to a skew curve Γ is always tangent to a fixed sphere whose center is O, show that the plane through the tangent perpendicular to the principal normal passes through O, and show that the ratio of the radius of curvature to the radius of torsion is a linear function of the arc. State and prove the converse theorems.

CHAPTER XII

SURFACES

I. CURVATURE OF CURVES DRAWN ON A SURFACE

239. Fundamental formula. Meusnier's theorem. In order to study the curvature of a surface at a non-singular point M, we shall suppose the surface referred to a system of rectangular coördinates such that the axis of z is not parallel to the tangent plane at M. If the surface is analytic, its equation may be written in the form

$$(1) \qquad z = F(x, y),$$

where $F(x, y)$ is developable in power series according to powers of $x - x_0$ and $y - y_0$ in the neighborhood of the point M (x_0, y_0, z_0) (§ 194). But the arguments which we shall use do not require the assumption that the surface should be analytic: we shall merely suppose that the function $F(x, y)$, together with its first and second derivatives, is continuous near the point (x_0, y_0) We shall use Monge's notation, p, q, r, s, t, for these derivatives.

It is seen immediately from the equation of the tangent plane that the direction cosines of the normal to the surface are proportional to p, q, and -1. If we adopt as the positive direction of the normal that which makes an acute angle with the positive z axis, the actual direction cosines themselves λ, μ, ν are given by the formulæ

$$(2) \quad \lambda = \frac{-p}{\sqrt{1 + p^2 + q^2}}, \quad \mu = \frac{-q}{\sqrt{1 + p^2 + q^2}}, \quad \nu = \frac{1}{\sqrt{1 + p^2 + q^2}}.$$

Let C be a curve on the surface S through the point M, and let the equations of this curve be given in parameter form; then the functions of the parameter which represent the coördinates of a point of this curve satisfy the equation (1), and hence their differentials satisfy the two relations

$$(3) \qquad dz = p\,dx + q\,dy,$$

$$(4) \qquad d^2z = p\,d^2x + q\,d^2y + r\,dx^2 + 2s\,dx\,dy + t\,dy^2.$$

The first of these equations means that the tangent to the curve C lies in the tangent plane to the surface. In order to interpret the second geometrically, let us express the differentials which occur in it in terms of known geometrical quantities. If the independent variable be the arc σ of the curve C, we shall have

$$\frac{dx}{d\sigma} = \alpha, \quad \frac{dy}{d\sigma} = \beta, \quad \frac{dz}{d\sigma} = \gamma, \quad \frac{d^2x}{d\sigma^2} = \frac{\alpha'}{R}, \quad \frac{d^2y}{d\sigma^2} = \frac{\beta'}{R}, \quad \frac{d^2z}{d\sigma^2} = \frac{\gamma'}{R},$$

where the letters α, β, γ, α', β', γ', R have the same meanings as in § 229. Substituting these values in (4) and dividing by $\sqrt{1 + p^2 + q^2}$, that equation becomes

$$\frac{\gamma' - p\alpha' - q\beta'}{R\sqrt{1 + p^2 + q^2}} = \frac{r\alpha^2 + 2s\alpha\beta + t\beta^2}{\sqrt{1 + p^2 + q^2}},$$

or, by (2),

$$\frac{\lambda\alpha' + \mu\beta' + \nu\gamma'}{R} = \frac{r\alpha^2 + 2s\alpha\beta + t\beta^2}{\sqrt{1 + p^2 + q^2}}.$$

But the numerator $\lambda\alpha' + \mu\beta' + \nu\gamma'$ is nothing but the cosine of the angle θ included between the principal normal to C and the positive direction of the normal to the surface; hence the preceding formula may be written in the form

$$(5) \qquad \frac{\cos\theta}{R} = \frac{r\alpha^2 + 2s\alpha\beta + t\beta^2}{\sqrt{1 + p^2 + q^2}}.$$

This formula is exactly equivalent to the formula (4); hence it contains all the information we can discover concerning the curvature of curves drawn on the surface. Since R and $\sqrt{1 + p^2 + q^2}$ are both essentially positive, $\cos\theta$ and $r\alpha^2 + 2s\alpha\beta + t\beta^2$ have the same sign, i.e. the sign of the latter quantity shows whether θ is acute or obtuse. In the first place, let us consider all the curves on the surface S through the point M which have the same osculating plane (which shall be other than the tangent plane) at the point M. All these curves have the same tangent, namely the intersection of the osculating plane with the tangent plane to the surface. The direction cosines α, β, γ therefore coincide for all these curves. Again, the principal normal to any of these curves coincides with one of the two directions which can be selected upon the perpendicular to the tangent line in the osculating plane. Let ω be the angle which the normal to the surface makes with one of these directions; then we shall have $\theta = \omega$ or $\theta = \pi - \omega$. But the sign of $r\alpha^2 + 2s\alpha\beta + t\beta^2$ shows whether the angle θ is acute or obtuse; hence the positive direction of the principal normal is the same for all these curves. Since θ is also the same for all the curves, the radius of curvature R is the same for them all; that is to say, *all the curves on the surface through the point M which have the same osculating plane have the same center of curvature.*

It follows that we need only study the curvature of the plane sections of the surface. First let us study the variation of the curvature of the sections of the surface by planes which all pass through the same tangent MT. We may suppose, without loss of generality, that $r\alpha^2 + 2s\alpha\beta + t\beta^2 > 0$, for a change in the direction of the z axis is sufficient to change the signs of r, s, and t. For all these plane sections we shall have, therefore, $\cos\theta > 0$, and the angle θ is acute. If R_1 be the radius of curvature of the section by the normal plane through MT, since the corresponding angle θ is zero, we shall have

$$\frac{1}{R_1} = \frac{r\alpha^2 + 2s\alpha\beta + t\beta^2}{\sqrt{1 + p^2 + q^2}}.$$

Comparing this formula with equation (5), which gives the radius of curvature of any oblique section, we find

$$(6) \qquad \frac{1}{R_1} = \frac{\cos\theta}{R},$$

or $R = R_1 \cos\theta$, which shows that *the center of curvature of any oblique section is the projection of the center of curvature of the normal section through the same tangent line.* This is Meusnier's theorem.

The preceding theorem reduces the study of the curvature of oblique sections to the study of the curvature of normal sections. We shall discuss directly the results obtained by Euler. First let us remark that the formula (5) will appear in two different forms for a normal section according as $r\alpha^2 + 2s\alpha\beta + t\beta^2$ is positive or negative. In order to avoid the inconvenience of carrying these two signs, we shall agree to affix the sign $+$ or the sign $-$ to the radius of curvature R of a normal section according as the direction from M to the center of curvature of the section is the same as or opposite to the positive direction of the normal to the surface. With this convention, R is given in either case by the formula

$$(7) \qquad \frac{1}{R} = \frac{r\alpha^2 + 2s\alpha\beta + t\beta^2}{\sqrt{1 + p^2 + q^2}},$$

which shows without ambiguity the direction in which the center of curvature lies.

From (7) it is easy to determine the position of the surface with respect to its tangent plane near the point of tangency. For if $s^2 - rt < 0$, the quadratic form $r\alpha^2 + 2s\alpha\beta + t\beta^2$ keeps the same sign — the sign of r and of t — as the normal plane turns around the normal; hence all the normal sections have their centers of curvature on the same side of the tangent plane, and therefore all lie on the same side of that plane: the surface is said to be *convex* at such a point, and the point is called an *elliptic* point. On the contrary, if $s^2 - rt > 0$, the form $r\alpha^2 + 2s\alpha\beta + t\beta^2$ vanishes for two particular positions of the normal plane, and the corresponding normal sections have, in general, a point of inflection. When the normal plane lies in one of the dihedral angles formed by these two planes, R is positive, and the corresponding section lies above the tangent plane; when the normal plane lies in the other dihedral angle, R is negative, and the section lies below the tangent plane. Hence in this case the surface crosses its tangent plane at the point of tangency. Such a point is called a *hyperbolic* point. Finally, if $s^2 - rt = 0$, all the normal sections lie on the same side of the tangent plane near the point of tangency except that one for which the radius of curvature is infinite. The latter section usually crosses the tangent plane. Such a point is called a *parabolic* point.

It is easy to verify these results by a direct study of the difference $u = z - z'$ of the values of z for a point on the surface and for the point on the tangent plane at M which projects into the same point (x, y) on the xy plane. For we have

$$z' = p(x - x_0) + q(y - y_0),$$

whence, for the point of tangency (x_0, y_0),

$$\frac{\partial u}{\partial x} = p - \frac{\partial z'}{\partial x} = 0, \qquad \frac{\partial u}{\partial y} = 0,$$

and

$$\frac{\partial^2 u}{\partial x^2} = r, \qquad \frac{\partial^2 u}{\partial x\, \partial y} = s, \qquad \frac{\partial^2 u}{\partial y^2} = t.$$

It follows that if $s^2 - rt < 0$, u is a maximum or a minimum at M (§ 56), and since u vanishes at M, it has the same sign for all other points in the neighborhood. On the other hand, if $s^2 - rt > 0$, u has neither a maximum nor a minimum at M, and hence it changes sign in any neighborhood of M.

240. Euler's theorems. The indicatrix. In order to study the variation of the radius of curvature of a normal section, let us take the
point M as the origin and the tangent plane at M as the xy plane.
With such a system of axes we shall have $p = q = 0$, and the
formula (7) becomes

$$(8) \qquad \frac{1}{R} = r \cos^2\phi + 2s \cos\phi \sin\phi + t \sin^2\phi,$$

where ϕ is the angle which the trace of the normal plane makes
with the positive x axis. Equating the derivative of the second
member to zero, we find that the points at which R may be a maximum or a minimum stand at right angles. The following geometrical picture is a convenient means of visualizing the variation of R.
Let us lay off, on the line of intersection of the normal plane with
the xy plane, from the origin, a length Om equal numerically to the
square root of the absolute value of the corresponding radius of curvature. The point m will describe a curve, which gives an instanta-
neous picture of the variation of the radius of curvature. This curve
is called the *indicatrix*. Let us examine the three possible cases.

1) $s^2 - rt < 0$. In this case the radius R has a constant sign, which
we shall suppose positive. The coördinates of m are $\xi = \sqrt{R} \cos\phi$
and $\eta = \sqrt{R} \sin\phi$; hence the equation of the *indicatrix* is

$$(9) \qquad r\xi^2 + 2s\xi\eta + t\eta^2 = 1,$$

which is the equation of an ellipse whose center is the origin. It is
clear that R is at a maximum for the section made by the normal
plane through the major axis of this ellipse, and at a minimum for
the normal plane through the minor axis. The sections made by two
planes which are equally inclined to the two axes evidently have the
same curvature. The two sections whose planes pass through the
axes of the indicatrix are called the *principal normal sections*, and
the corresponding radii of curvature are called the *principal radii of
curvature*. If the axes of the indicatrix are taken for the axes of x
and y, we shall have $s = 0$, and the formula (8) becomes

$$\frac{1}{R} = r \cos^2\phi + t \sin^2\phi.$$

With these axes the principal radii of curvature R_1 and R_2 correspond
to $\phi = 0$ and $\phi = \pi/2$, respectively; hence $1/R_1 = r$, $1/R_2 = t$, and

$$(10) \qquad \frac{1}{R} = \frac{\cos^2\phi}{R_1} + \frac{\sin^2\phi}{R_2}.$$

2) $s^2 - rt > 0$.   The normal sections which correspond to the values of ϕ which satisfy the equation

$$r \cos^2 \phi + 2s \cos \phi \sin \phi + t \sin^2 \phi = 0$$

have infinite radii of curvature.   Let $L_1'OL_1$ and $L_2'OL_2$ be the intersections of these two planes with the xy plane.   When the trace of the normal plane lies in the angle L_1OL_2, for example, the radius of curvature is positive.   Hence the corresponding portion of the indicatrix is represented by the equation

$$r \xi^2 + 2s \xi \eta + t \eta^2 = 1,$$

where ξ and η are, as in the previous case, the coördinates of the point m.   This is an hyperbola whose asymptotes are the lines $L_1'OL_1$ and $L_2'OL_2$.   When the trace of the normal plane lies in the other angle $L_2'OL_1$, R is negative, and the coördinates of m are

$$\xi = \sqrt{-R} \cos \phi, \qquad \eta = \sqrt{-R} \sin \phi.$$

Hence the corresponding portion of the indicatrix is the hyperbola

$$r \xi^2 + 2s \xi \eta + t \eta^2 = -1,$$

which is conjugate to the preceding hyperbola.   These two hyperbolas together form a picture of the variation of the radius of curvature in this case.   If the axes of the hyperbolas be taken as the x and y axes, the formula (8) may be written in the form (10), as in the previous case, where now, however, the principal radii of curvature R_1 and R_2 have opposite signs.

3) $s^2 - rt = 0$.   In this case the radius of curvature R has a fixed sign, which we shall suppose positive.   The indicatrix is still represented by the equation (9), but, since its center is at the origin and it is of the parabolic type, it must be composed of two parallel straight lines.   If the axis of y be taken parallel to these lines, we shall have $s = 0$, $t = 0$, and the general formula (8) becomes

$$\frac{1}{R} = r \cos^2 \phi,$$

or

$$\frac{1}{R} = \frac{\cos^2 \phi}{R_1}.$$

This case may also be considered to be a limiting case of either of the preceding, and the formula just found may be thought of as the limiting case of (10), when R_2 becomes infinite.

Euler's formulæ may be established without using the formula (5). Taking the point M of the given surface as the origin and the tangent plane as the xy plane, the expansion of z by Taylor's series may be written in the form

$$z = \frac{rx^2 + 2sxy + ty^2}{1 \cdot 2} + \cdots,$$

where the terms not written down are of order greater than two. In order to find the radii of curvature of the section made by a plane $y = x \tan \phi$, we may introduce the transformation

$$x = x' \cos \phi - y' \sin \phi, \qquad y = x' \sin \phi + y' \cos \phi,$$

and then set $y' = 0$. This gives the expansion of z in powers of x',

$$z = \frac{r \cos^2 \phi + 2s \sin \phi \cos \phi + t \sin^2 \phi}{1 \cdot 2} x'^2 + \cdots,$$

which, by § 214, leads to the formula (8).

Notes. The section of the surface by its tangent plane is given by the equation

$$0 = rx^2 + 2sxy + ty^2 + \phi_3(x, y) + \cdots,$$

and has a double point at the origin. The two tangents at this point are the asymptotic tangents. More generally, if two surfaces S and S_1 are both tangent at the origin to the xy plane, the projection of their curve of intersection on the xy plane is given by the equation

$$0 = (r - r_1)x^2 + 2(s - s_1)xy + (t - t_1)y^2 + \cdots,$$

where r_1, s_1, t_1 have the same meaning for the surface S_1 that r, s, t have for S. The nature of the double point depends upon the sign of the expression $(s - s_1)^2 - (r - r_1)(t - t_1)$. If this expression is zero, the curve of intersection has, in general, a cusp at the origin.

To recapitulate, there exist on any surface four remarkable positions for the tangent at any point: two perpendicular tangents for which the corresponding radii of curvature have a maximum or a minimum, and two so-called *asymptotic*, or *principal*,* tangents, for which the corresponding radii of curvature are infinite. The latter are to be found by equating the trinomial $r\alpha^2 + 2s\alpha\beta + t\beta^2$ to zero (§ 238). We proceed to show how to find the principal normal sections and the principal radii of curvature for any system of rectangular axes.

241. Principal radii of curvature. There are in general two different normal sections whose radii of curvature are equal to any given value of R. The only exception is the case in which the given value of R is one of the principal radii of curvature, in which case

---

* The reader should distinguish sharply the directions of the *principal tangents* (the *asymptotes* of the indicatrix) and the directions of the *principal normal sections* (the *axes* of the indicatrix). To avoid confusion we shall not use the term *principal tangent.* — TRANS.

only the corresponding principal section has the assigned radius of curvature. To determine the normal sections whose radius of curvature is a given number R, we may determine the values of α, β, γ by the three equations

$$\frac{\sqrt{1+p^2+q^2}}{R} = r\alpha^2 + 2s\alpha\beta + t\beta^2, \quad \gamma = p\alpha + q\beta, \quad \alpha^2 + \beta^2 + \gamma^2 = 1.$$

It is easy to derive from these the following homogeneous combination of degree zero in α and β:

$$(11) \qquad \frac{\sqrt{1+p^2+q^2}}{R} = \frac{r\alpha^2 + 2s\alpha\beta + t\beta^2}{\alpha^2 + \beta^2 + (p\alpha + q\beta)^2}.$$

It follows that the ratio β/α is given by the equation

$$\alpha^2(1 + p^2 - rD) + 2\alpha\beta(pq - sD) + \beta^2(1 + q^2 - tD) = 0,$$

where $R = D\sqrt{1+p^2+q^2}$. If this equation has a double root, that root satisfies each of the equations formed by setting the two first derivatives of the left-hand side with respect to α and β equal to zero:

$$(12) \qquad \begin{cases} \alpha(1 + p^2 - rD) + \beta(pq - sD) = 0, \\ \alpha(pq - sD) + \beta(1 + q^2 - tD) = 0. \end{cases}$$

Eliminating α and β and replacing D by its value, we obtain an equation for the principal radii of curvature:

$$(13) \qquad \begin{cases} (rt - s^2)R^2 - \sqrt{1+p^2+q^2}\,[(1+p^2)t + (1+q^2)r - 2pqs]\,R \\ \qquad\qquad\qquad\qquad\qquad\qquad\qquad + (1+p^2+q^2)^2 = 0. \end{cases}$$

On the other hand, eliminating D from the equations (12), we obtain an equation of the second degree which determines the lines of intersection of the tangent plane with the principal normal sections:

$$(14) \qquad \begin{cases} \alpha^2[(1+p^2)s - pqr] \\ \qquad + \alpha\beta[(1+p^2)t - (1+q^2)r] + \beta^2[pqt - (1+q^2)s] = 0. \end{cases}$$

From the very nature of the problem the roots of the equations (13) and (14) will surely be real. It is easy to verify this fact directly.

In order that the equation for R should have equal roots, it is necessary that the indicatrix should be a circle, in which case all the normal sections will have the same radius of curvature. Hence the second member of (11) must be independent of the ratio β/α, which necessitates the equations

$$(15) \qquad \frac{r}{1+p^2} = \frac{s}{pq} = \frac{t}{1+q^2}.$$

The points which satisfy these equations are called *umbilics*. At such points the equation (14) reduces to an identity, since every diameter of a circle is also an axis of symmetry.

It is often possible to determine the principal normal sections from certain geometrical considerations. For instance, if a surface S has a plane of symmetry through a point M on the surface, it is clear that the line of intersection of that plane with the tangent plane at M is a line of symmetry of the indicatrix; hence the section by the plane of symmetry is one of the principal sections. For example, on a surface of revolution the meridian through any point is one of the principal normal sections; it is evident that the plane of the other principal normal section passes through the normal to the surface and the tangent to the circular parallel at the point. But we know the center of curvature of one of the oblique sections through this tangent line, namely that of the circular parallel itself. It follows from Meusnier's theorem that the center of curvature of the second principal section is the point where the normal to the surface meets the axis of revolution.

At any point of a developable surface, $s^2 - rt = 0$, and the indicatrix is a pair of parallel straight lines. One of the principal sections coincides with the generator, and the corresponding radius of curvature is infinite. The plane of the second principal section is perpendicular to the generator. All the points of a developable surface are parabolic, and, conversely, these are the only surfaces which have that property (§ 222).

If a non-developable surface is convex at certain points, while other points of the surface are hyperbolic, there is usually a line of parabolic points which separates the region where $s^2 - rt$ is positive from the region where the same quantity is negative. For example, on the anchor ring, these parabolic lines are the extreme circular parallels.

In general there are on any convex surface only a finite number of umbilics. We proceed to show that the only real surface for which every point is an umbilic is the sphere. Let λ, μ, ν be the direction cosines of the normal to the surface. Differentiating (2), we find the formulæ

$$\frac{\partial \lambda}{\partial x} = \frac{pqs - (1 + q^2)r}{(1 + p^2 + q^2)^{\frac{3}{2}}}, \qquad \frac{\partial \lambda}{\partial y} = \frac{pqt - (1 + q^2)s}{(1 + p^2 + q^2)^{\frac{3}{2}}},$$

$$\frac{\partial \mu}{\partial x} = \frac{pqr - (1 + p^2)s}{(1 + p^2 + q^2)^{\frac{3}{2}}}, \qquad \frac{\partial \mu}{\partial y} = \frac{pqs - (1 + p^2)t}{(1 + p^2 + q^2)^{\frac{3}{2}}},$$

or, by (15),

$$\frac{\partial \lambda}{\partial y} = 0, \qquad \frac{\partial \mu}{\partial x} = 0, \qquad \frac{\partial \lambda}{\partial x} = \frac{\partial \mu}{\partial y}.$$

The first equation shows that λ is independent of y, the second that μ is independent of x; hence the common value of $\partial\lambda/\partial x$, $\partial\mu/\partial y$ is independent of both x and y, i.e. it is a constant, say $1/a$. This fact leads to the equations

$$\lambda = \frac{x - x_0}{a}, \qquad \mu = \frac{y - y_0}{a}, \qquad \nu = \frac{\sqrt{a^2 - (x - x_0)^2 - (y - y_0)^2}}{a},$$

$$p = -\frac{\lambda}{\nu} = -\frac{x - x_0}{\sqrt{a^2 - (x - x_0)^2 - (y - y_0)^2}},$$

$$q = -\frac{\mu}{\nu} = -\frac{y - y_0}{\sqrt{a^2 - (x - x_0)^2 - (y - y_0)^2}},$$

whence, integrating, the value of z is found to be

$$z = z_0 + \sqrt{a^2 - (x - x_0)^2 - (y - y_0)^2},$$

which is the equation of a sphere. It is evident that if $\partial\lambda/\partial x = \partial\mu/\partial y = 0$, the surface is a plane. But the equations (15) also have an infinite number of imaginary solutions which satisfy the relation $1 + p^2 + q^2 = 0$, as we can see by differentiating this equation with respect to x and with respect to y.

II. ASYMPTOTIC LINES   CONJUGATE LINES

242. Definition and properties of asymptotic lines. At every hyperbolic point of a surface there are two tangents for which the corresponding normal sections have infinite radii of curvature, namely the asymptotes of the indicatrix. The curves on the given surface which are tangent at each of their points to one of these asymptotic directions are called *asymptotic lines*. If a point moves along any curve on a surface, the differentials dx, dy, dz are proportional to the direction cosines of the tangent. For an asymptotic tangent $r\alpha^2 + 2s\alpha\beta + t\beta^2 = 0$; hence the differentials dx and dy at any point of an asymptotic line must satisfy the relation

$$(16) \qquad r\,dx^2 + 2s\,dx\,dy + t\,dy^2 = 0.$$

If the equation of the surface be given in the form $z = F(x, y)$, and we substitute for r, s, and t their values as functions of x and y, this equation may be solved for dy/dx, and we shall obtain the two solutions

$$(17) \qquad \frac{dy}{dx} = \phi_1(x, y), \qquad \frac{dy}{dx} = \phi_2(x, y).$$

We shall see later that each of these equations has an infinite number of solutions, and that every pair of values (x_0, y_0) determines in general one and only one solution. It follows that there pass through every point of the surface, in general, two and only two asymptotic lines : all these lines together form a double system of lines upon the surface.

Again, the asymptotic lines may be defined without the use of any metrical relation : *the asymptotic lines on a surface are those curves for which the osculating plane always coincides with the tangent plane to the surface.* For the necessary and sufficient condition that the osculating plane should coincide with the tangent plane to the surface is that the equations

$$dz - p\,dx - q\,dy = 0, \qquad d^2z - p\,d^2x - q\,d^2y = 0$$

should be satisfied simultaneously (see § 215). The first of these equations is satisfied by any curve which lies on the surface. Differentiating it, we obtain the equation

$$d^2z - p\,d^2x - q\,d^2y - dp\,dx - dq\,dy = 0,$$

which shows that the second of the preceding equations may be replaced by the following relation between the first differentials :

$$(18) \qquad dp\,dx + dq\,dy = 0,$$

an equation which coincides with (16). Moreover it is easy to explain why the two definitions are equivalent. Since the radius of curvature of the normal section which is tangent to an asymptote of the indicatrix is infinite, the radius of curvature of the asymptotic line will also be infinite, by Meusnier's theorem, at least unless the osculating plane is perpendicular to the normal plane, in which case Meusnier's theorem becomes illusory. Hence the osculating plane to an asymptotic line must coincide with the tangent plane, at least unless the radius of curvature is infinite ; but if this were true, the line would be a straight line and its osculating plane would be indeterminate. It follows from this property that any projective transformation carries the asymptotic lines into asymptotic lines. It is evident also that the differential equation is of the same form whether the axes are rectangular or oblique, for the equation of the osculating plane remains of the same form.

It is clear that the asymptotic lines exist only in case the points of the surface are hyperbolic. But when the surface is analytic the differential equation (16) always has an infinite number of solutions, real or imaginary, whether $s^2 - rt$ is positive or negative. As a generalization we shall say that any convex surface possesses two systems of imaginary asymptotic lines. Thus the asymptotic lines of an unparted hyperboloid are the two systems of rectilinear generators.

For an ellipsoid or a sphere these generators are imaginary, but they satisfy the differential equation for the asymptotic lines.

Example. Let us try to find the asymptotic lines of the surface

$$z = x^m y^n.$$

In this example we have

$$r = m(m-1)x^{m-2}y^n, \qquad s = mnx^{m-1}y^{n-1}, \qquad t = n(n-1)x^m y^{n-2},$$

and the differential equation (16) may be written in the form

$$m(m-1)\left(\frac{y\,dx}{x\,dy}\right)^2 + 2mn\left(\frac{y\,dx}{x\,dy}\right) + n(n-1) = 0.$$

This equation may be solved as a quadratic in $(y\,dx)/(x\,dy)$. Let h_1 and h_2 be the solutions. Then the two families of asymptotic lines are the curves which project, on the xy plane, into the curves

$$y^{h_1} = C_1 x, \qquad y^{h_2} = C_2 x.$$

243. Differential equation in parameter form. Let the equations of the surface be given in terms of two parameters u and v:

$$(19) \qquad x = f(u, v), \qquad y = \phi(u, v), \qquad z = \psi(u, v).$$

Using the second definition of asymptotic lines, let us write the equation of the tangent plane in the form

$$(20) \qquad A(X - x) + B(Y - y) + C(Z - z) = 0,$$

where A, B, and C satisfy the equations

$$(21) \qquad \begin{cases} A\dfrac{\partial f}{\partial u} + B\dfrac{\partial \phi}{\partial u} + C\dfrac{\partial \psi}{\partial u} = 0, \\[2mm] A\dfrac{\partial f}{\partial v} + B\dfrac{\partial \phi}{\partial v} + C\dfrac{\partial \psi}{\partial v} = 0, \end{cases}$$

which are the equations for A, B, and C found in § 39. Since the osculating plane of an asymptotic line is the same as this tangent plane, these same coefficients must satisfy the equations

$$\begin{aligned} A\,dx + B\,dy + C\,dz &= 0, \\ A\,d^2x + B\,d^2y + C\,d^2z &= 0. \end{aligned}$$

The first of these equations, as above, is satisfied identically. Differentiating it, we see that the second may be replaced by the equation

$$(22) \qquad dA\,dx + dB\,dy + dC\,dz = 0,$$

which is the required differential equation. If, for example, we set $C = -1$ in the equations (21), A and B are equal, respectively, to the partial derivatives p and q of z with respect to x and y, and the equation (22) coincides with (18).

Examples. As an example let us consider the conoid $z = \phi(y/x)$. This equation is equivalent to the system $x = u$, $y = uv$, $z = \phi(v)$, and the equations (21) become

$$A + Bv = 0, \qquad Bu + C\phi'(v) = 0.$$

These equations are satisfied if we set $C = -u$, $A = -v\phi'(v)$, $B = \phi'(v)$; hence the equation (22) takes the form

$$u\phi''(v)\,dv^2 - 2\phi'(v)\,du\,dv = 0.$$

One solution of this equation is $v = \text{const.}$, which gives the rectilinear generators. Dividing by dv, the remaining equation is

$$\frac{\phi''(v)\,dv}{\phi'(v)} = \frac{2\,du}{u},$$

whence the second system of asymptotic lines are the curves on the surface defined by the equation $u^2 = K\phi'(v)$, which project on the xy plane into the curves

$$x^2 = K\phi'\left(\frac{y}{x}\right).$$

Again, consider the surfaces discussed by Jamet, whose equation may be written in the form

$$xf\left(\frac{y}{x}\right) = F(z).$$

Taking the independent variables z and $u = y/x$, the differential equation of the asymptotic lines may be written in the form

$$\sqrt{\frac{F''(z)}{F(z)}}\,dz = \pm\,\sqrt{\frac{f''(u)}{f(u)}}\,du,$$

from which each of the systems of asymptotic lines may be found by a single quadrature.

A helicoid is a surface defined by equations of the form

$$x = \rho\cos\omega, \qquad y = \rho\sin\omega, \qquad z = f(\rho) + h\omega.$$

The reader may show that the differential equation of the asymptotic lines is

$$\rho f''(\rho)\,d\rho^2 - 2h\,d\omega\,d\rho + \rho^2 f'(\rho)\,d\omega^2 = 0,$$

from which ω may be found by a single quadrature.

244. Asymptotic lines on a ruled surface. Eliminating A, B, and C between the equations (21) and the equation

$$A\,d^2x + B\,d^2y + C\,d^2z = 0,$$

we find the general differential equation of the asymptotic lines:

$$(23) \qquad \begin{vmatrix} \dfrac{\partial f}{\partial u} & \dfrac{\partial \phi}{\partial u} & \dfrac{\partial \psi}{\partial u} \\[2mm] \dfrac{\partial f}{\partial v} & \dfrac{\partial \phi}{\partial v} & \dfrac{\partial \psi}{\partial v} \\[2mm] d^2x & d^2y & d^2z \end{vmatrix} = 0.$$

This equation does not contain the second differentials d^2u and d^2v, for we have

$$d^2x = \frac{\partial f}{\partial u}\,d^2u + \frac{\partial f}{\partial v}\,d^2v + \frac{\partial^2 f}{\partial u^2}\,du^2 + 2\,\frac{\partial^2 f}{\partial u\,\partial v}\,du\,dv + \frac{\partial^2 f}{\partial v^2}\,dv^2$$

and analogous expressions for d^2y and d^2z. Subtracting from the third row of the determinant (23) the first row multiplied by d^2u and the second row multiplied by d^2v, the differential equation becomes

$$\begin{vmatrix} \dfrac{\partial f}{\partial u} & \dfrac{\partial \phi}{\partial u} & \dfrac{\partial \psi}{\partial u} \\[2mm] \dfrac{\partial f}{\partial v} & \dfrac{\partial \phi}{\partial v} & \dfrac{\partial \psi}{\partial v} \\[2mm] \dfrac{\partial^2 f}{\partial u^2}\,du^2 + 2\,\dfrac{\partial^2 f}{\partial u\,\partial v}\,du\,dv + \dfrac{\partial^2 f}{\partial v^2}\,\partial v^2 & \cdots & \cdots \end{vmatrix} = 0.$$

Developing this determinant with respect to the elements of the first row and arranging with respect to du and dv, the equation may be written in the form

$$(24) \qquad D\,du^2 + 2D'\,du\,dv + D''\,dv^2 = 0,$$

where D, D', and D'' denote the three determinants

$$(25) \quad \begin{cases} D = \begin{vmatrix} \dfrac{\partial x}{\partial u} & \dfrac{\partial y}{\partial u} & \dfrac{\partial z}{\partial u} \\[2mm] \dfrac{\partial x}{\partial v} & \dfrac{\partial y}{\partial v} & \dfrac{\partial z}{\partial v} \\[2mm] \dfrac{\partial^2 x}{\partial u^2} & \dfrac{\partial^2 y}{\partial u^2} & \dfrac{\partial^2 z}{\partial u^2} \end{vmatrix}, \quad D' = \begin{vmatrix} \dfrac{\partial x}{\partial u} & \dfrac{\partial y}{\partial u} & \dfrac{\partial z}{\partial u} \\[2mm] \dfrac{\partial x}{\partial v} & \dfrac{\partial y}{\partial v} & \dfrac{\partial z}{\partial v} \\[2mm] \dfrac{\partial^2 x}{\partial u\,\partial v} & \dfrac{\partial^2 y}{\partial u\,\partial v} & \dfrac{\partial^2 z}{\partial u\,\partial v} \end{vmatrix}, \\[10mm] D'' = \begin{vmatrix} \dfrac{\partial x}{\partial u} & \dfrac{\partial y}{\partial u} & \dfrac{\partial z}{\partial u} \\[2mm] \dfrac{\partial x}{\partial v} & \dfrac{\partial y}{\partial v} & \dfrac{\partial z}{\partial v} \\[2mm] \dfrac{\partial^2 x}{\partial v^2} & \dfrac{\partial^2 y}{\partial v^2} & \dfrac{\partial^2 z}{\partial v^2} \end{vmatrix}. \end{cases}$$

As an application let us consider a ruled surface, that is, a surface whose equations are of the form

$$x = x_0 + \alpha u, \qquad y = y_0 + \beta u, \qquad z = z_0 + \gamma u,$$

where $x_0, y_0, z_0, \alpha, \beta, \gamma$ are all functions of a second variable parameter v. If we set $u = 0$, the point (x_0, y_0, z_0) describes a certain curve Γ which lies on the surface. On the other hand, if we set $v = \text{const.}$ and let u vary, the point (x, y, z) will describe a straight-

line generator of the ruled surface, and the value of u at any point
of the line will be proportional to the distance between the point
(x, y, z) and the point (x_0, y_0, z_0) at which the generator meets the
curve Γ.   It is evident from the formulæ (25) that $D = 0$, that D'
is independent of u, and that D'' is a polynomial of the second
degree in u:

$$D'' = \begin{vmatrix} \alpha & \cdots & \cdots \\ x_0' + \alpha'u & \cdots & \cdots \\ x_0'' + \alpha''u & \cdots & \cdots \end{vmatrix}.$$

Since dv is a factor of (24), one system of asymptotic lines consists
of the rectilinear generators $v = \text{const.}$ Dividing by dv, the remaining differential equation for the other system of asymptotic lines is
of the form

(26) $$\frac{du}{dv} + Lu^2 + Mu + N = 0,$$

where L, M, and N are functions of the single variable v.   An equation of this type possesses certain remarkable properties, which we
shall study later.   For example, we shall see that *the anharmonic
ratio of any four solutions is a constant.*   It follows that the anharmonic ratio of the four points in which a generator meets any four
asymptotic lines of the other system is the same for all generators,
which enables us to discover all the asymptotic lines of the second
system whenever any three of them are known.   We shall also
see that whenever one or two integrals of the equation (26) are
known, all the rest can be found by two quadratures or by a single
quadrature.   Thus, if all the generators meet a fixed straight line,
that line will be an asymptotic line of the second system, and all
the others can be found by two quadratures.   If the surface possesses two such rectilinear directrices, we should know two asymptotic lines of the second system, and it would appear that another
quadrature would be required to find all the others.   But we can
obtain a more complete result.   For if a surface possesses two
rectilinear directrices, a projective transformation can be found
which will carry one of them to infinity and transform the surface
into a conoid; but we saw in § 243 that the asymptotic lines on a
conoid could be found without a single quadrature.

245. Conjugate lines.   Any two conjugate diameters of the indicatrix at a point of a given surface S are called *conjugate tangents.*
To every tangent to the surface there corresponds a conjugate
tangent, which coincides with the first when and only when the given

tangent is an asymptotic tangent. Let $z = F(x, y)$ be the equation of
the surface S, and let m and m' be the slopes of the projections of
two conjugate tangents on the xy plane.   These projections on the
xy plane must be harmonic conjugates with respect to the projections of the two asymptotic tangents at the same point of the surface.   But the slopes of the projections of the asymptotic tangents
satisfy the equation

$$r + 2s\mu + t\mu^2 = 0.$$

In order that the projections of the conjugate tangents should be
harmonic conjugates with respect to the projections of the asymptotic tangents, it is necessary and sufficient that we should have

$$(27) \qquad r + s(m + m') + tmm' = 0.$$

If C be a curve on the surface S, the envelope of the tangent
plane to S at points along this curve is a developable surface which
is tangent to S all along C.   *At every point M of C the generator of
this developable is the conjugate tangent to the tangent to C.*   Along
C, x, y, z, p, and q are functions of a single independent variable α.
The generator of the developable is defined by the two equations

$$Z - z - p(X - x) - q(Y - y) = 0,$$
$$- dz + p\,dx + q\,dy - dp(X - x) - dq(Y - y) = 0,$$

the last of which reduces to

$$\frac{Y - y}{X - x} = -\frac{dp}{dq} = -\frac{r\,dx + s\,dy}{s\,dx + t\,dy}.$$

Let m be the slope of the projection of the tangent to C and m' the
slope of the projection of the generator.   Then we shall have

$$\frac{dy}{dx} = m, \qquad \frac{Y - y}{X - x} = m',$$

and the preceding equation reduces to the form (27), which proves
the theorem stated above.

Two one-parameter families of curves on a surface are said to
form a *conjugate network* if the tangents to the two curves of the
two families which pass through any point are conjugate tangents
at that point.   It is evident that there are an infinite number of
conjugate networks on any surface, for the first family may be
assigned arbitrarily, the second family then being determined by a
differential equation of the first order.

Given a surface represented by equations of the form (19), let us find the conditions under which the curves $u = $ const. and $v = $ const. form a conjugate network. If we move along the curve $v = $ const., the characteristic of the tangent plane is represented by the two equations

$$A(X - x) + B(Y - y) + C(Z - z) = 0,$$

$$\frac{\partial A}{\partial u}(X - x) + \frac{\partial B}{\partial u}(Y - y) + \frac{\partial C}{\partial u}(Z - z) = 0.$$

In order that this straight line should coincide with the tangent to the curve $u = $ const., whose direction cosines are proportional to $\partial x/\partial v$, $\partial y/\partial v$, $\partial z/\partial v$, it is necessary and sufficient that we should have

$$A\frac{\partial x}{\partial v} + B\frac{\partial y}{\partial v} + C\frac{\partial z}{\partial v} = 0,$$

$$\frac{\partial A}{\partial u}\frac{\partial x}{\partial v} + \frac{\partial B}{\partial u}\frac{\partial y}{\partial v} + \frac{\partial C}{\partial u}\frac{\partial z}{\partial v} = 0.$$

Differentiating the first of these equations with regard to u, we see that the second may be replaced by the equation

$$(28) \qquad A\frac{\partial^2 x}{\partial u\,\partial v} + B\frac{\partial^2 y}{\partial u\,\partial v} + C\frac{\partial^2 z}{\partial u\,\partial v} = 0,$$

and finally the elimination of A, B, and C between the equations (21) and (28) leads to the necessary and sufficient condition

$$\begin{vmatrix} \dfrac{\partial x}{\partial u} & \dfrac{\partial y}{\partial u} & \dfrac{\partial z}{\partial u} \\[2mm] \dfrac{\partial x}{\partial v} & \dfrac{\partial y}{\partial v} & \dfrac{\partial z}{\partial v} \\[2mm] \dfrac{\partial^2 x}{\partial u\,\partial v} & \dfrac{\partial^2 y}{\partial u\,\partial v} & \dfrac{\partial^2 z}{\partial u\,\partial v} \end{vmatrix} = 0.$$

This condition is equivalent to saying that x, y, z are three solutions of a differential equation of the form

$$(29) \qquad \frac{\partial^2 \theta}{\partial u\,\partial v} = M\frac{\partial \theta}{\partial u} + N\frac{\partial \theta}{\partial v},$$

where M and N are arbitrary functions of u and v. It follows that the knowledge of three distinct integrals of an equation of this form is sufficient to determine the equations of a surface which is referred to a conjugate network. For example, if we set $M = N = 0$, every integral of the equation (29) is the sum of a function of u and a function of v; hence, on any surface whose equations are of the form

$$(30) \qquad x = f(u) + f_1(v), \qquad y = \phi(u) + \phi_1(v), \qquad z = \psi(u) + \psi_1(v),$$

the curves (u) and (v) form a conjugate network.

Surfaces of the type (30) are called *surfaces of translation*. Any such surface may be described in two different ways by giving one rigid curve Γ a motion of translation such that one of its points moves along another rigid curve Γ'. For, let M_0, M_1, M_2, M be four points of the surface which correspond, respectively, to the four sets of values (u_0, v_0), (u, v_0), (u_0, v), (u, v) of the parameters u and v. By (30) these four points are the vertices of a plane parallelogram. If v_0 is fixed and u allowed to vary, the point M_1 will describe a curve Γ on the surface; like-wise, if u_0 is kept fixed and v is allowed to vary, the point M_2 will describe another curve Γ' on the surface. It follows that we may generate the surface by giving Γ a motion of translation which causes the point M_2 to describe Γ', or by giving Γ' a motion of translation which causes the point M_1 to describe Γ. It is evident from this method of generation that the two families of curves (u) and (v) are conjugate. For example, the tangents to the different positions of Γ' at the various points of Γ form a cylinder tangent to the surface along Γ; hence the tangents to the two curves at any point are conjugate tangents.

III. LINES OF CURVATURE

246. Definition and properties of lines of curvature. A curve on a given surface S is called a *line of curvature* if the normals to the surface along that curve form a developable surface. If $z = f(x, y)$ is the equation of the surface referred to a system of rectangular axes, the equations of the normal to the surface are

$$(31) \qquad \begin{cases} X = -pZ + (x + pz), \\ Y = -qZ + (y + qz). \end{cases}$$

The necessary and sufficient condition that this line should describe a developable surface is that the two equations

$$(32) \qquad \begin{cases} -Z\,dp + d(x + pz) = 0, \\ -Z\,dq + d(y + qz) = 0 \end{cases}$$

should have a solution in terms of Z (§ 223), that is, that we should have

$$\frac{d(x + pz)}{dp} = \frac{d(y + qz)}{dq},$$

or, more simply,

$$\frac{dx + p\,dz}{dp} = \frac{dy + q\,dz}{dq}.$$

Again, replacing dz, dp, and dq by their values, this equation may be written in the form

$$(33) \qquad \frac{(1 + p^2)\,dx + pq\,dy}{r\,dx + s\,dy} = \frac{pq\,dx + (1 + q^2)\,dy}{s\,dx + t\,dy}.$$

This equation possesses two solutions in dy/dx which are always real and unequal if the surface is real, except at an umbilic. For, if we replace dx and dy by α and β, respectively, the preceding equation coincides with the equation found above [(14), § 241] for the determination of the lines of intersection of the principal normal sections with the tangent plane. It follows that the tangents to the lines of curvature through any point coincide with the axes of the indicatrix. We shall see in the study of differential equations that there is one and only one line of curvature through every non-singular point of a surface tangent to each one of the axes of the indicatrix at that point, except at an umbilic. These lines are always real if the surface is real, and the network which they form is at once orthogonal and conjugate, — a characteristic property.

Example. Let us determine the lines of curvature of the paraboloid $z = xy/a$. In this example

$$p = \frac{y}{a}, \qquad q = \frac{x}{a}, \qquad r = t = 0, \qquad s = \frac{1}{a},$$

and the differential equation (33) is

$$(a^2 + y^2)\,dx^2 = (a^2 + x^2)\,dy^2 \qquad \text{or} \qquad \frac{dx}{\sqrt{x^2 + a^2}} \pm \frac{dy}{\sqrt{y^2 + a^2}} = 0.$$

If we take the positive sign for both radicals, the general solution is

$$\left(x + \sqrt{x^2 + a^2}\right)\left(y + \sqrt{y^2 + a^2}\right) = C,$$

which gives one system of lines of curvature. If we set

$$(34) \qquad \lambda = x\,\sqrt{y^2 + a^2} + y\,\sqrt{x^2 + a^2},$$

the equation of this system may be written in the form

$$\lambda + \sqrt{\lambda^2 + a^4} = C$$

by virtue of the identity

$$\left(x\,\sqrt{y^2 + a^2} + y\,\sqrt{x^2 + a^2}\,\right)^2 + a^4 = \left[xy + \sqrt{(x^2 + a^2)(y^2 + a^2)}\,\right]^2$$

It follows that the projections of the lines of curvature of this first system are represented by the equation (34), where λ is an arbitrary constant. It may be shown in the same manner that the projections of the lines of curvature of the other system are represented by the equation

$$(35) \qquad x\,\sqrt{y^2 + a^2} - y\,\sqrt{x^2 + a^2} = \mu.$$

From the equation $xy = az$ of the given paraboloid, the equations (34) and (35) may be written in the form

$$\sqrt{x^2 + z^2} + \sqrt{y^2 + z^2} = C, \qquad \sqrt{x^2 + z^2} - \sqrt{y^2 + z^2} = C'.$$

But the expressions $\sqrt{x^2 + z^2}$ and $\sqrt{y^2 + z^2}$ represent, respectively, the distances of the point (x, y, z) from the axes of x and y. It follows that *the lines of curvature on the paraboloid are those curves for which the sum or the difference of the distances of any point upon them from the axes of x and y is a constant.*

247. Evolute of a surface. Let C be a line of curvature on a surface S. As a point M describes the curve C, the normal MN to the surface remains tangent to a curve Γ. Let (X, Y, Z) be the coördinates of the point A at which MN is tangent to Γ. The ordinate Z is given by either of the equations (32), which reduce to a single equation since C is a line of curvature. The equations (32) may be written in the form

$$Z - z = \frac{(1 + p^2)\,dx + pq\,dy}{r\,dx + s\,dy} = \frac{pq\,dx + (1 + q^2)\,dy}{s\,dx + t\,dy}.$$

Multiplying each term of the first fraction by dx, each term of the second by dy, and then taking the proportion by composition, we find

$$Z - z = \frac{dx^2 + dy^2 + (p\,dx + q\,dy)^2}{r\,dx^2 + 2s\,dx\,dy + t\,dy^2}.$$

Again, since dx, dy, and dz are proportional to the direction cosines α, β, γ of the tangent, this equation may be written in the form

$$Z - z = \frac{\alpha^2 + \beta^2 + (p\alpha + q\beta)^2}{r\alpha^2 + 2s\alpha\beta + t\beta^2} = \frac{1}{r\alpha^2 + 2s\alpha\beta + t\beta^2}.$$

Comparing this formula with (7), which gives the radius of curvature R of the normal section tangent to the line of curvature, with the proper sign, we see that it is equivalent to the equation

$$(36) \qquad Z - z = \frac{R}{\sqrt{1 + p^2 + q^2}} = R\nu,$$

where ν is the cosine of the acute angle between the z axis and the positive direction of the normal. But $z + R\nu$ is exactly the value of Z for the center of curvature of the normal section under consideration. It follows that *the point of tangency A of the normal MN to its envelope Γ coincides with the center of curvature of the principal normal section tangent to C at M.* Hence the curve Γ is the locus of these centers of curvature. If we consider all the lines of curvature of the system to which C belongs, the locus of the corresponding curves Γ is a surface Σ to which every normal to the given surface S is tangent. For the normal MN, for example, is tangent at A to the curve Γ which lies on Σ.

The other line of curvature C' through M cuts C at right angles. The normal to S along C' is itself always tangent to a curve Γ' which is the locus of the centers of curvature of the normal sections tangent to C'. The locus of this curve Γ' for all the lines of curvature of the system to which C' belongs is a surface Σ' to which all the normals to S are tangent. The two surfaces Σ and Σ' are not usually analytically distinct, but form two nappes of the same surface, which is then represented by an irreducible equation.

The normal MN to S is tangent to each of these nappes Σ and Σ' at the two principal centers of curvature A and A' of the surface S at the point M. It is easy to find the tangent planes to the two nappes at the points A and A' (Fig. 51). As the point M describes the curve C, the normal MN describes the developable surface D whose edge of regression is Γ; at the same time the point A' where MN touches Σ' describes a curve γ' distinct from Γ', since the straight line MN cannot remain tangent to two distinct curves Γ and Γ'. The developable D and the surface Σ' are tangent at A'; hence the tangent plane to Σ' at A' is tangent to D all along MN. It follows that it is the plane NMT, which passes through the tangent to C. Similarly, it is evident that the tangent plane to Σ at A is the plane NMT' through the tangent to the other line of curvature C'.

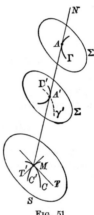

FIG. 51

The two planes NMT and NMT' stand at right angles. This fact leads to the following important conception. Let a normal OM be dropped from any point O in space on the surface S, and let A and A' be the principal centers of curvature of S on this normal. The tangent planes to Σ and Σ' at A and A', respectively, are perpendicular. Since each of these planes passes through the given point O, it is clear that *the two nappes of the evolute of any surface S, observed from any point O in space, appear to cut each other at right angles.* The converse of this proposition will be proved later.

248. Rodrigues' formulæ. If λ, μ, ν denote the direction cosines of the normal, and R one of the principal radii of curvature, the corresponding principal center of curvature will be given by the formulæ

$$(37) \qquad X = x + R\lambda, \qquad Y = y + R\mu, \qquad Z = z + R\nu.$$

As the point (x, y, z) describes a line of curvature tangent to the normal section whose radius of curvature is R, this center of curvature, as we have just seen, will describe a curve Γ tangent to the normal MN; hence we must have

$$\frac{dX}{\lambda} = \frac{dY}{\mu} = \frac{dZ}{\nu},$$

or, replacing X, Y, and Z by their values from (37) and omitting the common term dR,

$$\frac{dx + R\,d\lambda}{\lambda} = \frac{dy + R\,d\mu}{\mu} = \frac{dz + R\,d\nu}{\nu}.$$

The value of any of these ratios is zero, for if we take them by composition after multiplying each term of the first ratio by λ, of the second by μ, and of the third by ν, we obtain another ratio equal to any of the three; but the denominator of the new ratio is unity, while the numerator

$$\lambda\,dx + \mu\,dy + \nu\,dz + R(\lambda\,d\lambda + \mu\,d\mu + \nu\,d\nu)$$

is identically zero. This gives immediately the formulæ of Olinde Rodrigues:

$$(38) \quad dx + R\,d\lambda = 0, \qquad dy + R\,d\mu = 0, \qquad dz + R\,d\nu = 0,$$

which are very important in the theory of surfaces. It should be noticed, however, that these formulæ apply only to a displacement of the point (x, y, z) along a line of curvature.

249. Lines of curvature in parameter form. If the equations of the surface are given in terms of two parameters u and v in the form (19), the equations of the normal are

$$\frac{X - x}{A} = \frac{Y - y}{B} = \frac{Z - z}{C},$$

where A, B, and C are determined by the equations (21). The necessary and sufficient condition that this line should describe a developable surface is, by § 223,

$$(39) \qquad \begin{vmatrix} dx & dy & dz \\ A & B & C \\ dA & dB & dC \end{vmatrix} = 0,$$

where x, y, z, A, B, and C are to be replaced by their expressions in terms of the parameters u and v; hence this is the differential equation of the lines of curvature.

As an example let us find the lines of curvature on the helicoid

$$z = a \arctan \frac{y}{x},$$

whose equation is equivalent to the system

$$x = \rho \cos \theta, \qquad y = \rho \sin \theta, \qquad z = a\theta.$$

In this example the equations for A, B, and C are

$$A \cos \theta + B \sin \theta = 0, \qquad - A\rho \sin \theta + B\rho \cos \theta + Ca = 0.$$

Taking $C = \rho$, we find $A = a \sin \theta$, $B = - a \cos \theta$. After expansion and simplification the differential equation (39) becomes

$$d\rho^2 - (\rho^2 + a^2)\, d\theta^2 = 0 \qquad \text{or} \qquad d\theta = \pm \frac{d\rho}{\sqrt{\rho^2 + a^2}}.$$

Choosing the sign $+$, for example, and integrating, we find

$$\rho + \sqrt{\rho^2 + a^2} = ae^{\theta - \theta_0}, \qquad \text{or} \qquad \rho = \frac{a}{2}\left[e^{\theta - \theta_0} - e^{-(\theta - \theta_0)} \right].$$

The projections of these lines of curvature on the xy plane are all spirals which are easily constructed.

The same method enables us to form the equation of the second degree for the principal radii of curvature. With the same symbols A, B, C, λ, μ, ν we shall have, except for sign,

$$\lambda = \frac{A}{\sqrt{A^2 + B^2 + C^2}}, \qquad \mu = \frac{B}{\sqrt{A^2 + B^2 + C^2}}, \qquad \nu = \frac{C}{\sqrt{A^2 + B^2 + C^2}}.$$

We shall adopt as the positive direction of the normal that which is given by the preceding equations. If R is a principal radius of curvature, taken with its proper sign, the coördinates of the corresponding center of curvature are

$$X = x + \rho A, \qquad Y = y + \rho B, \qquad Z = z + \rho C,$$

where

$$R = \rho \sqrt{A^2 + B^2 + C^2}.$$

If the point (x, y, z) describes the line of curvature tangent to the principal normal section whose radius of curvature is R, we have seen that the point (X, Y, Z) describes a curve Γ which is tangent to the normal to the surface. Hence we must have

$$\frac{dx + \rho\, dA + A\, d\rho}{A} = \frac{dy + \rho\, dB + B\, d\rho}{B} = \frac{dz + \rho\, dC + C\, d\rho}{C},$$

or, denoting the common values of these ratios by $d\rho + K$,

$$(40) \quad \begin{cases} dx + \rho\, dA - AK = 0, \\ dy + \rho\, dB - BK = 0, \\ dz + \rho\, dC - CK = 0. \end{cases}$$

Eliminating ρ and K from these three equations, we find again the differential equation (39) of the lines of curvature. But if we replace dx, dy, dz, dA, dB, and dC by the expressions

$$\frac{\partial x}{\partial u}\, du + \frac{\partial x}{\partial v}\, dv, \qquad \cdots, \qquad \frac{\partial C}{\partial u}\, du + \frac{\partial C}{\partial v}\, dv,$$

respectively, and then eliminate du, dv, and K, we find an equation for the determination of ρ :

$$(41) \quad \begin{vmatrix} \dfrac{\partial x}{\partial u} + \rho\, \dfrac{\partial A}{\partial u} & \dfrac{\partial x}{\partial v} + \rho\, \dfrac{\partial A}{\partial v} & A \\[2ex] \dfrac{\partial y}{\partial u} + \rho\, \dfrac{\partial B}{\partial u} & \dfrac{\partial y}{\partial v} + \rho\, \dfrac{\partial B}{\partial v} & B \\[2ex] \dfrac{\partial z}{\partial u} + \rho\, \dfrac{\partial C}{\partial u} & \dfrac{\partial z}{\partial v} + \rho\, \dfrac{\partial C}{\partial v} & C \end{vmatrix} = 0.$$

If we replace ρ by $R / \sqrt{A^2 + B^2 + C^2}$, this equation becomes an equation for the principal radii of curvature.

The equations (39) and (41) enable us to answer many questions which we have already considered. For example, the necessary and sufficient condition that a point of a surface should be a parabolic point is that the coefficient of ρ^2 in (41) should vanish. In order that a point be an umbilic, the equation (39) must be satisfied for all values of du and dv

As an example let us find the principal radii of curvature of the rectilinear helicoid. With a slight modification of the notation used above, we shall have in this example

$$x = u \cos v, \qquad y = u \sin v, \qquad z = av,$$
$$A = a \sin v, \qquad B = -a \cos v, \qquad C = u,$$

and the equation (41) becomes

$$a^2 \rho^2 = a^2 + u^2,$$

whence $R = \pm (a^2 + u^2)/a$. *Hence the principal radii of curvature of the helicoid are numerically equal and opposite in sign.*

250. Joachimsthal's theorem. The lines of curvature on certain surfaces may be found by geometrical considerations. For example, it is quite evident that the lines of curvature on a surface of revolution are the meridians and the parallels of the surface, for each of these curves is tangent at every point to one of the axes of the indicatrix at that point. This is again confirmed by the remark that the normals along a meridian form a plane, and the normals along a parallel form a circular cone, — in each case the normals form a developable surface.

On a developable surface the first system of lines of curvature consists of the generators. The second system consists of the orthogonal trajectories of the generators, that is, of the involutes of the edge of regression (§ 231). These can be found by a single quadrature. If we know one of them, all the rest can be found without even one quadrature. All of these results are easily verified directly.

The study of the theory of evolutes of a skew curve led Joachimsthal to a very important theorem, which is often used in that theory. Let S and S' be two surfaces whose line of intersection C is a line of curvature on each surface. The normal MN to S along C describes a developable surface, and the normal MN' to S' along C describes another developable surface. But each of these normals is normal to C. It follows from § 231 that *if two surfaces have a common line of curvature, they intersect at a constant angle along that line.*

Conversely, *if two surfaces intersect at a constant angle, and if their line of intersection is a line of curvature on one of them, it is also a line of curvature on the other.* For we have seen that if one family of normals to a skew curve C form a developable surface, the family of normals obtained by turning each of the first family through the same angle in its normal plane also form a developable surface.

Any curve whatever on a plane or on a sphere is a line of curvature on that surface. It follows as a corollary to Joachimsthal's theorem that *the necessary and sufficient condition that a plane curve or a spherical curve on any surface should be a line of curvature is that the plane or the sphere on which the curve lies should cut the surface at a constant angle.*

251. Dupin's theorem. We have already considered [§§ 43, 146] triply orthogonal systems of surfaces. The origin of the theory of such systems lay in a noted theorem due to Dupin, which we shall proceed to prove:

Given any three families of surfaces which form a triply orthogonal system: the intersection of any two surfaces of different families is a line of curvature on each of them.

We shall base the proof on the following remark. Let $F(x, y, z) = 0$ be the equation of a surface tangent to the xy plane at the origin. Then we shall have, for $x = y = z = 0$, $\partial F/\partial x = 0$, $\partial F/\partial y = 0$, but $\partial F/\partial z$ does not vanish, in general, except when the origin is a singular point. It follows that the necessary and sufficient condition that the x and y axes should be the axes of the indicatrix is that $s = 0$. But the value of this second derivative $s = \partial^2 z/\partial x\, \partial y$ is given by the equation

$$\frac{\partial^2 F}{\partial x\, \partial y} + \frac{\partial^2 F}{\partial x\, \partial z}\, q + \frac{\partial^2 F}{\partial y\, \partial z}\, p + \frac{\partial^2 F}{\partial z^2}\, pq + \frac{\partial F}{\partial z}\, s = 0.$$

Since p and q both vanish at the origin, the necessary and sufficient condition that s should vanish there is that we should have

$$(42) \qquad\qquad \frac{\partial^2 F}{\partial x\, \partial y} = 0.$$

Now let the three families of the triply orthogonal system be given by the equations

$$F_1(x, y, z) = \rho_1, \qquad F_2(x, y, z) = \rho_2, \qquad F_3(x, y, z) = \rho_3,$$

where F_1, F_2, F_3 satisfy the relation

$$(43) \qquad \frac{\partial F_1}{\partial x}\frac{\partial F_2}{\partial x} + \frac{\partial F_1}{\partial y}\frac{\partial F_2}{\partial y} + \frac{\partial F_1}{\partial z}\frac{\partial F_2}{\partial z} = 0$$

and two other similar relations obtained by cyclic permutation of the subscripts 1, 2, 3. Through any point M in space there passes, in general, one surface of each of the three families. The tangents to the three curves of intersection of these three surfaces form a trirectangular trihedron. In order to prove Dupin's theorem, it will be sufficient to show that each of these tangents coincides with one of the axes of the indicatrix on each of the surfaces to which it is tangent.

In order to show this, let us take the point M as origin and the edges of the trirectangular trihedron as the axes of coördinates; then the three surfaces pass through the origin tangent, respectively, to the three coördinate planes. At the origin we shall have, for example,

$$\left(\frac{\partial F_1}{\partial x}\right)_0 = 0, \qquad \left(\frac{\partial F_1}{\partial y}\right)_0 = 0, \qquad \left(\frac{\partial F_1}{\partial z}\right)_0 \gtrless 0,$$

$$\left(\frac{\partial F_2}{\partial x}\right)_0 \gtrless 0, \qquad \left(\frac{\partial F_2}{\partial y}\right)_0 = 0, \qquad \left(\frac{\partial F_2}{\partial z}\right)_0 = 0,$$

$$\left(\frac{\partial F_3}{\partial x}\right)_0 = 0, \qquad \left(\frac{\partial F_3}{\partial y}\right)_0 \gtrless 0, \qquad \left(\frac{\partial F_3}{\partial z}\right)_0 = 0.$$

The axes of x and y will be the axes of the indicatrix of the surface $F(x, y, z) = 0$ at the origin if $(\partial^2 F_1/\partial x\,\partial y)_0 = 0$.   To show that this is the case, let us differentiate (43) with respect to y, omitting the terms which vanish at the origin; we find

$$\left(\frac{\partial F_2}{\partial x}\right)_0 \left(\frac{\partial^2 F_1}{\partial x\,\partial y}\right)_0 + \left(\frac{\partial F_1}{\partial z}\right)_0 \left(\frac{\partial^2 F_2}{\partial y\,\partial z}\right)_0 = 0,$$

or

(44)
$$\frac{\left(\dfrac{\partial^2 F_1}{\partial x\,\partial y}\right)_0}{\left(\dfrac{\partial F_1}{\partial z}\right)_0} + \frac{\left(\dfrac{\partial^2 F_2}{\partial y\,\partial z}\right)_0}{\left(\dfrac{\partial F_2}{\partial x}\right)_0} = 0.$$

From the two relations analogous to (43) we could deduce two equations analogous to (44), which may be written down by cyclic permutation:

(45)
$$\frac{\left(\dfrac{\partial^2 F_2}{\partial y\,\partial z}\right)_0}{\left(\dfrac{\partial F_2}{\partial x}\right)_0} + \frac{\left(\dfrac{\partial^2 F_3}{\partial z\,\partial x}\right)_0}{\left(\dfrac{\partial F_3}{\partial y}\right)_0} = 0, \qquad \frac{\left(\dfrac{\partial^2 F_3}{\partial z\,\partial x}\right)_0}{\left(\dfrac{\partial F_3}{\partial y}\right)_0} + \frac{\left(\dfrac{\partial^2 F_1}{\partial x\,\partial y}\right)_0}{\left(\dfrac{\partial F_1}{\partial z}\right)_0} = 0.$$

From (44) and (45) it is evident that we shall have also

$$\left(\frac{\partial^2 F_1}{\partial x\,\partial y}\right)_0 = 0, \qquad \left(\frac{\partial^2 F_2}{\partial y\,\partial z}\right)_0 = 0, \qquad \left(\frac{\partial^2 F_3}{\partial z\,\partial x}\right)_0 = 0,$$

which proves the theorem.

A remarkable example of a triply orthogonal system is furnished by the confocal quadrics discussed in § 147.   It was doubtless the investigation of this particular system which led Dupin to the general theorem.   It follows that the lines of curvature on an ellipsoid or an hyperboloid (which had been determined previously by Monge) are the lines of intersection of that surface with its confocal quadrics.

The paraboloids represented by the equation

$$\frac{y^2}{p - \lambda} + \frac{z^2}{q - \lambda} = 2x - \lambda,$$

where λ is a variable parameter, form another triply orthogonal system, which determines the lines of curvature on the paraboloid. Finally, the system discussed in § 246,

$$\frac{xy}{z} = \alpha, \quad \sqrt{x^2 + z^2} + \sqrt{y^2 + z^2} = \beta, \quad \sqrt{x^2 + z^2} - \sqrt{y^2 + z^2} = \gamma,$$

is triply orthogonal.

The study of triply orthogonal systems is one of the most interesting and one of the most difficult problems of differential geometry. A very large number of memoirs have been published on the subject, the results of which have been collected by Darboux in a recent work.* Any surface S belongs to an infinite number of triply orthogonal systems. One of these consists of the family of surfaces parallel to S and the two families of developables formed by the normals along the lines of curvature on S. For, let O be any point on the normal MN to the surface S at the point M, and let MT and MT' be the tangents to the two lines of curvature C and C' which pass through M; then the tangent plane to the parallel surface through O is parallel to the tangent plane to S at M, and the tangent planes to the two developables described by the normals to S along C and C' are the planes MNT and MNT', respectively. These three planes are perpendicular by pairs, which shows that the system is triply orthogonal.

An infinite number of triply orthogonal systems can be derived from any one known triply orthogonal system by means of successive inversions, since any inversion leaves all angles unchanged. Since any surface whatever is a member of some triply orthogonal system, as we have just seen, it follows that *an inversion carries the lines of curvature on any surface over into the lines of curvature on the transformed surface.* It is easy to verify this fact directly.

252. Applications to certain classes of surfaces. A large number of problems have been discussed in which it is required to find all the surfaces whose lines of curvature have a preassigned geometrical property. We shall proceed to indicate some of the simpler results.

First let us determine all those surfaces for which one system of lines of curvature are circles. By Joachimsthal's theorem, the plane of each of the circles must cut the surface at a constant angle. Hence all the normals to the surface along any circle C of the system must meet the axis of the circle, i.e. the perpendicular to its plane at its center, at the same point O. The sphere through C about O as center is tangent to the surface all along C; hence the required surface must be the envelope of a one-parameter family of spheres. Conversely, any surface which is the envelope of a one-parameter family of spheres is a solution of the problem, for the characteristic curves, which are circles, evidently form one system of lines of curvature.

Surfaces of revolution evidently belong to the preceding class. Another interesting particular case is the so-called *tubular surface*, which is the envelope of a sphere of constant radius whose center describes an arbitrary curve Γ. The characteristic curves are the circles of radius R whose centers lie on Γ and whose planes are normal to Γ. The normals to the surface are also normal to Γ;

---

* *Leçons sur les systèmes orthogonaux et les coordonnées curvilignes*, 1898.

hence the second system of lines of curvature are the lines in which the surface is cut by the developable surfaces which may be formed from the normals to Γ.

If both systems of lines of curvature on a surface are circles, it is clear from the preceding argument that the surface may be thought of as the envelope of either of two one-parameter families of spheres. Let S_1, S_2, S_3 be any three spheres of the first family, C_1, C_2, C_3 the corresponding characteristic curves, and M_1, M_2, M_3 the three points in which C_1, C_2, C_3 are cut by a line of curvature C' of the other system. The sphere S' which is tangent to the surface along C' is also tangent to the spheres S_1, S_2, S_3 at M_1, M_2, M_3, respectively. Hence *the required surface is the envelope of a family of spheres each of which touches three fixed spheres.* This surface is the well-known *Dupin cyclide.* Mannheim gave an elegant proof that any Dupin cyclide is the surface into which a certain anchor ring is transformed by a certain inversion. Let γ be the circle which is orthogonal to each of the three fixed spheres S_1, S_2, S_3. An inversion whose pole is a point on the circumference of γ carries that circle into a straight line OO', and carries the three spheres S_1, S_2, S_3 into three spheres $\Sigma_1, \Sigma_2, \Sigma_3$ orthogonal to OO', that is, the centers of the transformed spheres lie on OO'. Let C_1', C_2', C_3' be the intersections of these spheres with any plane through OO', C' a circle tangent to each of the circles C_1', C_2', C_3', and Σ' the sphere on which C' is a great circle. It is clear that Σ' remains tangent to each of the spheres $\Sigma_1, \Sigma_2, \Sigma_3$ as the whole figure is revolved about OO', and that the envelope of Σ' is an anchor ring whose meridian is the circle C'.

Let us now determine the surface for which all of the lines of curvature of one system are plane curves whose planes are all parallel. Let us take the xy plane parallel to the planes in which these lines of curvature lie, and let

$$x \cos \alpha + y \sin \alpha = F(\alpha, z)$$

be the tangential equation of the section of the surface by a parallel to the xy plane, where $F(\alpha, z)$ is a function of α and z which depends upon the surface under consideration. The coördinates x and y of a point of the surface are given by the preceding equation together with the equation

$$- x \sin \alpha + y \cos \alpha = \frac{\partial F}{\partial \alpha}.$$

The formulæ for x, y, z are

$$(46) \quad x = F \cos \alpha - \frac{\partial F}{\partial \alpha} \sin \alpha, \qquad y = F \sin \alpha + \frac{\partial F}{\partial \alpha} \cos \alpha, \qquad z = z.$$

Any surface may be represented by equations of this form by choosing the function $F(\alpha, z)$ properly. The only exceptions are the ruled surfaces whose directing plane is the xy plane. It is easy to show that the coefficients A, B, C of the tangent plane may be taken to be

$$A = \cos \alpha, \qquad B = \sin \alpha, \qquad C = - \frac{\partial F}{\partial z};$$

hence the cosine of the angle between the normal and the z axis is

$$\nu = \frac{- F_z(\alpha, z)}{\sqrt{1 + F_z^2(\alpha, z)}}.$$

In order that all the sections by planes parallel to the xy plane be lines of curvature, it is necessary and sufficient, by Joachimsthal's theorem, that each of these planes cut the surface at a constant angle, i.e. that ν be independent of α. This is equivalent to saying that $F_z(\alpha, z)$ is independent of α, i.e. that $F(\alpha, z)$ is of the form

$$F(\alpha, z) = \phi(z) + \psi(\alpha),$$

where the functions ϕ and ψ are arbitrary. Substituting this value in (46), we see that the most general solution of the problem is given by the equations

(47)
$$\begin{cases} x = \psi(\alpha)\cos\alpha - \psi'(\alpha)\sin\alpha + \phi(z)\cos\alpha, \\ y = \psi(\alpha)\sin\alpha + \psi'(\alpha)\cos\alpha + \phi(z)\sin\alpha, \\ z = z. \end{cases}$$

These surfaces may be generated as follows. The first two of equations (47), for z constant and α variable, represent a family of parallel curves which are the projections on the xy plane of the sections of the surface by planes parallel to the xy plane. But these curves are all parallel to the curve obtained by setting $\phi(z) = 0$. Hence the surfaces may be generated as follows : *Taking in the xy plane any curve whatever and its parallel curves, lift each of the curves vertically a distance given by some arbitrary law; the curves in their new positions form a surface which is the most general solution of the problem.*

It is easy to see that the preceding construction may be replaced by the following : *The required surfaces are those described by any plane curve whose plane rolls without slipping on a cylinder of any base.* By analogy with plane curves, these surfaces may be called *rolled surfaces* or *roulettes.* This fact may be verified by examining the plane curves $\alpha = \text{const.}$ The two families of lines of curvature are the plane curves $z = \text{const.}$ and $\alpha = \text{const.}$

IV. FAMILIES OF STRAIGHT LINES

The equations of a straight line in space contain four variable parameters. Hence we may consider one-, two-, or three-parameter families of straight lines, according to the number of given relations between the four parameters. A one-parameter family of straight lines form a ruled surface. A two-parameter family of straight lines is called a *line congruence*, and, finally, a three-parameter family of straight lines is called a *line complex.*

253. Ruled surfaces. Let the equations of a one-parameter family of straight lines (G) be given in the form

(48) $x = az + p, \qquad y = bz + q,$

where a, b, p, q are functions of a single variable parameter u. Let us consider the variation in the position of the tangent plane to the surface S formed by these lines as the point of tangency moves along any one of the generators G. The equations (48), together with the equation $z = z$, give the coördinates x, y, z of a point M on S in terms of the two parameters z and u; hence, by § 39, the equation of the tangent plane at M is

$$\begin{vmatrix} X - x & Y - y & Z - z \\ a & b & 1 \\ a'z + p' & b'z + q' & 0 \end{vmatrix} = 0,$$

where a', b', p', q' denote the derivatives of a, b, p, q with respect to u. Replacing x and y by $az + p$ and $bz + q$, respectively, and simplifying, this equation becomes

$$(49) \quad (b'z + q')(X - aZ - p) - (a'z + p')(Y - bZ - q) = 0.$$

In the first place, we see that this plane always passes through the generator G, which was evident *a priori*, and moreover, that the plane turns around G as the point of tangency M moves along G, at least unless the ratio $(a'z + p')/(b'z + q')$ is independent of z, i.e. unless $a'q' - b'p' = 0$, — we shall discard this special case in what follows. Since the preceding ratio is linear in z, every plane through a generator is tangent to the surface at one and only one point. As the point of tangency recedes indefinitely along the generator in either direction the tangent plane P approaches a limiting position P', which we shall call *the tangent plane at the point at infinity* on that generator. The equation of this limiting plane P' is

$$(50) \quad b'(X - aZ - p) - a'(Y - bZ - q) = 0.$$

Let ω be the angle between this plane P' and the tangent plane P at a point M (x, y, z) of the generator. The direction cosines $(\alpha', \beta', \gamma')$ and (α, β, γ) of the normals to P' and P are proportional to

$$b', \qquad -a', \qquad a'b - ab'$$

and

$$b'z + q', \quad -(a'z + p'), \quad b(a'z + p') - a(b'z + q'),$$

respectively; hence

$$\cos \omega = \alpha \alpha' + \beta \beta' + \gamma \gamma' = \frac{Az + B}{\sqrt{A} \sqrt{Az^2 + 2Bz + C}},$$

where

$$A = a'^2 + b'^2 + (ab' - ba')^2,$$
$$B = a'p' + b'q' + (ab' - ba')(aq' - bp'),$$
$$C = p'^2 + q'^2 + (aq' - bp')^2.$$

After an easy reduction, we find, by Lagrange's identity (§ 131),

$$(51) \quad \tan \omega = \frac{\sqrt{AC - B^2}}{Az + B} = \frac{(a'q' - b'p')\sqrt{1 + a^2 + b^2}}{Az + B}.$$

It follows that the limiting plane P' is perpendicular to the tangent plane P_1 at a point O_1 of the generator whose ordinate z_1 is given by the formula

$$(52) \qquad z_1 = -\frac{B}{A} = -\frac{a'p' + b'q' + (ab' - ba')(aq' - bp')}{a'^2 + b'^2 + (ab' - ba')^2}.$$

The point O_1 is called the *central point* of the generator, and the tangent plane P_1 at O_1 is called the *central plane*. The angle θ between the tangent plane P at any point M of the generator and this central plane P_1 is $\pi/2 - \omega$, and the formula (51) may be replaced by the formula

$$\tan \theta = \frac{A(z - z_1)}{\sqrt{AC - B^2}} = \frac{[a'^2 + b'^2 + (ab' - ba')^2](z - z_1)}{(a'q' - b'p')\sqrt{1 + a^2 + b^2}}.$$

Let ρ be the distance between the central point O_1 and the point M, taken with the sign $+$ or the sign $-$ according as the angle which $O_1 M$ makes with the positive z axis is acute or obtuse. Then we shall have $\rho = (z - z_1)\sqrt{1 + a^2 + b^2}$, and the preceding formula may be written in the form

$$(53) \qquad \tan \theta = k\rho,$$

where k, which is called the *parameter of distribution*, is defined by the equation

$$(54) \qquad k = \frac{a'^2 + b'^2 + (ab' - ba')^2}{(a'q' - b'p')(1 + a^2 + b^2)}.$$

The formula (53) expresses in very simple form the manner in which the tangent plane turns about the generator. It contains no quantity which does not have a geometrical meaning: we shall see presently that k may be defined geometrically. However, there remains a certain ambiguity in the formula (53), for it is not immediately evident in which sense the angle θ should be counted. In other words, it is not clear, *a priori*, in which direction the tangent plane turns around the generator as the point moves along the generator. The sense of this rotation may be determined by the sign of k.

In order to see the matter clearly, imagine an observer lying on a generator G. As the point of tangency M moves from his feet toward his head he will see the tangent plane P turn either from his left to his right or *vice versa*. A little reflection will show that the sense of rotation defined in this way remains unchanged if the observer turns around so that his head and feet change places. Two hyperbolic paraboloids having a generator in common and lying symmetrically with respect to a plane through that generator give a clear idea of the two possible situations. Let us now move the axes in such a way that the new origin is at the central point O_1, the new z axis is the generator G itself, and the xz plane is the central plane P_1. It is evident that the value of the parameter of distribution (54) remains unchanged during this movement of the axes, and that the formula (53) takes the form

$$(53') \qquad\qquad \tan \theta = kz,$$

where θ denotes the angle between the xz plane P_1 and the tangent plane P, counted in a convenient sense. For the value of u_0 which corresponds to the z axis we must have $a = b = p = q = 0$, and the equation of the tangent plane at any point M of that axis becomes

$$(b'z + q')X - (a'z + p')Y = 0.$$

In order that the origin be the central point and the xz plane the central plane, we must have also $a' = 0$, $q' = 0$; hence the equation of the tangent plane reduces to $Y = (b'z/p')X$, and the formula (54) gives $k = -b'/p'$. It follows that the angle θ in (53') should be counted positive in the sense from Oy toward Ox. If the orientation of the axes is that adopted in § 228, an observer lying in the z axis will see the tangent plane turn from his left toward his right if k is positive, or from his right toward his left if k is negative.

The locus of the central points of the generators of a ruled surface is called the *line of striction*. The equations of this curve in terms of the parameter u are precisely the equations (48) and (52).

Note. If $a'q' = b'p'$ for a generator G, the tangent plane is the same at any point of that generator. If this relation is satisfied for every generator, i.e. for all values of u, the ruled surface is a developable surface (§ 223), and the results previously obtained can be easily verified. For if a' and b' do not vanish simultaneously, the tangent plane is the same at all points of any generator G, and becomes indeterminate for the point $z = -p'/a' = -q'/b'$, i.e. for the point where the generator touches its envelope. It is easy to show that this value for z is the same as that given by (52) when $a'q' = b'p'$. It follows that the line of striction becomes the edge of regression on a developable surface. The parameter of distribution is infinite for a developable.

If $a' = b' = 0$ for every generator, the surface is a cylinder and the central point is indeterminate.

254. Direct definition of the parameter of distribution. The central point and the parameter of distribution may be defined in an entirely different manner. Let G and G_1 be two neighboring generators corresponding to the values u and $u + h$ of the parameter, respectively, and let G_1 be given by the equations

$$(55) \quad x = (a + \Delta a)z + p + \Delta p, \qquad y = (b + \Delta b)z + q + \Delta q.$$

Let δ be the shortest distance between the two lines G and G_1, α the angle between G and G_1, and (X, Y, Z) the point where G meets the common perpendicular. Then, by well-known formulæ of Analytic Geometry, we shall have

$$Z = -\frac{\Delta a\,\Delta q + \Delta b\,\Delta p + (a\,\Delta b - b\,\Delta a)[(a + \Delta a)\Delta q - (b + \Delta b)\Delta p]}{(\Delta a)^2 + (\Delta b)^2 + (a\,\Delta b - b\,\Delta a)^2},$$

$$\delta = \frac{\Delta a\,\Delta q - \Delta b\,\Delta p}{\sqrt{(\Delta a)^2 + (\Delta b)^2 + (a\,\Delta b - b\,\Delta a)^2}},$$

$$\sin\alpha = \frac{\sqrt{(\Delta a)^2 + (\Delta b)^2 + (a\,\Delta b - b\,\Delta a)^2}}{\sqrt{a^2 + b^2 + 1}\,\sqrt{(a + \Delta a)^2 + (b + \Delta b)^2 + 1}}.$$

As h approaches zero, Z approaches the quantity z_1 defined by (52), and $(\sin\alpha)/\delta$ approaches k. Hence the central point is the limiting position of the foot of the common perpendicular to G and G_1, while the parameter of distribution is the limit of the ratio $(\sin\alpha)/\delta$.

In the expression for δ let us replace Δa, Δb, Δp, Δq by their expansions in powers of h:

$$\Delta a = ha' + \frac{h^2}{1 \cdot 2}\,a'' + \cdots$$

and the similar expansions for Δb, Δp, Δq. Then the numerator of the expression for δ becomes

$$\Delta a\,\Delta q - \Delta b\,\Delta p = h^2(a'q' - b'p') + \frac{h^3}{2}\,(a''q' + a'q'' - b''p' - b'p'') + \cdots,$$

while the denominator is always of the first order with respect to h. It is evident that δ is in general an infinitesimal of the first order with respect to h, except for developable surfaces, for which $a'q' = b'p'$. But the coefficient of $h^3/2$ is the derivative of $a'q' - b'p'$; hence this coefficient also vanishes for a developable, and the shortest distance between two neighboring generators is of the third order (§ 230). This remark is due to Bouquet, who also showed that if this distance is constantly of the fourth order, it must be precisely zero; that is, that in that case the given straight lines are the tangents to a plane curve or to a conical surface. In order to prove this, it is sufficient to carry the development of $\Delta a\, \Delta q - \Delta b\, \Delta p$ to terms of the fourth order.

255. Congruences. Focal surface of a congruence. Every two-parameter family of straight lines

$$(56) \qquad x = az + p, \qquad y = bz + q,$$

where a, b, p, q depend on two parameters α and β, is called a *line congruence*. Through any point in space there pass, in general, a certain number of lines of the congruence, for the two equations (56) determine a certain number of definite sets of values of α and β when x, y, and z are given definite values. If any relation between α and β be assumed, the equations (56) will represent a ruled surface, which is not usually developable. In order that the surface be developable, we must have

$$da\, dq - db\, dp = 0,$$

or, replacing da by $(\partial a/\partial \alpha)\, d\alpha + (\partial a/\partial \beta)\, d\beta$, etc.,

$$(57) \qquad \begin{cases} \left(\dfrac{\partial a}{\partial \alpha}\, d\alpha + \dfrac{\partial a}{\partial \beta}\, d\beta\right)\left(\dfrac{\partial q}{\partial \alpha}\, d\alpha + \dfrac{\partial q}{\partial \beta}\, d\beta\right) \\ \qquad - \left(\dfrac{\partial b}{\partial \alpha}\, d\alpha + \dfrac{\partial b}{\partial \beta}\, d\beta\right)\left(\dfrac{\partial p}{\partial \alpha}\, d\alpha + \dfrac{\partial p}{\partial \beta}\, d\beta\right) = 0. \end{cases}$$

This is a quadratic equation in $d\beta/d\alpha$. Solving it, we should usually obtain two distinct solutions,

$$(58) \qquad \frac{d\beta}{d\alpha} = \psi_1(\alpha, \beta), \qquad \frac{d\beta}{d\alpha} = \psi_2(\alpha, \beta),$$

either of which defines a developable surface. Under very general limitations, which we shall state precisely a little later and which we shall just now suppose fulfilled, each of these equations is satisfied by an infinite number of functions of α, and each of them has one and only one solution which assumes a given value β_0 when $\alpha = \alpha_0$. It follows that every straight line G of the congruence belongs to two developable surfaces, all of whose generators are members of the congruence. Let Γ and Γ' be the edges of regression of these two developables, and A and A' the points where G touches Γ and Γ', respectively. The two points A and A' are called the *focal points* of the generator G. They may be found as follows without integrating the equation (57). The ordinate z of one of these points must satisfy both of the equations

$$z\, da + dp = 0, \qquad z\, db + dq = 0,$$

or, replacing da, db, dp, dq by their developments,

$$z\left(\frac{\partial a}{\partial \alpha}\, d\alpha + \frac{\partial a}{\partial \beta}\, d\beta\right) + \frac{\partial p}{\partial \alpha}\, d\alpha + \frac{\partial p}{\partial \beta}\, d\beta = 0,$$

$$z\left(\frac{\partial b}{\partial \alpha}\, d\alpha + \frac{\partial b}{\partial \beta}\, d\beta\right) + \frac{\partial q}{\partial \alpha}\, d\alpha + \frac{\partial q}{\partial \beta}\, d\beta = 0.$$

Eliminating z between these two equations, we find again the equation (57). But if we eliminate $d\beta/d\alpha$ we obtain an equation of the second degree

$$(59)\quad \left(z\frac{\partial a}{\partial \alpha} + \frac{\partial p}{\partial \alpha}\right)\left(z\frac{\partial b}{\partial \beta} + \frac{\partial q}{\partial \beta}\right) - \left(z\frac{\partial a}{\partial \beta} + \frac{\partial p}{\partial \beta}\right)\left(z\frac{\partial b}{\partial \alpha} + \frac{\partial q}{\partial \alpha}\right) = 0,$$

whose two solutions are the values of z for the focal points.

The locus of the focal points A and A' consists of two nappes Σ and Σ' of a surface whose equations are given in parameter form by the formulæ (56) and (59). These two nappes are not in general two distinct surfaces, but constitute two portions of the same analytic surface. The whole surface is called the *focal surface*. It is evident that the focal surface is also the locus of the edges of regression of the developable surfaces which can be formed from the lines of the congruence. For by the very definition of the curve Γ the tangent at any point a is a line of the congruence; hence a is a focal point for that line of the congruence. Every straight line of the congruence is tangent to each of the nappes Σ and Σ', for it is tangent to each of two curves which lie on these two nappes, respectively.

By an argument precisely similar to that of § 247 it is easy to determine the tangent planes at A and A' to Σ and Σ' (Fig. 51). As the line G moves, remaining tangent to Γ, for example, it also remains tangent to the surface Σ'. Its point of tangency A' will describe a curve γ' which is necessarily distinct from Γ'. Hence the developable described by G during this motion is tangent to Σ' at A', since the tangent planes to the two surfaces both contain the line G and the tangent line to γ'. It follows that the tangent plane to Σ' at A' is precisely the osculating plane of Γ at A. Likewise, the tangent plane to Σ at A is the osculating plane of Γ' at A'. These two planes are called the *focal planes* of the generator G.

It may happen that one of the nappes of the focal surface degenerates into a curve C. In that case the straight lines of the congruence are all tangent to Σ, and merely *meet* C. One of the families of developables consists of the cones circumscribed about Σ

whose vertices are on C. If both of the nappes of the focal surface degenerate into curves C and C', the two families of developables consist of the cones through one of the curves whose vertices lie on the other. If both the curves C and C' are straight lines, the congruence is called a *linear congruence*.

256. Congruence of normals. The normals to any surface evidently form a congruence, but the converse is not true: there exists no surface, in general, which is normal to every line of a given congruence. For, if we consider the congruence formed by the normals to a given surface S, the two nappes of the focal surface are evidently the two nappes Σ and Σ' of the evolute of S (§ 247), and we have seen that the two tangent planes at the points A and A' where the same normal touches Σ and Σ' stand at right angles. This is a characteristic property of a congruence of normals, as we shall see by trying to find the condition that the straight line (56) should always remain normal to the surface. The necessary and sufficient condition that it should is that there exist a function $f(\alpha, \beta)$ such that the surface S represented by the equations

$$(60) \qquad x = az + p, \qquad y = bz + q, \qquad z = f(\alpha, \beta)$$

is normal to each of the lines (G). It follows that we must have

$$a \frac{\partial x}{\partial \alpha} + b \frac{\partial y}{\partial \alpha} + \frac{\partial z}{\partial \alpha} = 0,$$

$$a \frac{\partial x}{\partial \beta} + b \frac{\partial y}{\partial \beta} + \frac{\partial z}{\partial \beta} = 0,$$

or, replacing x and y by $az + p$ and $bz + q$, respectively, and dividing by $\sqrt{a^2 + b^2 + 1}$,

$$(61) \qquad \begin{cases} \dfrac{\partial}{\partial \alpha} \left(z \sqrt{a^2 + b^2 + 1} \right) + \dfrac{a \dfrac{\partial p}{\partial \alpha} + b \dfrac{\partial q}{\partial \alpha}}{\sqrt{a^2 + b^2 + 1}} = 0, \\[4ex] \dfrac{\partial}{\partial \beta} \left(z \sqrt{a^2 + b^2 + 1} \right) + \dfrac{a \dfrac{\partial p}{\partial \beta} + b \dfrac{\partial q}{\partial \beta}}{\sqrt{a^2 + b^2 + 1}} = 0. \end{cases}$$

The necessary and sufficient condition that these equations be compatible is

$$(62) \qquad \frac{\partial}{\partial \beta} \left(\frac{a \dfrac{\partial p}{\partial \alpha} + b \dfrac{\partial q}{\partial \alpha}}{\sqrt{a^2 + b^2 + 1}} \right) = \frac{\partial}{\partial \alpha} \left(\frac{a \dfrac{\partial p}{\partial \beta} + b \dfrac{\partial q}{\partial \beta}}{\sqrt{a^2 + b^2 + 1}} \right).$$

If this condition is satisfied, z can be found from (61) by a single quadrature. The surfaces obtained in this way depend upon a constant of integration and form a one-parameter family of parallel surfaces.

In order to find the geometrical meaning of the condition (62), it should be noticed that that condition, by its very nature, is independent of the choice of axes and of the choice of the independent variables. We may therefore choose the z axis as a line of the congruence, and the parameters α and β as the coördinates of the point where a line of the congruence pierces the xy plane. Then we shall have $p = \alpha$, $q = \beta$, and a and b given functions of α and β which vanish for $\alpha = \beta = 0$. It follows that the condition of integrability, for the set of values $\alpha = \beta = 0$, reduces to the equation $\partial a/\partial \beta = \partial b/\partial \alpha$. On the other hand, the equation (57) takes the form

$$\frac{\partial a}{\partial \beta}\, d\beta^2 + \left(\frac{\partial a}{\partial \alpha} - \frac{\partial b}{\partial \beta}\right) d\alpha\, d\beta - \frac{\partial b}{\partial \alpha}\, d\alpha^2 = 0,$$

which is the equation for determining the lines of intersection of the xy plane with the developables of the congruence after α and β have been replaced by x and y, respectively. The condition $\partial a/\partial \beta = \partial b/\partial \alpha$, for $\alpha = \beta = 0$, means that the two curves of this kind which pass through the origin intersect at right angles; that is, the tangent planes to the two developable surfaces of the congruence which pass through the z axis stand at right angles. Since the line taken as the z axis was any line of the congruence, we may state the following important theorem:

The necessary and sufficient condition that the straight lines of a given congruence be the normals of some surface is that the focal planes through every line of the congruence should be perpendicular to each other.

Note. If the parameters α and β be chosen as the cosines of the angles which the line makes with the x and y axes, respectively, we shall have

$$a = \frac{\alpha}{\sqrt{1 - \alpha^2 - \beta^2}}, \qquad b = \frac{\beta}{\sqrt{1 - \alpha^2 - \beta^2}}, \qquad \sqrt{1 + a^2 + b^2} = \frac{1}{\sqrt{1 - \alpha^2 - \beta^2}},$$

and the equations (61) become

$$(63) \qquad \begin{cases} \dfrac{\partial}{\partial \alpha}\left(\dfrac{z}{\sqrt{1 - \alpha^2 - \beta^2}}\right) + \alpha \dfrac{\partial p}{\partial \alpha} + \beta \dfrac{\partial q}{\partial \alpha} = 0, \\[2ex] \dfrac{\partial}{\partial \beta}\left(\dfrac{z}{\sqrt{1 - \alpha^2 - \beta^2}}\right) + \alpha \dfrac{\partial p}{\partial \beta} + \beta \dfrac{\partial q}{\partial \beta} = 0. \end{cases}$$

Then the condition of integrability (62) reduces to the form $\partial q/\partial\alpha = \partial p/\partial\beta$, which means that p and q must be the partial derivatives of the same function $F(\alpha, \beta)$:

$$p = \frac{\partial F}{\partial \alpha}, \qquad q = \frac{\partial F}{\partial \beta},$$

where $F(\alpha, \beta)$ can be found by a single quadrature. It follows that z is the solution of the total differential equation

$$d\left(\frac{z}{\sqrt{1 - \alpha^2 - \beta^2}}\right) = -\left(\alpha\frac{\partial^2 F}{\partial \alpha^2} + \beta\frac{\partial^2 F}{\partial \alpha\, \partial \beta}\right)d\alpha - \left(\alpha\frac{\partial^2 F}{\partial \alpha\, \partial \beta} + \beta\frac{\partial^2 F}{\partial \beta^2}\right)d\beta,$$

whence

$$z = \sqrt{1 - \alpha^2 - \beta^2}\left(C + F - \alpha\frac{\partial F}{\partial \alpha} - \beta\frac{\partial F}{\partial \beta}\right),$$

where C is an arbitrary constant.

257. Theorem of Malus. If rays of light from a point source are reflected (or refracted) by any surface, the reflected (or refracted) rays are the normals to each of a family of parallel surfaces. This theorem, which is due to Malus, has been extended by Cauchy, Dupin, Gergonne, and Quetelet to the case of any number of successive reflections or refractions, and we may state the following more general theorem :

If a family of rays of light are normal to some surface at any time, they retain that property after any number of reflections and refractions.

Since a reflection may be regarded as a refraction of index -1, it is evidently sufficient to prove the theorem for a single refraction. Let S be a surface normal to the unrefracted rays, mM an incident ray which meets the surface of separation Σ at a point M, and MR the refracted ray. By Descartes' law, the incident ray, the refracted ray, and the normal MN lie in a plane, and the angles i and r (Fig. 52) satisfy the relation $n \sin i = \sin r$. For definiteness we shall suppose, as in the figure, that n is less than unity. Let l denote the distance Mm, and let us lay off on the refracted ray extended a length $l' = Mm'$ equal to k times l, where k is a constant factor which we shall determine presently. The point m' describes a surface S'. We shall proceed to show that k may be chosen in such a way that Mm' is normal to S'. Let C be any curve on S. As the point m describes C the point M describes a curve Γ on the surface Σ, and the corresponding point m' describes another curve C' on S'. Let s, σ, s' be the lengths of the arcs of the three curves C, Γ, C' measured from corresponding fixed points on those curves, respectively, ω the angle which the tangent MT_1 to Γ makes with the tangent MT to the normal section by the normal plane through the incident ray, and ϕ and ϕ' the angles which MT_1 makes with Mm and Mm', respectively. In order to find $\cos\phi$, for example, let us lay off on Mm a unit length and project it upon MT_1,

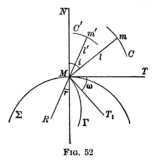

FIG. 52

first directly, then by projecting it upon MT and from MT upon MT_1. This, and the similar projection from Mm' upon MT_1, give the equations

$$\cos \phi = \sin i \cos \omega, \qquad \cos \phi' = \sin r \cos \omega.$$

Applying the formula (10′) of § 82 for the differential of a segment to the segments Mm and Mm', we find

$$dl = -d\sigma \cos \omega \sin i,$$
$$dl' = -d\sigma \cos \omega \sin r - ds' \cos \theta,$$

where θ denotes the angle between $m'M$ and the tangent to C'. Hence, replacing dl' by $k\,dl$, we find

$$\cos \omega\, d\sigma(k \sin i - \sin r) = ds' \cos \theta,$$

or, assuming $k = n$,

$$ds' \cos \theta = 0.$$

It follows that Mm' is normal to C', and, since C' is any curve whatever on S', Mm' is also normal to the surface S'. This surface S' is called the *anticaustic* surface, or the *secondary caustic*. It is clear that S' is the envelope of the spheres described about M as center with a radius equal to n times Mm; hence we may state the following theorem:

Let us consider the surface S which is normal to the incident rays as the envelope of a family of spheres whose centers lie on the surface of separation Σ. Then the anticaustic for the refracted rays is the envelope of a family of spheres with the same centers, whose radii are to the radii of the corresponding spheres of the first family as unity is to the index of refraction.

This envelope is composed of two nappes which correspond, respectively, to indices of refraction which are numerically equal and opposite in sign. In general these two nappes are portions of the same inseparable analytic surface.

258. Complexes. A *line complex* consists of all the lines of a three-parameter family. Let the equations of a line be given in the form

$$(64) \qquad\qquad x = az + p, \qquad y = bz + q.$$

Any line complex may be defined by means of a relation between a, b, p, q of the form

$$(65) \qquad\qquad F(a, b, p, q) = 0,$$

and conversely. If F is a polynomial in a, b, p, q, the complex is called an *algebraic complex*. The lines of the complex through any point (x_0, y_0, z_0) form a cone whose vertex is at that point; its equation may be found by eliminating a, b, p, q between the equations (64), (65), and

$$(66) \qquad\qquad x_0 = az_0 + p, \qquad y_0 = bz_0 + q.$$

Hence the equation of this *cone of the complex* is

$$(67) \qquad F\left(\frac{x - x_0}{z - z_0}, \frac{y - y_0}{z - z_0}, \frac{x_0 z - xz_0}{z - z_0}, \frac{y_0 z - yz_0}{z - z_0}\right) = 0.$$

Similarly, there are in any plane in space an infinite number of lines of the complex; these lines envelop a curve which is called *a curve of the complex*. If the complex is algebraic, *the order of the cone of the complex is the same as the class of the curve of the complex.* For, if we wish to find the number of lines of the complex which pass through any given point A and which lie in a plane P through that point, we may either count the number of generators in which P cuts the cone of the complex whose vertex is at A, or we may count the number of tangents which can be drawn from A to the curve of the complex which lies in the plane P. As the number must be the same in either case, the theorem is proved.

If the cone of the complex is always a plane, the complex is said to be *linear*, and the equation (65) is of the form

(68) $$Aa + Bb + Cp + Dq + E(aq - bp) + F = 0.$$

Then the locus of all the lines of the complex through any given point (x_0, y_0, z_0) is the plane whose equation is

(69) $$\begin{cases} A(x - x_0) + B(y - y_0) + C(x_0 z - z_0 x) \\ \qquad + D(y_0 z - z_0 y) + E(y_0 x - x_0 y) + F(z - z_0) = 0. \end{cases}$$

The curve of the complex, since it must be of class unity, degenerates into a point, that is, all the lines of the complex which lie in a plane pass through a single point of that plane, which is called the *pole* or the *focus*. A linear complex therefore establishes a correspondence between the points and the planes of space, such that any point in space corresponds to a plane through that point, and any plane to a point in that plane. A correspondence is also established among the straight lines in space. Let D be a straight line which does not belong to the complex, F and F' the foci of any two planes through D, and Δ the line FF'. Every plane through Δ has its focus at its point of intersection ϕ with the line D, since each of the lines ϕF and $\phi F'$ evidently belongs to the complex. It follows that every line which meets both D and Δ belongs to the complex, and, finally, that the focus of any plane through D is the point where that plane meets Δ. The lines D and Δ are called *conjugate lines;* each of them is the locus of the foci of all planes through the other.

If the line D recedes to infinity, the planes through it become parallel, and it is clear that the foci of a set of parallel planes lie on a straight line. There always exists a plane such that the locus of the foci of the planes parallel to it is perpendicular to that plane. If this particular line be taken as the z axis, the plane whose focus is any point on the z axis is parallel to the xy plane. By (69) the necessary and sufficient condition that this should be the case is that $A = B = C = D = 0$, and the equation of the complex takes the simple form

(70) $$aq - bp + K = 0.$$

The plane whose focus is at the point (x, y, z) is given by the equation

(71) $$Xy - Yx + K(Z - z) = 0,$$

where X, Y, Z are the running coördinates.

As an example let us determine the curves whose tangents belong to the preceding complex. Given such a curve, whose coördinates x, y, z are known functions of a variable parameter, the equations of the tangent at any point are

$$\frac{X - x}{dx} = \frac{Y - y}{dy} = \frac{Z - z}{dz}.$$

The necessary and sufficient condition that this line should belong to the given complex is that it should lie in the plane (71) whose focus is the point (x, y, z), that is, that we should have

(72) $$x\,dy - y\,dx = K\,dz.$$

We saw in § 218 how to find all possible sets of functions x, y, z of a single parameter which satisfy such a relation; hence we are in a position to find the required curves.

The results of § 218 may be stated in the language of line complexes. For example, differentiating the equation (72) we find

(73) $$x\,d^2y - y\,d^2x = K\,d^2z,$$

and the equations (72) and (73) show that the osculating plane at the point (x, y, z) is precisely the tangent plane (71); hence we may state the following theorem :

If all the tangents to a skew curve belong to a linear line complex, the osculating plane at any point of that curve is the plane whose focus is at that point.

(APPELL.)

Suppose that we wished to draw the osculating planes from any point O in space to a skew curve Γ whose tangents all belong to a linear line complex. Let M be the point of contact of one of these planes. By Appell's theorem, the straight line MO belongs to the complex ; hence M lies in the plane whose focus is the point O. Conversely, if the point M of Γ lies in that plane, the straight line MO, which belongs to the complex, lies in the osculating plane at M ; hence that osculating plane passes through O. It follows that the required points are the intersections of the curve with the plane whose focus is the point O (see § 218).

Linear line complexes occur in many geometrical and mechanical applications. The reader is referred, for example, to the theses of Appell and Picard.*

EXERCISES

1. Find the lines of curvature of the developable surface which is the envelope of the family of planes defined in rectangular coördinates by the equation

$$z = \alpha x + y\,\phi(\alpha) + R\sqrt{1 + \alpha^2 + \phi^2(\alpha)}\,,$$

where α is a variable parameter, $\phi(\alpha)$ an arbitrary function of that parameter, and R a given constant.

[*Licence*, Paris, August, 1871.]

2. Find the conditions that the lines $x = az + \alpha$, $y = bz + \beta$, where a, b, α. β are functions of a variable parameter, should form a developable surface for which all of the system of lines of curvature perpendicular to the generators lie on a system of concentric spheres.

[*Licence*, Paris, July, 1872.]

---

* *Annales scientifiques de l'École Normale supérieure*, 1876 and 1877.

3. Determine the lines of curvature of the surface whose equation in rectangular coördinates is

$$e^z = \cos x \cos y.$$

[*Licence*, Paris, July, 1875.]

4. Consider the ellipsoid of three unequal axes defined by the equation

$$\frac{x^2}{a^2} + \frac{y^2}{b^2} + \frac{z^2}{c^2} - 1 = 0,$$

and the elliptical section E in the xz plane. Find, at each point M of E: 1) the values of the principal radii of curvature R_1 and R_2 of the ellipsoid, 2) the relation between R_1 and R_2, 3) the loci of the centers of curvature of the principal sections as the point M describes the ellipse E.

[*Licence*, Paris, November, 1877.]

5. Derive the equation of the second degree for the principal radii of curvature at any point of the paraboloid defined by the equation

$$\frac{x^2}{a} + \frac{y^2}{b} = 2z.$$

Also express, in terms of the variable z, each of the principal radii of curvature at any point on the line of intersection of the preceding paraboloid and the paraboloid defined by the equation

$$\frac{x^2}{a - \lambda} + \frac{y^2}{b - \lambda} = 2z - \lambda.$$

[*Licence*, Paris, November, 1880.]

6. Find the loci of the centers of curvature of the principal sections of the paraboloid defined by the equation $xy = az$ as the point of the surface describes the x axis.

[*Licence*, Paris, July, 1883.]

7. Find the equation of the surface which is the locus of the centers of curvature of all the plane sections of a given surface S by planes which all pass through the same point M of the surface.

8. Let MT be any tangent line at a point M of a given quadric surface, O the center of curvature of the section of the surface by any plane through MT, and O' the center of curvature of the evolute of that plane section. Find the locus of O' as the secant plane revolves about MT.

[*Licence*, Clermont, July, 1883.]

9. Find the asymptotic lines on the anchor ring formed by revolving a circle about one of its tangents.

[*Licence*, Paris, November, 1882.]

10. Let C be a given curve in the xz plane in a system of rectangular coördinates. A surface is described by a circle whose plane remains parallel to the xy plane and whose center describes the curve C, while the radius varies in such a way that the circle always meets the z axis. Derive the differential equation of the asymptotic lines on this surface, taking as the variable parameters the coördinate z of any point, and the angle θ which the radius of the circle through the point makes with the trace of the plane of the circle on the xz plane.

Apply the result to the particular case where the curve C is a parabola whose vertex is at the origin and whose axis is the x axis.

[*Licence*, Paris, July, 1880.]

11. Determine the asymptotic lines on a ruled surface which is tangent to another ruled surface at every point of a generator Δ of the second surface, every generator of the first surface meeting Δ at some point.

12. Determine the curves on a rectilinear helicoid whose osculating plane always contains the normal to the surface.

[*Licence*, Paris, July, 1876.]

13. Find the asymptotic lines on the ruled surface defined by the equations

$$x = (1 + u)\cos v, \qquad y = (1 - u)\sin v, \qquad z = u.$$

[*Licence*, Nancy, November, 1900.]

14*. The sections of a surface S by planes through a straight line Δ and the curves of contact of the cones circumscribed about S with their vertices on Δ form a conjugate network on the surface.

[Koenigs.]

15*. As a rigid straight line moves in such a way that three fixed points upon it always remain in three mutually perpendicular planes, the straight line always remains normal to a family of parallel surfaces. One of the family of surfaces is the locus of the middle point of the segment of the given line bounded by the point where the line meets one of the coördinate planes and by the foot of the perpendicular let fall upon the line from the origin of coördinates.

[Darboux, *Comptes rendus*, Vol. XCII, p. 446, 1881.]

16*. On any surface one imaginary line of curvature is the locus of the points for which the equation $1 + p^2 + q^2 = 0$ is satisfied.

[In order to prove this, put the differential equation of the lines of curvature in the form

$$(dp\,dy - dq\,dx)(1 + p^2 + q^2) + (p\,dy - q\,dx)(p\,dp + q\,dq) = 0.]$$

[Darboux, *Annales de l'École normale*, 1864.]

INDEX

[Titles in italic are proper names; numbers in italic are page numbers; and numbers in roman type are paragraph numbers, which are the same as in the original edition.]

548 INDEX

A CATALOGUE OF SELECTED
DOVER SCIENCE BOOKS

A CATALOGUE OF SELECTED
DOVER SCIENCE BOOKS

Physics: The Pioneer Science, Lloyd W. Taylor. Very thorough non-mathematical survey of physics in a historical framework which shows development of ideas. Easily followed by laymen; used in dozens of schools and colleges for survey courses. Richly illustrated. Volume 1: Heat, sound, mechanics. Volume 2: Light, electricity. Total of 763 illustrations. Total of cvi + 847pp.

60565-5, 60566-3 Two volumes, Paperbound 5.50

THE RISE OF THE NEW PHYSICS, A. d'Abro. Most thorough explanation in print of central core of mathematical physics, both classical and modern, from Newton to Dirac and Heisenberg. Both history and exposition: philosophy of science, causality, explanations of higher mathematics, analytical mechanics, electromagnetism, thermodynamics, phase rule, special and general relativity, matrices. No higher mathematics needed to follow exposition, though treatment is elementary to intermediate in level. Recommended to serious student who wishes verbal understanding. 97 illustrations. Total of ix + 982pp.

20003-5, 20004-3 Two volumes, Paperbound $5.50

INTRODUCTION TO CHEMICAL PHYSICS, John C. Slater. A work intended to bridge the gap between chemistry and physics. Text divided into three parts: Thermodynamics, Statistical Mechanics, and Kinetic Theory; Gases, Liquids and Solids; and Atoms, Molecules and the Structure of Matter, which form the basis of the approach. Level is advanced undergraduate to graduate, but theoretical physics held to minimum. 40 tables, 118 figures. xiv + 522pp.

62562-1 Paperbound $4.00

BASIC THEORIES OF PHYSICS, Peter C. Bergmann. Critical examination of important topics in classical and modern physics. Exceptionally useful in examining conceptual framework and methodology used in construction of theory. Excellent supplement to any course, textbook. Relatively advanced.
Volume 1. Heat and Quanta. Kinetic hypothesis, physics and statistics, stationary ensembles, thermodynamics, early quantum theories, atomic spectra, probability waves, quantization in wave mechanics, approximation methods, abstract quantum theory. 8 figures. x + 300pp. 60968-5 Paperbound $2.00
Volume 2. Mechanics and Electrodynamics. Classical mechanics, electro- and magnetostatics, electromagnetic induction, field waves, special relativity, waves, etc. 16 figures, viii + 260pp. 60969-3 Paperbound $2.75

FOUNDATIONS OF PHYSICS, Robert Bruce Lindsay and Henry Margenau. Methods and concepts at the heart of physics (space and time, mechanics, probability, statistics, relativity, quantum theory) explained in a text that bridges gap between semi-popular and rigorous introductions. Elementary calculus assumed. "Thorough and yet not over-detailed," *Nature*. 35 figures. xviii + 537 pp.

60377-6 Paperbound $3.50

FUNDAMENTAL FORMULAS OF PHYSICS, edited by Donald H. Menzel. Most useful reference and study work, ranges from simplest to most highly sophisticated operations. Individual chapters, with full texts explaining formulae, prepared by leading authorities cover basic mathematical formulas, statistics, nomograms, physical constants, classical mechanics, special theory of relativity, general theory of relativity, hydrodynamics and aerodynamics, boundary value problems in mathematical physics, heat and thermodynamics, statistical mechanics, kinetic theory of gases, viscosity, thermal conduction, electromagnetism, electronics, acoustics, geometrical optics, physical optics, electron optics, molecular spectra, atomic spectra, quantum mechanics, nuclear theory, cosmic rays and high energy phenomena, particle accelerators, solid state, magnetism, etc. Special chapters also cover physical chemistry, astrophysics, celestian mechanics, meteorology, and biophysics. Indispensable part of library of every scientist. Total of xli + 787pp.
60595-7, 60596-5 Two volumes, Paperbound $5.00

INTRODUCTION TO EXPERIMENTAL PHYSICS, William B. Fretter. Detailed coverage of techniques and equipment: measurements, vacuum tubes, pulse circuits, rectifiers, oscillators, magnet design, particle counters, nuclear emulsions, cloud chambers, accelerators, spectroscopy, magnetic resonance, x-ray diffraction, low temperature, etc. One of few books to cover laboratory hazards, design of exploratory experiments, measurements. 298 figures. xii + 349pp.
(EUK) 61890-0 Paperbound $2.50

CONCEPTS AND METHODS OF THEORETICAL PHYSICS, Robert Bruce Lindsay. Introduction to methods of theoretical physics, emphasizing development of physical concepts and analysis of methods. Part I proceeds from single particle to collections of particles to statistical method. Part II covers application of field concept to material and non-material media. Numerous exercises and examples. 76 illustrations. x + 515pp. 62354-8 Paperbound $4.00

AN ELEMENTARY TREATISE ON THEORETICAL MECHANICS, Sir James Jeans. Great scientific expositor in remarkably clear presentation of basic classical material: rest, motion, forces acting on particle, statics, motion of particle under variable force, motion of rigid bodies, coordinates, etc. Emphasizes explanation of fundamental physical principles rather than mathematics or applications. Hundreds of problems worked in text. 156 figures. x + 364pp. 61839-0 Paperbound $2.50

THEORETICAL MECHANICS: AN INTRODUCTION TO MATHEMATICAL PHYSICS, Joseph S. Ames and Francis D. Murnaghan. Mathematically rigorous introduction to vector and tensor methods, dynamics, harmonic vibrations, gyroscopic theory, principle of least constraint, Lorentz-Einstein transformation. 159 problems; many fully-worked examples. 39 figures. ix + 462pp. 60461-6 Paperbound $3.00

THE PRINCIPLE OF RELATIVITY, Albert Einstein, Hendrick A. Lorentz, Hermann Minkowski and Hermann Weyl. Eleven original papers on the special and general theory of relativity, all unabridged. Seven papers by Einstein, two by Lorentz, one each by Minkowski and Weyl. "A thrill to read again the original papers by these giants," *School Science and Mathematics*. Translated by W. Perret and G. B. Jeffery. Notes by A. Sommerfeld. 7 diagrams. viii + 216pp.
60081-5 Paperbound $2.00

EINSTEIN'S THEORY OF RELATIVITY, Max Born. Relativity theory analyzed, explained for intelligent layman or student with some physical, mathematical background. Includes Lorentz, Minkowski, and others. Excellent verbal account for teachers. Generally considered the finest non-technical account. vii + 376pp.
60769-0 Paperbound $2.50

PHYSICAL PRINCIPLES OF THE QUANTUM THEORY, Werner Heisenberg. Nobel Laureate discusses quantum theory, uncertainty principle, wave mechanics, work of Dirac, Schroedinger, Compton, Wilson, Einstein, etc. Middle, non-mathematical level for physicist, chemist not specializing in quantum; mathematical appendix for specialists. Translated by C. Eckart and F. Hoyt. 19 figures. viii + 184pp.
60113-7 Paperbound $2.00

PRINCIPLES OF QUANTUM MECHANICS, William V. Houston. For student with working knowledge of elementary mathematical physics; uses Schroedinger's wave mechanics. Evidence for quantum theory, postulates of quantum mechanics, applications in spectroscopy, collision problems, electrons, similar topics. 21 figures. 288pp.
60524-8 Paperbound $3.00

ATOMIC SPECTRA AND ATOMIC STRUCTURE, Gerhard Herzberg. One of the best introductions to atomic spectra and their relationship to structure; especially suited to specialists in other fields who require a comprehensive basic knowledge. Treatment is physical rather than mathematical. 2nd edition. Translated by J. W. T. Spinks. 80 illustrations. xiv + 257pp.
60115-3 Paperbound $2.00

ATOMIC PHYSICS: AN ATOMIC DESCRIPTION OF PHYSICAL PHENOMENA, Gaylord P. Harnwell and William E. Stephens. One of the best introductions to modern quantum ideas. Emphasis on the extension of classical physics into the realms of atomic phenomena and the evolution of quantum concepts. 156 problems. 173 figures and tables. xi + 401pp.
61584-7 Paperbound $2.50

ATOMS, MOLECULES AND QUANTA, Arthur E. Ruark and Harold C. Urey. 1964 edition of work that has been a favorite of students and teachers for 30 years. Origins and major experimental data of quantum theory, development of concepts of atomic and molecular structure prior to new mechanics, laws and basic ideas of quantum mechanics, wave mechanics, matrix mechanics, general theory of quantum dynamics. Very thorough, lucid presentation for advanced students. 230 figures. Total of xxiii + 810pp.
61106-X, 61107-8 Two volumes, Paperbound $6.00

INVESTIGATIONS ON THE THEORY OF THE BROWNIAN MOVEMENT, Albert Einstein. Five papers (1905-1908) investigating the dynamics of Brownian motion and evolving an elementary theory of interest to mathematicians, chemists and physical scientists. Notes by R. Fürth, the editor, discuss the history of study of Brownian movement, elucidate the text and analyze the significance of the papers. Translated by A. D. Cowper. 3 figures. iv + 122pp.
60304-0 Paperbound $1.50

MATHEMATICAL FOUNDATIONS OF STATISTICAL MECHANICS, A. I. Khinchin. Introduction to modern statistical mechanics: phase space, ergodic problems, theory of probability, central limit theorem, ideal monatomic gas, foundation of thermodynamics, dispersion and distribution of sum functions. Provides mathematically rigorous treatment and excellent analytical tools. Translated by George Gamow. viii + 179pp.   60147-1 Paperbound $2.00

INTRODUCTION TO PHYSICAL STATISTICS, Robert B. Lindsay. Elementary probability theory, laws of thermodynamics, classical Maxwell-Boltzmann statistics, classical statistical mechanics, quantum mechanics, other areas of physics that can be studied statistically. Full coverage of methods; basic background theory. ix + 306pp.   61882-X Paperbound $2.75

DIALOGUES CONCERNING TWO NEW SCIENCES, Galileo Galilei. Written near the end of Galileo's life and encompassing 30 years of experiment and thought, these dialogues deal with geometric demonstrations of fracture of solid bodies, cohesion, leverage, speed of light and sound, pendulums, falling bodies, accelerated motion, etc. Translated by Henry Crew and Alfonso de Salvio. Introduction by Antonio Favaro. xxiii + 300pp.   60099-8 Paperbound $2.25

FOUNDATIONS OF SCIENCE: THE PHILOSOPHY OF THEORY AND EXPERIMENT, Norman R. Campbell. Fundamental concepts of science examined on middle level: acceptance of propositions and axioms, presuppositions of scientific thought, scientific law, multiplication of probabilities, nature of experiment, application of mathematics, measurement, numerical laws and theories, error, etc. Stress on physics, but holds for other sciences. "Unreservedly recommended," *Nature* (England). Formerly *Physics: The Elements.* ix + 565pp.   60372-5 Paperbound $4.00

THE PHASE RULE AND ITS APPLICATIONS, Alexander Findlay, A. N. Campbell and N. O. Smith. Findlay's well-known classic, updated (1951). Full standard text and thorough reference, particularly useful for graduate students. Covers chemical phenomena of one, two, three, four and multiple component systems. "Should rank as the standard work in English on the subject," *Nature*. 236 figures. xii + 494pp.   60091-2 Paperbound $3.50

THERMODYNAMICS, Enrico Fermi. A classic of modern science. Clear, organized treatment of systems, first and second laws, entropy, thermodynamic potentials, gaseous reactions, dilute solutions, entropy constant. No math beyond calculus is needed, but readers are assumed to be familiar with fundamentals of thermometry, calorimetry. 22 illustrations. 25 problems. x + 160pp.
60361-X Paperbound $2.00

TREATISE ON THERMODYNAMICS, Max Planck. Classic, still recognized as one of the best introductions to thermodynamics. Based on Planck's original papers, it presents a concise and logical view of the entire field, building physical and chemical laws from basic empirical facts. Planck considers fundamental definitions, first and second principles of thermodynamics, and applications to special states of equilibrium. Numerous worked examples. Translated by Alexander Ogg. 5 figures. xiv + 297pp.   60219-2 Paperbound $2.50

MICROSCOPY FOR CHEMISTS, Harold F. Schaeffer. Thorough text; operation of microscope, optics, photomicrographs, hot stage, polarized light, chemical procedures for organic and inorganic reactions. 32 specific experiments cover specific analyses: industrial, metals, other important subjects. 136 figures. 264pp.
61682-7 Paperbound $2.50

THE ELECTRONIC THEORY OF ACIDS AND BASES, by William F. Luder and Saverio Zuffanti. Full, newly revised (1961) presentation of a still controversial theory. Historical background, atomic orbitals and valence, electrophilic and electrodotic reagents, acidic and basic radicals, titrations, displacement, acid catalysis, etc., are discussed. xi + 165pp.
60201-X Paperbound $2.00

OPTICKS, Sir Isaac Newton. A survey of 18th-century knowledge on all aspects of light as well as a description of Newton's experiments with spectroscopy, colors, lenses, reflection, refraction, theory of waves, etc. in language the layman can follow. Foreword by Albert Einstein. Introduction by Sir Edmund Whittaker. Preface by I. Bernard Cohen. cxxvi + 406pp.
60205-2 Paperbound $3.50

LIGHT: PRINCIPLES AND EXPERIMENTS, George S. Monk. Thorough coverage, for student with background in physics and math, of physical and geometric optics. Also includes 23 experiments on optical systems, instruments, etc. "Probably the best intermediate text on optics in the English language," *Physics Forum*. 275 figures. xi + 489pp.
60341-5 Paperbound $3.50

PIEZOELECTRICITY: AN INTRODUCTION TO THE THEORY AND APPLICATIONS OF ELECTROMECHANICAL PHENOMENA IN CRYSTALS, Walter G. Cady. Revised 1963 edition of most complete, most systematic coverage of field. Fundamental theory of crystal electricity, concepts of piezoelectricity, including comparisons of various current theories; resonators; oscillators; properties, etc., of Rochelle salt; ferroelectric crystals; applications; pyroelectricity, similar topics. "A great work," *Nature*. Many illustrations. Total of xxx + 840pp.
61094-2, 61095-0 Two volumes, Paperbound $6.00

PHYSICAL OPTICS, Robert W. Wood. A classic in the field, this is a valuable source for students of physical optics and excellent background material for a study of electromagnetic theory. Partial contents: nature and rectilinear propagation of light, reflection from plane and curved surfaces, refraction, absorption and dispersion, origin of spectra, interference, diffraction, polarization, Raman effect, optical properties of metals, resonance radiation and fluorescence of atoms, magneto-optics, electro-optics, thermal radiation. 462 diagrams, 17 plates. xvi + 846pp.
61808-0 Paperbound $4.25

MIRRORS, PRISMS AND LENSES: A TEXTBOOK OF GEOMETRICAL OPTICS, James P. C. Southall. Introductory-level account of modern optical instrument theory, covering unusually wide range: lights and shadows, reflection of light and plane mirrors, refraction, astigmatic lenses, compound systems, aperture and field of optical system, the eye, dispersion and achromatism, rays of finite slope, the microscope, much more. Strong emphasis on earlier, elementary portions of field, utilizing simplest mathematics wherever possible. Problems. 329 figures. xxiv + 806pp.
61234-1 Paperbound $3.75

THE PSYCHOLOGY OF INVENTION IN THE MATHEMATICAL FIELD, Jacques Hadamard. Important French mathematician examines psychological origin of ideas, role of the unconscious, importance of visualization, etc. Based on own experiences and reports by Dalton, Pascal, Descartes, Einstein, Poincaré, Helmholtz, etc. xiii + 145pp. 20107-4 Paperbound $1.50

INTRODUCTION TO CHEMICAL PHYSICS, John C. Slater. A work intended to bridge the gap between chemistry and physics. Text divided into three parts: Thermodynamics, Statistical Mechanics, and Kinetic Theory; Gases, Liquids and Solids; and Atoms, Molecules and the Structure of Matter, which form the basis of the approach. Level is advanced undergraduate to graduate, but theoretical physics held to minimum. 40 tables, 118 figures. xiv + 522pp.
62562-1 Paperbound $4.00

POLAR MOLECULES, Pieter Debye. Explains some of the Nobel Laureate's most important theories on dielectrics, including fundamental electrostatic field relations, polarization and molecular structure, measurements of polarity, constitution of simple polar molecules, anomalous dispersion for radio frequencies, electrical saturation effects, connections with quantum theory, energy levels and wave mechanics, rotating molecules. 33 figures. 172pp. 60064-5 Paperbound $2.00

THE CONTINUUM AND OTHER TYPES OF SERIAL ORDER, Edward V. Huntington. Highly respected systematic account of modern theory of the continuum as a type of serial order. Based on the Dedekind-Cantor ordinal theory. Mathematics held to an elementary level. vii + 82pp. 60130-7 Paperbound $1.00

CONTRIBUTIONS TO THE FOUNDING OF THE THEORY OF TRANSFINITE NUMBERS, Georg Cantor. The famous articles of 1895-1897 which founded a new branch of mathematics, translated with 82-page introduction by P. Jourdain. Not only a great classic but still one of the best introductions for the student. ix + 211pp.
60045-9 Paperbound $2.00

ESSAYS ON THE THEORY OF NUMBERS, Richard Dedekind. Two classic essays, on the theory of irrationals, giving an arithmetic and rigorous foundation; and on transfinite numbers and properties of natural numbers. Translated by W. W. Beman. iii + 115pp. 21010-3 Paperbound $1.50

GEOMETRY OF FOUR DIMENSIONS, H. P. Manning. Part verbal, part mathematical development of fourth dimensional geometry. Historical introduction. Detailed treatment is by synthetic method, approaching subject through Euclidean geometry. No knowledge of higher mathematics necessary. 76 figures. ix + 348pp.
60182-X Paperbound $3.00

AN INTRODUCTION TO THE GEOMETRY OF N DIMENSIONS, Duncan M. Y. Sommerville. The only work in English devoted to higher-dimensional geometry. Both metric and projective properties of n-dimensional geometry are covered. Covers fundamental ideas of incidence, parallelism, perpendicularity, angles between linear space, enumerative geometry, analytical geometry, polytopes, analysis situs, hyperspacial figures. 60 diagrams. xvii + 196pp. 60494-2 Paperbound $1.50

A TREATISE ON THE DIFFERENTIAL GEOMETRY OF CURVES AND SURFACES, Luther P. Eisenhart. Detailed, concrete introductory treatise on differential geometry, developed from author's graduate courses at Princeton University. Thorough explanation of the geometry of curves and surfaces, concentrating on problems most helpful to students. 683 problems, 30 diagrams. xiv + 474pp.
60667-8 Paperbound $2.75

AN ESSAY ON THE FOUNDATIONS OF GEOMETRY, Bertrand Russell. A mathematical and physical analysis of the place of the a priori in geometric knowledge. Includes critical review of 19th-century work in non-Euclidean geometry as well as illuminating insights of one of the great minds of our time. New foreword by Morris Kline. xx + 201pp.
60233-8 Paperbound $2.00

INTRODUCTION TO THE THEORY OF NUMBERS, Leonard E. Dickson. Thorough, comprehensive approach with adequate coverage of classical literature, yet simple enough for beginners. Divisibility, congruences, quadratic residues, binary quadratic forms, primes, least residues, Fermat's theorem, Gauss's lemma, and other important topics. 249 problems, 1 figure. viii + 183pp.
60342-3 Paperbound $2.00

AN ELEMENTARY INTRODUCTION TO THE THEORY OF PROBABILITY, B. V. Gnedenko and A. Ya. Khinchin. Introduction to facts and principles of probability theory. Extremely thorough within its range. Mathematics employed held to elementary level. Excellent, highly accurate layman's introduction. Translated from the fifth Russian edition by Leo Y. Boron. xii + 130pp.
60155-2 Paperbound $1.75

SELECTED PAPERS ON NOISE AND STOCHASTIC PROCESSES, edited by Nelson Wax. Six papers which serve as an introduction to advanced noise theory and fluctuation phenomena, or as a reference tool for electrical engineers whose work involves noise characteristics, Brownian motion, statistical mechanics. Papers are by Chandrasekhar, Doob, Kac, Ming, Ornstein, Rice, and Uhlenbeck. Exact facsimile of the papers as they appeared in scientific journals. 19 figures. v + 337pp. $6\frac{1}{8}$ x $9\frac{1}{4}$.
60262-1 Paperbound $3.00

STATISTICS MANUAL, Edwin L. Crow, Frances A. Davis and Margaret W. Maxfield. Comprehensive, practical collection of classical and modern methods of making statistical inferences, prepared by U. S. Naval Ordnance Test Station. Formulae, explanations, methods of application are given, with stress on use. Basic knowledge of statistics is assumed. 21 tables, 11 charts, 95 illustrations. xvii + 288pp.
60599-X Paperbound $2.00

MATHEMATICAL FOUNDATIONS OF INFORMATION THEORY, A. I. Khinchin. Comprehensive introduction to work of Shannon, McMillan, Feinstein and Khinchin, placing these investigations on a rigorous mathematical basis. Covers entropy concept in probability theory, uniqueness theorem, Shannon's inequality, ergodic sources, the E property, martingale concept, noise, Feinstein's fundamental lemma, Shanon's first and second theorems. Translated by R. A. Silverman and M. D. Friedman. iii + 120pp.
60434-9 Paperbound $1.75

A COURSE IN MATHEMATICAL ANALYSIS, Edouard Goursat. *The entire "Cours d'analyse" for students with one year of calculus, offering an exceptionally wide range of subject matter on analysis and applied mathematics. Available for the first time in English. Definitive treatment.*

VOLUME I: Applications to geometry, expansion in series, definite integrals, derivatives and differentials. Translated by Earle R. Hedrick. 52 figures. viii + 548pp.   60554-X Paperbound $3.00

VOLUME II, PART I: Functions of a complex variable, conformal representations, doubly periodic functions, natural boundaries, etc. Translated by Earle R. Hedrick and Otto Dunkel. 38 figures. x + 259pp.   60555-8 Paperbound $2.25

VOLUME II, PART II: Differential equations, Cauchy-Lipschitz method, non-linear differential equations, simultaneous equations, etc. Translated by Earle R. Hedrick and Otto Dunkel. 1 figure. viii + 300pp.   60556-6 Paperbound $2.50

VOLUME III, PART I: Variation of solutions, partial differential equations of the second order. Poincaré's theorem, periodic solutions, asymptotic series, wave propagation, Dirichlet's problem in space, Newtonian potential, etc. Translated by Howard G. Bergmann. 15 figures. x + 329pp.   61176-0 Paperbound $3.00

VOLUME III, PART II: Integral equations and calculus of variations: Fredholm's equation, Hilbert-Schmidt theorem, symmetric kernels, Euler's equation, transversals, extreme fields, Weierstrass's theory, etc. Translated by Howard G. Bergmann. Note on Conformal Representation by Paul Montel. 13 figures. xi + 389pp.
61177-9 Paperbound $3.00

ELEMENTARY STATISTICS: WITH APPLICATIONS IN MEDICINE AND THE BIOLOGICAL SCIENCES, Frederick E. Croxton. Presentation of all fundamental techniques and methods of elementary statistics assuming average knowledge of mathematics only. Useful to readers in all fields, but many examples drawn from characteristic data in medicine and biological sciences. vii + 376pp.
60506-X Paperbound $2.25

ELEMENTS OF THE THEORY OF FUNCTIONS. A general background text that explores complex numbers, linear functions, sets and sequences, conformal mapping. Detailed proofs. Translated by Frederick Bagemihl. 140pp.
60154-4 Paperbound $1.50

THEORY OF FUNCTIONS, PART I. Provides full demonstrations, rigorously set forth, of the general foundations of the theory: integral theorems, series, the expansion of analytic functions. Translated by Federick Bagemihl. vii + 146pp.
60156-0 Paperbound $1.50

INTRODUCTION TO THE THEORY OF FOURIER'S SERIES AND INTEGRALS, Horatio S. Carslaw. A basic introduction to the theory of infinite series and integrals, with special reference to Fourier's series and integrals. Based on the classic Riemann integral and dealing with only ordinary functions, this is an important class text. 84 examples. xiii + 368pp.   60048-3 Paperbound $3.00

AN INTRODUCTION TO FOURIER METHODS AND THE LAPLACE TRANSFORMATION, Philip Franklin. Introductory study of theory and applications of Fourier series and Laplace transforms, for engineers, physicists, applied mathematicians, physical science teachers and students. Only a previous knowledge of elementary calculus is assumed. Methods are related to physical problems in heat flow, vibrations, eletcrical transmission, electromagnetic radiation, etc. 828 problems with answers. Formerly *Fourier Methods.* x + 289pp. 60452-7 Paperbound $2.50

INFINITE SEQUENCES AND SERIES, Konrad Knopp. Careful presentation of fundamentals of the theory by one of the finest modern expositors of higher mathematics. Covers functions of real and complex variables, arbitrary and null sequences, convergence and divergence. Cauchy's limit theorem, tests for infinite series, power series, numerical and closed evaluation of series. Translated by Frederick Bagemihl. v + 186pp. 60153-6 Paperbound $2.00

INTRODUCTION TO THE DIFFERENTIAL EQUATIONS OF PHYSICS, Ludwig Hopf. No math background beyond elementary calculus is needed to follow this classroom or self-study introduction to ordinary and partial differential equations. Approach is through classical physics. Translated by Walter Nef. 48 figures. v + 154pp. 60120-X Paperbound $1.45

DIFFERENTIAL EQUATIONS FOR ENGINEERS, Philip Franklin. For engineers, physicists, applied mathematicians. Theory and application: solution of ordinary differential equations and partial derivatives, analytic functions. Fourier series, Abel's theorem, Cauchy Riemann differential equations, etc. Over 400 problems deal with electricity, vibratory systems, heat, radio; solutions. Formerly *Differential Equations for Electrical Engineers.* 41 illustrations. vii + 299pp. 60601-5 Paperbound $2.00

THEORY OF FUNCTIONS, PART II. Single- and multiple-valued functions; full presentation of the most characteristic and important types. Proofs fully worked out. Translated by Frederick Bagemihl. x + 150pp. 60157-9 Paperbound $1.50

PROBLEM BOOK IN THE THEORY OF FUNCTIONS, I. More than 300 elementary problems for independent use or for use with "Theory of Functions, I." 85pp. of detailed solutions. Translated by Lipman Bers. viii + 126pp. 60158-7 Paperbound $1.50

PROBLEM BOOK IN THE THEORY OF FUNCTIONS, II. More than 230 problems in the advanced theory. Designed to be used with "Theory of Functions, II" or with any comparable text. Full solutions. Translated by Frederick Bagemihl. 138pp. 60159-5 Paperbound $1.50

INTRODUCTION TO THE THEORY OF EQUATIONS, Florian Cajori. Classic introduction by leading historian of science covers the fundamental theories as reached by Gauss, Abel, Galois and Kronecker. Basics of equation study are followed by symmetric functions of roots, elimination, homographic and Tschirnhausen transformations, resolvents of Lagrange, cyclic equations, Abelian equations, the work of Galois, the algebraic solution of general equations, and much more. Numerous exercises include answers. ix + 239pp. 62184-7 Paperbound $2.75

LAPLACE TRANSFORMS AND THEIR APPLICATIONS TO DIFFERENTIAL EQUATIONS, N. W. McLachlan. Introduction to modern operational calculus, applying it to ordinary and partial differential equations. Laplace transform, theorems of operational calculus, solution of equations with constant coefficients, evaluation of integrals, derivation of transforms, of various functions, etc. For physics, engineering students. Formerly *Modern Operational Calculus*. xiv + 218pp.

60192-7 Paperbound $2.50

PARTIAL DIFFERENTIAL EQUATIONS OF MATHEMATICAL PHYSICS, Arthur G. Webster. Introduction to basic method and theory of partial differential equations, with full treatment of their applications to virtually every field. Full, clear chapters on Fourier series, integral and elliptic equations, spherical, cylindrical and ellipsoidal harmonics, Cauchy's method, boundary problems, method of Riemann-Volterra, many other basic topics. Edited by Samuel J. Plimpton. 97 figures. vii + 446pp.

60263-X Paperbound $2.75

PRINCIPLES OF STELLAR DYNAMICS, Subrahmanyan Chandrasekhar. Theory of stellar dynamics as a branch of classical dynamics; stellar encounter in terms of 2-body problem, Liouville's theorem and equations of continuity. Also two additional papers. 50 illustrations. x + 313pp. 5⅝ x 8⅜.

60659-7 Paperbound $3.00

CELESTIAL OBJECTS FOR COMMON TELESCOPES, T. W. Webb. The most used book in amateur astronomy: inestimable aid for locating and identifying hundreds of celestial objects. Volume 1 covers operation of telescope, telescope photography, precise information on sun, moon, planets, asteroids, meteor swarms, etc.; Volume 2, stars, constellations, double stars, clusters, variables, nebulae, etc. Nearly 4,000 objects noted. New edition edited, updated by Margaret W. Mayall. 77 illustrations. Total of xxxix + 606pp.

20917-2, 20918-0 Two volumes, Paperbound $5.00

A SHORT HISTORY OF ASTRONOMY, Arthur Berry. Earliest times through the 19th century. Individual chapters on Copernicus, Tycho Brahe, Galileo, Kepler, Newton, etc. Non-technical, but precise, thorough, and as useful to specialist as layman. 104 illustrations, 9 portraits, xxxi + 440 pp.

20210-0 Paperbound $3.00

ORDINARY DIFFERENTIAL EQUATIONS, Edward L. Ince. Explains and analyzes theory of ordinary differential equations in real and complex domains: elementary methods of integration, existence and nature of solutions, continuous transformation groups, linear differential equations, equations of first order, non-linear equations of higher order, oscillation theorems, etc. "Highly recommended," *Electronics Industries*. 18 figures. viii + 558pp.

60349-0 Paperbound $3.50

DICTIONARY OF CONFORMAL REPRESENTATIONS, H. Kober. Laplace's equation in two dimensions for many boundary conditions; scores of geometric forms and transformations for electrical engineers, Joukowski aerofoil for aerodynamists, Schwarz-Christoffel transformations, transcendental functions, etc. Twin diagrams for most transformations. 447 diagrams. xvi + 208pp. 6⅛ x 9¼.

60160-9 Paperbound $2.50

ALMOST PERIODIC FUNCTIONS, A. S. Besicovitch. Thorough summary of Bohr's theory of almost periodic functions citing new shorter proofs, extending the theory, and describing contributions of Wiener, Weyl, de la Vallée, Poussin, Stepanoff, Bochner and the author. xiii + 180pp. 60018-1 Paperbound $1.75

AN INTRODUCTION TO THE STUDY OF STELLAR STRUCTURE, S. Chandrasekhar. A rigorous examination, using both classical and modern mathematical methods, of the relationship between loss of energy, the mass, and the radius of stars in a steady state. 38 figures. 509pp. 60413-6 Paperbound $3.25

INTRODUCTION TO THE THEORY OF GROUP'S OF FINITE ORDER, Robert D. Carmichael. Progresses in easy steps from sets, groups, permutations, isomorphism through the important types of groups. No higher mathematics is necessary. 783 exercises and problems. xiv + 447pp. 60300-8 Paperbound $3.50

THE SOLUBILITY OF NONELECTROLYTES, Joel H. Hildebrand and Robert L. Scott. Classic, pioneering work discusses in detail ideal and nonideal solutions, intermolecular forces, structure of liquids, athermal mixing, hydrogen bonding, equations describing mixtures of gases, high polymer solutions, surface phenomena, etc. Originally published in the American Chemical Society Monograph series. New authors' preface and new paper (1964). 148 figures, 88 tables. xiv + 488pp. 61125-6 Paperbound $3.00

INTRODUCTION TO APPLIED MATHEMATICS, Francis D. Murnaghan. Introduction to advanced mathematical techniques—vector and matrix analysis, partial differential equations, integral equations, Laplace transform theory, Fourier series, boundary-value problems, etc.—particularly useful to physicists and engineers. 41 figures. ix + 389pp. 61042-X Paperbound $2.25

ELEMENTARY MATHEMATICS FROM AN ADVANCED STANDPOINT: VOLUME I— ARITHMETIC, ALGEBRA, ANALYSIS, Felix Klein. Second-level approach, illuminated by graphical and geometrical interpretation. Covers natural and complex numbers, real equations with real unknowns, equations in the field of complex quantities, logarithmic and exponential functions, goniometric functions, infinitesimal calculus, transcendence of e and π. Concept of function introduced immediately. Translated by E. R. Hedrick and C. A. Noble. 125 figures. ix + 274pp.
(USO) 60150-1 Paperbound $2.25

ELEMENTARY MATHEMATICS FROM AN ADVANCED STANDPOINT: VOLUME II— GEOMETRY, Feliex Klein. Using analytical formulas, Klein clarifies the precise formulation of geometric facts in chapters on manifolds, geometric and higher point transformations, foundations. "Nothing comparable," *Mathematics Teacher*. Translated by E. R. Hedrick and C. A. Noble. 141 figures. ix + 214pp.
(USO) 60151-X Paperbound $2.25

ENGINEERING MATHEMATICS, Kenneth S. Miller. Most useful mathematical techniques for graduate students in engineering, physics, covering linear differential equations, series, random functions, integrals, Fourier series, Laplace transform, network theory, etc. "Sound and teachable," Science. 89 figures. xii + 417pp. 6 x 8½. 61121-3 Paperbound $3.00

INTRODUCTION TO ASTROPHYSICS: THE STARS, Jean Dufay. Best guide to observational astrophysics in English. Bridges the gap between elementary popularizations and advanced technical monographs. Covers stellar photometry, stellar spectra and classification, Hertzsprung-Russell diagrams, Yerkes 2-dimensional classification, temperatures, diameters, masses and densities, evolution of the stars. Translated by Owen Gingerich. 51 figures, 11 tables. xii + 164pp.
(USCO) 60771-2 Paperbound $2.00

INTRODUCTION TO BESSEL FUNCTIONS, Frank Bowman. Full, clear introduction to properties and applications of Bessel functions. Covers Bessel functions of zero order, of any order; definite integrals; asymptotic expansions; Bessel's solution to Kepler's problem; circular membranes; etc. Math above calculus and fundamentals of differential equations developed within text. 636 problems. 28 figures. x + 135pp.
60462-4 Paperbound $1.75

DIFFERENTIAL AND INTEGRAL CALCULUS, Philip Franklin. A full and basic introduction, textbook for a two- or three-semester course, or self-study. Covers parametric functions, force components in polar coordinates, Duhamel's theorem, methods and applications of integration, infinite series, Taylor's series, vectors and surfaces in space, etc. Exercises follow each chapter with full solutions at back of the book. Index. xi + 679pp.
62520-6 Paperbound $4.00

THE EXACT SCIENCES IN ANTIQUITY, O. Neugebauer. Modern overview chiefly of mathematics and astronomy as developed by the Egyptians and Babylonians. Reveals startling advancement of Babylonian mathematics (tables for numerical computations, quadratic equations with two unknowns, implications that Pythagorean theorem was known 1000 years before Pythagoras), and sophisticated astronomy based on competent mathematics. Also covers transmission of this knowledge to Hellenistic world. 14 plates, 52 figures. xvii + 240pp.
22332-9 Paperbound $2.50

THE THIRTEEN BOOKS OF EUCLID'S ELEMENTS, translated with introduction and commentary by Sir Thomas Heath. Unabridged republication of definitive edition based on the text of Heiberg. Translator's notes discuss textual and linguistic matters, mathematical analysis, 2500 years of critical commentary on the Elements. Do not confuse with abridged school editions. Total of xvii + 1414pp.
60088-2, 60089-0, 60090-4 Three volumes, Paperbound $8.50

AN INTRODUCTION TO SYMBOLIC LOGIC, Susanne K. Langer. Well-known introduction, popular among readers with elementary mathematical background. Starts with simple symbols and conventions and teaches Boole-Schroeder and Russell-Whitehead systems. 367pp.
60164-1 Paperbound $2.25

Prices subject to change without notice.

Available at your book dealer or write for free catalogue to Dept. Sci, Dover Publications, Inc., 180 Varick St., N.Y., N.Y. 10014. Dover publishes more than 150 books each year on science, elementary and advanced mathematics, biology, music, art, literary history, social sciences and other areas.